An ICMA Green Book

Managing FIRE and EMERGENCY Services

An ICMA Green Book

Managing FIRE and EMERGENCY Services

Edited by

Adam K. Thiel
Fire Chief
FACETS Consulting, LLP

Charles R. Jennings
Associate Professor
John Jay College of Criminal Justice
City University of New York

Leaders at the Core of Better Communities

ICMA, the International City/County Management Association, advances professional local government worldwide. Our mission is to create excellence in local governance by developing and advancing professional management to create sustainable communities that improve lives worldwide. ICMA provides member support; publications; data and information; peer and results-oriented assistance; and training and professional development to nearly 9,000 city, town, and county experts and other individuals and organizations throughout the world. The management decisions made by ICMA's members affect millions of individuals living in thousands of communities, from small villages and towns to large metropolitan areas.

Library of Congress Cataloging-in-Publication Data

Managing fire and emergency services / edited by Adam K. Thiel, Charles R. Jennings.—1st ed.
p. cm.
Includes bibliographical references and index.
ISBN 978-0-87326-763-2 (alk. paper)
1. Fire departments—Management. 2. Personnel management. 3. Emergency communication systems. I. Thiel, Adam K. II. Jennings, Charles R.
TH9145.M2526 2012
363.37'8068—dc23

2011037769

Printed in the United States of America
2018 2017 2016 2015 2014 2013 2012
5 4 3 2 1

ABOUT THE EDITORS

Adam K. Thiel has spent twenty years in the fire and emergency services across four states and in numerous capacities, including fire chief for a diverse and densely populated urban community in the National Capital Region; operations deputy chief for a fast-growing Arizona city; executive director of the Virginia Department of Fire Programs; firefighter, paramedic, hazardous materials technician, and company officer with the Fairfax County (Virginia) Fire and Rescue Department; deputy fire chief for a small combination fire department in North Carolina; and volunteer firefighter/rescuer in Montgomery County, Maryland.

For the past fifteen years, Chief Thiel has provided strategy, planning, leadership, and management consulting to international organizations, nonprofits, government agencies at all levels, educational institutions, and private firms. He currently chairs the National Fire Protection Association (NFPA) Technical Committee on Emergency Services Organization Risk Management, is a member of the NFPA Fire Service Section board, serves as vice-chair for the National Fire Academy Board of Visitors, is a Fire 20/20 board member, and serves on the steering committee for the George Washington University's Homeland Security Policy Institute. He has authored numerous publications, writes a regular column in *Fire Chief* magazine, and has presented at conferences throughout the country. He teaches graduate-level public administration courses, teaches in the International Association of Fire Chiefs (IAFC) New Chiefs Leadership and Executive Edge programs, and is an IAFC/International Association of Fire Fighters (IAFF) Labor-Management Initiative facilitator.

Chief Thiel earned undergraduate degrees in history and fire science from the University of North Carolina at Chapel Hill and the University of Maryland University College, respectively; he holds a master's degree in public administration from George Mason University, is finishing his doctoral degree in public administration at Arizona State University, and has completed the Virginia Executive Institute and Harvard University's Kennedy School of Government Program for Senior Executives in State and Local Government.

Charles R. Jennings, MIFireE, CFO, is an associate professor at John Jay College of Criminal Justice of the City University of New York, teaching in the fire science, protection management, and public administration programs. He also serves as director of the Christian Regenhard Center for Emergency Response Studies, a first-responder policy research center located at the college. His teaching and research interests include risk analysis, management, emergency service deployment, and relating community fire loss with community characteristics. With over twenty years of active service as a firefighter and officer in New York and Maryland, Dr. Jennings has held a number of fire service positions, most recently as deputy commissioner of public safety for the city of White Plains, New York. He was also chairman of the Board of Fire Commissioners for the city of Ithaca, New York, and is currently principal of Manitou, Inc., a public safety consulting firm in North America.

Dr. Jennings earned a BS in journalism from the University of Maryland; an MS in fire protection management from John Jay College of Criminal Justice; and a master's degree in regional planning and a PhD in city and regional planning from Cornell University.

Green Books—Authoritative source books on local government management

ICMA's "Green Books" (a designation derived from the original bright green cloth covers) have a long history as the authoritative source on local government management. They are used by local government managers in cities and counties worldwide, by university professors and students as textbooks for undergraduate and graduate courses, and by public safety professionals in preparation for promotional exams. The Green Books cover the range of local government functions, linking the latest theories and research to specific examples of day-to-day decision making and the nuts and bolts of management. Current titles in the Green Book series include

Emergency Management: Principles and Practice for Local Government, 2nd edition

Local Government Police Management, 4th edition

Local Planning: Contemporary Principles and Practice

Management Policies in Local Government Finance, 5th edition

Other recent titles

Capital Budgeting and Finance: A Guide for Local Governments, 2nd edition

Citizen Surveys for Local Government: A Comprehensive Guide to Making Them Matter

Economic Development: Strategies for State and Local Practice, 2nd edition

The Effective Local Government Manager, 3rd edition

Effective Supervisory Practices, 4th edition

Homeland Security: Best Practices for Local Government, 2nd edition

Human Resource Management in Local Government: An Essential Guide, 3rd edition

Leading Performance Management in Local Government

Leading Your Community: A Guide for Local Elected Leaders

Managing Local Government: Cases in Effectiveness

Managing Local Government Services: A Practical Guide

Service Contracting: A Local Government Guide

Statistics for Public Administration: Practical Uses for Better Decision Making

Learn about these and other titles at bookstore.icma.org.

CONTENTS

Sidebars

Chapter 1 Contemporary Fire and Emergency Services

Chapter 2 Emergency Management and Homeland Security for Fire Services

Chapter 3 Evaluating and Managing Local Risks

Chapter 4 Organizing and Deploying Resources

Chapter 5 Emergency Medical Services

Chapter 6 Comprehensive Prevention Programs

Figures

Tables

FOREWORD

ICMA is proud to release the fourth iteration of its fire "Green Book," the first of which, *Managing Fire Services,* was published in 1967. The last version, *Managing Fire and Rescue Services,* was completed just after September 11, 2001, and long before Hurricane Katrina and the economic disaster of 2007. As the editors of this current version note in their preface, much has changed over the last decade, and some of that change is reflected in the new title: *Managing Fire and Emergency Services.* Acknowledging the growing integration of emergency services in the fire service, this latest volume accounts for yet another milestone in the evolution of the field from its volunteer roots to the complex, multidisciplinary profession it is today.

Often the fire service is perceived in overly simplistic terms of brute strength and raw courage—characteristics that remain very much a part of fire and emergency work. But today's highly complex world of innovative construction, electrical and alternative fuel vehicles, and biological and chemical threats requires professionals who are not only brave but also highly trained and appropriately equipped and deployed. During my tenure as county manager of Arlington, Virginia, I surveyed numerous fire scenes, ranging from a kitchen fire contained in a single room to the massive destruction wreaked by the terrorist attack on the Pentagon. I vividly remember being at the Pentagon on September 12 as firefighters fought a complex and tenacious fire on the roof. Upon receiving an emergency alarm that an unidentified aircraft was headed toward the Pentagon, the incident commander, Assistant Chief James Schwartz, reluctantly called for an evacuation of the fire ground, with dozens of firefighters stranded on the roof. Fortunately, it was a false alarm—a federal aircraft had failed to get proper clearance—but a firefighter who had been on the roof told me afterward that he had struggled with the decision to stay on the roof or jump five floors. Later, at the insistence of the firefighters, I went up on the roof to get a better sense of the danger and complexity of the fire they were fighting. It was clearly a job for a special kind of person.

The dangers of fire and emergency services became much more poignant when I attended the first post-9/11 annual ceremony for fallen firefighters. There I realized fully and consciously for the first time that the number of New York City firefighters who were lost in the World Trade Center attack was equivalent to the entire Arlington County fire department.

The complexity of today's response was also illustrated at the Pentagon, as I learned from Capt. William (Scotty) McKay, head of Arlington's technical rescue team. Once it was safe to do, Captain McKay arranged for me to go through the structure; among other elements of the response, he wanted me to understand the extensive construction work needed to stabilize the building—literally rebuilding the Pentagon's support columns with heavy lumber—to avoid further collapse. Complexity was apparent as well in the range of protective gear in use and the protocols for decontamination of all crews after exiting the building.

The incidents at the Pentagon and World Trade Center on 9/11, and across the Gulf Coast following Hurricane Katrina, were all large-scale events, but the same level of complexity can be found in any community: at a big-box store, a manufacturing plant, or a train crossing, and, unfortunately, in a home or apartment where someone is doing something unwise or illegal. The convergence of modern construction with other hazards creates threats that require sophisticated skills, quick thinking, the ability to work together, and a high degree of overall professionalism for all firefighters and emergency medical responders—qualities that are necessary for their own safety as well as for that of the communities in which they serve.

For this edition of *Managing Fire and Emergency Services,* Fire Chief Adam K. Thiel and Professor Charles R. Jennings have used their combined knowledge and expertise as practitioner and academic to assemble the latest leading practices in fire and emergency services. Drawing from a diverse group of leaders in the field, these editors have done an excellent job in capturing the full breadth of skills demanded by today's fire and emergency services.

This book provides a valuable insight into the fire and emergency services from people who know it best. Designed for fire professionals who aspire to managerial and chief positions, it is also an excellent source for city/county managers, budget directors, and others who interact with fire and emergency service organizations. Local government managers will find that the editors and authors are concerned about many of the same issues as they are. I discovered this same alignment in early 2011, when I participated in a training workshop for new fire chiefs, sponsored by the International Association of Fire Chiefs. I attended presentations by a number of the most respected fire chiefs in the field and was struck by the similarity of their message to what city and county managers were stressing: the importance of data-driven decision making, of working across boundaries, of performance assessment, and of efficiency and the creation of good value for taxpayers. They all expressed a deep understanding of competition for scarce resources for staffing, training, and equipment within the fire service as well as with other important public services. Fire chiefs realize the fiscal realities that the editors note in their preface: that in this economic environment, officials "are increasingly interested in agency performance and demand justification for expenditures" as opposed to "traditional appeals to emotion or unsubstantiated assertions."

Fire chiefs, local government managers, and elected officials all have a responsibility to protect the lives of the men and women in the fire and emergency services as well as of the citizens in their communities. At the same time, city and county managers need to be able to ask the right questions and fully understand the real and potential consequences of the decisions they make and the recommendations they formulate for elected officials. The chapters in this volume should be a valuable resource for these leaders. Part One examines the actual issues facing today's fire and emergency services, including homeland security, local risks, organization and deployment of resources, emergency medical services, and comprehensive prevention programs. In Part Two, managers will find organizational leadership concepts and human resource concerns consistent with their own training, while Chapters 9, 10, and 11 discuss issues related to training, regulations, and worker safety. Part Three addresses the intricacies of budgeting and capital planning for fire and emergency services, and Part Four helps to illuminate some of the challenges inherent in technology and communications. I particularly recommend Chapter 15 on information systems; essential for providing the data necessary for informed decision making, information systems are a needed investment for many fire and emergency service departments.

ICMA is grateful for the outstanding contributions of the editors and authors, a number of whom I have had the privilege of working with personally. I also appreciate the continuing contributions of Ann Mahoney, director of publications; Christine Ulrich, a former ICMA staff member who served as the book's substantive editor; senior editor Jane Cotnoir; and Valerie Hepler and Charles Mountain, who led the book's creative design. Tom Wieczorek, a former fire chief himself, was a valuable in-house resource.

Finally, ICMA expresses its deep appreciation and respect for all the men and women who serve our communities as firefighters, rescue workers, and emergency medical providers. We value what they do every day to keep our communities safe. We sincerely hope that this book—written by their peers and by other professionals who care deeply about fire and emergency services—will help them advance in their careers as they may desire. Most importantly, we hope that this book provides valuable insight and guidance to keep them and their colleagues safe in a profession where lives are put at risk every day.

Ron Carlee
Chief Operating Officer
ICMA

PREFACE

This edition of the classic ICMA series on fire and rescue services carries a new name, *Managing Fire and Emergency Services,* reflecting the transition of traditional fire service agencies to multihazard emergency service organizations. The previous edition, *Managing Fire and Rescue Services,* addressed a profession on the brink of change following the tragic events of September 11, 2001. This edition reflects the continuing transformation of fire services, fueled by decreased federal funding and increasing expectations for local emergency services, as expressed in policies and regulations from agencies such as the U.S. Department of Homeland Security, itself formed in 2002. While some discussion of government regulation and funding is specific to the United States, this volume was designed to be useful in a North American context, reflecting the mission and membership of ICMA.

Events since 2001 have reinforced the continuing challenges for fire and emergency services—for example, fiscal scarcity and increasing demands for accountability—and raised new ones, such as terrorism and large-scale incident response and management. The attacks of September 11 and subsequent terrorist attempts against the United States have highlighted the role of fire and emergency services in managing terrorism incidents, as well as the need to prepare for mass violence against the public. The birth of "homeland security" and the global war on terror signal long-term shifts in the service delivery environment and new requirements for local emergency services.

Events such as Hurricane Katrina and more recent hurricanes, earthquakes, floods, and tornadoes have heightened awareness of the need to prepare for and manage large-scale emergencies. Local agencies' tradition of operating as independent entities is giving way to regional approaches to emergency preparedness and response. Arrangements that are acceptable for day-to-day operations may not be sufficient for large-scale events.

The collapse of the housing market since 2008 and its effects on the larger economy have constrained government revenues. Fiscal scarcity, especially in local government, has created challenges for existing working arrangements and compensation structures. Within fire and emergency service agencies, it has meant widespread layoffs and constrained budgets, which may continue for several years. In the new economic environment, the public seems less willing to support steady increases in the cost of providing basic services, so increasingly the fire and emergency services must compete with other societal needs as local governments try to balance public safety, education, health care, and social services.

Performance management systems have demonstrated their worth in many settings and are penetrating local government agencies. Backed by the public and the media, elected officials are increasingly interested in agency performance and demand justification for expenditures. More and more, a chief's ability to justify requests for resources depends on sound, quantitative measures of performance rather than on traditional appeals to emotion or unsubstantiated assertions.

Finally, establishing and maintaining legitimacy with the public and elected officials remain paramount. Failures to meet public expectations are publicized not only in the traditional media but also through social media, creating a more challenging climate for agency managers.

About the Text

Managing Fire and Emergency Services is a reference for chief officers and local government officials, a textbook for students, and essential reading for those preparing for promotional examinations. The text is designed to meet the National Fire Academy's Fire and Emergency Services Higher Education (FESHE) model curriculum guidelines for its course, "Fire and Emergency Services Administration."

The 2011 edition was substantially reorganized and includes two new chapters. The first, "Emergency Management and Homeland Security for Fire Services," recognizes the immersion of all fire services in the realm of emergency management, and the importance of funding streams and policy and program guidance in this area. The second, "Emergency Medical Services," responds to the trend among fire agencies toward greater involvement in emergency medical services and the accompanying challenges.

The text is organized into four major areas:

Part One, "Policy and Organizational Environment for Fire and Emergency Services," looks at the major service considerations that affect fire and emergency services management. It describes modern fire protection and the role of emergency management in homeland security; explains the issues involved in evaluating and managing local risks and in organizing and deploying resources; discusses the role of emergency medical services in the fire service; and addresses the value of comprehensive prevention programs.

Part Two, "Organizational Leadership," defines the principles and practices of leadership and management in the new fire and emergency services environment; introduces the essential concerns of human resource management; lays out the framework for professional development; updates the reader on regulations, standards, and liability; and presents a comprehensive approach to health, safety, and survival.

Part Three, "Managing Fiscal Resources," contains chapters on fiscal management, including budgeting, and on capital resource management.

Part Four, "Critical Support Systems and Functions," offers completely revised chapters on performance management, information systems, and communications systems and emergency communication centers.

Continuing the practice from previous editions, each chapter provides an overview of the topic at a level sufficient for understanding and action. Emergent issues are reviewed, and examples of best practices from local case studies are included where appropriate. Each chapter emphasizes innovation, collaboration, and the advancement of professional knowledge and skills, looking toward the future. Further readings are included for those seeking more information. Effort was made to include scholarly publications and "best in class" examples, even when they were not specifically designed for fire and emergency service audiences.

A host of regulatory and legal changes have occurred since the previous edition. This volume presents the latest developments of this kind that affect human resource management, candidate selection, firefighter safety, and grants management. Information and communication technologies have advanced as well. Special emphasis is given to updating terminology, discussing new policies, and describing challenges that arise as the line between information and communications technology begins to blur. The chapter on communications emphasizes organizational dynamics and management of combined multidisciplinary communication centers, which we expect to become more common for financial reasons and also because staffing and technology requirements are becoming too heavy for some small stand-alone centers.

Each generation tends to imagine that the challenges it faces are unprecedented. This generation is no exception. The fire chief of tomorrow must be equipped to operate in an environment that is more dynamic, more challenging, and more unforgiving than in the past. Mastery of technology, intergovernmental relations, regulatory compliance, human resource management and labor relations, and safe and efficient delivery of high-quality services has perhaps never been more important to a chief's success. But while our challenges are real and novel, the opportunity for the fire and emergency services profession to mobilize around meaningful and effective change is also great. We can look to the rich history of the fire service for examples of the kind of collaboration, innovation, and professional development that we need now.

Effective agencies are those with strong linkages to the communities they serve—those that are able to operate with neighboring agencies and allied organizations to deliver service. Effective agencies are also those that are able to measure, document, and improve their performance. Above all, the ability to define and adapt the role of fire and emergency services within the context of local government and economic development is crucial. The fire and emergency services are capable of great things, but whether we are viewed by the public and local leaders as engaged in solving problems in our communities or as defensively clinging to the past is in the balance

Acknowledgments

The authors for this text reflect the diversity of fire and emergency services leadership as well as our aspiration to produce a "leading" publication—not merely a reflection of the "way it is" but a call to excellence in all dimensions of management. The authors are united in their commitment to rigorously researched and documented guidance for fire and emergency service managers. The editors thank them for their diligence and commitment.

As co-editors of the new *Managing Fire and Emergency Services,* we would like to express our appreciation not only to the authors of the current edition but also to the ICMA staff, particularly Ron Carlee, Ann Mahoney, Christine Ulrich, and Jane Cotnoir, who assisted in the preparation of this volume. The editorial process and review has produced what we believe readers will find to be a useful, authoritative text. Finally, we would like to acknowledge the foundation built by editors and authors of previous editions of this venerable and influential series that has become synonymous with progressive management of fire services. It has been our distinct privilege to join the ranks of this prestigious group of fire service leaders.

Adam K. Thiel
Fairfax, Virginia

Charles R. Jennings
New York, New York

PART ONE

Policy and Organizational Environment for Fire and Emergency Services

CHAPTER 1

Contemporary Fire and Emergency Services

Adam K. Thiel

This chapter provides an understanding of

- The role of fire and emergency services as part of the community government and comprehensive plan
- Direct and indirect costs associated with fire
- The importance of a good working relationship with public officials and the community as a whole
- The assumptions underlying community-based local government
- Strategies for developing good working relationships with public officials and the community
- The role of fire and emergency services in the community's economic development and neighborhood preservation programs
- Ways to take a proactive role in local, state, and national organizations.

The need to protect communities from the ravages of uncontrolled fire was acknowledged soon after the founding of European colonies in North America. At first, in the absence of organized fire departments, community protection from hostile fires took the literal form of neighbors helping neighbors. When a fire was reported in a town or village, able-bodied residents would quickly band together and contribute to its extinguishment. Leather fire buckets stood by the doors of early homes, ready to be grabbed on the way outside to fight a fire (Figure 1–1).

Given the highly combustible nature of early building construction and the limited effectiveness of bucket brigades, there was low tolerance for human behavior that might increase the community's risk of a conflagration affecting life, property, and the economy. In the British colonies that joined to form the United States, the need for regulations to protect residents was an expected facet of the basic fire protection scheme. According to William J. Novak's research on nineteenth-century America, providing public safety, especially as related to fire protection, has long been a principal role of government (see Figure 1–2): "Fire emerged early as one of the crucial public safety concerns of the young republic. Fire did not merely endanger the people's health or economy or morality; it threatened their very being, their existence."[1] Through the Civil War, the Industrial Revolution, and a tumultuous twentieth century, fire remained a concern for many Americans.

After the first decade of the twenty-first century, despite major advances in fire and building protection technology, the United States leads the world in direct fire losses and fire deaths. From 2005 to 2007, the United States recorded 1.23 fire deaths per 100,000 population.[2] Over the same time period, for example, the United Kingdom had a fire death rate of 0.82 per 100,000 population; Germany, 0.68; France, 1.02; Greece, 1.52; and Singapore, 0.19.[3] Contrary to the perception that fire occurrence is continually decreasing, the number of reported U.S. fire incidents actually increased 1 percent over the five years from 2003 through 2007.[4] During the same period, annual averages of 3,635 civilian fire deaths and 17,600 civilian fire injuries were reported to the U.S. Fire Administration (USFA).[5]

Figure 1-1 Leather buckets were used to fight fires in colonial America.

Photo by Adam K. Thiel

Direct property losses account for a relatively small percentage of the total cost of fire. According to National Fire Protection Association (NFPA) estimates for 2008, direct property loss accounted for only $17.6 billion (4.9 percent) of the $362 billion total annual cost of fire in the United States.[6] As depicted in Figure 1–3, the balance represents indirect costs arising from insurance, fire department infrastructure, fire protection systems installed in buildings, other economic costs (e.g., lost business after a commercial fire), the value of time donated by volunteer firefighters, and the monetary value of fire-related deaths and injuries.

Notwithstanding the magnitude of the U.S. fire problem, which represents an estimated average of 2.5 percent of annual U.S. gross domestic product (GDP),[7] twenty-first-century fire and emergency service organizations are increasingly expected to safely, effectively, and efficiently address emergencies arising from a wide range of hazards. The list of events to which contemporary fire and emergency service departments

---

Portions of this chapter were substantially reproduced and/or adapted from Chapter 3, "Leadership Strategies for the Political Process," by Steven C. Carter and Lyle J. Sumek, and Chapter 8, "Leading and Managing," by Bob Hart and Robin Paulsgrove, in the 2002 edition of this volume.

respond includes fires, medical illnesses and traumatic injuries, hazardous materials (HAZMAT) releases, explosions, vehicle crashes, building and trench collapses, confined space entrapments, and all manner of natural and technological disasters.

An increased awareness of the potential benefits of fire and injury prevention has spurred many U.S. fire and emergency service departments to focus on engineering, education, and enforcement as part of a proactive effort to reduce community losses from fires and other emergencies. At the same time, these departments have placed a renewed emphasis on protecting their own members through initiatives to reduce the approximately 100 firefighter fatalities[8] and estimated 80,000 firefighter injuries[9] occurring each year in this country.

This chapter introduces the origins, evolution, and current state of contemporary fire and emergency services. It then presents foundational information on the public policy environment in which fire and emergency service departments operate, as well as the relationship of those departments to federal, state, and local governance. It briefly describes the organizational environment of a fire and emergency services department (elaborated upon in subsequent chapters), along with trends and challenges facing fire and emergency service leaders in the future.

Photo by Adam K. Thiel

Figure 1-2 The second fire station built by the Friendship Fire Company in Alexandria, Virginia, ca. 1855, still stands today.

Origins of contemporary fire and emergency services

Having advanced well beyond the leather fire buckets and hand-operated pumps of colonial times, contemporary fire and emergency service departments today provide a wide range of services. In addition to fire suppression, many departments also provide emergency medical services, HAZMAT response, technical rescue, fire code enforcement, and public fire/life safety education to their communities. In notable examples from coast to coast, local jurisdictions

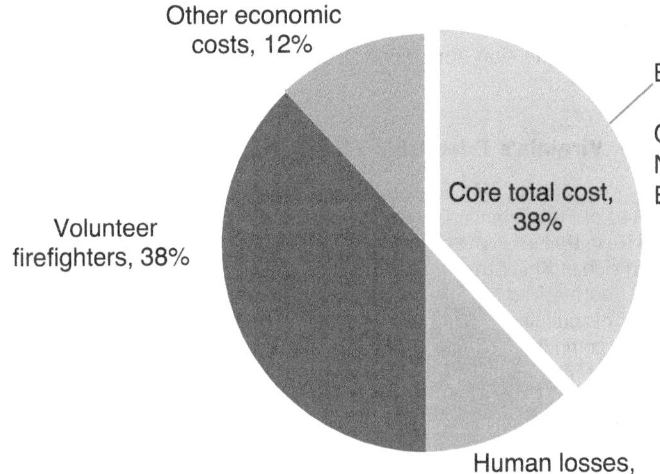

Source: Reproduced with permission from *The Total Cost of Fire in the United States*, by John R. Hall Jr. (Quincy, Mass.: National Fire Protection Association, February 2011), iii, nfpa.org/assets/files/PDF/totalcostsum.pdf. Copyright © 2011, National Fire Protection Association.

Figure 1-3 The total cost of fire in the United States in 2008 was an estimated $362 billion.

cooperatively provide a full spectrum of fire and emergency services by engaging in mutual aid agreements that enhance daily efficiency as well as offer mutual support for major incidents that can quickly outstrip their individual resources.

The rapid pace of technological development since the Industrial Revolution has also influenced the provision of contemporary fire and emergency services. Twenty-first-century buildings are notably safer than buildings of the eighteenth and nineteenth centuries. Continued advances in fire detection and suppression systems—notably, residential fire sprinklers—hold great promise for mitigating the consequences of structural fires. Today's fire and emergency apparatus are highly sophisticated vehicles that provide capabilities once unimaginable, including digital controls, mobile computer terminals, interoperable radio systems, and large-volume fire pumps. Technology also now allows firefighters to advance directly into burning buildings to search for trapped occupants, confine and extinguish fires by applying water and other extinguishing agents, rescue fire victims, ventilate smoke and toxic gases, protect adjacent structures, and save property through salvage and overhaul.

Despite the emergence of previously inconceivable threats, some things have not changed through the years. Billions of people around the globe saw New York City firefighters—along with their colleagues in Northern Virginia—respond to the September 11, 2001, terrorist attacks on the World Trade Center and the Pentagon. Similarly, firefighters were among the first responders who remained at their posts to provide essential fire and emergency services during Hurricane Katrina in 2005. Beyond these high-profile tragedies, an estimated 1,148,100 U.S. firefighters[10] respond 24 hours a day, 365 days per year, to an annual average of 1.6 million fires[11] and countless other emergencies of all descriptions. The courage and professionalism demonstrated by these twenty-first-century heroes continue an unbroken legacy that can be traced back directly to the founders of the United States.

Volunteer fire companies

As the population and land area of the North American colonies expanded, cities and towns became more dense and their economies diversified. It was no longer reasonable to expect everyone in the community to respond to fires, so the first volunteer fire companies were organized in burgeoning cities and towns.

Despite an overall decline in the number of volunteer firefighters nationwide during the past decades, an estimated 71 percent (812,150) of U.S. firefighters in 2009 were volunteers.[12] In fact, the greater part of the United States, in terms of land area, is still protected by volunteer fire departments. However, the majority of the U.S. population, including the populations in the largest cities, is served by career firefighters.

Insurance industry

Insurance companies formed to help protect property owners from economic losses due to fires and other hazards. Many early insurance companies provided fire suppression services through local fire companies, as denoted by firemarks on colonial-era structures (Figure 1–4); buildings without firemarks may or may not have received protection from the local department when a fire occurred.

The formation of Alexandria, Virginia's Friendship Fire Company in 1774

The Friendship Fire Company was organized in 1774. The company purchased the city's first fire engine the next year from Mr. Gibbs of Philadelphia. The engine was kept in a structure on Royal Street on Market Square until 1838. In that year, the company merged with the Crescent Fire Company and moved to the north side of King Street near Columbus Street. In 1851, the company moved to the present location on South Alfred Street. The engine house at that time was a two-story frame house with a steeple. This building was "greatly damaged" by fire in March 1855. On April 5th, the company appointed a committee to petition the City Council "to have built for us a two story brick Engine House." Events moved quickly, and the company held the first meeting in the new engine house on October 29th of that year. The cost of this new building was paid for by grants from the City Council, banks and insurance companies, contributions from the members and citizens, and a "Fair held by the Ladies." This Fair was held during the week of November 5, 1855 at the Sarepta Hall and raised almost $600.00 of the total cost of $2,000.00.

Source: T. Michael Carter, "Forming a More Perfect Community: An Early History of the Friendship Fire Company," *Historic Alexandria Quarterly* (Summer 2002): 2, alexandriava.gov/uploadedfiles/historic/haq/haqsum02.pdf (accessed May 13, 2011).

As fire and emergency response became primarily a local government responsibility, the insurance industry continued its close involvement with community fire protection in several ways. Today insurance agents, underwriters, adjusters, and investigators raise awareness of fire protection and may work closely with fire and emergency service department personnel after an incident. Several national insurance firms offer grant programs to assist fire service organizations with fire prevention and control efforts. Some states have special programs, established in state law and administered by state agencies, that are funded by levies on insurance policies and dedicated to enhancing fire department capabilities.

Photo by Adam K. Thiel

Figure 1-4 The firemark was used in the colonial era to signal that the building would receive fire suppression services through the local fire company.

In perhaps the most visible community interaction with the fire and emergency service, Insurance Services Office, Inc. maintains a Public Protection Classification™ (PPC™) program to provide insurers with information about the fire loss characteristics of jurisdictions throughout the country. The PPC™ descends from a program developed by the National Board of Fire Underwriters, which was established in 1866, after a series of disastrous fires, to evaluate fire risk in U.S. cities.

The insurance industry remains a key stakeholder concerned with the provision of fire and emergency services in communities across the United States and Canada.

Career firefighters

As cities grew ever more dense and the number of fires increased nationwide, volunteer fire companies were challenged to keep pace with service demands and were gradually replaced by paid, full-time career firefighters using specialized equipment. The city of Cincinnati, Ohio, claims the title of the first "fully paid fire department in the United States."[13]

City of Cincinnati Fire Department

On April 1, 1853, Cincinnati, Ohio, established the first professional and fully paid fire department in the United States. Miles Greenwood, co-inventor of the first practical steam fire engine, served as the department's first chief.

One of the principal reasons for creation of a professional and fully paid fire department in Cincinnati was a fire that occurred in 1852 at Miles Greenwood's Eagle Ironworks. The fire destroyed much of Greenwood's business, prompting him to seek new and better ways to fight fires. On March 2, 1852, three Cincinnati residents, Abel Shawk, Alexander Bonner Latta, and Greenwood, began construction of the world's first practical steam-powered fire engine. Shawk was a locksmith, and Latta was a locomotive builder. Greenwood's Eagle Ironworks manufactured the engines. Earlier inventors had manufactured steam-powered fire engines, but the Cincinnati version proved to be much more practical, as the steam engine could begin pumping water out of a water source in ten minutes. Earlier engines took significantly longer.

After the three men demonstrated their finished engine to the Cincinnati City Council, the council members contracted for an engine. The fire engine was presented to the Cincinnati Fire Department on January 1, 1853, making Cincinnati the first city in the world to use steam fire engines. This first engine was named "Uncle Joe Ross" after a city council member. In 1854, Cincinnati residents raised enough funds to allow the Fire department to purchase a second steam fire engine. This engine was known as "Citizen's Gift."

The steam fire engine forever changed firefighting in Cincinnati. Pleased with the engine, local government leaders decided to form a professional fire department rather than relying on volunteers.

Source: City of Cincinnati, "Fire Department: History" (n.d.), cincinnati-oh.gov/cityfire/pages/-16094-/ (accessed January 28, 2011).

Seventy-three percent of the NFPA-estimated 335,950 U.S. career firefighters serve communities with populations greater than 25,000.[14] Even in smaller communities that still rely heavily on volunteers, career firefighters are sometimes employed on a full- or part-time basis to conduct routine training, maintenance, and inspection duties, along with ensuring the initial response of fire apparatus when volunteer staff is unavailable—often during the daytime hours.

The estimated number of career firefighters in the United States increased 40 percent from 1983 to 2008.[15] This upward trend is expected to continue as demand rises for fire and emergency services, fire and emergency service department roles and responsibilities expand, legal liability increases, additional training and certification mandates are implemented, community expectations are raised, and overall volunteerism in American society declines.

The public policy environment

Public expectations for fire and emergency services remain extremely high. In a 2009 international survey performed by the GFK Group, firefighters in sixteen of seventeen countries worldwide (including the United States) received respondents' highest marks for trustworthiness.[16] In the United States, most citizens hold a bedrock belief that when they call 911, the local fire and emergency service department will respond quickly and effectively to any situation, anytime, anywhere.

Notwithstanding citizens' trust and expectations, fire and emergency services are not delivered in a vacuum. The public policy environment where twenty-first-century fire and emergency service departments operate is characterized by the complex interaction of politics, economics, demographics, geography, and sociology.

Politics

It is impossible to ignore the role of politics in the administration of fire and emergency services. As the word is used in this chapter, *politics* describes the processes that citizens use to make policy choices about how their communities are governed. Ultimately, the political process defines how fire and emergency services are delivered to residents, businesses, and visitors in local jurisdictions across North America.

In contrast to some other countries, where fire and emergency services are provided by national organizations or subject to meaningful national regulations, in the United States and Canada these services are a state or provincial responsibility that is generally delegated to localities with a great degree of flexibility. State constitutions vary in their treatment of fire and emergency services, with some states taking more or less statutory responsibility than others.

Local governance is the responsibility of elected officials—the mayor and city council, board of aldermen, county commission, county board of supervisors, board of fire trustees, and so forth. Governance focuses on defining what the local government is going to be: its vision for the future, goals for the community, allocation of resources, and decisions on key policy issues. The governing process has nine basic elements, and each elected body has its own style of governing. In addition, elected boards all have in common a standard life cycle that reflects the phases of the political season.

The nine basic elements by which elected bodies govern are (1) listening to the community (making themselves available to hear the ideas and concerns of a wide variety of citizens); (2) informing citizens about the local government, its vision and goals, policies and plans, programs and services; (3) defining the future direction of the community by articulating a focused vision that is simple, understandable, and usable and has outcome-based goals for which there are benchmarks of future success; (4) making decisions on policy direction, resource allocation, solutions to problems, issues to be addressed during the next year, and level of services; (5) setting the tone for the way business is conducted in the local government and for the image of government that is transmitted in the community and to the outside world; (6) representing the local government—serving as its spokesperson—to federal and state officials, to other local governments at the elected-official level, and to the outside world (including businesses that desire to relocate to the local community); (7) monitoring the performance of the local government (the results of local government services and actions and the effects on, and reactions of, citizens); (8) seeking feedback from citizens and adjusting policies and resources accordingly; and (9) mobilizing support from community partners—community groups, public institutions, schools, key businesses and business leaders, neighborhood associations—who can help achieve a goal.

Each elected body develops its own style of carrying out these basic elements of governing. Even in situations in which only one or two positions change after an election cycle, the style and process of governing will change. A fire and emergency services manager can define his or her elected body's own style of governing by observing the governing process and determining whether the elected officials

- Are problem solvers, focusing on specific problems and expecting quick and timely action by staff
- Are crisis managers, responding to the phone calls and complaints of citizens by directing staff to take short-term actions
- Are visionaries, developing long-term goals and bringing into focus a vision for the community's future
- Are legislative leaders, balancing long-term goals with short-term results, and individual citizens' desires with what the legislators see as best for the overall community.

Every elected body has a dominant style, and it is important that fire and emergency service administrators understand the style of the elected body and, in working with the elected officials, adapt their approach to that style. For example, if the members of the elected body do not read the agenda and supporting materials, the manager should think about alternative ways to provide information on a policy issue—perhaps by taking them on a field trip, meeting with them one-on-one to discuss the issue, and so forth. However, fire service managers' actions should be guided by this principle: think political (put yourself in their shoes) but act apolitical (focus on the policy background rather than on lobbying).

Economics

As previously mentioned, the economic cost of fire is staggering. According to the USFA, a federal agency responsible for supporting state and local fire services, the estimated direct value of property lost in U.S. fires was $15 billion for 2007; in the five years from 2003 to 2007, the direct cost of fire losses in the United States, when adjusted for inflation, increased 8 percent.[17]

Since fire protection is generally considered a "public good," local governments bear the lion's share of the cost of providing fire and emergency services across the United States and Canada. In 2008, continuing a decades-long trend, local governments in the United States spent $39.7 billion on direct expenditures to protect their communities from fire (Table 1–1).[18]

Some people may look at local budget dollars spent on fire protection (including fire prevention and life safety education) as wasted in light of other possible uses. A consideration of the potential economic and social downsides of failing to adequately protect communities from fire, however, may lend a different perspective. As illustrated in Figure 1–3, the immediate and visible consequences of direct fire losses pale in comparison to the indirect losses, which include business interruption, health care costs, and lost wages.

Demographics

The population of the United States is in a continual state of flux. U.S. Census Bureau projections anticipate sweeping demographic changes across the entire nation in the decades to come. By 2039, the U.S. population is expected to reach the 400 million mark. All of the baby boom generation—nearly one in five U.S. residents—will be 65 and older by 2030. By 2050, the 65-plus age group will double its 2008 count to 38.7 million. The minorities—taken together, currently about one-third of the nation's population—are expected to become the majority in 2042; projections suggest that the United States will be 54 percent "minority" by 2050. The working-age population (18–64) is expected to decline from 63 to 57 percent by 2050.[19]

These changes will directly or indirectly affect the provision of fire and emergency services in local communities; in some ways the impacts will be subtle, in other ways quite obvious. Generally speaking, population drives demand for fire and emergency service departments. As population increases with its attendant effects (e.g., new buildings, increased density, traffic

Table 1-1 Direct expenditures on local fire protection, 1980-2008

Year	Expenditures (in $ billions)	Expenditures (in $ billions) adjusted for inflation*
1980	5.7	5.7
1981	6.3	5.7
1982	7.0	6.0
1983	7.6	6.3
1984	8.2	6.5
1985	8.5	6.5
1986	9.6	7.2
1987	10.5	7.9
1988	11.8	8.2
1989	11.9	7.9
1990	13.2	8.3
1991	13.8	8.3
1992	14.4	8.5
1993	15.4	9.0
1994	16.1	9.0
1995	17.0	9.2
1996	17.7	9.3
1997	19.4	10.0
1998	20.3	10.3
1999	21.3	10.5
2000	23.1	11.1
2001	25.0	11.6
2002	26.0	11.9
2003	27.9	12.5
2004	28.4	12.4
2005	30.7	13.0
2006	34.2	14.0
2007	36.8	14.6
2008	39.7	15.2

Source: U.S. Bureau of the Census, Governments Division.

*Adjustments were made to 1980 dollars using the Consumer Price Index.

Source: Reproduced with permission from *U.S. Fire Department Profile through 2009*, by Michael J. Karter and Gary P. Stein (Quincy, Mass.: NFPA, October 2010), 29, firecompany4.com/wp-content/uploads/2010/07/National-Volunteer-Firefighters-Profile-2009.pdf (accessed January 28, 2011).

congestion, etc.), so too does the demand for fire and emergency services. The socioeconomic characteristics of a local jurisdiction's population also affect its fire risk and service demand profile, as discussed later in this section.

Geography

The global recession that started in 2008 will also likely affect the delivery of fire and emergency services for years to come. Writing for the *Atlantic Monthly* magazine in March 2009, noted urbanist Richard Florida asserted that recovery from the "crash of 2008" will fundamentally reshape America's geography:

> If there is one constant in the history of capitalist development, it is the ever-more-intensive use of space. Today, we need to begin making smarter use of both our urban spaces and the suburban rings that surround them—packing in more people, more affordably, while at the same time improving their quality of life. That means liberal zoning and building codes within cities to allow more residential development, more mixed-use development in suburbs and cities alike, the in-filling of suburban cores near rail links, new investment in rail, and congestion pricing for travel on our roads. Not everyone wants to live in city centers, and the suburbs are not about to disappear. But we can do a much better job of connecting suburbs to cities and to each other, and allowing regions to grow bigger and denser without losing their velocity.[20]

The implications of these changes for the delivery of local fire protection and emergency services can already be seen in many areas of the country. Urban redevelopment and the movement of people back to central cities are occurring as a reaction against suburban sprawl and are being spurred by urban planners' promotion of "new urbanism" and more densely populated, transit-oriented, mixed-use communities.

Sociology

Fire damages the social fabric of communities in many ways. The societal impact of fires, while difficult to quantify, is no less important than the economic impact. Burned-out buildings can lead to neighborhood blight; families are displaced from their friends and neighbors; and burn victims wear their scars forever (see Figure 1–5).

The USFA publishes a periodic report, *Fire in the United States,* on fire outcomes, and the report consistently points to disparities in fire losses for certain groups:

> Fire losses affect all groups and races, rich and poor, North and South, urban and rural. But the problem is higher for some groups than for others. African-Americans and American Indian males have much higher fire death rates than the national average. African-Americans comprise a large and disproportionate share of total fire deaths, accounting for 22 percent of fire deaths—nearly twice as high as their share of the overall population (13 percent).[21]

The report goes on to identify the higher probability, compared to the general population, of fire deaths and injuries for adults over age 65.

Understanding the socioeconomic factors influencing fire losses and deaths can help fire and emergency service departments with community risk assessment, resource deployment, and delivery of public fire and life safety education to high-risk community members.

Public policy issues

Beyond those specific to the departments themselves, numerous other public policy issues can influence the delivery of fire and emergency services. Telecommunications policy, for example, affects many fire and emergency service departments and their partner agencies as they work to

Photo by Adam K. Thiel

Figure 1-5 This fire caused almost $1 million in direct property loss and displaced four families.

Major fire issues for the public arena

- **Mission and range of services** Services provided by fire and emergency service departments have expanded considerably in the last thirty years. Fire responses now account for a decreasing percentage of activity in most agencies and have been exceeded particularly by emergency medical calls. What should the fire service's mission be? What services should it provide? How will the answers to these questions affect the local community?
- **Funding** Few agencies would admit to having adequate funding. When economic conditions are weak or funding is limited, agencies sometimes experience serious budget reductions. Or they are required to provide services for a rapidly expanding population while resources remain static. What alternative funding options are there? Are fees consistent with the mission? Where will funds be spent most effectively? If funding is not adequate, what is the most reasonable place to reduce expenditures? Would privatizing or alternative organizational arrangements be more cost-effective?
- **Regional cooperation** Potentially greater effectiveness and efficiency are two strong inducements for increasing regional cooperation. Would greater cooperation benefit citizens? What type of cooperation would be most effective—consolidation, functional consolidation, mutual aid, automatic aid, or some other type? (Consolidation is the merging of two or more agencies; functional consolidation is the merging of a function, such as training, of two or more agencies; mutual aid is an agreement between departments to respond when specific assistance is requested; and automatic aid is having the closest unit automatically respond to a call regardless of political boundaries.)
- **Privatization and contracting** A number of communities have considered privatization or contracting. Are there services or activities that others can provide more cost-effectively—for example, emergency medical response, fire code inspection, training of fire personnel, or public education? Some communities contract with private organizations for all their fire services. Other communities have chosen to retain certain fire functions internally, such as fire prevention and code enforcement, while contracting for the remainder. More commonly, communities contract for specific functions, such as emergency medical service or airport fire service.
- **Entrepreneurship** Some agencies have developed more of a private enterprise approach themselves, offering their services to other jurisdictions for a fee, selling public information programs they have developed, and so forth. Is this sort of thing appropriate for public agencies?
- **Diversity** Census numbers show that communities and their workforces are becoming increasingly diverse, yet the workforces of many agencies still do not reflect the diversity of the communities they serve. In many instances this has resulted in litigation; perhaps more important, a lack of diversity has negatively affected the relationship between the agency and segments of the community. (The International Association of Black Professional Fire Fighters, the National Association of Hispanic Firefighters, and the International Association of Women in the Fire and Emergency Services have an increasing presence in departments nationwide.) How do community groups feel about such underrepresentation? Is there an ongoing, constructive dialogue on this issue in the department? In the community?
- **Facilities** The growth of communities has strained the fire service's capacity, as the cost of new stations and staffing is high. In older sections of the community, stations built thirty or more years ago may no longer be adequate for new service, equipment, staffing, and health and safety needs. How can these needs be addressed? Are stations located where they need to be? Some municipalities construct stations jointly, to be staffed by departments in both municipalities.
- **Equipment and technology** Purchase of a new or replacement ladder truck at almost a million dollars is a major expenditure in many communities. Specialized functions (e.g., water rescue, high-angle rescue) create additional funding needs. New technology is constantly being introduced. How does the agency decide when to purchase new equipment or technology, and how is the purchase funded?
- **Staffing, compensation, and work hours** Increases in costs of fire and emergency services are due mainly to labor costs, including salaries, health care costs, and postemployment benefits. Some departments have begun to consider alternative staffing arrangements, including a combination of paid and volunteer staff, use of paid on-call employees (paid by the hour or incident for responding to alarms or participating in drills), or staffing shared with other jurisdictions.
- **Working conditions and safety** Outside agencies, such as the National Fire Protection Association and the federal Occupational Safety and Health Administration, have set standards and requirements that significantly affect local operations. How can local agencies address these requirements?

Source: Adapted from Steven C. Carter and Lyle J. Sumek, "Leadership Strategies for the Political Process," in *Managing Fire and Rescue Services*, ed. Dennis Compton and John Granito (Washington, D.C.: ICMA, 2002), 67-69.

build and maintain interoperable voice/data communications networks; health care policy has an obvious impact on the fire and emergency services, especially those providing emergency medical care and transport of the sick and injured; and transportation policy affects fire and emergency responders in terms of traffic congestion and regulations governing HAZMAT transport.

Environmental policy has also become increasingly relevant as fire and emergency service delivery is affected by efforts to combat global warming. Effects include the impact of green building technologies on firefighting strategy and tactics, and of regulations governing emissions for large vehicles such as heavy fire apparatus.

Local government and community expectations

Since the majority of fire and emergency service organizations in the United States and Canada are agencies of, or affiliated with, local government, this section examines several aspects of local governance with salience for most fire and emergency service department leaders. It is important to understand that while a comprehensive treatment of local government management is beyond the scope of this book, executive-level fire and emergency service administrators are expected to function as public administrators akin to any other city or county department head.

Background: Professional local government

Starting in about 1960, most local governments tried to attain and sustain a professional approach to government in the face of increasing demands for, and the resulting complexity of, a broad array of services. Professional local government assumed the desirability of

- Separation between politics (elected officials) and administration (managers), with policy set by the elected officials and implemented by staff
- Centralization of organizational processes (including employee recruitment and selection, salary policy and administration, and purchasing and financial management)
- Development of professionally based standards (such as zoning, development standards, life safety codes, sprinkler ordinances)
- Increased emphasis on and resources for employee development (e.g., fire academies for new firefighters, in-service training programs to expand skills)
- Support for technology (e.g., new safety equipment, more highly engineered fire apparatus, and computers in vehicles) as a tool for management and fire suppression
- Greater emphasis on planning for the future (preincident planning, participation of fire managers in reviewing development plans and land use proposals, studies of the locations of fire stations, and so forth)
- Experimentation with innovative programs (such as water rescue units, technical rescue, and HAZMAT programs)
- Expansion of services and service areas (by incorporating full emergency medical services in the fire department, contracting for service outside the jurisdictional boundaries, and so forth)
- Limitation of citizen involvement to large formal committees or the public hearing process.

The fire service was changed for the better by these efforts and now has a strong professional foundation.

In the late 1980s, however, individual citizens and community groups increasingly challenged professional government, arguing that local governments had become insensitive to the needs of their communities and to the effects that their services and actions had on citizens. Basically, in many communities citizens felt that local government officials had gone too far in professionalizing. Citizens cited the following perceptions:

- Arrogance of local government officials (from elected officials to managers to employees) in minimizing citizen concerns or issues

- Bureaucratic approach to rules and procedures, reflecting a rigidity that sometimes led to decisions or actions that made no sense to the community
- Seemingly predetermined outcomes in decision making, with the "participative" process simply an attempt by the professionals to manipulate and placate citizens
- Punitive actions toward the average citizen, especially in code enforcement and inspections
- Patronizing attitude—belief that the professionals know what is best for the community
- Inbreeding of membership on boards and commissions, giving the impression that citizen involvement was for the select few
- Decision making based on thorough research and analysis but paying no attention and giving no weight to citizen concerns.

Certainly, some staffs and elected officials assumed less visible roles than their more political predecessors had, and participated less in community events. As for fire chiefs and managers, they spent more of their spare time on professional activities and matters related to professional associations. This emphasis was encouraged by local government managers and elected bodies, who put a high value on recognition by peers and professional organizations. As fire departments got caught up in the drive for an internally prized professionalism, fewer fire suppression personnel were involved or known in the community. In some places, the image of the firefighter as the trusted friend in the community faded.

Emergence of community-based local government

During the 1990s, local elected officials and managers began to reemphasize the importance of community. In this now-prevalent model of local governance, the professional approach is balanced with what is best for the community as determined by the elected officials. This balancing sometimes means that the line between policy and administration is blurred.

The community-based model rests on the following assumptions:

- Every locality consists of a number of communities, defined by geography, race or ethnicity, age, income, and so forth.
- Local governments need to reach out to citizens, inviting them to participate as partners.
- Local government employees should be empowered to use their discretion to proactively solve problems in the community.
- Elected officials, managers, and employees must listen to citizens' expressions of their needs and desires, help them define problems that require attention, and help them clarify their expectations of local government and the outcomes they want.
- Citizens need to be included in a decision-making process early, not just when it is time to react to the final report.
- Goals should focus on outcomes for the communities and be checked out with citizens.
- Staff members should focus their energy on meeting the community's needs first and other needs later.
- Values and goals should take priority over rules and regulations.
- Local officials and managers need to increase their visibility in the community by participating in community events or celebrations, becoming active in service or civic organizations, attending meetings, and listening.
- Evaluating and adjusting services and programs are essential to success.

Community-based government in action

How does community-based local government really work? The foundation is the community, beginning with citizens who form neighborhood associations, cultural/religious organizations, or special-interest groups that advocate for a specific cause. There are also numerous civic and community groups that have access to and participate in local government decision making. In addition, elected officials appoint committees and task forces as well as boards and com-

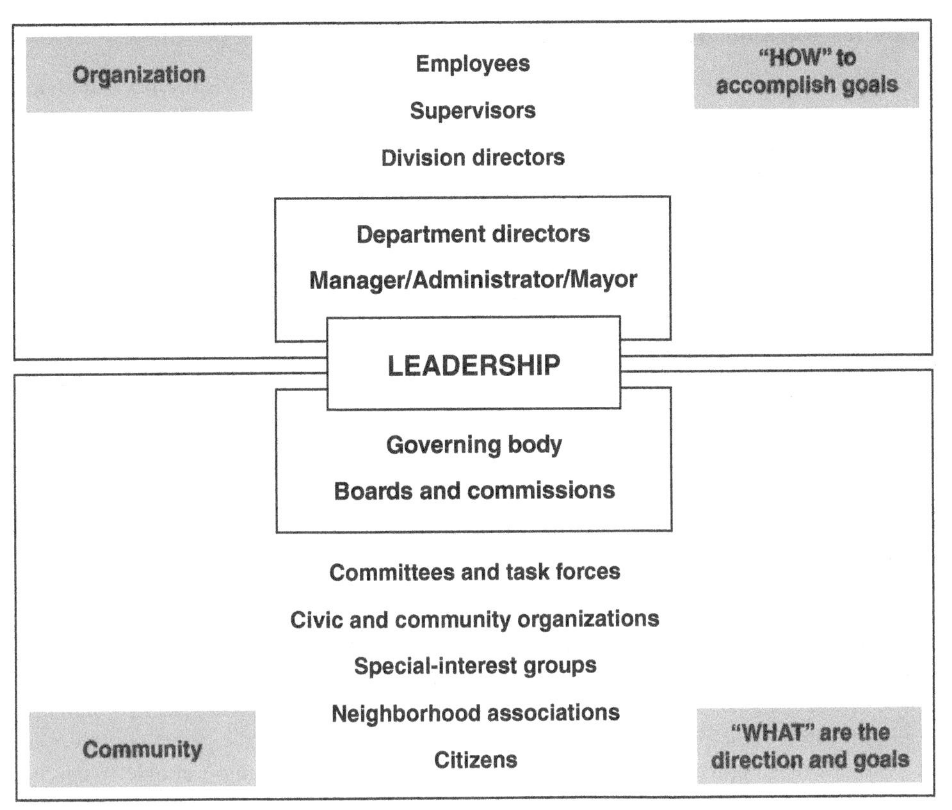

Courtesy of Lyle Sumek Associates, Inc., 2000

Figure 1-6 The relationship between citizens, their representatives, and the governing body is depicted in this chart showing how community-based local government works.

missions to help them (the officials) in the governing process. The ultimate representatives of the community are the individuals who are elected to the governing body, and it is they who decide what is going to get accomplished (see lower half of Figure 1–6).

The local government organization (top half of Figure 1–6) is represented first by the employees who are in the field, providing services and delivering products. Supervisors and division directors translate the goals, mission, and values of the organization to employees. Department directors have the dual concern of supporting policy development and leading the departmental organization. The city manager or administrator is the organization's key link to the governing body and the political process. The organization's purpose is to determine how to accomplish goals set, and implement decisions made, by the governing body.

Under the model of community-based local government, fire service managers should be guided by the following "commandments":

1. Know your communities: who they are, what is unique to each, who their leaders are, what they perceive to be their problems and needs.
2. Define desired outcomes for community goals and fire service goals, with measurable benchmarks.
3. Involve citizens in fire and emergency service decisions and programs as appropriate.
4. Make decisions about what is best that balance professional standards and community needs.
5. Empower employees and managers to solve problems and make decisions.
6. When necessary, negotiate on policy decisions to achieve a viable, realistic outcome whenever possible.
7. Develop approaches to educating citizens about the fire and emergency services department and its services.
8. Anticipate community issues and opportunities that lie over the horizon.
9. Evaluate the effect that programs have on the community.
10. Build a personal presence in the community.

Tools for working with communities

Fire and emergency service department managers have used many tools to understand and respond to their different communities. No one set of tools will work in all locales or for all communities, but tools that have worked for some fire and emergency service managers are presented below. Beyond the specifics of these six tools lies the fact that each locale, and the public arena along with it, is changing. The fire and emergency service needs to be sensitive to its community's future needs as well as to its present needs.

Tool 1: Develop a community profile Fire department managers, working with the city manager and other departments or with their own staffs, can develop a profile of who really makes up their communities and how their communities are changing. In many cases, perceptions do not match the reality. Fire and emergency service managers should begin with basic demographic data, such as age, educational level, and income level; establish a baseline; and examine trends over time. They should then expand the profile to identify expectations of local government, including programs and service delivery mechanisms. This information can guide them as they define their mission (Tool 2) or develop a new program (Tool 4).

Tool 2: Reevaluate the departmental mission and core values Managers should look up on the wall and dust off the old mission statement. Most fire departments have mission statements and statements of core operating values, but many of those statements are generic and look alike or were developed years ago. Fire and emergency service managers need to begin by looking at the current needs and expectations of their own communities and citizens (see Figure 1-7). An aging housing supply or a population of elderly people calls for a different mission from that of a department in a community with newer homes built under modern codes and a younger citizenry. Core values, too, should be reviewed: how should the fire and emergency services department provide services and work with citizens? How the department does its work will determine its image in the community. Managers need to align the department's values with the community's values, as reflected by the next four tools.

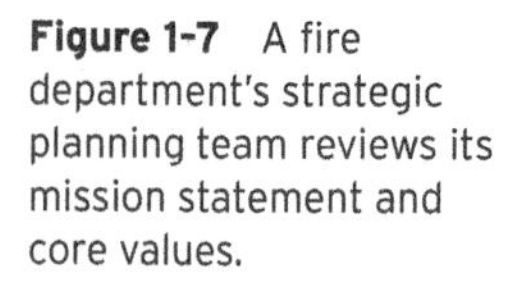

Figure 1-7 A fire department's strategic planning team reviews its mission statement and core values.

Photo by Adam K. Thiel

Tool 3: Create a citizen task force Fire managers have continuing opportunities to involve citizens through task forces. (Some task forces may be created by the elected officials, others by the fire and emergency services organization.) A task force has (1) a specific assignment (usually to define the problems or issues, to bring into focus desired outcomes for the community, to identify and evaluate options, and to make recommendations); (2) small membership (seven to nine is optimal, there should be no more than eleven, and members should be identified not by special interest but by communities to be represented; elected officials can be asked to identify potential members); (3) a defined time frame (three to six months is best, and twelve months is the absolute limit); (4) regular agendas (prepared in advance of all meetings) and minutes (recording the decisions made); and (5) for complex issues, special reports to serve as discussion guides. The key for citizens is that their participation on a task force makes a difference and produces tangible results.

Tool 4: Develop a community-based program Identifying a community issue that relates to fire and emergency services and developing a neighborhood-based program in response is a way for fire department managers to engage the community proactively (see Figure 1–8).

The keys to community-based programs are

- Developing and maintaining a philosophy within the department that supports community-based programs, as demonstrated by an enthusiastic commitment of resources and staff time
- Addressing "real" community issues and concerns (see Tool 6)
- Involving citizens as partners so that they have a responsible role
- Producing results that are visible in the community, generating a sense of making progress
- Making the experience positive and fun for both citizens and firefighters.

Tool 5: Maintain a greater community presence Fire managers should get out into the community, setting the example by increasing their personal presence and staff's presence in the community. They should begin by drawing up a list of key community events or festivals, key civic and community organizations, and key businesses and institutions. Next they should

Photo by Adam K. Thiel

Figure 1-8 Community volunteers prepare to deliver fire safety literature in neighborhoods.

evaluate the involvement of the fire and emergency service organizations with an eye to who should be involved and to what extent.

Community presence may include

- Visiting community organizations
- Meeting one-on-one with citizens, including key community leaders
- Participating in community events (e.g., celebrations, parades, festivals)
- Opening fire and emergency service stations to the community (the chief alone cannot be everywhere, but the department's presence can be enhanced)
- Developing a department website, blog, Facebook group, or Twitter feed.

Tool 6: Check out citizens' needs and satisfaction Fire department managers should survey their citizens. Many local jurisdictions conduct regular surveys of the community, and fire managers can participate in these efforts by incorporating questions related to fire and emergency services—or they can develop their own surveys. These surveys are a reality check and can provide valuable feedback to enhance management and service delivery. Their results can be discussed in staff meetings and used in developing programs and budgets. One alternative to general surveys is periodic phone surveys on specific issues (the scope needs to be narrowly defined). To get more in-depth feedback, another alternative is to use focus groups. In all cases, the key is listening to communities and using the messages received in managing fire and emergency services.

Seven major roles of effective chiefs and managers

Depending on the size and type of department, as well as on its relationship to the broader local government, the job of a fire chief or manager can be very different from that of an operationally focused company or chief officer. This is not to say that understanding, and sometimes commanding, fire and emergency incidents is not important. However, fire chiefs and managers who are effective in the public arena, whether at the local, state, or national level, usually assume one or more other roles as well. Style and approach may differ, and the fairly common roles described below are not mutually exclusive. They overlap and reinforce each other; successful chiefs and managers will combine aspects of several of them and may also delegate some roles to subordinates.

Community ambassador

Community ambassadors work with their communities. They begin by getting to know the community: identifying it; listening to it; helping it focus on issues and problems related to the fire and emergency services; and getting to know influential individuals, groups, and organizations. They also represent the fire and emergency services department to the community, serving as spokespersons, sharing information about the department and its services, and functioning as symbolic leaders who are present in the community. They assume responsibility for educating citizens about the fire department and fire-related issues. They make sure that key citizens and stakeholders are brought to the table with staff to define issues and explore opportunities. They are recognized by people in the community and are invited to participate in community activities. The role of community ambassador, therefore, requires a presence in the community, a willingness to listen, the ability to relate to an individual as a person, and the ability to communicate ideas through brief messages.

Futurist

Futurists have their eyes on the horizon. With regard to the community, they anticipate potential policy or political issues that may affect and should involve the fire and emergency services department. With regard to the profession, through professional organizations and journals they keep abreast of innovations in the fire service and of services that might be useful to the community. They anticipate change and plan for it. They work with the community and staff to test new ideas—to see whether those ideas might add value to fire and emergency service programs and services, and whether they are likely to work in the particular community. After determining that a concept is worth pursuing, they frame the issue and present it to the elected officials and the community. Being a futurist requires reading; taking a proactive role in local, state, and national organizations; attending professional meetings; searching for real opportunities; separating fad from fact; and being willing to take risks and experiment.

Political strategist

Political strategists work with elected officials and community leaders, with whom they have developed credible relationships based on mutual trust and consideration. They respect role boundaries. They help the elected officials define the problem and bring possible outcomes into focus, and once goals are decided on, they make suggestions and advise these leaders on everything from involving the community to building support for action. Political strategists must be able to relate to various kinds of people, find personal links, think strategy and not just project or program, develop an action plan, and advise without directing. In fulfilling this role, fire and emergency service leaders must consider the broader context and community plans, including the comprehensive plan, working alongside their colleagues in other departments to address planning, zoning, transportation, infrastructure, and other policy issues—with oversight and direction from elected officials.

Negotiator

Negotiators represent the fire and emergency services department to other agencies and organizations, and represent the local government to other public or private entities. They help negotiate local agreements on fire and emergency services, contracts with other entities (such as hospitals), arrangements for emergency medical and labor contracts, and so forth. This role requires the ability to seek options and arrive at a compromise—a compromise that must be represented to, and owned by, the department and must be acceptable to elected officials and community. Negotiators must be willing and able to be part of a negotiating team, articulate and argue a point of view, seek a middle ground, and sell the agreement to others.

Lobbyist

Lobbyists work with state and federal governments to make decisions that affect the fire and emergency service's responsibilities, capabilities, and resources. These lobbying efforts are generally made through professional organizations and take place both at the legislative level and with agencies. Legislative lobbying involves representing defined positions on legislative proposals, monitoring potential and proposed legislation, drafting bills and potential amendments, and taking time to develop personal relationships. Agency lobbying focuses on administrative regulations and requirements, identifies programs to improve safety, and supports funding for desirable programs. Lobbying requires an outgoing personality, the ability to develop personal relations and credibility with a variety of politicians of different personality types, the ability to translate technical issues into easily understandable messages, a tolerance for ambiguity, and a willingness to act without needing to see results.

Navigator

Navigators first help others focus on the end results and desired outcomes, and then help them maneuver through obstacles in the community and the political arena. They develop the process—how to get to the defined destination. Recognizing that the political environment is fluid and can change at a moment's notice, navigators monitor the community and the political arena for these changes and, when they happen, suggest alternative routes for consideration by elected officials and managers. Navigators need an astute political sense, a concern for the process, flexibility in proposing alternatives, the ability to suggest a route without asserting control, and a willingness to remain in the background so that elected officials and managers take credit for the progress and final results.

Relationship between the fire chief and the local government manager

All public officials, not only fire chiefs, are charged with doing their part to make their communities safe and livable. Local government managers share many objectives with fire chiefs, but differences in perspective can inhibit communication. In addition, fire chiefs and other local government officials are human beings, and like everyone else, for the sake of efficiency, they may form opinions on the basis of limited experiences and paint entire professions with a broad brush.

Local government managers may view fire chiefs as inflexible or assume that their scope of interests and concerns is limited. Fire chiefs may see local government managers as transient, searching for short-term wins. For both leaders, meeting changing needs and maintaining a successful peer relationship with the other are challenges. However, some fire chiefs and local government managers have built and maintained very effective working partnerships.

Such peer relationships are possible if questions are asked that test understanding and alignment.

In particular, a local government manager, concerned about the "traditional" fire service, may wonder whether the fire chief has a vision for the future of the local fire service. If the chief is asked, "On what does the future of the fire service depend?" he or she should be prepared to respond. And if the question is not asked directly, the chief should be prepared to volunteer thoughtful ideas about what the community's fire and emergency services ought to look like in the future and why.

The fire chief's perspective

Most fire chiefs want to be heard, respected, trusted, and treated as professional peers. They have dedicated their careers to a specific technical discipline. They do not want someone to evaluate, label, or dismiss them on the basis of their uniform or occupation.

Local government managers should be mindful of the situation in which they may put their fire chiefs. Chiefs are often asked to position their departments for the future by looking beyond their own needs and developing interdepartmental systems to serve the community. City and county managers have asked for analyses of bureaucratic structures, with management layers eliminated or consolidated to become more efficient and responsive. They have asked for budgets framed by affordability, with reductions in funding. But as chiefs reposition their departments, appropriately questioning existing assumptions, they must not compromise the safety of the community or of their firefighters. The fire chief has to make difficult choices, balancing a commitment to being a responsible, responsive member of the manager's team with a desire to maintain an effective organization while managing an increasingly anxious workforce.

For fire service leaders to stand for safety seems fundamental. On consensus issues—those on which the population at large is in general agreement and where the interests of the fire service and other government agencies are identical—it is comparatively easy to do this. The real test of leadership may come when a leader must stand alone on difficult issues—for example, balancing code compliance with legitimate business concerns. Within the context of local government as a whole, a fire chief's understanding of the sensitive political issues in a dynamic government and community environment is fundamental to leadership success. A leader should be able to both identify multiple solutions and modify a position when additional information is provided. But adopting a position solely because it is politically popular, or changing a position as a result of inappropriate pressure, can be an abdication of leadership. A credible leader is defined by the ability to balance two extremes within personal and professional ethical standards.

Champion

Champions are boosters of the fire and emergency services, the fire and emergency services department, and the local government without being self-promoting. They look at ways of getting others to believe in the department and of inspiring others to act in support of its mission. They seek or create opportunities to celebrate successes in the community, the local government, and the department—successes such as the completion of projects and the accomplishment of established goals. Rather than claiming personal credit, champions thank partners and supporters and share successes with others. Champions need an optimistic outlook, skills in marketing, and the willingness to take time for the little niceties of thanking others and celebrating success.

Fire and emergency service organizations today

It is difficult to generalize about the organizational environment for fire and emergency services across the United States. Local communities generally provide these services in whatever manner their citizens select through the public policy process. Some communities rely on a collection of essentially independent fire and emergency service organizations (using volunteers, career firefighters, or a combination of both); others contract with neighboring jurisdictions, special districts, or private firms; and others develop (and fund) sophisticated, all-hazards fire and emergency response agencies attuned to twenty-first-century challenges.

The local government manager's perspective

From the point of view of the city or county manager, the key to a successful working relationship with the fire chief is the chief's credibility. Fire chiefs can improve their credibility with local government managers by avoiding a self-righteous communications style and remembering that they are not the only ones concerned about community safety; managers share this commitment and responsibility.

Credibility begins with telling the truth without a "spin," having one's facts straight, nondefensively evaluating systems and structures, and candidly responding to questions. Credibility means giving the manager the same assistance that the chief expects from his or her own staff: multiple options with a thorough analysis of the alternatives.

Participating more in the public policy debate by providing factual data is also important. For instance, the manager expects the fire chief to be forthcoming about the effect that fire department staffing and other budgetary decisions (station locations, new equipment, and so forth) will have on insurance rates paid by home owners. The manager's aim is to seek an equitable balance among the community's fire rating, insurance rates paid, and expenditures; and data from the fire chief can help in that regard. Each budgetary decision relating to the fire and emergency service will affect the financial burden that every citizen and property owner bears in supporting local government services, and the manager's goal is to ensure that this financial burden produces the necessary services while being neither excessive nor unwarranted.

In addition, the fire chief should remember that in the context of local government, fire and emergency services represent the expenditure of a relatively large amount of money. More important, however, is the fact that the staffing of a fire and emergency services department is different from that of other city or county departments. This traditional difference—twenty-four-hour, or overnight, shifts in the fire service—necessitates a different method of calculating overtime, standard workweek, holiday pay, and budget expenditures. Consequently, comparisons made by other employee groups may create conflict.

As technology evolves in the areas of fire suppression equipment and fire/smoke detection and in the building and trades industry, the manager expects the fire and emergency services department to stay up-to-date. Although much is said about fire prevention, too often (partly because of tradition and partly because of staff orientation) suppression consumes a larger portion of the department's budget. The manager expects the chief to be creative in using firefighters—and in partnership with the building and trades community—to bridge the gap between suppression and prevention, strengthening education about fire prevention so as to meet broader local government objectives. This use of firefighters could include code enforcement activities as well as emergency preparedness, education, and prevention efforts. Through prefire and emergency response planning, it could also include identifying hazards that confront the community. (For details on comprehensive fire and injury prevention, see Chapter 6.)

Finally, if the local fire service assumes responsibility for emergency medical response, the manager expects the chief to play a role within the broader context of community health. The emergency response program must be integrated closely and coordinated with community health services as a whole to ensure the adequate and equitable delivery of overall comprehensive health services within the community.

Source: Adapted from Bob Hart and Robin Paulsgrove, "Leading and Managing," in *Managing Fire and Rescue Services*, ed. Dennis Compton and John Granito (Washington, D.C.: ICMA, 2002), 263-265.

The range of services provided by contemporary fire and emergency service departments spans several discrete lines of business.

Fire suppression

The vast majority of fire departments in the United States consider fire suppression to be their core mission (see Figure 1-9). While the range of services they provide is much broader than just responding to fires, fire departments are, by and large, the only local government entity with primary responsibility for suppressing fires in buildings, vehicles, and outdoors. (Chapters 3, 4, and 12 provide detailed information on evaluating fire risk and deploying resources to safely accomplish fire suppression.)

Community risk reduction

In contrast to many other industrialized nations, where fire prevention and the overall reduction of community risk is seen as the fire department's core mission, the United States puts comparatively little emphasis on this important facet of protecting the community, but that emphasis is increasing (see Figure 1-10). (Chapter 6 provides a comprehensive overview of fire prevention and life safety education provided by fire and emergency service organizations.)

Beyond the obvious importance of protecting lives and property from the ravages of fire and other hazards, contemporary fire and emergency service organizations play a critical role

Photo by Adam K. Thiel

Figure 1-9 Fire suppression is a principal fire department responsibility.

Photo by Adam K. Thiel

Figure 1-10 Firefighters proactively engage in community risk reduction.

in sustaining the overall economic vitality of their communities. The impact of fire on businesses, large and small, can be substantial in terms of lost sales, supply chain interruption, and temporary (or permanent) worker layoffs; recovering from a significant fire can take months, and many small businesses never reopen. These negative effects can translate to the broader public policy environment through unrealized tax revenues, difficulty in attracting new businesses, blighted or vacant properties, reduced tourism, and increased unemployment.

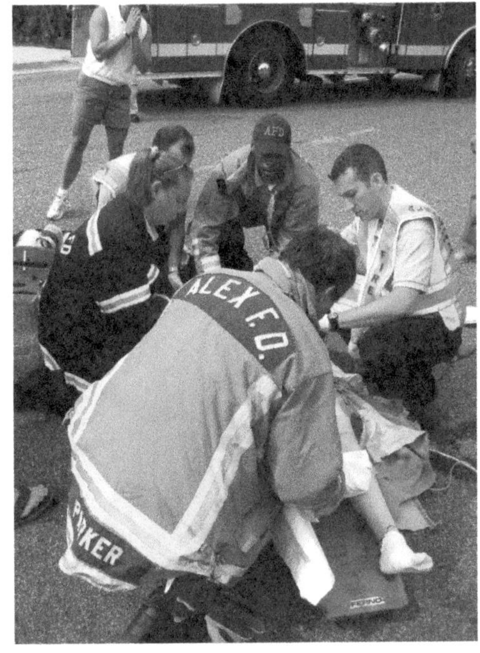

Photo by Adam K. Thiel

Figure 1-11 Paramedics and firefighters train together to provide emergency medical services.

Emergency medical services

The inclusion of emergency medical service (EMS) delivery in the mission of local fire and emergency service departments varies, although 59 percent of U.S. fire departments provide some form of emergency medical services to their communities.[22] In 2008, these services accounted for an estimated 65 percent of total fire department workload in the United States.[23] The design of fire-based EMS systems can vary from providing basic first responder services, with ambulance transport by another organization, to providing highly sophisticated advanced life support across multiple platforms on the ground, in the air, and on the water (see Figure 1-11). (Chapter 5 delivers an overview of essential EMS information for fire and emergency service managers.)

Technical rescue

Technical rescue encompasses a range of services, including response to structural collapse, trench collapse, high-angle (rope) rescues, confined-space emergencies, and water-related (swift-water and underwater rescue/recovery) incidents. Most fire departments deal with these incidents as first responders, and many provide all or some of these services themselves or as part of a regional response team (see Figure 1-12).

Hazardous materials

Fire departments have always responded to events where hazardous chemicals and other materials were spilled or released from their containers, violently or otherwise. In the late 1970s, awareness of hazardous materials as a specialized response discipline prompted many fire departments to embrace HAZMAT response as part of their mission. The advent of federal regulations surrounding the protection of life, property, and the environment from HAZMAT releases drove them to acquire specialized training (Figure 1-13) and equipment—often on a regional basis given the relative infrequency of HAZMAT incidents. State emergency management and other agencies are also often involved in HAZMAT emergencies, usually in concert with local jurisdictions.

Emergency management

In some respects, local fire and emergency service departments have been closely associated with the specialized discipline of emergency management since its inception in the mid-twentieth century. In other ways, despite interdependent missions and an obvious need for coordination before, during, and after an incident, local emergency management authorities and fire departments can tend to drift apart until brought together under exigent circumstances during major disasters or emergencies (see Figure 1-14). Renewed participation by local fire and emergency service organizations in the broader emergency management picture was accelerated by the tragic

Figure 1-12 Firefighters and paramedics from multiple jurisdictions work at a building collapse.

Photo by Adam K. Thiel

Figure 1-13 Firefighters cross-train as hazardous materials technicians.

Photo by Adam K. Thiel

Figure 1-14 Fire department personnel help staff a local emergency operations center.

Photo by Adam K. Thiel

events of September 11, 2001 (9/11), and solidified over the 2005 hurricane season in the Gulf Coast. (Chapter 2 is devoted to emergency management and homeland security as critical topic areas influencing contemporary fire and emergency service organizations.)[24]

Terrorism and weapons of mass destruction

Well before 9/11, local fire and emergency service organizations were engaged in managing the consequences of incidents arising from terrorism or involving weapons of mass destruction (WMD). In the 1993 bombings of the Alfred P. Murrah Federal Building in Oklahoma City, Oklahoma, and the World Trade Center in New York, and the 1994 bombing of Atlanta's Centennial Park during the Summer Olympics, local firefighters and EMS workers were first responders; others provided specialized assistance as part of the Federal Emergency Management Agency's Urban Search and Rescue Response System.

In the aftermath of 9/11, firefighters across the United States increased their efforts to prepare for terrorist events. Federal grant programs supplied many fire and emergency service departments with specialized training, equipment, and vehicles to address WMD events involving chemical, biological, radiological, nuclear, and explosive (CBRNE) materials. Continued concerns about terrorism, both foreign and domestic, challenge fire and emergency service leaders, with their law enforcement and emergency management counterparts, to address these threats as well as the potential for attacks like that launched in Mumbai, India, in 2008.

Emerging issues and themes

The first decade of the twenty-first century was marked by tremendous geopolitical and economic turmoil and upheaval. Many consider this far from an anomaly and see it instead as the "new normal." As the old adage suggests, the only constant for contemporary fire and emergency service agencies during the coming years will be change. In an era of increasing globalization, expanding service demand, and shrinking budgets, fire and emergency service administrators will face tremendous challenges in calibrating their services to meet community needs and citizen expectations.

"All-hazards" fire and emergency services

While there are many fire and emergency service departments across the United States with missions restricted to basic fire suppression, the clear trend is for local departments to embrace multiple roles and responsibilities in the mission areas described in the preceding section. The term coined to describe such departments is "all-hazards," meaning that firefighters are trained and equipped to address emergencies arising from any type of hazard, natural or technological, accidental or intentional.

Collaboration

The need for collaboration among local fire and emergency service departments, their partner disciplines, other local government agencies, not-for-profit organizations, and the private sector was made apparent in the lessons learned from 9/11. If anyone missed those lessons, the 2005 response to Hurricane Katrina put a fine point on the matter. Mobilized through the Emergency Management Assistance Compact, fire and emergency service organizations from around the United States converged on Louisiana and Mississippi to provide basic fire and emergency services in devastated areas. Regional technical rescue and specialized teams were also mobilized and deployed to disaster areas (see Figure 1–15).

Collaboration in the fire and emergency services reaches far beyond disasters. The need for mutual aid is a given in most areas of the United States and Canada; a number of sophisticated regional organizations have been developed over the years to foster regional partnerships that aid response to the daily emergencies facing all communities.

Throughout this book there are many examples of collaboration at multiple levels: interlocal cooperation, regional collaboration, state-local cooperation, and partnerships among national-level organizations and entities. This is not a coincidence: successful fire and emergency service organizations have learned that no matter how big or small they are, nobody can stand alone.

Innovation

Facing the fact that the world is rapidly changing, fire and emergency service leaders must embrace innovation. Sometimes innovation stems from technical advances in science and engineering, such as the development of next-generation structural firefighter protective

Figure 1-15 Fire departments from multiple jurisdictions address a hazardous materials incident.

Photo by Adam K. Thiel

Central Arizona Life Safety Council

The Central Arizona Life Safety Council is a long-standing consortium of twenty-two local jurisdictions in the Phoenix, Arizona, metropolitan region. The jurisdictions' fire and emergency service departments participate together in an automatic mutual aid system designed to provide "seamless service" and bring a number of stated benefits to area residents, businesses, and visitors across the Phoenix "Valley."

- When an emergency occurs, the firefighters that are closest to the emergency respond. In many communities in the United States, jurisdictional lines prevent firefighters from another city or town who are closer to an emergency from responding to that emergency. In the Valley, the closest firefighters are dispatched, regardless of jurisdictional considerations.
- Automatic Aid reduces the number of fire stations that are needed to serve the community as a whole. Through coordinated planning, fire stations are located and built in a way that serves the entire community, not just the citizens of one city or fire district. An average fire station costs $5-$6 million to construct and approximately $1.5 million a year to operate.
- Coordinated training and procedures help firefighters do their jobs better. All Valley firefighters receive the same basic training and use the same daily procedures to respond to emergencies. Chiefs from all Valley fire departments receive the same training and command incidents according to the same procedures.
- Firefighters work together every day on routine emergencies so that they work better together at larger emergencies. Firefighters are used to working together with firefighters from other communities. This familiarity helps when larger emergencies occur.
- Automatic Aid makes sure that all fire department units have similar capabilities. In order to be a member of the Automatic Aid system, fire departments are required to equip and staff their fire trucks in a standard way. This assures that all firefighters have similar equipment and the same number of firefighters on all fire trucks. The number of firefighters on a fire truck translates to the number and types of work that can be performed.
- Support functions such as dispatch and communications are coordinated. The fire service in the Valley utilizes two dispatch centers for almost all of the communities in the Valley, rather than having to maintain and operate a communications center for each fire department. This service eliminates duplication, increases efficiency, and saves money.
- Joint purchasing leads to savings. The Automatic Aid system uses its purchasing power to buy things like protective clothing for firefighters. Most Valley firefighters use the same protective clothing. Everyone pays a lower price since so much of the equipment is purchased. Manufacturers compete for the contract.
- Specialized fire fighting and rescue teams are shared. No single community can afford to keep enough firefighters on hand to respond to every specialized emergency. Incidents like leaks of hazardous materials and building collapses occur less often than fires. The fire departments in the Automatic Aid system work together to respond to specialized emergencies. This cooperation saves money and helps firefighters work more efficiently and safely at these unusual incidents.
- Nonemergency resources such as training facilities, health centers, and other support systems can be shared to reduce expense and standardize programs.

Source: Central Arizona Life Safety Council, *Managing Fire & EMS Service Delivery in These Tough Economic Times* (Phoenix: Phoenix Fire Department, 2009), 9–10, daisymountainfire.org/pages/documents/tough_times.pdf (accessed February 7, 2011).

clothing and self-contained breathing apparatus. In other cases, proven technology such as residential fire sprinklers must be adopted through the political and regulatory processes. At all times, however, human judgment plays the key role in whether to embrace innovation or continue with the status quo ante.

It is no longer viable to wear the phrase "200 years of tradition, unimpeded by progress" as a badge of honor. Instead, fire and emergency service departments must find new ways to provide safe, effective, and efficient service to their communities.

Professionalization

As a corollary to innovation, the increasing professionalization of the fire and emergency services is essential for meeting the changing demands of the twenty-first century. Without highly trained, educated, and experienced leaders, local fire and emergency service departments—volunteer, career, or combination—will not be able to keep pace with changes in society or in technology to meet their communities' high expectations for safe, effective, and efficient service across the wide range of mission areas with which they are increasingly tasked.

(Chapter 9 gives a basic overview of professional development considerations for the fire and emergency services.)

Summary

Providing fire protection and emergency services is a core function of local government, rooted in colonial times. But in the twenty-first century, the United States has a severe, albeit little understood, fire problem. The complex public policy environment where today's fire and emergency service managers must operate is influenced by politics, economics, demographics, geography, and sociology. A number of public policy issues can affect localities as they deliver a wide range of services to address emergencies arising from all hazards.

To be successful in leading their organizations, fire and emergency service leaders must become well versed in a variety of subjects. There is no substitute for a solid base of technical expertise in firefighting strategy and tactics, safety practices, building construction, incident command, emergency medical services, fire prevention and life safety education, HAZMAT response, technical rescue, and the many other aspects of providing frontline service to the community.

Just as important, however, is developing the capacity to be a capable public administrator in a complicated world. Fire chiefs and aspiring fire and emergency service officers must understand key facets of public budgeting and finance, public management, risk analysis, leadership, strategic planning, and many other administrative topics.

This chapter provides a brief introduction to the political and organizational environments where twenty-first-century fire chiefs and managers must work. Although the balance of the book provides more detailed information on a variety of essential topics, it still must be considered an overview that should be followed with continuous training and education, a variety of challenging experiences, and ongoing self-development.

Notes

1. William J. Novak, *The People's Welfare: Law and Regulation in Nineteenth-Century America* (Chapel Hill: University of North Carolina Press, 1996), 54.
2. World Fire Statistics Centre, "Table 4: Population Comparisons for Fire Deaths (2005–07)," *World Fire Statistics, No. 26*, Geneva Association Newsletter (London: International Association for the Study of Insurance Economics, October 2010), 7, genevaassociation.org/PDF/WFSC/GA2010-FIRE26.pdf (accessed February 13, 2011).
3. Ibid.
4. U.S. Fire Administration (USFA)/National Fire Data Center, *Fire in the United States, 2003–2007,* 15th ed., FA-325 (Emmitsburg, Md.: USFA, 2009), 29, usfa.dhs.gov/downloads/pdf/statistics/fa_325.pdf.
5. Ibid., 27.
6. John R. Hall Jr., *The Total Cost of Fire in the United States* (Quincy, Mass.: National Fire Protection Association [NFPA], February 2011), iii, nfpa.org/assets/files/PDF/totalcostsum.pdf.
7. Ibid.
8. Rita F. Fahy, Paul R. LeBlanc, and Joseph L. Molis, *Firefighter Fatalities in the United States—2009* (Quincy, Mass.: NFPA, June 2010), 1, nfpa.org/assets/files/pdf/osfff.pdf.
9. Michael J. Karter Jr., and Joseph L. Molis, *U.S. Firefighter Injuries—2009* (Quincy, Mass.: NFPA, October 2010), 4, nfpa.org/assets/files//PDF/OS.FFInjuries.pdf.
10. Michael J. Karter Jr. and Gary P. Stein, *U.S. Fire Department Profile through 2009* (Quincy, Mass.: NFPA, October 2010), ii, firecompany4.com/wp-content/uploads/2010/07/National-Volunteer-Firefighters-Profile-2009.pdf.
11. USFA, *Fire in the United States*, 1.
12. Karter and Stein, *U.S. Fire Department Profile through 2009.*
13. City of Cincinnati, "Fire Department: History" (n.d.), cincinnati-oh.gov/cityfire/pages/-16094-/ (accessed January 28, 2011).
14. NFPA, The U.S. Fire Service, "The U.S. Fire Service, 2009," nfpa.org/categoryList.asp?categoryID=955&%3BURL=Research%20&%3B%20Reports/Fire%20statistics/The%20U.S.%20fire%20service&cookie%5Ftest=1.
15. NFPA, U.S. Fire Service, "Firefighters and Fire Departments (U.S.)," nfpa.org/itemDetail.asp?categoryID=955&itemID=23688&URL=Research/Fire%20statistics/The%20U.S.%20fire%20service (accessed January 28, 2011).
16. GfK Group, "Firefighters Are the Most Trusted Group," *GfK Trust Index* 2009 (2009), gfk.ua/imperia/md/content/gfkukraine/pressreleases/pm_trust_index_june_2009_efin.pdf.
17. USFA, *Fire in the United States*, 29.
18. Karter and Stein, *U.S. Fire Department Profile through 2009*, 29.
19. U.S. Census Bureau, "An Older and More Diverse Nation by Mid-Century," news release, August 14, 2008, census.gov/newsroom/releases/archives/population/cb08-123.html.
20. Richard Florida, "How the Crash Will Reshape America," *Atlantic Monthly*, March 2009, 22, theatlantic.com/doc/200903/meltdown-geography (accessed February 14, 2011).
21. USFA, *Fire in the United States*, 4.
22. Karter and Stein, *U.S. Fire Department Profile through 2009.*
23. Michael J. Karter Jr., *Fire Loss in the United States during 2009* (Quincy, Mass.: NFPA, August 2010), 26, nfpa.org/assets/files/pdf/os.fireloss.pdf.
24. *Emergency Management: Principles and Practice for Local Government*, a companion "green book" to this volume, is available from ICMA Press and should be required reading for aspiring fire and emergency service leaders and local government managers.

CHAPTER 2

Emergency Management and Homeland Security for Fire Services

Jeffrey D. Stern

This chapter provides an understanding of

- The concept of emergency management, including mitigation, preparedness, response, and recovery
- The concept of homeland security, including prevention, protection, response, and recovery
- The similarities and differences between emergency management and homeland security
- The various roles of the fire service in emergency management and in homeland security
- The fire service's roles in activities before, during, and after an emergency management or homeland security incident.

Emergency management and homeland security have developed rapidly over the past decade. While emergency management as a discipline can trace its roots to national security challenges during World War II, it has evolved since the 1970s from Cold War civil defense programs to modern, "all-hazards" programs that address natural disasters, such as hurricanes, floods, and tornadoes, as well as man-made technological hazards, such as chemical and nuclear accidents and intentional events like terrorism. The broader mission of homeland security was developed in response to the terrorist attacks of September 11, 2001 (9/11), which led to changes in U.S. domestic security management and the desire to make a specific, concerted effort to deter, detect, and disrupt terrorist activity, especially that involving potential weapons of mass destruction, such as nuclear, biological, and chemical weapons.

Although they differ in some respects, emergency management and homeland security have many concepts in common. Both fields are continuing to evolve, and the fire service must play a key role in helping to ensure a robust emergency management system and effective homeland security in the United States. National emergency management is built on the foundation of local preparedness; similarly, national homeland security will not be possible without achieving a certain level of hometown security.

This chapter provides an overview of the fields of emergency management and homeland security. It discusses the role of the fire service in both fields; introduces readers to commonly used concepts and terminology for both fields; and discusses the fire service's role before, during, and after an incident as related to both emergency management and homeland security.

Emergency management

The International Association of Emergency Managers defines emergency management as the "managerial function charged with creating the framework within which communities reduce vulnerability to hazards and cope with disasters."[1]

Emergency management is an approach to all hazards that involves planning, coordinating, training, and exercising for a wide variety of both predictable and unforeseen emergencies. These activities take place in four phases: mitigation, preparedness, response, and recovery. Collectively, these phases make up an integrated approach called comprehensive emergency management.

Mitigation

Mitigation is the effort to reduce the overall effect of a hazard before an event occurs. Mitigation programs in emergency management have included efforts to remove buildings from flood-prone areas and to build storm runoff zones to prevent damage from floods (see Figure 2-1). Mitigation can include prevention efforts as well as protective efforts. Reducing heavy fuel loads near houses in the wildland-urban interface or banning the use of wood roof shingles are fire service–specific examples of mitigation efforts to reduce the spread of wildfire.

In emergency management, mitigation programs are often designed to address historical hazards and threats—for example, hurricanes on the East Coast and earthquakes on the West Coast. Federal grant programs, such as the Hazard Mitigation Grant Program, help communities after an incident reduce the likelihood of damage from a similar event in the future; they also prevent collateral damage from cascade events—sequential consequences that result from the original emergency. For example, programs to seed grasses and plants in areas destroyed by wildfires are intended to mitigate against the cascade events of flash flooding and landslides, which often occur after a wildfire destroys local vegetation and exposes soil to rainwater.

Preparedness

Preparedness activities include all efforts—planning, equipping, training, educating, public communications, exercising, and like activities—directed toward ensuring readiness for a particular hazard. Preparedness can include designating evacuation routes and shelter locations, and stockpiling supplies such as food, water, and fuel. Personal preparedness activities include developing a family contact or reunification plan to use after an emergency, maintain-

Photo by Adam K. Thiel

Figure 2-1 This flood control weir was constructed using a FEMA mitigation grant to help prevent downstream flooding during seasonal rainstorms.

ing personal emergency supplies such as food and water, and putting together a "go-kit" with personal items in case of evacuation with limited warning. The section "Before the Incident," beginning on page 36, describes important mitigation and preparedness activities.

Response

Response describes the operational phase of reacting to an emergency to save lives, property, and the environment. This phase includes declaring an emergency, activating emergency operations plans, opening and staffing an emergency operations center to coordinate response actions, alerting and notifying the public and the media, and prioritizing actions. Specific response activities may include ordering evacuations and opening shelters, and initiating continuity-of-government or continuity-of-operations plans. National response actions are guided by the National Response Framework (NRF) and the National Incident Management System (NIMS) developed by the Federal Emergency Management Agency (FEMA). The section titled "During the Incident," beginning on page 49, addresses many aspects of response.

Recovery

Recovery describes the short- and long-term efforts to restore the normal activities of everyday life, including repairing or rebuilding infrastructure and housing; reopening businesses and reinvigorating the economic life of a community; and reestablishing social structures such as government, schools, religious organizations, and other activities that make up a community. The section titled "After the Incident," beginning on page 59, discusses recovery considerations.

The role of the fire service

In the United States, emergency management takes place at the local, state, and federal levels. Responsibilities vary depending on the level of government. Private companies also have special risk, emergency, or crisis management teams to implement their own emergency management programs.

Principles of emergency management

Definition

Emergency management is the managerial function charged with creating the framework within which communities reduce vulnerability to hazards and cope with disasters.

Vision

Emergency management seeks to promote safer, less vulnerable communities with the capacity to cope with hazards and disasters.

Mission

Emergency management protects communities by coordinating and integrating all activities necessary to build, sustain, and improve the capability to mitigate against, prepare for, respond to, and recover from threatened or actual natural disasters, acts of terrorism, or other man-made disasters.

Principles

Emergency management must be

1. **Comprehensive:** Emergency managers consider and take into account all hazards, all phases, all stakeholders and all impacts relevant to disasters.
2. **Progressive:** Emergency managers anticipate future disasters and take preventive and preparatory measures to build disaster-resistant and disaster-resilient communities.
3. **Risk-driven:** Emergency managers use sound risk management principles (hazard identification, risk analysis, and impact analysis) in assigning priorities and resources.
4. **Integrated:** Emergency managers ensure unity of effort among all levels of government and all elements of a community.
5. **Collaborative:** Emergency managers create and sustain broad and sincere relationships among individuals and organizations to encourage trust, advocate a team atmosphere, build consensus, and facilitate communication.
6. **Coordinated:** Emergency managers synchronize the activities of all relevant stakeholders to achieve a common purpose.
7. **Flexible:** Emergency managers use creative and innovative approaches in solving disaster challenges.
8. **Professional:** Emergency managers value a science and knowledge-based approach based on education, training, experience, ethical practice, public stewardship and continuous improvement.

Source: International Association of Emergency Managers, "Principles of Emergency Management Supplement" (September 11, 2007), 4, iaem.com/publications/documents/PrinciplesofEmergencyManagement.pdf.

The fire service always has a role to play in emergency management; however, that role differs widely from community to community depending on the organization of the government and the authority and responsibilities delegated to the fire service.

At the local level At the local level, the senior elected or appointed official is generally designated as the emergency management director or coordinator. This official might be a mayor, a city or county manager, or another senior official; the title varies depending on each individual state's laws. This senior official bears ultimate responsibility for the local jurisdiction's emergency management program; however, the actual day-to-day responsibility for running the program is often delegated to a department head.

For example, in some communities, the fire chief or fire department holds responsibility for the entire community's emergency management function. In other communities, that function might be handled in the police department or sheriff's office. In still other communities, a distinct, independent emergency management department reports directly to the senior government official, just like the police or fire department does; in these communities, the fire service plays a supporting role. But wherever the emergency management function is located, the fire service remains the principal agency charged with managing fire emergencies, and in many jurisdictions, it also bears responsibility for managing medical service emergencies, hazardous materials (HAZMAT) incidents, and emergencies requiring technical or special rescue capabilities.

At the state level At the state level, the governor is the key official with overarching responsibility for emergency management. Each state has a dedicated emergency manager to lead the program for the governor; in each state, however, this position differs in scope and authority. In some states, the state emergency manager reports directly to the governor; in other states, the position is part of a state department of public safety; and in still other states, the emergency manager reports directly to the adjutant general, who heads the state's National Guard. Sometimes the adjutant general is also the emergency manager. Some state emergency management programs are combined with the state's homeland security program (as in California); in other states, the two programs are distinct.

At the federal level At the federal level, the president directs emergency management activities across the entire government, with key responsibilities delegated through presidential staff at the White House and through cabinet-level departments such as the Department of Homeland Security (DHS). The president's National Security Staff is responsible for oversight of emergency management programs.

All federal cabinet agencies have various responsibilities during a national emergency. These responsibilities are designated in the NRF and in various executive orders signed by the president, as well as in such legislation as the Robert T. Stafford Disaster Relief and Emergency Assistance Act of 1988, the Homeland Security Act of 2002, and the Post-Katrina Emergency Management Reform Act of 2006.

The secretary of DHS serves as the domestic incident manager for national emergencies and is empowered to coordinate across cabinet agencies. The administrator of FEMA reports to the secretary of DHS; during a Stafford Act declaration, however, the administrator may report directly to the president. FEMA is responsible for coordinating emergency management activities across the United States, carrying out its mission with state, local, and tribal governments through ten regional offices. These regional offices are led by regional directors who work closely with state agencies and local jurisdictions on a wide array of programs to mitigate, prepare for, respond to, and recover from emergencies.

While other cabinet agencies share responsibility for various emergency management programs, several key agencies take on leadership roles for some domestic emergencies. For example, the Department of Health and Human Services plays an important role in health emergencies such as pandemics, and the Department of Defense (DOD) takes a major role in providing defense support to civil authorities. Federal firefighting efforts are coordinated by the Department of Interior and the Department of Agriculture through the National Interagency Fire Center, located in Boise, Idaho.

Homeland security

President George W. Bush's *National Strategy for Homeland Security* (2007) defined homeland security as a "concerted national effort to prevent terrorist attacks within the United States, reduce America's vulnerability to terrorism, and minimize the damage and recover from attacks that do occur."[2] Since Hurricane Katrina, however, policy makers, academics, and practitioners have debated whether the government should focus homeland security efforts only on terrorism or take an all-hazards approach to security. President Barack Obama released guidance in Presidential Policy Directive (PPD) 1 in 2009, which goes further to integrate homeland security within the framework of America's long-standing national security structure. DHS describes the concept of homeland security as "the intersection of evolving threats and hazards with traditional governmental and civic responsibilities for civil defense, emergency response, law enforcement, customs, border control, and immigration."[3] There are many issues yet to be resolved related to the interrelationships among emergency management, homeland security, and national security, but in general terms, homeland security addresses terrorism *and* other hazards, including those that are natural and those that are man-made, whether accidental or intentional. There is, therefore, much overlap between the new and rapidly evolving field of homeland security and the slightly older field of emergency

Table 2-1 Homeland security and emergency management organizations

Level of government	Key leader	Homeland security key organizations	Emergency management key organizations
Federal	President	Department of Homeland Security Department of Justice (FBI) Department of Defense Intelligence community	Department of Homeland Security (FEMA) Department of Defense Department of Health and Human Services National Weather Service U.S. Geological Survey
State	Governor	Homeland security advisor State police National Guard	State emergency management National Guard
Local	Mayor/city Manager/county Manager	Law enforcement	Emergency management office Fire department Law enforcement Emergency medical services

management. The key distinguishing features for the fire service are the types of activities required of it in each field (see Table 2-1).

The White House sets federal direction for homeland security efforts as described in a series of presidential national strategies and presidential directives. Congress also establishes programs and authorizes funding through federal legislation.

Like emergency management, which has a comprehensive four-stage approach that consists of mitigation, preparedness, response, and recovery, the 2007 *National Strategy for Homeland Security* describes a common approach with three pillars: "to prevent and disrupt terrorist attacks; protect the American people, critical infrastructure, and key resources; and respond to and recover from incidents that do occur."[4] The replacement of the concepts of "mitigation" and "preparedness" with those of "protection" and "prevention" reflects the shift to a security-centered approach after 9/11. The Obama administration has reemphasized mitigation through its own presidential directives—notably, PPD 8, which superseded Homeland Security Presidential Directive 8 in 2011. A challenge over the next decade for policy makers and practitioners will be either to integrate all the approaches to maximize the use of resources, or to more clearly define the line between them and eliminate redundancies (Figure 2-2).

Protection

Protection refers to efforts and activities to secure people as well as critical infrastructure and key resources (CIKR) from terrorism and other threats. Critical infrastructure are key components of society necessary for the maintenance of government, the economic life of the

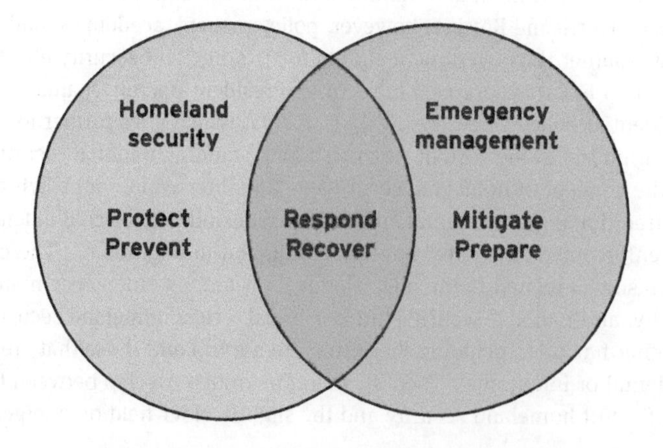

Figure 2-2 The circles depict the overlapping responsibilities of homeland security and emergency management.

Critical infrastructure and key resources sectors

Agriculture and food
Banking and finance
Chemical
Commercial facilities
Communications
Critical manufacturing
Dams
Defense industrial base
Emergency services
Energy
Government facilities
Health care and public health
Information technology
National monuments and icons
Nuclear reactors, materials, and waste
Postal and shipping
Transportation systems
Water

Source: Department of Homeland Security, "Critical Infrastructure and Key Resources" (last updated November 30, 2010), dhs .gov/files/programs/gc_1189168948944.shtm.

country, and national security; they include specific sites (e.g., dams) in addition to networks of facilities necessary for a particular function—for example, the energy distribution network. Key resources are individual targets, such as national symbols, icons, and monuments, "whose destruction . . . could create local disaster or profoundly damage our Nation's morale or confidence."[5] The federal government identifies key resources and critical infrastructures in eighteen specific sectors, listed in the accompanying sidebar.

Protection can be seen as a form of mitigation, reducing the vulnerability of various installations to attack or damage by strengthening them or limiting access. Fire departments are often involved in protective homeland security measures, helping to identify CIKR such as HAZMAT storage facilities and then working with responsible authorities to identify how hazardous materials may be more safely and securely stored. Emergency services are considered a critical infrastructure, and so efforts to control access to stations or apparatus, to provide identification and credentials to personnel, and to secure items such as uniforms or badges are considered protective homeland security measures.

Prevention

Prevention refers to activities to identify, deter, disrupt, or defeat acts of terrorism before they occur, as well as to prevent other types of hazardous events. Information collection, information and data sharing, and public education are all aspects of prevention. While law enforcement may take more defensive antiterrorism actions, and the military and federal law enforcement may take offensive counterterrorism actions, generally the fire service's role in prevention of terrorism is limited to its involvement in information-sharing processes and programs and in coordinating with terrorism task forces. In these areas, fire service personnel may play key roles in helping law enforcement determine the potential consequences of terrorist actions—for example, the extent of danger from an attack on a chemical facility or fuel depot. They may also track arson and related crimes that often serve as tools of domestic terror groups such as the Earth Liberation Front (ELF). (Because terrorism is defined as a criminal act carried out for political motives, groups ranging from the ELF to al-Qaeda are considered terrorist groups. A fire set by an ELF cell is a terrorist act as well as a criminal act because of the political motive. However, arson committed to claim insurance funds is a criminal act, not a terrorist act, because it lacks a political motive.)

In recent years, fire chiefs and counterterrorism policy makers have debated whether fire service personnel should be actively trained to look for and report on potential terrorist activities. Proponents hold that the fire service provides a set of eyes and ears in the community as it responds to millions of emergencies each year, and thus it should be able to report suspicious activity to law enforcement. Opponents argue that the fire service holds a unique public trust and should not risk that trust by reporting on citizens. In either event, it is prudent that every fire department, especially in higher-risk areas, incorporate some basic training in terrorism, terrorist motivations, and terrorist target hazards into its curriculum for officers and staff. Senior fire officers should know who handles terrorism prevention issues in the community at the local, state, and federal levels, and should build relationships with those people and organizations. Two key groups are the closest Joint Terrorism Task

Force (JTTF), which is led by the Federal Bureau of Investigation (FBI), and the fire department's own state or local intelligence fusion center (both of which are discussed further on in the section titled "Intelligence and Information Sharing," beginning on page 48).

Response and recovery

The response and recovery phases for homeland security include the same activities as they do for emergency management. In the specific case of a terrorist incident, however, the FBI has a legally mandated lead role in managing the response. In all other incidents, authorities follow the general guidelines of the NRF and the NIMS, which direct that the incident be managed at the lowest governmental level by the local incident commander, supported by various organizational structures up through the state and federal levels. The fire service plays a key role in responding to any terrorist event, and in some cases, it will provide overall command of the incident during rescue operations, when the focus is on life safety and incident stabilization. Then, as the incident transitions from response to recovery, the fire service will transfer the lead within a unified command structure to federal law enforcement, as occurred during the response to the 9/11 attack on the Pentagon.

The fire service also plays a key role in recovery from a terrorist event. That role ranges from helping remediate chemical or biological hazards and other hazardous materials, to supporting the removal of debris, to protecting workers at the incident site. Additionally, the fire department may provide psychological support to its members and their families, along with various other recovery services.

Preparedness and resilience

Preparedness, one of the four stages of emergency management, is not identified as one of the four phases of homeland security; instead, it is considered a broader, cross-cutting endeavor. Efforts to prevent, protect, respond, and recover are all efforts at building a more prepared community. Emergency management and homeland security efforts to mitigate, prepare, prevent, protect, respond, and recover all contribute to resilience, creating a community and systems of infrastructure that can quickly adapt and bounce back from hazards, no matter what their cause.

Developing disaster-resilient communities should be an overarching goal of all emergency management and homeland security programs. A disaster-resilient community is one that can quickly reestablish normal community functions after an emergency. This might mean the adoption of building codes that require new construction to meet a certain degree of resistance to storm winds, for example. Some nations, such as Britain and Israel, create psychological resilience to terrorism by quickly reopening businesses and restoring normal community functions, often within hours or days of a terrorist attack.

The goal of any fire chief should be to create a resilient department and community that can respond to any event and, once the crisis has ended, return to normal duties and functions in the shortest amount of time. Fire chiefs should promote efforts to protect and mitigate against hazards, educate and prepare citizens on protective actions when an emergency strikes, and work to build relationships with other communities, nonprofit groups, utility companies, and the private sector to increase preparedness. These efforts help to enhance the disaster resilience within a community.

Before the incident

Since homeland security and emergency management encompass overlapping activities such as planning, fire service leadership can benefit from understanding the basic activities that take place before any incident, no matter what the cause.

Planning

Planning is one of the most basic emergency management and homeland security activities. Fire service personnel should be familiar with planning models for both functions.

Emergency management planning at the local level starts with the development of an emergency operations plan (EOP). The EOP describes the roles and responsibilities for different leaders and organizations at the local level. It also describes the process for declaring emergencies; activating local resources; and requesting additional aid from other local jurisdictions, the state or federal level, the private sector, or nonprofit organizations such as the Red Cross. EOPs often contain detailed information, such as the location of the local emergency operations center (EOC), methods to activate the EOC, and methods to coordinate with incident commanders managing field response.

The local emergency management authority (LEMA) usually develops the EOP. The LEMA is the organization that has the authority to manage the jurisdiction's emergency management program. In many jurisdictions, this organization is the fire department. The EOP describes the jurisdiction's organization for emergencies and contains functional annexes that detail specific actions, activities, or responsibilities (such as how the EOC will be organized), as well as hazard-specific annexes that identify historical or specific hazards in the community and the plan for organizing a response to those specific hazards. For example, a community with a nuclear power plant may have a hazard-specific annex in its EOP that deals solely with an emergency at that power plant, while another community may have an annex that deals specifically with general flooding. State or local law generally requires that the EOP be updated on a regular basis and approved by elected officials, such as a county or city council. Some federal grant funding is tied to maintaining an updated and current EOP.

There are many methods for developing plans. In general, organizations start with their own historical plans; they may also copy other jurisdictions' plans that are considered "best practices" and model their own plans in similar fashion. Often, subject matter experts or consultants are employed to assist with developing the plan. For specific hazards, there are planning tools such as computer programs based on geographic information systems that help map hazards in the community, or software that can model potential consequences, such as where chemical plumes may drift. Other software can simulate scenarios to determine how long it might take to evacuate people from a particular building or a section of a city. Common emergency management tools include FEMA's HAZUS program, a risk assessment tool that helps estimate potential losses from floods, hurricane winds, and earthquakes.[6] Floodplain maps developed by FEMA are another planning tool. Specific tools can be used to build plans for specific hazards. However, it is not always necessary to use tools to develop a basic EOP.

The private sector also uses EOPs for specific locations such as factories, industrial complexes, and office buildings. Fire chiefs should collaborate with facility managers to review and help design these EOPs.

FEMA requires jurisdictions to complete hazard mitigation plans in order to receive certain annual grant funds. These plans typically outline the specific local, historical hazards that the jurisdiction faces and the efforts to mitigate the damage they could cause.

Planning for large events and mass gatherings is an important preincident duty for emergency managers and homeland security professionals. Such events could include routine occurrences, such as football games or other sporting events, as well as rare visits by distinguished visitors, such as the president or the pope. Emergency managers and homeland security professionals should plan for such occasions in keeping with the various phases of preparedness, mitigation, prevention, protection, response, and recovery. Certain large events, such as the Olympics, may take years of planning. Managers responsible for planning for them often visit cities that have had experience with similar events. For example, cities that are scheduled to host the Super Bowl in the future usually send a delegation to observe the preparations and activities under way in the city that is currently preparing to host it.

Each year, the secretary of DHS designates about a dozen events as National Special Security Events (NSSEs) because their high visibility might attract terrorist activity. Since 9/11, it has become commonplace for the Super Bowl and other specific sporting events to be declared NSSEs. The president's annual State of the Union address to Congress and certain other events when the country's leaders are gathered together may also be so designated. The declaration of an NSSE places the U.S. Secret Service in charge of planning the operations for the event. The Secret Service designates a special agent-in-charge to work with those responsible for the security and safety of the venue, including fire and medical services, local and state emergency managers, and the homeland security community. Fire departments in metropolitan areas are very likely to be involved in supporting an NSSE at some point.

Other important preparations include continuity-of-operations (COOP) plans and continuity-of-government (COG) plans. A COOP plan details the means of relocating government programs and documents to alternative work sites so that government operations may continue from a safe area (see Figure 2–3). COG plans involve the relocation of key elected and appointed government officials to safe areas so that the local, state, or federal government can continue to operate through a crisis. A fire department may need COOP plans to relocate its station staffing to safe areas or may need to institute COG plans for command teams supporting policy makers. During 9/11, when many of the New York Fire Department's commanders were killed, a COG plan for the department might have assisted with the rapid identification and deployment of new leadership.

Handling individuals with special needs is another important planning function. Citizens with special needs come from all walks of life and may require medical attention, specialty care, or ambulatory support. Some have disabilities or are elderly. (Information on handling people with special needs can be found on FEMA's website.)[7]

There are many other types of plans for use in homeland security and emergency management. Fire service leaders should become familiar with these plans and the planning processes used to create them.

Coordination and oversight

Many entities are involved in the coordination and oversight of emergency management and homeland security activities at the local level. Fire services often are members of these groups or may chair or facilitate their activities.

All jurisdictions are required to have a local emergency planning committee (LEPC). This group generally consists of community members from government organizations, industry, and nonprofit groups as well as individual citizens. LEPCs came into existence in the 1970s as a requirement of the Superfund Amendments and Reauthorization Act of 1986 (SARA), Title III, and originally existed to help oversee and plan for incidents involving hazardous sites. Today LEPCs play different roles in different jurisdictions, but generally they advise and review the various emergency plans in their local communities.

Figure 2-3 A fire station may be damaged during a storm, requiring implementation of a continuity-of-operations (COOP) plan.

Photo by Jeffrey D. Stern

Several regions in the country have developed regional homeland security advisory councils to discuss and plan for a broad range of homeland security emergencies. These groups help build relationships between various response agencies, the private sector, and the nonprofit sector. In addition, each of FEMA's ten regions has a regional advisory council that provides advice and builds relationships with FEMA regional administration staff. Fire service representatives are part of these councils.

Numerous other bodies around the country work to enhance coordination and build networks among potential agencies and leaders in emergency management and homeland security. Many metropolitan areas have regional councils of governments and standing committees that oversee emergency management and homeland security issues. One specific regional coordinating group exists in major metropolitan areas that receive Urban Area Security Initiative (UASI) funding from DHS (see the accompanying sidebar). In cities where more than one jurisdiction is part of the UASI, regional committees are often formed to oversee their collaborative homeland security efforts. Fire service leaders should be aware of their local, state, and regional advisory and oversight groups, and work with them to develop robust relationships and emergency management and homeland security plans.

Areas eligible for Urban Area Security Initiative funding

The Urban Area Security Initiative (UASI) is designed to enhance preparedness in regions centered on major cities. The program is limited to the highest-risk urban areas, as defined by the Department of Homeland Security. Risk rankings are based on population, vulnerability to attack, and presence of critical infrastructure or key assets. Tier 1 designates the urban areas considered to be at highest risk; these areas receive the majority of total program funds. In 2009, sixty-two urban areas were deemed eligible for UASI grants.

FY 2009 Tier 1 UASI areas

(CA) Los Angeles/Long Beach Area
(CA) Bay Area
(DC) National Capital Region
(IL) Chicago Area
(NJ) Jersey City/Newark Area
(NY) New York City Area
(TX) Houston Area

FY 2009 Tier 2 UASI areas

(AZ) Phoenix Area
(AZ) Tucson Area
(CA) Anaheim/Santa Ana Area
(CA) Oxnard Area
(CA) Riverside Area
(CA) Sacramento Area
(CA) San Diego Area
(CO) Denver Area
(CT) Bridgeport Area
(CT) Hartford Area
(FL) Fort Lauderdale Area
(FL) Jacksonville Area
(FL) Miami Area
(FL) Orlando Area
(FL) Tampa Area
(GA) Atlanta Area
(HI) Honolulu Area
(IN) Indianapolis Area
(KY) Louisville Area
(LA) Baton Rouge Area
(LA) New Orleans Area
(MA) Boston Area
(MD) Baltimore Area
(MI) Detroit Area
(MN) Twin Cities Area
(MO) Kansas City Area
(MO) St. Louis Area
(NC) Charlotte Area
(NV) Las Vegas Area
(NY) Albany Area
(NY) Buffalo Area
(NY) Rochester Area
(NY) Syracuse Area
(OH) Cincinnati Area
(OH) Cleveland Area
(OH) Columbus Area
(OH) Toledo Area
(OK) Oklahoma City Area
(OK) Tulsa Area
(OR) Portland Area
(PA) Philadelphia Area
(PA) Pittsburgh Area
(PR) San Juan Area
(RI) Providence Area
(TN) Memphis Area
(TN) Nashville Area
(TX) Austin Area
(TX) Dallas/Fort Worth/Arlington Area
(TX) El Paso Area
(TX) San Antonio Area
(UT) Salt Lake City Area
(VA) Norfolk Area
(VA) Richmond Area
(WA) Seattle Area
(WI) Milwaukee Area

Source: Department of Homeland Security, *Fiscal Year 2009: Urban Areas Security Initiative Nonprofit Security Grant Program: Guidance and Application Kit* (Washington, D.C.: FEMA Grant Programs Directorate, November 2008), 4, fema.gov/pdf/government/grant/uasi/fy09_uasi__nsgp_guidance.pdf.

The Metropolitan Medical Response System (MMRS) is another program that has been created to develop and coordinate response plans, especially those for mass casualty and health events. Funded by the federal government in the nation's largest urban areas, the MMRS is designed to support a regional approach to strengthen emergency medical services, hospitals, and public health systems in the event of a biological terrorist event such as an anthrax attack, or of a large public health emergency such as a pandemic flu.

Intergovernmental agreements and collaboration

Another pre-event activity that involves emergency management and homeland security is the creation of intergovernmental agreements. These agreements, which often take the form of memorandums of understanding (MOUs), may be made between departments, between governments, or between governments and taxing districts (e.g., an independent school board), the private sector, or nonprofit groups. For example, a local emergency management organization may develop an MOU among the jurisdiction, a school board, and a nonprofit group to permit the school to be used as a shelter during an emergency and the nonprofit group to provide staffing for it in accordance with guidelines from the local jurisdiction. There are many successful models for MOUs that can be adapted for use in a specific local jurisdiction. The fire department's legal advisors should help review and develop MOUs to ensure that they adequately address the terms of the agreement, statutory authority, liability protection, and, if necessary, financial reimbursement issues.

Local jurisdictions may also enter into agreements with military bases located in or near the jurisdiction. Often, these agreements can be mutually beneficial. For example, the Los Angeles County Fire Department has an agreement with the U.S. Marine Corps for fire engines to be ferried to Catalina Island in the event of wildfires on the island. Because local base commanders around the country are legally authorized to provide direct, lifesaving actions to neighboring areas when necessary, without seeking time-consuming authorization from the military chain of command through the secretary of defense, establishing proactive agreements ahead of time on how to share available resources can be of benefit when an incident occurs.

Because it has many resources that can be deployed during an emergency, either through the National Guard or through regular military forces, the military plays an essential role in both emergency management and homeland security. Fire departments should familiarize themselves with the military resources available locally and in the state, and should learn how those resources can be activated. Coordinated planning, training, and exercises should be done before an emergency occurs.

Public health departments also play an essential role in supporting emergency management and homeland security activities. Depending on state law, local and state public health officials have key responsibilities and authorities for monitoring and tracking disease outbreaks and directing responses to address public health emergencies. Fire service leaders should familiarize themselves with the organizations and individuals who lead their local public health response and develop joint preparations for public health emergencies. Public health officials also have essential legal authorities to quarantine individuals or areas in a community during a public health emergency; fire services should be familiar with these legal authorities and know when they can be employed.

Hospital health care systems and emergency medical services need to be closely involved in emergency management and homeland security preparations. They must be prepared for a medical surge, which would occur in the event of mass casualties or a pandemic or biological incident, when large numbers of patients would require a rapid increase in medical capacity. Medical surge events often require specialty medical facilities, such as trauma centers or burn centers, which are routinely in short supply in the normal day-to-day operations of many areas of the country. Fire service emergency managers and homeland security professionals must work with medical officials from their areas to prepare for medical management of mass casualty events from any cause.

Risk assessment and hazard vulnerability analysis

Risk assessment, also known as risk analysis, is a fundamental activity for both emergency management and homeland security. While there are many different methods for risk assessment, the basic activity involves determining the likelihood or probability of a particular hazard occurring, assessing vulnerability to that hazard, and determining the consequences should that threat or hazard actually occur. For example, the failure of a dam could lead to catastrophic flooding. Conducting a risk assessment also includes developing a plan to reduce vulnerabilities where possible through emergency management and homeland security strategies such as protection or mitigation. Risk assessment is thus an important ongoing task as communities seek to direct limited resources toward emergency management and homeland security needs. (Further information on risk assessment can be found in Chapter 3.)

Each community faces many common hazards, such as fire or a HAZMAT incident that might result from a truck or rail crash. Each community also has unique hazards specific to its own location and history. Hazards are typically divided into natural hazards, such as hurricanes, floods, tornadoes, and earthquakes, and man-made hazards, such as toxic industrial accidents, chemical spills, and terrorist events. Terms such as *technological* or *human caused* are sometimes substituted for the term *man-made hazards,* and some people further divide man-made hazards into intentional hazards and unintentional hazards. For example, a dam failure could be the result of a design failure, an earthquake, or an intentional act, resulting in a flood (a natural hazard) that is caused by an accident (infrastructure decay or design flaw), or a natural event (earthquake), or a nefarious act (terrorist sabotage). The flooding after Hurricane Katrina (a natural hazard) caused a technological failure in the levees (a failure that was partially attributed to poor engineering design and poor construction, as well as to the forces of the hurricane).[8]

The following is a catalog of many common natural and man-made hazards faced by communities in the United States.

Floods Flooding is the most costly and deadly natural hazard in the United States, causing hundreds of millions of dollars each year in damage and claiming hundreds of lives. Most lives lost during Hurricane Katrina, for example, were lost not to the storm winds but to the flooding that occurred when the levees failed after the storm. Flash flooding can occur in almost every community in the United States.

A fire department needs to know the flooding dangers in its community and put in place education programs (e.g., teaching the public not to drive on flooded roadways), protection measures (e.g., identifying roads that should be closed in the event of flooding), and mitigation measures (e.g., helping local officials identify flood-prone areas and improve runoff or sewer systems to reduce flooding). Departments with persistent flood dangers should train all personnel how to safely respond to flood emergencies. Many departments have created specially trained swift-water rescue teams to respond to flood emergencies. The Charlotte (North Carolina) Fire Department, for example, has built a robust and systematic swift-water response capability: gauges monitor rising waters in flood-prone areas and trigger warnings; all department personnel receive a basic level of flood awareness training; specialty companies are trained to do intermediate rescue work; and a special swift-water rescue team handles advanced rescue operations.

Fires Wildfires, including those in the wildland-urban interface, are becoming a growing challenge for emergency management and homeland security. Several factors are contributing to this challenge, including the increasing presence of full-time residents moving into rural, fire-prone areas, expanding the size of the interface; decades of aggressive wildfire management focused on suppression that has disrupted the natural cycles of clearance by allowing the buildup of ladder fuels in areas where fires occur; climate changes that have increased the length of the fire season and the extent of areas normally prone to wildfires; and infestations of invasive species, such as the bark beetle currently decimating forests in the Rocky Mountain states and leaving behind dead trees that will fuel fires for decades to come until different tree species reforest affected areas.

Wildland fire specialists have become increasingly concerned about the danger of megafires that burn uncontrolled. Such firestorms are possible in areas of the West and Northwest, including Alaska. Fire managers at the federal level also are beginning to speak of a year-round fire season, as fire seasons in all parts of the country are extended and as the cycles of fire throughout the calendar year move from one area of the country to another—from the grasslands of the Southeast, to the mountains of the West, to the coast of California.

Wildfires are also burning in areas where fire departments have not traditionally faced such threats, thereby creating challenges for training and equipping firefighters to respond to this emerging hazard.

Suburban interface areas create conditions in which fires can routinely destroy hundreds of homes and cause dozens of deaths. Fire departments must not only be ready to respond to these kinds of emergencies but also become involved in the emergency management aspects of planning for and managing them. They must be prepared to warn citizens, provide protective instructions on evacuation routes and shelter locations, provide information on how to create defensible spaces around homes, and assist with developing model building codes that make neighborhoods more resilient against the fire threat. Their responsibilities cover the entire range from mitigation, preparedness, prevention, and protection to response and recovery from threat of large fires.

Modern building codes and professional fire departments have reduced the threat of large, urban conflagrations like the Great Chicago Fire of 1871 or the fire that destroyed San Francisco after the 1906 earthquake. However, the threat still exists in sections of our older cities, as was demonstrated in Richmond, Virginia, in 2004, and in Grand Forks, North Dakota, in 1997. Urban conflagrations can also be sparked by civil disorder, as happened during the Los Angeles riots in 1992.

Hurricanes Hurricanes provide a special challenge for fire departments along the East Coast, in the Gulf states, and in Hawaii. Hurricane Katrina revealed the challenges in Louisiana and Mississippi as fire departments throughout the nation offered assistance (Figure 2–4).

The biggest challenge is ensuring that the fire department itself maintains the ability to serve the community after the storm. Fire stations must be designed and built to withstand hurricane-force winds, and plans and operational procedures must be in place to help the department determine when it can respond to an emergency, when it must wait out the worst of the winds, and when it can safely go into a community to assess damages. Plans must be developed to ensure that communications systems—from radios to cell phones to the entire 911 phone system—will function throughout a storm and that, should those systems fail, backup systems and methods are in place to allow the department to function in a decen-

Figure 2-4 Fire departments from Illinois, Maryland, and New York provided mutual aid to New Orleans in 2005.

Photo by Jeffrey D. Stern

tralized fashion until the primary systems can be restored. Since fire stations are located in neighborhoods, fire service managers must expect that residents will go to the stations to request assistance, find shelter, and get information, and so managers must plan accordingly. They should also be ready for surges in mutual aid as responders arrive from other localities and states and must be integrated into operations.

Fire departments often overlook the need to ensure the welfare of the families of their own personnel. A large hurricane is likely to damage the homes of many responders and place their families at risk, so robust plans must be in place well ahead of storms to ensure that personnel have the opportunity to take care of their homes and families. This is especially a challenge in areas where the fire department relies heavily on volunteers. Many departments have developed family networks so that department members' families can assist each other, allowing the members to work. Early requests for mutual aid resources from areas that have not been affected may be one of the best ways to ensure that the community's emergency response needs are met while local responders attend to their own families, homes, and businesses. The need to look after the families of fire service personnel, a lesson learned during Hurricane Katrina, is relevant in other catastrophic hazards as well, such as earthquakes, pandemics, and terror attacks.

Tornadoes Tornadoes are devastating wind events that cause some of the greatest destruction of any natural forces on earth. Departments in tornado-prone areas should use early warning systems from the National Weather Service and coordinate with their local emergency management communities. Operational plans and procedures for response and damage assessment, as well as shelter for members, must be paramount priorities for any fire departments that face potential tornado events.

Volcanoes While rare, volcanoes do exist in the United States, especially in Hawaii and the Pacific Northwest. The eruption of Mount St. Helens in Washington in 1980 killed fifty-seven people and destroyed hundreds of homes.

Tsunamis Tsunamis are large tidal waves that result from earthquakes, underwater volcanoes, or landslides that occur in or near the ocean. They can strike without warning in coastal areas. The coastal United States, as well as Hawaii and U.S. territories in the Pacific, are subject to tsunami hazards: a 2009 tsunami did significant damage to American Samoa and killed over 100 people. The 2004 tsunami in the Indian Ocean killed more than 250,000 people. The West Coast of the United States has a tsunami warning system that is overseen by the National Oceanic and Atmospheric Administration.

Hazardous materials and toxic industrial chemicals In the last thirty years, fire departments have developed HAZMAT response teams to deal with toxic and industrial chemicals, radiological emergencies, and biological pathogens. Emergency management professionals have long concerned themselves with technological disasters, taking lessons from events like the partial reactor meltdown at the Three Mile Island nuclear plant near Harrisburg, Pennsylvania, in 1979 and the *Exxon Valdez* oil spill in Prince William Sound, Alaska, in 1989. The more recent focus on homeland security has raised the profile of specific, intentional hazards involving chemical, biological, radiological, nuclear, or explosive (CBRNE) materials. Homeland security officials are especially concerned with a subset of CBRNE known as weapons of mass destruction (WMDs), which could kill thousands of people. Another subset is labeled weapons of mass effect (WMEs) because of the psychological and economic damage they may cause.

Mutual aid programs

The International Association of Fire Chiefs has been working with fire departments across the United States to develop fire service mutual aid programs. The National Fire Service Intrastate Mutual Aid System is a program funded by the Department of Homeland Security to develop intrastate and interstate mutual aid systems. Model programs exist in California and Illinois. More information can be obtained from the association at iafc.org.

Chemical incidents (C) Fire service HAZMAT teams respond to thousands of chemical emergencies each week across the United States. Routinely used toxic industrial chemicals pose many hazards to the public and to responders. In 1984, in one of the worst industrial accidents in modern history, several thousand people were killed in Bhopal, India, when a toxic industrial chemical was accidently released. Fire services play a key role in identifying hazardous chemicals in their communities, tracking and marking their storage or transport, and working with emergency personnel on contingency and response plans.

The use of chemical weapons by terrorists is a concern of homeland security officials. Chemical incidents could stem from the use of industrial chemicals found in many parts of the United States, such as chlorine, or of military-grade weapons such as nerve gas. In the past decade, attackers in Iraq have attempted to blow up chlorine tanker trucks. The use of sarin gas in a Tokyo subway in 1995 prompted many U.S. cities to begin to prepare for chemical incidents. Fire departments should ensure that first responders have training in how to recognize such incidents. HAZMAT response teams and emergency medical services should be equipped to respond to chemical incidents and manage contaminated victims. Many fire departments have developed plans for mass decontamination of people at large public gatherings or in transportation systems that might be targeted in a chemical attack.

Biological incidents (B) Biological pathogens have been used in attacks in the United States, the most well known being the anthrax incidents in 2001. Biological pathogens pose a unique challenge to responders. They are not easily detected, and often symptoms do not appear until after an incubation period, which may take place over hours, days, or weeks. Biological pathogens can also occur naturally, so it may be difficult to distinguish a naturally occurring event, such as a flu pandemic or disease outbreak, from a man-made terrorist event.

Fire services should prepare to deal with the effects of biological incidents, planning in coordination with emergency medical services, local hospitals, public health authorities, and local law enforcement. Public health officials can help with medical monitoring of disease outbreaks and advise on proper courses of treatment. Fire departments should also have plans in place to protect firefighters and rescue workers, either by providing prophylactic treatment for a particular disease (e.g., annual flu shots) or by maintaining stockpiles of treatment regimens (e.g., doxycycline for anthrax exposure). They should also be prepared to deal with a potential reduction in their own workforce should a pandemic occur. Health officials estimate that a flu outbreak could affect 20–40 percent of the workforce, as workers themselves fall ill or take leave to care for sick family members.

Radiological incidents (R) Fire departments routinely face the hazard of radiological emergencies. Virtually all health facilities that contain x-ray equipment or other scanning systems contain radiological isotopes. University labs, industrial facilities, and construction sites often contain radiological instruments. Departments in areas near nuclear power plants train for radiological emergencies.

Detection of radiological emergencies is a key responsibility of responders, who are also trained to consider time of exposure, distance, and shielding when confronting such emergencies. In the case of a terrorist incident, radiation poses a dangerous psychological hazard in addition to its physical effects and thus is considered a WME. Depending on the type of isotope used, radiation may injure or kill people who come into direct contact with it, and while it is unlikely that terrorists could obtain enough radiation to inflict massive radiation-caused casualties, unlikely does not mean impossible. Radiation can be spread to a large area if the radiological source is combined with an explosive, as in a radiological dispersal device (RDD) (i.e., a dirty bomb). While most of the casualties will likely be due to the explosion and resulting blast damage, the resulting radioactive contamination can cause severe, long-term economic and psychological damage because of public reluctance to return to a contaminated area. Public officials may have difficulty convincing the public that an area is safe to return to, even when contamination is slight. Several cities are working with the federal government to develop maps detailing naturally occurring background radiation so that they can accurately measure postevent contamination should an event occur. A strong public communications effort will be an essential part of the response to use of an RDD.

Nuclear incidents (N) Nuclear incidents are radiological events. However, nuclear weapons or improvised nuclear devices differ from RDDs because they create an atomic chain reaction that results in a thermonuclear explosion, whereas an RDD just spreads the radioactive source materials but does not create the nuclear chain reaction. Nuclear accidents happen irregularly in the United States, but they do happen,[9] the most notable being the incident at the Three Mile Island nuclear power plant. Elsewhere, the incident at Chernobyl in Ukraine (then the USSR) in 1986 is said to have caused fewer than fifty direct deaths (although figures vary depending on source) but at least 4,000 indirect deaths.[10] Fire departments in the vicinity of nuclear power plants should familiarize themselves with the personnel and safety procedures at those plants. (Nuclear power generators or materials can also be found at military, university, and research facilities.)

The thought of a nuclear bomb exploding in the United States presents a grave image, and fire services have been preparing for such an event since the Cold War. Prevention and deterrence of a nuclear explosion is the responsibility of the federal government, but there are many planning and response issues that have yet to be developed to handle the aftermath of a terrorist-caused nuclear incident in America. This is an area that will require great attention in the coming decade. Should an event occur, the fire service will play a key role, assessing damage, conducting radiation surveys, searching for and rescuing survivors, suppressing fires and firestorms, and beginning to rebuild.

Explosives (E) Fire departments respond to explosive incidents—from fireworks to homemade pipe bombs to more sophisticated and dangerous bombs. One form of explosive threat, the improvised explosive device (IED), is common outside the United States, challenging U.S. forces operating in Iraq and Afghanistan as it has become a weapon of choice among terrorists. Suicide bombers commonly employ IEDs that are built into clothing, such as bomb vests, belts, or jackets. Backpacks can also be used to carry an IED, as was the case in the Centennial Olympic Park bombing in Atlanta, Georgia, in 1996 and in the bombing of trains in Madrid, Spain, in 2004 and in London, England, in 2005. An IED can be made to look like almost any object. Terrorist Richard Reid tried to explode a shoe bomb on an airplane flying from Britain to the United States in 2001. In 2006, concerns that terrorists were developing liquid explosives that could be mixed and detonated on an airplane prompted homeland security officials to limit air travelers to carrying three-ounce liquid containers.

When an IED is built into a motor vehicle, it becomes a vehicle-borne improvised explosive device (VBIED), commonly referred to as a car or truck bomb. VBIEDs can be very destructive because of the amount of explosives that can be carried in vehicles. Truck bombs were used in the first attack on the World Trade Center in New York in 1993 and in the bombing of the Alfred P. Murrah Federal Building in Oklahoma City in 1995. A small boat was turned into a VBIED in the attack on the USS *Cole* in Yemen in 2000.

Most fire departments have encountered some kind of IED; the most common is the pipe bomb, which is made by stuffing explosive materials into a common pipe and threading detonators onto the end caps. Other types of IEDs have been used to guard drug laboratories or drug houses. Departments should ensure that they have close relationships with local and regional explosive ordinance disposal teams (bomb squads). Many U.S. fire departments have their own FBI-certified bomb squads. Departments should train personnel in responding to incidents that involve explosives and determining safe operating distances. They should also train personnel to maintain awareness when responding to incidents involving IEDs; increasingly, attackers have placed secondary explosive devices at incident scenes to target first responders.

Civil disorder Riots and other civil disturbances also pose man-made hazards to communities. Historic events can lead to rioting, as occurred across the United States after the assassination of Dr. Martin Luther King Jr. in 1968. Special events can attract protestors, anarchists, and others. In Washington, D.C., for example, where demonstrations and protests are commonplace, the District of Columbia Fire Department works collaboratively with many federal and local police agencies to ensure that the department can support law enforcement operations. Sometimes rescue personnel are requested to train police forces to use special equipment to remove chains and other self-imposed restraints from protestors, a common tactic deployed by protest groups. Some cities have annual events that bring large crowds and require special planning and the deployment of special resources. College spring break and Mardi Gras are examples of events that require fire departments to be ready to work with police forces in handling crowds that may become unruly.

Resource shortages Fire departments should be prepared to face resource shortages that may occasionally strike certain parts of the United States—for example, shortages of fuel, water, and food as well as the disruption of power supplies. A resource shortage can occur as an initial event (such as the Northeast power outage in 2003) or as a cascade event from a prior incident (such as the disruption of fuel supplies after a hurricane). As supply chains for various goods become increasingly interdependent and responsive to just-in-time needs, the chance of system failure increases, leading to the potential for resource shortages from time to time if the supply chain is interrupted.

War Fire service officials may not think of war as one of the key hazards to which they may be vulnerable. However, it is important to realize that emergency management has its roots in World War II planning for the allocation of limited resources during wartime, and many departments were involved in civil defense planning during the Cold War. In the modern era, many departments face the deployment of their own personnel as part of U.S. military efforts since 9/11.

Mitigation and preparedness programs in the preincident period

Preemergency mitigation and preparedness are essential to readiness for emergencies of all kinds and are two of the underlying pillars of comprehensive emergency management. A study based on the Hazard Mitigation Grant Program, the Flood Mitigation Assistance Program, and FEMA's Project Impact, a mitigation program in place during the 1990s that largely targeted natural hazards such as floods, estimated that for every dollar spent on mitigation efforts, four dollars were saved in reduced costs or damages when an incident occurred.[11] As Benjamin Franklin, founder of the America Fire Service, famously aphorized, "An ounce of prevention is worth a pound of cure."

Preparedness efforts are directed at citizens, the business community, and government employees. Citizens should receive information about the various potential hazards in their community, the protective actions that they can take before an emergency occurs, where they can get information, and how they can make themselves safer during an emergency.

In addition, governments are increasingly involving citizens in basic training so that when disaster strikes, they can assist in initial response efforts. The most prominent program is known as the Community Emergency Response Team (CERT). CERTs were first developed in California's earthquake-prone areas to train citizens to take lifesaving action (such as shutting off gas utilities or providing basic first aid) in the immediate aftermath of an earthquake. The CERT program now exists nationwide as part of a system coordinated through the Citizen Corps Councils. The Citizen Corps Councils also include Neighborhood Watch, the Medical Reserve Corps, and Citizens in Community Policing groups.

The federal government maintains the Ready.gov website, which keeps up-to-date preparedness information for citizens and businesses. The American Red Cross and other nonprofit organizations provide information and tools for individuals, families, businesses, and schools. Fire departments can use these materials to help with prevention and preparedness efforts. One program, the Ready Rating Program (readyrating.org), was developed by the Red Cross to help schools and businesses become more prepared.

Training and exercises

Emergency management and homeland security training and exercises are another important element of pre-event activities. The goal of exercises is to test plans, operations, and assumptions; build relationships; discover potential weaknesses in response efforts; and develop corrective actions based on after-action reports.

An important and often neglected step in exercises is developing a comprehensive training program around the specific areas in the exercise. Too often, exercises are like a final exam administered before the course is delivered; without preparatory training, they are not as effective as they could be. For example, an exercise for response to a potential HAZMAT incident should be preceded by a review of HAZMAT response plans and equipment. While occasional "surprise" exercises are important to test readiness, they should be the exception, not the norm.

Grants and grant management

Numerous grant programs are available to fire departments for homeland security and emergency management. All fire departments should research these programs and use available grants to enhance their response capabilities. In addition to programs available before incidents occur, special grants and funding may be available after an incident occurs. The accompanying sidebar lists the most common grants.

Fire departments that use federal grant funds for homeland security and emergency management must have a grant management program in place to ensure that these public funds are spent appropriately, within the guidelines of the grant program and federal law. Most individual grant programs have different rules and regulations on how program monies can be allocated and how they must be tracked. Federal grants are often audited, so departments must have proper accounting systems set up to track the funds and maintain detailed records showing how they were spent—whether on equipment or training or other department needs. Misuse of federal funds is not only embarrassing for the fire chief; it can also be a criminal act. It can jeopardize the ability of the jurisdiction to receive grant funds in the future. (More information on financial management can be found in Chapter 12.)

Homeland security and emergency management grants

The following list is just a sample of the many Department of Homeland Security-administered grant programs that have significant bearing on the fire and emergency service.

Assistance to Firefighters Grant Program

Buffer Zone Protection Program (BZPP)

Citizen Corps

Commercial Equipment Direct Assistance Program (CEDAP)

Competitive Training Grants Program (CTGP)

Emergency Management Performance Grant (EMPG) Program

Emergency Operations Center (EOC) Grant Program

Fire Prevention and Safety Grants

Hazard Mitigation Grant Program (HMGP)

Homeland Security Grant Program (HSGP)

Interoperable Emergency Communications Grant Program (IECGP)

Metropolitan Medical Response System (MMRS)

Regional Catastrophic Preparedness Grant Program (RCPGP)

SAFER (Staffing for Adequate Fire and Emergency Response)

State Homeland Security Program (SHSP)

State Homeland Security Program–Tribal (SHSP Tribal)

Urban Area Security Initiative (UASI)

Details on these programs can be obtained from numerous sources, including the Department of Homeland Security at fema.gov/government/grant/hsgp/index.shtm and the U.S. government at grants.gov.

Some jurisdictions have begun to consolidate their homeland security and emergency management grant programs across their various agencies. This enables them to allocate funds for maximum impact in the jurisdiction and to increase operability across agencies. If the police department and fire department are both requesting chemical protective equipment, for example, a consolidated program can ensure that compatible protective equipment is purchased rather than equipment that cannot be easily interchanged in the event of an incident. Some jurisdictions are also cooperating across jurisdictional boundaries to facilitate mutual aid interoperability. For example, departments in the Washington, D.C., metropolitan area have been collaborating to purchase similar self-contained breathing apparatus and other equipment that can be used interchangeably by personnel from different agencies during a large incident.

Intelligence and information sharing

One of the cornerstone responsibilities in homeland security is to ensure that a system for intelligence and information sharing is established. All fire departments, even those without other homeland security responsibilities, should be involved in information-sharing programs with homeland security agencies.

Intelligence collection and analysis is usually the role of law enforcement agencies. Within constitutional limits, intelligence analysts in these agencies collect information on potential criminal or terrorist activities, usually from crime databases, suspicious activity reports, and open-source (public) materials on the Internet, as well as from closed-source materials, such as law enforcement–sensitive reports and documents. From these sources the analysts develop various bulletins and reports on potential threats. For example, an analyst may receive a report that ammonium nitrate has been stolen from a construction site. Ammonium nitrate is a key ingredient in homemade bombs like the one used in the 1995 Oklahoma City bombing (which was a combination of ammonium nitrate and fertilizer, or ANFO). The analyst may then attempt to determine if there have been other thefts, how much has been stolen, and whether there are any reports of potential terrorist activity using ammonium nitrate. Then the analyst produces an intelligence report on the theft and potential threat, if one exists.

Intelligence analysts usually work in fusion centers, where members of different organizations involved in homeland security analyze various threats and then share information.[12] Although a relatively new concept in the United States, fusion centers exist in every state and in several major cities and regions. Currently, there are no standards for how to operate a fusion center; some centers focus specifically on terrorism, others have an "all-crimes" focus, and others emphasize "all crimes, all hazards." However, these centers are playing a growing role in analyzing and sharing homeland security information. Many fusion centers have fire service personnel who are assigned to them or who participate in their operations.

Fusion centers typically share information they produce on secure, web-based platforms built specifically for law enforcement use. Several platforms in use include the Homeland Security Information Network and the FBI's e-Guardian system. Networks among different departments and agencies in the intelligence community are constantly evolving. Fire and emergency management departments involved in homeland security activities should develop access to these systems, or work with their local and state law enforcement agencies to ensure that they are alerted when pertinent information is exchanged.

One of the challenges in homeland security is the process of administering clearances and classification systems that allow or deny access to information. Traditionally, the national security intelligence community (the FBI, the Central Intelligence Agency, and others) has been guided by a "need to know" culture and has had difficulty in the homeland security environment transitioning to a "need to share" culture. *Clearances* are applied to people and indicate the access level of a classified document or information that a person may be granted permission to see or hear. There are many levels of clearance, but in general, the basic level is "secret." People with secret-level clearance have generally undergone a background check by either the FBI or the U.S. Office of Personnel Management investigative services. *Classification* refers to documents or information within a sensitive program. There are over 400 different classification systems in the federal government, and the entire system was under review starting in 2009. Not all information must be classified, but a report must carry the highest level of classification given to any information it contains. Failure to maintain proper security of classified information is a violation of federal law, and people receiving clearances undergo specific training in their responsibilities to keep classified information secure.

While there are many classifications for documents, most homeland security information is placed under the heading of "Law Enforcement Sensitive" (LES) or "For Official Use Only" (FOUO). Neither of these is a secret-level classification requiring recipients to have a secret-level clearance or even to be part of law enforcement.

Fire services should work with local, state, and federal law enforcement to ensure that appropriate personnel have been granted appropriate clearances and access to certain classified information. Fire service leaders must understand the clearance and classification process and develop relationships that allow them to exchange information. Most important, they need to find out what kind of information is getting "fused," what kind of reports are being developed, what kind of information might be useful to them, and what kind of information they may be able to provide. The intelligence community depends on the exchange of information, so fire service leaders should be prepared to provide their knowledge and experience to assist in intelligence and information sharing. For example, the fire service can provide valuable information on hazards that can help law enforcement analysts determine the risk that a specific threat might pose.

Another resource for intelligence and information sharing is the FBI's Joint Terrorism Task Force (JTTF), organized in most major cities in the United States. Each task force combines federal, state, and local law enforcement personnel to investigate potential terrorist activities. Fire service leaders should know who the members of their closest JTTF are and proactively build relationships.

During the incident

During a homeland security incident or emergency management event, fire service leaders must rely on the plans, procedures, preparation, training, and relationships that they have made prior to the incident. Often, leaders will need to be flexible in their approaches to incidents. If the traditional role of the fire chief is coordinating the efforts of the fire trucks, the role of the emergency manager can be seen as coordinating the efforts of all the trucks: fire trucks, public works trucks, buses—in short, everything. The role of the homeland security professional is evolving, but it will focus on assessing the situation, sharing information, disrupting ongoing threats, and rapidly moving to reestablish security.

Detection

The determination that an event is occurring is made at the beginning of the incident. This may happen before the event, such as when a hurricane begins to form in the ocean and the first storm projections are made, or there may be no advance notice, as in the case of an earthquake or a bombing. The goal of both the emergency management and homeland security

9/11 information sharing on the front lines

One of the early lessons about information sharing involving the fire service came from the Pentagon on 9/11, where the Arlington County incident commander and a special agent of the Federal Bureau of Investigation (FBI) stood side by side from the initial moments of the attack and response. The special agent provided the incident commander with immediate information, including reports of additional hijacked planes that might be headed toward the incident scene, in exchange for updates on rescue operations so that the FBI could begin immediate evidence retrieval once the area was safe. This cooperation was forged in the years prior to the attack through preexisting relationships that the special agent had formed with the area fire departments when he served as an FBI liaison to the region's fire services in Washington, D.C.[1]

1 Arlington County, *After-Action Report on the Response after the September 11 Terrorist Attack on the Pentagon* (n.d.), arlingtonva.us/departments/Fire/Documents/after_report.pdf.

Standards for emergency management and homeland security

Consensus and accreditation standards in the fields of emergency management and homeland security are emerging. Additional standards that apply to the fire service are referenced in Chapter 10.

The Emergency Management Accreditation Program

The Emergency Management Accreditation Program (EMAP), developed by an independent, nonprofit organization in association with the National Emergency Management Association, originally focused on state-level emergency management programs. It did not apply to federal or local programs or to the private sector.

EMAP has been evolving and now can be used to assess local programs and specific agencies. Fire departments that have oversight of emergency management programs in their communities should look to the EMAP standards for an overview of how to build a comprehensive emergency management program, even if they do not wish to seek accreditation for their local jurisdictions. (More information can be found at emaponline.org.)

The Certified Emergency Manager® program

The International Association of Emergency Managers oversees the Certified Emergency Manager® (CEM®) program, a peer-reviewed program that assesses the professional development of emergency managers in several key areas. The CEM® designation lasts for five years. There is also an Associate Emergency Manager® credential for personnel who do not possess a baccalaureate degree. (More information can be found at iaem.com/certification/generalinfo/intro.htm.)

National Fire Protection Association

The National Fire Protection Association has developed NFPA 1600, Standard on Disaster/ Emergency Management and Business Continuity Programs (2010 ed.). (More information can be found at nfpa.org/assets/files/pdf/nfpa1600.pdf.)

communities is to determine when events are about to happen and either disrupt them (in the case of an attack) or provide enough advance warning so that protective measures can be taken. Detecting the event and determining its magnitude are critical responsibilities for emergency management programs.

Weather events and natural hazards are often detected by federal agencies or local news agency meteorologists, and are then passed on to the public and to state and local agencies. The National Weather Service, for example, monitors weather conditions; issues advisories, alerts, and warnings; and works closely with the emergency management community. The U.S. Geological Survey monitors for earthquakes and also sends out alerts and information. The Centers for Disease Control and Prevention monitors for outbreaks of contagious diseases around the world. Other federal agencies use various instruments and computer models to monitor and predict a variety of natural hazards. Monitoring stations exist, for example, to indicate when floods are occurring in many parts of the country.

Man-made hazards are harder to predict, but various methods have been developed to speed detection of these kinds of threats as well. In recent years, major cities have set up chemical monitors in transportation systems and public areas to detect chemical releases. Similar programs, such as the federal BioWatch program, have been set up to detect the release of biological pathogens; and public health and homeland security officials monitor the frequency of disease around the country and around the world to detect abnormal patterns that may indicate the occurrence of a biological incident. Radiation monitors have been placed in major ports of entry around the country, and many cities have issued portable radiation monitors for first responders.

Detection also requires constant monitoring for unfolding events. Some emergency management and homeland security agencies have established watch centers, where desk officers monitor media services, public sector radio bands, and detection devices, and use online information-sharing systems to rapidly detect and then alert both government leaders and citizens about a developing incident. During an incident, these watch centers often help maintain updated situational awareness and situation status reports for the responders, incident commanders, and policy makers dealing with the event.

Public warning, alert, and notification

As soon as it is determined that an event is imminent or has already occurred, emergency managers are usually responsible for activating public alert, warning, and notification systems. These systems vary widely, and emerging technology is rapidly changing how warning information can be disseminated. Homeland security officials may recommend increasing protective actions, such as security, screening, or police patrols. Fire service leaders should be prepared to increase response readiness and staffing levels, or to request additional resources in anticipation of needs during an unfolding event. The concept of "leaning forward" in preparation for possible requests for service has become a widely accepted doctrine in emergency management and homeland security.

Emergency managers may send emergency alerts to the public advising of the incident; giving information about immediate lifesaving actions, such as instructions to evacuate or shelter-in-place; and telling where to seek additional information. The emergency alert system is a nationwide system that can be activated locally to broadcast emergency information over the radio and television networks.

Many communities still maintain siren systems for outdoor alerting. Modern sirens can be programmed to make different sounds and broadcast voice messages, and they can be tested silently. However, human behavior and local custom must be considered when using sirens. In the tornado-prone Midwest, people understand that a siren means to seek shelter; in a town near a nuclear power plant, however, it may mean to evacuate the area. Emergency managers must tailor warning systems to local needs and make sure that visitors and new residents know what the various warnings mean.

With the growing use of cell phones, the Internet, e-mail, text messaging, and social networks, alert and notification systems have expanded to leverage these new technologies. Early systems, often referred to as "reverse 911" systems, could call landline phones with a safety message created by the emergency managers. More recent systems can send a variety of custom or prescripted messages not only to landline phones but also to cell phones, e-mail accounts, and even social networking sites. (An overview of emerging technologies for the fire service can be found in Chapter 16.)

Emergency managers and homeland security officials will also notify other government agencies, the private sector, response partners such as the Red Cross, and neighboring jurisdictions. If the incident demands, emergency managers may institute COOP or COG plans.

Incident management

During an unfolding incident, emergency managers and homeland security officials work closely with field incident command, unified command, or area command to keep situational awareness; they can inform command posts of additional information they receive and can prepare to request additional resources. Homeland security officials will often try to gain information from information-sharing systems, fusion centers, and law enforcement partners. Emergency managers typically bear the responsibility for handling mutual aid requests and initiating a local jurisdiction's disaster declaration process, should an incident be large enough to warrant a request for outside local, state, or federal resources. Incident management should conform to guidelines laid out in the NRF and NIMS.

National Response Framework FEMA's NRF, which replaced the National Response Plan in the aftermath of Hurricane Katrina, is an effort to align roles and responsibilities among federal agencies, and to provide guidance on how they can integrate with state and local responders during large emergencies.

National Incident Management System The federal government's NIMS is an effort to align the organization, doctrine, and operations of responders at various levels of government by providing a lexicon and a common set of definitions and procedures to guide the management of incidents. The NIMS is based on the Incident Command System (ICS), which is used widely in the fire service.

Disaster declaration

Emergency managers are responsible for the process used to declare that a disaster has occurred. While there are small variations in each state's disaster declaration process, in general the person responsible for directing a local jurisdiction's emergency management program (usually the highest elected or appointed official, such as a mayor or a city or county manager) makes a formal request for a disaster declaration to the state governor. The request is transmitted by the local and state emergency managers. In some states, a disaster declaration empowers local and state leaders to bring additional aid and resources in to assist with the emergency or to make changes to certain legal rules (e.g., declaring a curfew) for its duration.

At the state level, a request for a federal disaster declaration is transmitted from the governor to the president. A Presidential Disaster Declaration allows federal assistance and opens up federal funding streams, depending on the type of disaster. Disasters have been declared for emergencies such as hurricanes and wildfires, for terrorist incidents such as 9/11, and even for drought. In an unfolding emergency, a Presidential Disaster Declaration invokes the Stafford Act, which prescribes certain activities that FEMA and DHS can take to support the state government, and it allows funding and resources to be directed to the stricken area.

States may request resources from the federal government for a variety of missions and needs. They may also request aid from other states through the Emergency Management Assistance Compact (EMAC), the legal agreement between states for sharing state and local resources.

For fire departments involved in any large emergency, and especially for those departments that oversee emergency management programs, it is important to keep track of costs incurred once a disaster has been declared. Good records will be required when the department seeks reimbursement for activities during disaster response. Poor records can greatly reduce or delay reimbursement, sometimes for many years.

Emergency operations center

One of the activities that may take place during an emergency is the activation of the EOC (see Figures 2-5 and 2-6). Despite the "operations" name, the EOC is actually a center for coordinating disaster response activities, and it often functions as a multiagency coordination center (MACC). Some EOCs do have decisional, command roles in carrying out their func-

Figure 2-5 Mobile command units are often deployed during large-scale disasters.

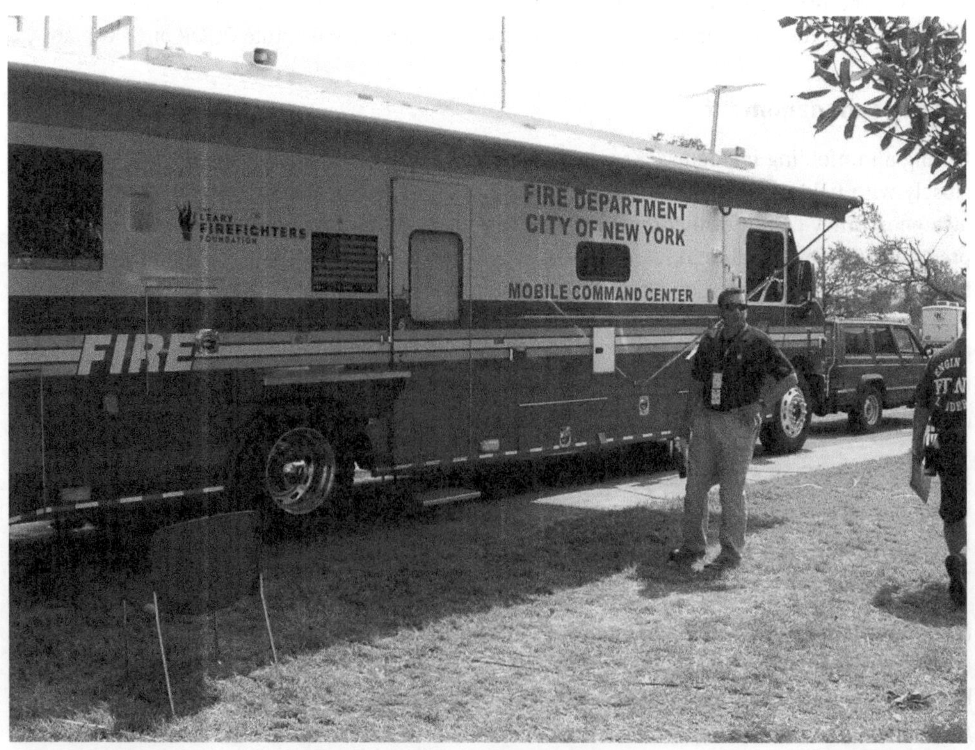

Photo by Jeffrey D. Stern

Figure 2-6 A briefing is held in an emergency operations center.

Photo by Jeffrey D. Stern

tions, in supporting field response, or in supporting elected officials in their decision making. The role of the EOC varies by state and jurisdiction.

Representatives from government departments and agencies, liaisons from the private and nonprofit sectors, and volunteers staff the EOC, helping to track resource requests and keep leadership informed of ongoing needs. Fire departments participating in EOC operations should ensure that the personnel assigned to the EOC have the command authority to speak and make decisions on behalf of the department and the chief, especially if the chief is not present.

Many EOCs have transitioned to the ICS, dividing EOC functions into operations, logistics, finance/administration, and planning/intelligence. (For more on the ICS, see Chapter 16.) There are no set standards for EOCs; in general, each center is uniquely tailored to the size and needs of the local jurisdiction. Many EOCs also operate using emergency support functions (ESFs), which are stove-piped functions led or supported by one or more agencies. At the federal level, ESFs are designated in the NRF. At the state and local levels, they generally mirror the federal ESFs with minor variations (see the accompanying sidebar).

ICS, which grew out of the wildland firefighting community, is based on a century-old military model for organizing to create mission cohesion, spans of control, and efficient unity of effort. The ESF system, which grew out of federal responsibilities and the development of the field of emergency management, was mainly designed to integrate support from the federal government to the states. Rather than developing a new system of coordinated effort from scratch, the NIMS and the NRF attempt to blend these two systems together. It works, but it is not seamless, and it will continue to evolve. Fire service leadership must play a key role in facilitating this integration.

EOCs, like fusion centers, are unique, but increasingly emergency managers and homeland security professionals are looking for ways to standardize their operations so that staff members can easily be assigned to any EOC when responding to a mutual aid request during an event, and liaisons from state and federal agencies can fit seamlessly into EOC operations. One of the biggest challenges in the next decade will be to further integrate the operations of local, state, federal, nonprofit, and private sector personnel by defining and clarifying the linkages and operations among field incident, unified, and area commands; EOCs; federal joint field offices (JFOs); and other MACCs that have various roles and responsibilities in disaster response.

Emergency support functions (ESFs) in the National Response Framework

ESF #1-Transportation

Aviation/airspace management and control
Transportation safety
Restoration/recovery of transportation infrastructure
Movement restrictions
Damage and impact assessment

ESF #2-Communications

Coordination with telecommunications and information technology industries
Restoration and repair of telecommunications infrastructure
Protection, restoration, and sustainment of national cyber and information technology resources
Oversight of communications within the federal incident management and response structures

ESF #3-Public Works and Engineering

Infrastructure protection and emergency repair
Infrastructure restoration
Engineering services and construction management
Emergency contracting support for life-saving and life-sustaining services

ESF #4-Firefighting

Coordination of federal firefighting activities
Support to wildland, rural, and urban firefighting operations

ESF #5-Emergency Management

Coordination of incident management and response efforts
Issuance of mission assignments
Resource and human capital
Incident action planning
Financial management

ESF #6-Mass Care, Emergency Assistance, Housing, and Human Services

Mass care
Emergency assistance
Disaster housing
Human services

ESF #7-Logistics Management and Resource Support

Comprehensive, national incident logistics planning, management, and sustainment capability
Resource support (facility space, office equipment and supplies, contracting services, etc.)

During an incident, the EOC, using ICS principles, will generally produce an incident action plan (IAP) with overall goals and objectives. It will also use the operational planning cycle to keep track of ongoing events and reprioritize resources and actions on a daily basis. The IAP is a component of operational planning (sometimes also called "crisis action planning"), describing strategy, tactics, tasks, and resources that are assigned to meet incident goals and objectives. The IAP differs from the types of plans created prior to an incident, such as EOPs, which fall under the category of deliberate planning that occurs during steady-state, routine periods between events. While fire services are used to producing IAPs for field events, EOC IAPs are generally more strategic in nature, helping to guide the entire response effort for the disaster. An EOC's IAP might include priorities to be carried out by several agencies, such as police, fire, public works, and public health. Often, incident objectives listed in the EOC's IAP will be assigned or approved by political leadership, such as a mayor. Additional information on incident organization can be found in many sources, including the NRF, available at fema.gov.

Evacuate, shelter, or shelter-in-place

Emergency managers are often responsible for issuing instructions on protective lifesaving actions. However, emergency managers must often issue these orders on the basis of the par-

ESF #8-Public Health and Medical Services

Public health
Medical
Mental health services
Mass fatality management

ESF #9-Search and Rescue

Life-saving assistance
Search and rescue operations

ESF #10-Oil and Hazardous Materials Response

Oil and hazardous materials (chemical, biological, radiological, etc.) response
Environmental short- and long-term cleanup

ESF #11-Agriculture and Natural Resources

Nutrition assistance
Animal and plant disease and pest response
Food safety and security
Natural and cultural resources and historic properties protection and restoration
Safety and well-being of household pets

ESF #12-Energy

Energy infrastructure assessment, repair, and restoration
Energy industry utilities coordination
Energy forecast

ESF #13-Public Safety and Security

Facility and resource security
Security planning and technical resource assistance
Public safety and security support
Support to access, traffic, and crowd control

ESF #14-Long-Term Community Recovery

Social and economic community impact assessment
Long-term community recovery assistance to states, local governments, and the private sector
Analysis and review of mitigation program implementation

ESF #15-External Affairs

Emergency public information and protective action guidance
Media and community relations
Congressional and international affairs
Tribal and insular affairs

Source: Federal Emergency Management Agency, "Emergency Support Function Annexes: Introduction" (January 2008), E-i to E-ii, fema.gov/pdf/emergency/nrf/nrf-esf-intro.pdf.

ticular situation faced. Depending on the organization within a jurisdiction, these orders may come from a field incident commander to be transmitted through the emergency manager. In some cases, the emergency manager has the authority to issue orders.

An evacuation order typically asks civilians and nonessential emergency personnel to leave a geographic area until the hazard is over. Sheltering involves finding areas of safety where people can be protected, housed, and fed for hours, days, weeks, or even months. Ideally, evacuation routes and shelters have been preidentified. Shelter-in-place orders protect people by asking them to stay in a safe location for a period of hours or days—often in a specific, protected area or room and usually at the same location they were in when the incident occurred.

Who's in charge?

"Who's in charge" is a common question in emergency management and homeland security events, and the answer—familiar to fire service personnel used to operating in a unified command environment—is, "it depends." A better question to answer is probably, "Who is in charge of what, and when?"

Generally, according to the principles that guide emergency management in the United States, control rests with the lowest governmental and organization level—hence, the designation of the incident commander or unified command team in the field. However, governors retain broad authorities in many states and are the linchpin for effective local, state, and federal coordination. In the event of a terrorist incident, federal law places the FBI in charge of the response effort. In other cases, such as natural disasters or accidents, the response is led by DHS with support of other federal agencies. Ultimately, the president is responsible for the response of the various federal agencies.

During a large-scale emergency, there are many decentralized decision-making authorities. A goal of the emergency management community is to ensure that these authorities are all aware of each other and are operating with some degree of coordination. Ideally, a unified command system will be set up, and at different stages of the incident, a different agency head may serve as incident commander; in reality, individual teams are working within their established chains of command. However, emergency management and homeland security leaders must understand that the public and political pressures often demand a strong leadership presence. Emergency managers and homeland security personnel must therefore be prepared to fill this role, either by designating an appropriate incident commander, designating a single spokesperson, or supporting public elected officials as they assume their role in leading the government response to the specific incident.

The fire service is used to operating in a hierarchical, paramilitary-style, centralized command-and-control fashion, as reflected in the ICS. Emergency managers more often operate in a decentralized, coordinated fashion, working to establish collaborative networks with distributed decision-making, control, and resource activities. Successful incident management requires a blend of both, and fire service personnel must become adept at operating within decentralized network systems while maintaining appropriate organizational control. This is an evolving and ever-present issue that challenges response operations and leaders alike.

Public information and managing the media

Often, responders will set up a joint information center to coordinate public information and provide a point where leaders can keep the public updated with directions and information. Management of public information and the media is a critical and ongoing task during any emergency, and the emergence of new media technologies means that if incident commanders respond to only the traditional twenty-four-hour news cycle, they will be a day late in keeping the public and media informed. Incident managers are still grappling with how to improve public communications and media relations as communication technologies evolve and news is reported ever faster. Many departments are beginning to experiment with using social media sites such as Facebook and Twitter to both receive and distribute information during emergencies.

Requesting help and additional resources

After an incident has been detected, alerts and notifications have been disseminated, appropriate disaster or emergency declarations have been enacted at the appropriate government level, and the EOC and field commands are operating, the role of the emergency managers and homeland security staff will be to handle requests for aid and information. If outside resources are required, they can be requested through one of several mechanisms.

Jurisdictions can directly solicit aid from the private sector or from nonprofit organizations. Usually, this aid is available through preplanned MOUs or agreements, but it can also be contracted after an incident occurs. Some private aid providers are reimbursed under contracts for service; some private aid is provided without reimbursement as a community service. The jurisdiction may also request aid from surrounding jurisdictions via either automatic aid or mutual aid systems established before the incident.

Citizen roles Citizens have been asked to play an increasing role in emergency management and homeland security, and they may become involved in response efforts. CERT, Volunteers in Police Services, Neighborhood Watch, and the Medical Reserve Corps are programs that help train and organize citizens to assist with various homeland security and emergency management efforts.

Nonprofit or nongovernmental organizations and volunteers Many citizens participate through nonprofit organizations such as the Red Cross, faith-based organizations such as the Salvation Army, or their own houses of worship. Emergency managers coordinate with these groups in the wake of an incident. Many of the nonprofit charity organizations that participate in response are members of the National Voluntary Organizations Active for Disasters (nvoad.org/).

The private sector The role of the private sector is increasing in homeland security and emergency management. Incidents such as Hurricane Katrina have revealed that a vibrant economic life is essential to the rapid recovery of communities after a disaster. During a disaster, the private sector can provide essential services such as food, water, and fuel. The government's role should be to help coordinate with the private sector so that businesses can keep their supply chains open. It is much easier for an emergency manager to provide food by helping to keep the local supermarket open than it is to set up a food distribution system.

Increasingly, emergency management and homeland security personnel are meeting with private sector companies to discuss the roles of the private sector and the government sector and figure out how they can be complementary. One national group that helps the private sector facilitate these discussions and prepare for homeland security emergencies is the Business Executives for National Security (bens.org).

State resources Jurisdictions may request state aid from the governor. In many states, the governor has direct legal authority to intercede even without requests from the local government, so it is important that officials know their state constitutions and laws that determine when authority is maintained by the governor and when it remains with local officials. The governor may assist with state resources such as state police and the National Guard, and he or she may request additional resources from other states, either through the EMAC process or from the federal government by requesting a Presidential Disaster Declaration. Each state National Guard also has a small civil support team that can be deployed for CBRNE incidents, for example.

Federal resources Fire service leaders are very familiar with federal support provided by FEMA's Urban Search and Rescue Response System. There are many other federal resources that can be tapped in an emergency, and leaders with homeland security and emergency management responsibilities should become familiar with those as well. In the course of planning for, or responding to, an emergency management or homeland security incident, fire service leaders may work with several types of federal teams that have been specifically developed in the past decade to provide support for civilian authorities. When a Stafford Act declaration takes place, the president will appoint a principal federal official to oversee the coordination of the entire federal response. This position, established just prior to Hurricane Katrina in a revision of the older National Response Plan, was controversial, yet it remains in existence. FEMA will also appoint a federal coordinating officer, whose role is to oversee Stafford Act support to the affected states.

DOD will assign a defense coordinating officer to assist with military support to civil authorities. This officer is a liaison who handles military forces that are under the direct control of the secretary of defense and, ultimately, the president (as stipulated in *United States Code* [*U.S.C.*] Title 10); these forces are often referred to as "Title-10 forces." The governor of the affected state retains control of National Guard troops (as stipulated in *U.S.C.* Title 32) from that state or operating on mutual aid through the EMAC system; these troops are referred to as "Title-32 forces." National Guard troops may also be "federalized," which means they are placed under Title 10 and the control of the president.

After 9/11, DOD established NORTHCOM (Northern Command), which oversees the defense of North America and defense support to civil authorities. Additional specialty resources are available from the military. For example, the Marine Corps' Chemical Biological Incident Response Force, which was established in 1996 in the aftermath of the sarin gas attack on a Tokyo subway in 1995, is available to respond to U.S. facilities worldwide and to support civilian authorities for incidents that might involve chemical, biological, or radiological materials. It often deploys on training or exercise missions in proximity to national events in order to be available more quickly should state or local authorities request its assistance. And the U.S. Army and the National Guard Bureau have been developing a homeland response force to be available to respond to a CBRNE incident; its capabilities will include search and rescue, decontamination, medical, aviation, communications, and logistical support during a WMD event.

The attorney general at the Department of Justice will also appoint a senior federal law enforcement officer to coordinate and oversee federal law enforcement resources.

There remains some overlap among these different positions, and over the next decade there will likely be minor adjustments as the federal government strives to makes its disaster response more effective and efficient. The question of who is in charge remains problematic, but the fire service will remain in charge of the fire service role.

Federal resources will generally be coordinated through a joint field office (JFO), federal law enforcement activities through a joint operations center (JOC), federal military forces through a joint task force (JTF), and federal information through a joint information center (JIC). One challenge for local leaders will be to ensure that local and state efforts are coordinated with these entities. Ideally, the JFO, JOC, JTF, and JIC will be co-located with or near state and local EOCs and the command post; however, this does not generally happen, and widely distributed national disasters, such as a pandemic flu, pose a challenge to this concept of organizing. One of the most important things that a local emergency manager can do is to ensure that liaisons are exchanged among all the established field offices, command posts, and coordination centers during a large-scale incident. The sooner that formal and informal networks among the entities can be established, the sooner that the response effort will be more effectively organized.

Access control and credentials

Establishing the identification of authorized personnel through the credentialing of responders during an incident is a common activity. Efforts have been under way since 9/11 to preidentify authorized personnel. The wildfire community has had a "red card" system for many decades that credentials personnel, confirming firefighter qualifications for different roles at a wildfire. It is important to set up a field credentialing system to track authorized entrants into a disaster area or the site of a homeland security incident.

Access controls often need to be established for residents, civilian workers, government personnel, and contractors during responses. Sadly, there are criminals who, in the aftermath of a disaster, seek to exploit vulnerable citizens. Such criminals range from unscrupulous contractors to scam artists to those who commit fraud by claiming damages they did not incur. Part of the emergency manager's role following an emergency is to ensure that the public is made aware of potential criminal activity. Law enforcement will be a key partner in these efforts. It is common after large emergencies, for example, for official credentials to be issued to authorized, licensed contractors. Emergency managers should be prepared to work with contractors, local building officials, and law enforcement to ensure that proper credentials are provided only to qualified persons who have a legitimate reason to be in the disaster zone.

Access controls are also often used to limit "freelancing" of emergency response crews. During a large emergency, many unsolicited volunteers, good Samaritans, and even emergency responders will descend on a community to render assistance. During 9/11, emergency units from outside the jurisdictional response area responded to the Pentagon in Virginia and to New York City without being requested.[13] A credentialing program initiated by the city of New Orleans in the wake of Hurricane Katrina revealed that there were about 5,000 local and state law enforcement officers from around the country operating in the city in the two weeks after the disaster, yet fewer than 1,000 had been officially requested under mutual aid agreements.[14]

While the effort is well-intentioned, freelancing poses the same challenges in disasters as it does on the fire ground. Issues of safety, liability, coordination of effort, and tracking of resources all arise. Emergency management and homeland security personnel need to expect that this will happen and be ready to account for these personnel and resources, integrate them into the effort, or send them home if appropriate. Determining who is operating at the disaster site is essential. Mechanisms for incorporating individual volunteers into productive and coordinated activities must be planned before the event and implemented during it. Volunteers and freelancing responders must be identified, tracked, and accounted for during and after an incident, and may require long-term monitoring if the incident involved exposure to toxic or hazardous materials.

After the incident

In the immediate, mid-term, and long-term aftermath of an event, fire service personnel will be challenged to meet a series of objectives.

Damage assessment

Immediately following an incident, an ongoing series of damage assessments needs to be conducted. These assessments may initially be dashboard surveys conducted by fire or police personnel driving prescribed routes to assess damage and report back to an incident command post or EOC. Aerial and satellite images taken after the incident are often used to compare against images from before the incident (Figure 2-7). Detailed assessments take place in the days, weeks, and months after an incident. The initial damage assessments provide the scope and scale of the disaster; later assessments help to determine the extent of financial assistance for which individuals or communities may be eligible. They also provide information that may assist with developing successful mitigation strategies to reduce the impact of similar incidents in the future. State and federal officials, as well as the insurance industry, will often send damage assessment teams to the area.

Donations management

Communities hit by major disasters tend to be swamped with donated goods—often unsolicited—in the wake of an emergency, and community emergency managers often

Figure 2-7 Aerial damage assessments can be useful for surveying large areas during disasters.

Photo by Jeffrey D. Stern

establish an ESF to handle donated goods and services. Because of the logistical challenges in managing large amounts of miscellaneous donated goods such as clothing, many communities, as well as the federal government and nonprofits, are increasingly asking citizens to donate cash instead.

Reentry controls

Often leaders focus on the need to evacuate areas when necessary, but an overlooked challenge is controlling the reentry of those who have been evacuated. People are anxious to check on their homes and businesses, but in the wake of a disaster, there are many hazards that must be remediated before the public can be safely allowed back into the disaster zone. Informing citizens and businesses about reentry plans is a postevent task.

Disaster housing

Postdisaster housing is a challenge for the long-term management of catastrophes. It is distinguished from short-term shelters, which are designed to provide immediate, safe housing for victims of a catastrophe. However, long-term housing needs must be tailored to each community: trailers and manufactured homes may not be a viable option in an urban environment, for example. Long-term disaster housing strategies are part of the emergency manager's responsibility in coordination with building officials, the private sector, land use planners, and other officials. Fire service personnel and their families may be among those needing help with housing.

Family reunification and pets

Families, children, and pets often become separated in the wake of an emergency. A core component of postincident actions is the implementation of a family reunification program. This could entail phone banks or an Internet site where families can look for other family members, pets, friends, and co-workers. Several nonprofit groups can help in this endeavor.

The management of pets poses a special challenge after an incident, and plans should be in place to care for pets, establish "pet-friendly" shelters, and reunite lost pets with their owners. Veterinarians, animal control agencies, and nonprofits can assist with these efforts.

Debris management

Managing the removal of debris after natural disasters usually requires the work of contractors. In a homeland security incident, debris may include toxic materials that require special handling. Additionally, evidence must be found and preserved, as was the case at both the World Trade Center and the Pentagon after 9/11. Public works agencies and the private sector are heavily involved in the handling and removal of debris, and may require close coordination with fire service HAZMAT specialists.

Counseling services and health monitoring

Responders, their families, and members of the community may be psychologically affected by a major incident. Services must be made available to help everyone affected deal with what occurred. The psychological effects of a disaster can increase the incidence of mental illness; however, good psychological and behavioral health counseling can reduce these effects. Incident managers should be open to inviting professional mental health counselors to conduct workshops and studies, not only to help those affected but also to aid those who may be involved in future incidents, thereby increasing the psychological resilience of the community to future events.

Additionally, the fire service must ensure that the physical health of responders is assessed and monitored—sometimes for many years. Responders are often exposed to unique and unstudied mixtures of toxic industrial chemicals, pollutants, building debris, and other pathogens that can affect them over the course of their lives.

Cost recovery and funding

Recovering costs after an incident can be a frustrating process that can take several years. The jurisdiction, each responding agency, and private citizens must account properly for their losses and the costs of response and reconstruction. The fire and emergency services must work closely with jurisdiction management and budget and finance experts to facilitate reimbursement. Emergency managers are often responsible for aggregating cost reimbursement information and working with local financial managers, especially when requesting federal reimbursement from FEMA or through the EMAC system.

Lessons learned

Determining the lessons from an incident and channeling those lessons back into new policies and training are important parts of the emergency management and homeland security endeavor. Often, public safety officials conduct a hotwash, or postincident analysis, immediately after an incident. The hotwash focuses on the key successes, failures, challenges, and perspectives of those involved. Emergency managers or fire service incident commanders may facilitate these reviews. Lessons from these quick critiques can be rapidly developed and disseminated. This is especially important when events are unfolding, as was the case during the anthrax incidents in 2001, when use of Level A personal protective equipment was gradually reduced to Level B and then to Level C protection as more information was gathered about the threat. A more detailed after-action report or critical incident analysis then generally takes place, often facilitated or written by outside experts, historians, or academics who can develop a more comprehensive and strategically detailed lesson from the incident and tie it to lessons from other events. For some incidents, historical analysis will continue for many years.

Long-term recovery

A challenge for all communities after an incident is its long-term recovery. Long-term recovery—the effort to restore the routines of everyday life—involves the social and economic sectors of the community. For individuals, it may include psychological and financial assistance. Some communities will never go back to the way things were, but they can embrace and learn from the incident and move toward a better future. The most salient example is the town of Greensburg, Kansas, which was completely destroyed by a tornado in 2007 and is rebuilding itself as a "green" community that will be an example for towns of the future. How quickly the community can restore its way of life is a measure of its resilience.

Emergency managers and homeland security officials share a key role in long-term recovery to ensure that vulnerabilities to hazards discovered during the disaster are mitigated during the rebuilding, and that the government and private sector collaborate to create a plan and process that work to restore the community's economic vitality, sense of place, and vision for a new, rebuilt future. Catastrophic events provide an opportunity for communities to reinvent their future, and fire service leadership can play a key role in participating in the process of recovery, helping to identify opportunities to mitigate hazards and create a safer, more resilient community.

Notes

1. International Association of Emergency Managers, "Principles of Emergency Management Supplement" (September 11, 2007), 4, iaem.com/publications/documents/PrinciplesofEmergencyManagement.pdf.
2. Homeland Security Council, *National Strategy for Homeland Security* (Washington, D.C.: The White House, October 2007), 3, dhs.gov/xlibrary/assets/nat_strat_homelandsecurity_2007.pdf.
3. *Quadrennial Homeland Security Review Report: A Strategic Framework for a Secure Homeland* (Washington, D.C.: Department of Homeland Security, February 2010), viii, dhs.gov/xlibrary/assets/qhsr_report.pdf.
4. Homeland Security Council, *National Strategy for Homeland Security,* 13.
5. Homeland Security Council, *National Strategy for Homeland Security* (Washington, D.C.: The White House, July 2002), 31, dhs.gov/xlibrary/assets/nat_strat_hls.pdf.
6. See Federal Emergency Management Agency (FEMA), HAZUS, at fema.gov/plan/prevent/hazus/.
7. FEMA, "People with Disabilities and Other Access and Functional Needs," at fema.gov/plan/prepare/specialplans.shtm.
8. Interagency Performance Evaluation Task Force, *Performance Evaluation of the New Orleans and Southeast Louisiana Hurricane Protection System* (Vicksburg, Miss.: Coastal and Hydraulics Laboratory, U.S. Army Corps of Engineers, June 6, 2006).

9. Charles Perrow, *Normal Accidents: Living with High-Risk Technologies* (Princeton, N.J.: Princeton University Press, 1999).
10. International Atomic Energy Agency, World Health Organization, and United Nations Development Programme, "Press Release: Chernobyl: The True Scale of the Accident 20 Years Later," September 5, 2005, iaea.org/NewsCenter/Focus/Chernobyl/pdfs/pr.pdf.
11. Multihazard Mitigation Council, *Natural Hazard Mitigation Saves: An Independent Study to Assess the Future Savings from Mitigation Activities*, vol. 1, *Findings, Conclusions, and Recommendations* (Washington, D.C.: National Institute of Building Sciences, 2005), 5, available at floods.org/PDF/MMC_Volume1_FindingsConclusionsRecommendations.pdf.
12. See, for example, Kevin D. Eack, "State and Local Fusion Centers: Emerging Trends and Issues," *Homeland Security Affairs Journal* 4, suppl. 2 (August 2008).
13. Arlington County, *After-Action Report on the Response after the September 11 Terrorist Attack on the Pentagon* (n.d.), arlingtonva.us/departments/Fire/Documents/after_report.pdf.
14. Author's personal observations, September 2005.

CHAPTER 3

Evaluating and Managing Local Risks

Charles R. Jennings

This chapter provides an understanding of

- The historical approaches to community risk assessment
- Ways to evaluate the severity of losses in the context of the community, for the property owner or resident, and from the perspective of the fire and emergency services
- Ways to evaluate protective or preventive programs
- Classifications and measures of community risk for structural fire, emergency medical services, and other hazards
- The importance of engaging the public and other stakeholders in decisions about community risk and risk reduction
- The steps in risk management.

Perhaps the most fundamental task for a fire and emergency services organization is to evaluate the risks that confront the community. This chapter focuses on fundamental physical risks: risk of injury, property loss, and death. Using an assessment of those risks and a process of public consultation via elected or appointed officials, the fire and emergency services department must define the resources necessary for addressing risks within the community. It does this after setting goals for service levels, response time, staffing, performance on limiting fire loss, reduction of injuries to the public, etc., and in accordance with legal requirements for delivery of services.

Risks can be considered from the external perspective of the public or from the internal perspective of the fire and emergency services department. This chapter emphasizes the community perspective. This is because managing internal risk begins with a solid understanding of the risks facing the community, and because many fundamental management activities within the fire and emergency services already support the practice of organizational risk management.

All fire and emergency service organizations provide fire suppression services, and almost all provide numerous other services that may require specialized equipment, training, or other resources. Some of these services will be specific to a particular community, reflecting its particular risks or hazards. While many risks are common to many communities, unique aspects of each community's population, economic structure, topography, building stock, and even weather affect the type and level of risk management approaches within that community. For example, a community with significant waterways might provide marine firefighting services using a fireboat. Likewise, a community in a mountain resort might provide specialized search and emergency services using snowmobiles (snow machines).

Fire services have traditionally been distinguished by a "can do" attitude and an entrepreneurial approach to service delivery. The extension of additional services to the public shows that the fire and emergency services department is responsive to the community; it also builds public support. However, a department must carefully consider new services or initiatives not only in light of existing commitments and constraints but also in terms of money, personnel, and time. Unavoidably, department managers must face the possibility that they may be unable to do everything they would like to do given the limited resources at their disposal. The risk management process offers a tool for choosing among service options.

Managing local risks entails several steps, including identification of risks, evaluation of current efforts and programs, and consultation with fire employees and community members to determine what levels of risk are acceptable as well as what levels of service and performance the community wants and is willing to pay for. These findings should be incorporated into a plan that includes strategies for reducing specific risks.

Evolution of community fire risk analysis

Community risk analysis has a long history. Many communities engaged in a casual form of risk analysis when they first decided to establish formal fire protection, which often happened after a large fire had galvanized public support for improvements (see Figure 3–1). The founding stories of many fire departments begin with a destructive fire that led to efforts to establish or improve a local fire department.

The insurance industry developed some of the earliest third-party standards for municipal fire protection. These standards were largely designed to avoid the prospect of a conflagration and to ensure that minimum required water, equipment, and personnel were available and maintained to respond promptly to a fire.

As new services have come into being, the demand for service and the factors encompassed in "community risk" have grown larger. Today, the typical fire and emergency services department provides a wide range of services to its community. In many communities, the demand for emergency medical services and the response to automatic alarms now dominate the demand placed on local protective resources, affecting overall community risk and the fire and emergency services department's response to or preparedness for these demands in ways that may be poorly understood.

At the same time, advances in technology and computing power have made possible the analysis of fire-related data at levels of detail that were completely impractical just five or ten

Courtesy of the Library of Congress, Prints and Photographs Division (LC-B2-2193-4)

Figure 3-1 A large fire devastated Bangor, Maine, in 1911.

years ago, thereby enabling fire and emergency service managers to better understand the risks in their communities. With a more complete picture of actual risk and a greater range of service choices, managers must have a clear objective in mind as they allocate resources to address those risks. The practice of evaluating and managing community risks is essential to properly allocating resources and attention, and to ensuring that local services are able to meet community expectations.

The process for community risk assessment is ongoing: it must be repeated as the community changes. Generally, the process should be reviewed on an annual basis. The evaluation and management of risks in the community should be fundamental to many aspects of fire and emergency services management, including budgeting, capital planning, training, and fire prevention efforts.

Definitions and types of community fire risk

Definitions of terms used to define and describe risk vary. This book relies on the National Fire Protection Association (NFPA) Standard 1250, Recommended Practice in Emergency Service Organization Risk Management (2010 ed.), whose definitions generally conform to those of the insurance industry. Precision in terminology is crucial to being able to clearly conceptualize and analyze community risk. The key terms are "risk," "hazard," "exposure," "peril," and "risk control."

Risk

A measure of the probability and severity of adverse effects that result from an exposure to a hazard (3.3.20). Risks can be expressed from the perspective of a particular person, a particular property, or a class of properties, or for the entire population of people or buildings in a community. The perspective selected can vary, depending on the purpose of the analysis. If one is concerned with fire safety in a local stadium, the perspective of a particular property is appropriate. However, if one is interested in residential fire safety, risk could be expressed by averaging the number of incidents of interest over the number of properties in order to develop a likelihood or probability of loss.

Probability can be calculated by dividing the number of events of interest (fires, casualties, or vehicle accidents) by the number of exposure units (buildings, people, or vehicles). Severity is a function of the magnitude and consequence of the loss.

For most fire incidents, there are two types of loss: direct and indirect, or consequential. Direct losses are inflicted on the property or persons affected, usually close in time to the incident. Indirect, or consequential, losses are in addition to direct losses and include loss of business, missed opportunities, and additional costs associated with restoring the direct loss. Often, particularly in business settings, the dollar value of indirect losses may exceed that of direct losses by many multiples. Imagine the cost of an electrical short circuit in a panel feeding cash registers at a department store. The consequential cost of the disruption in service until the electrical panel is repaired will likely far exceed the direct cost of replacing the damaged equipment.

Deaths and injuries can be given a dollar value, and although many in the fire service may find it distasteful, economic valuation of life is an accepted practice in the benefit-cost analysis of any new or expanded regulation. In most cases and for the vast majority of departments, there will be no need to monetize the value of injuries or deaths, although in performing a benefit-cost analysis to select among different preventive activities, such information could prove useful in predicting which activity will have the largest effect. The less rigorous technique of cost-effectiveness analysis may be sufficient in most cases where the benefits of competing programs are the same or a decision has already been made to provide a particular program (see the accompanying sidebar).

Consequential losses are more difficult to establish than direct losses. Conditions particular to a loss must be known and judgment is required. While it may not be possible to consider the whole range of losses suggested by humanity and common sense, from the community risk planning perspective, impacts on the community should definitely be considered.

The consequences of two events that have the same dollar loss can vary greatly. For example, depending on the magnitude of the loss versus the total value of the structure, the consequences of a $10,000 loss could range from minor to catastrophic. A $10,000 loss in a small, uninsured retail establishment might cause the business to fail, while a similar loss in a well-capitalized and insured business might cause only a limited disruption to the business. Loss of a neighborhood food store might be a severe blow to residents who can't drive, especially if the area is not served by mass transit. However, loss of a similar establishment in a neighborhood with multiple retail outlets might cause minimal disruption to the community.

Characteristics typically used in establishing consequences on a community basis include impact on employment, destruction of cultural or identity value, and effects on surrounding properties and residents. Fire service managers should know the major employers and taxpayers in the community. Appropriate steps should be taken during the prefire planning phase as well as after a fire to avoid disruption of key assets, to promptly identify fire-related disruptions, and to involve other elements of government to minimize those disruptions.

Hazard

A condition, situation, attitude, or action that creates or increases expected loss frequency or severity (3.3.10). Examples of hazards include cigarette smoking or the use of highly flammable materials. Some hazards are a direct result of business activity or normal life and are thus unavoidable. Many hazards can be controlled. For example, poor housekeeping or poor property maintenance can increase the likelihood of a loss and should be monitored and corrected, where possible. Removal or control of hazards is one of the primary goals of most building fire inspection programs.

Exposure

The state of being exposed to loss because of some hazard or contingency (3.3.8). Depending on how specific our definition of a peril may be, an individual's exposure can be fairly uniform or can vary. For example, risk of exposure to lightning would be much the same for most people; however, risk of exposure to hazardous chemicals would typically be greater

Benefit-cost analysis and cost-effectiveness analysis

Benefit-cost analysis is an important technique that can help an organization select among competing alternatives for improving fire safety. The following is taken from the U.S. Office of Management and Budget, "Guidelines and Discount Rates for Benefit-Cost Analysis of Federal Programs."

Net present value and related outcome measures

The standard criterion for deciding whether a government program can be justified on economic principles is *net present value*—the discounted monetized value of expected net benefits (i.e., benefits minus costs). Net present value is computed by assigning monetary values to benefits and costs, discounting future benefits and costs using an appropriate discount rate, and subtracting the sum total of discounted costs from the sum total of discounted benefits. Discounting benefits and costs transforms gains and losses occurring in different time periods to a common unit of measurement. Programs with positive net present value increase social resources and are generally preferred. Programs with negative net present value should generally be avoided [if there are more effective alternatives available]....

Although net present value is not always computable..., efforts to measure it can produce useful insights even when the monetary values of some benefits or costs cannot be determined. In these cases:

1. A *comprehensive enumeration* of the different types of benefits and costs, monetized or not, can be helpful in identifying the full range of program effects.
2. *Quantifying* benefits and costs is worthwhile, even when it is not feasible to assign monetary values; *physical measurements* may be possible and useful.

Other *summary effectiveness measures* can provide useful supplementary information to net present value....Examples include the number of injuries prevented per dollar of cost (both measured in present value terms) or a project's internal rate of return.

Cost-effectiveness analysis

A program is cost-effective if, on the basis of *life cycle cost* analysis of competing alternatives, it is determined to have the lowest costs expressed in present value terms for a given amount of benefits. Cost-effectiveness analysis is appropriate whenever it is unnecessary or impractical to consider the dollar value of the benefits provided by the alternatives under consideration. This is the case whenever (i) each alternative has the same annual benefits expressed in monetary terms; or (ii) each alternative has the same annual affects [*sic*], but dollar values cannot be assigned to their benefits. Analysis of alternative defense systems often falls in this category.

Cost-effectiveness analysis can also be used to compare programs with identical costs but differing benefits. In this case, the decision criterion is the discounted present value of benefits. The alternative program with the largest benefits would normally be favored.

Source: U.S. Office of Management and Budget, "Guidelines and Discount Rates for Benefit-Cost Analysis of Federal Programs," Circular Number A-94 (Revised), Transmittal Memo No. 64 (October 29, 1992), 4-5, whitehouse.gov/omb/assets/a94/a094.pdf.

for people living near facilities that treat, use, or store such goods, as well as for people who live along transport routes for such materials, than for the population at large. Exposures can also vary greatly in intensity: while exposure to an aircraft accident is greatest for people and properties along flight paths and near airports, there is nonetheless a small risk for all people, regardless of where they live or whether they fly.

Peril

An active cause of loss, such as a hurricane, fire, or accident (3.3.15). Perils can include severe weather, flooding, lightning strikes, fires, automobile accidents, and even accidental injury. Fire and emergency service departments, which are typically responders to almost all perils, will aggregate or combine perils to ease analysis, especially since the actions taken are often the same for broad classes of perils.

Risk control

The management of risk through stopping losses via exposure avoidance, prevention of loss (addressing frequency) and reduction of loss (addressing severity), segregation of exposures, and contractual transfer techniques (3.3.22). The fire and emergency services generally have the ability to use contractual risk transfer as insurance as a means for community risk reduction. Communities use building, zoning, and fire codes to segregate exposures of widely varying risk profiles. For example, explosives manufacture or storage is not allowed near residential areas.

Fire service risk control techniques are often a mix of actions to reduce the severity and/or the frequency of losses. Fire suppression systems do not reduce the frequency of fires, but they do act to limit their severity. Many public education programs act on both frequency and severity. For example, educational programs may combine fire prevention messages (don't use candles) with messages designed to inspire behavior that can reduce the severity of events (if you have a fire, close your apartment door as you exit).

In terms of practical usage, a building may be exposed to the hazard of an inoperative fire alarm system, which greatly increases the building's risk of fire. However, this risk might be mitigated if a risk control mechanism in the form of a sprinkler system were installed. Even though the inactive fire alarm is a hazard, the risk control mechanism limits the risk to the building by reducing the severity of a fire, should one occur.

Risk can be viewed from the perspective of a particular property (structure) or of an individual or group of individuals. The methods used to address risk can vary as well. For the peril of fire, for example, cooking introduces an exposure that heightens the likelihood of a loss. A local government can reduce exposure by prohibiting cooking in certain places, or can reduce loss by requiring smoke detectors or initiating a public education campaign to make building occupants more careful when they are cooking, thus reducing the frequency and severity of loss.

Risk can be characterized according to frequency and severity of consequence. Figure 3-2 shows the frequency-versus-severity matrix used to classify risks. Structure fires are a classic example of a low-frequency, high-severity event. This quadrant is where fire and emergency service departments spend much of their time. A high-frequency, low-severity event might be an overheated light ballast. Low-frequency, low-severity events generally do not get much attention, and high-frequency, high-severity events should be targeted for risk control measures to reduce both frequency and severity.

Figure 3-2 This matrix looks at frequency versus severity in order to classify risk.

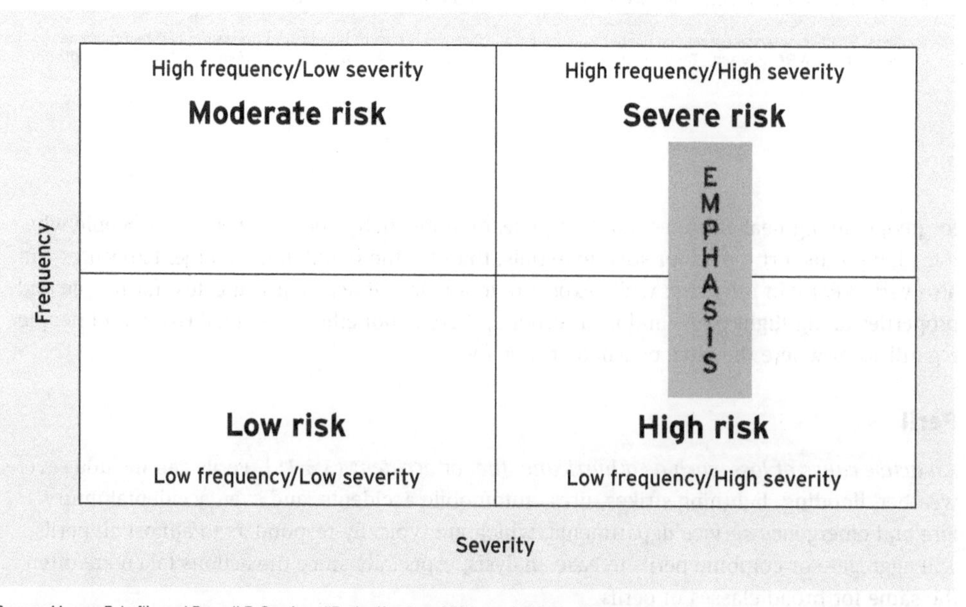

Source: Murrey E. Loflin and Russell E. Sanders, "Evaluating Local Risks and Planning for Necessary Resources," in *Managing Fire and Rescue Services*, ed. Dennis Compton and John Granito (Washington, D.C.: ICMA, 2002), 42.

According to the U.S. Fire Administration's report *Risk Management Practices in the Fire Service*, measures for controlling risks can be evaluated by several criteria:

- *Predicted effect:* Is the measure likely to be highly effective, such as installing sprinklers, or less so, such as posting warning signs?
- *Time required:* Will the measure be effective immediately, or will it require years to be effective?
- *Time to results:* Once implemented, how long will it take before results are achieved?
- *Effort required:* How much labor is required to implement the measure?
- *Associated costs:* What are the direct and indirect costs of the measure?
- *Insurance costs:* Are there changes in insurance costs associated with the measure?[1]

Community fire risk assessment

The contours of fire risk can be thought of as overlays on a map. Potential risk is the risk arising from the interaction of the built environment, topography, and human activity. The cumulative actual number of incidents in a given area can be thought of as actualized risk. In most cases, the potential risk is greater than the actualized risk.

Traditional fire risk assessment methodologies focus primarily on the property dimensions of risk. Larger structures are generally regarded as bigger risks than smaller structures. Fire flows are traditionally an important component of measuring fire risk for a specific property. Fire flow is the amount of water, expressed as gallons per minute, that is necessary to extinguish a fire in a structure. The use of projected or calculated fire flows as a proxy for risk carries some significant limitations. An understanding of fire flow requirements or needs is important, but it should not be the sole measure of risk.

Studies have consistently shown that there is a distinct socioeconomic component to fire risk. Variations in the frequency per capita of fires correlate with variations in socioeconomic status. Similarly, as noted above, dollar loss is not always a valid measure of the severity of risks or losses. Dollar loss, more commonly known as direct loss, is only one dimension of total loss. In most communities, property risk and life risk are not distributed equally; in fact, properties that have the lowest economic values may pose the highest risk for loss of life.

Risk identification

Risk identification for a community relies on a number of sources of information. Usually of most concern are fires originating in the built environment—that is, man-made structures. These structures present a risk based on their type of construction, any protective features they have incorporated, and their proximity to each other. Upkeep of these structures, as well as of electrical and mechanical systems within them, also plays an important role in determining risk. Sources of information on the built environment, particularly the building stock, include departmental and municipal tax or assessor's records, local utilities, housing agencies, and planning organizations.

The human dimension of risk is also an important component of risk identification. People play a major role in influencing risk patterns, and while past research has emphasized that criteria such as age of housing increase risk, it is often the condition of housing that is more important. Fire risk is generally greater for households with lower relative incomes, although the interaction of fire risk and income is influenced by numerous behavioral and residential characteristics. Fire officials should be very cautious not to apply generalizations from high-level studies to particular individuals within the community. (Inappropriate application of group data to individuals is known as the ecological fallacy.)

The protective infrastructure of a community must also be understood. Availability of fire suppression resources, including water supplies, equipment, and personnel, must be taken into account. As these resources are considered to be part of the community's response to mitigate risks, however, they will not be considered further here.

Identifying elements of risk

Building stock elements of risk	Human elements of risk
Building size and height	Number of occupants
Construction type	Physical or mental limitations that may affect ability to detect problems and evacuate without assistance
Protection systems in place/operational status	Presence of children, especially when undersupervised or unsupervised
Building access	Presence of elderly
Proximity of exposures	Household structure
Use of the building, including economic activity	Level of basic safety knowledge of community members
Vacant or disused properties	Prevalence of smoking, alcohol, drug use, or other activities that heighten risk

Risk analysis: Frequency and severity

Once a community has identified its risks, it must then analyze those risks to produce some estimates of their frequency and severity. A record of historical losses within the community can be developed from the National Fire Incident Reporting System (NFIRS) or other data sources. A community need not rely solely on its own data, however. For newly developing areas or for novel risks within the community, loss data from national sources can be used to explore the risks posed by certain populations, building types, or activities. Such data sources include national statistics; magazine articles or reports on similar incidents; fire and emergency service agencies in similar communities with experience with that type of property or risk; and regulatory, trade, or industry association data.

For each risk, a record, usually tied to a property, is developed. This record, which can be integrated into a prefire planning process, contains detailed information on all the characteristics identified in the sidebar above. The record might also include information on valuable or sensitive equipment, or on processes that should be safeguarded or that may require assistance from experts, as well as consequence information such as employment and historical or cultural value. In this way, risk profiles are developed for individual buildings, for subdivisions or developments, or for a neighborhood.

Risk classification and pattern identification

Once detailed risk information is developed for a number of buildings within a community and the assessment of risk—frequency and severity—for each property is complete, properties or areas can be ordered from highest to lowest risk. Classification of areas by risk level is used in deployment of resources at both the operational and planning stages.

Years ago, small areas of a community were known as box areas, corresponding literally to electromechanical fire reporting systems: each area was served by a box. In "high-value" areas, special boxes were dedicated to factories or other major structures. Signals from individual boxes could be used to assign a mix of apparatus and personnel, primarily on the basis of location, but also on the basis of risks particular to the area or building served by each box. A "running card" was developed listing a predetermined order of companies to respond on the initial and extra alarms from particular boxes. Even in communities that never had street-corner fire alarm boxes, the terms "box area" and "running card" persist. Today, box areas are also known as demand zones or fire management zones or something similar.

The practice of assigning units to an alarm on the basis of geographic area, a practice that has also carried forward into the design of computer-aided dispatch (CAD) systems, influenced early efforts to analyze the deployment of fire and emergency services. Limitations in computing power required that the myriad potential locations from and to which distances must be calculated be reduced to a manageable number of geographic areas or zones. The aggregation of risks into small areas of uniform composition is embedded in current risk classification and prioritization. A qualitative level of risk—low, medium, high, and extreme—is assigned to each small area, and a corresponding level of resources is identified in accordance with the type of emergency reported.

CAD systems can use dispatching protocols that are based on risk factors. For example, a CAD system can be programmed to send extra units to multistory buildings that do not have standpipes and that thus require fire personnel to stretch hose lines from the street to extinguish a fire.

The large amount of data generated in a community risk assessment can be very easily analyzed and presented using a geographic information system (GIS). GIS software displays spatially coded information from a database on an area map, enabling viewers to see spatial patterns. Beginning with a "base map," which usually shows streets, major natural features, and boundaries, the GIS user can add additional information—for example, zoning designations, employment, and building heights—in "layers." These layers can be turned on and off, and the display can be customized for maximum clarity. Vast amounts of data can be represented using this technology. GIS maps are an intuitive format for the display and presentation of data to elected officials and the public.

Figure 3-3 (see page 72) shows a GIS map representing the proposed floor area in dispatch zones in Surrey, British Columbia. Each dispatch zone corresponds to a unique assignment of resources in the agency's CAD system. This map, showing permitted new construction, indicates how the growth in the community is distributed and how additional resources may be required to meet likely growth in the demand for service. Fire stations are designated by the Maltese crosses.

This discussion has so far considered only responsive resources. Community risk analysis and prioritization can also be used for planning fire prevention programs and for identifying potential amendments to building and fire codes.

Balancing risks from different sources

In addition to fire risks, local fire officials must consider other risks to which fire and emergency services respond. Examples are medical emergencies, hazardous materials emergencies, and emergencies requiring technical rescue.

Firefighting dominates the deployment of most fire and emergency service organizations because of the large complement of personnel and multiple pieces of apparatus needed for each incident. However, in many communities emergency medical system (EMS) transport places a heavy demand on response system resources that will influence deployment for fires and other emergencies.

For each type of nonfire risk, the relevant characteristics of the risk should be documented and historical data reviewed. While the risk of fire is probably most closely tied to building stock, nonfire risks are more closely linked to human activity and therefore are more dynamic.

In most communities, the variance in nonfire, non-EMS transport risks tends to even out; major differences in deployment of staff are not necessary. These risks can be considered as evenly distributed throughout the community. Specialized apparatus and equipment for these specialized risks can be centrally located.

However, risks may change temporally or seasonally. A beach resort or ski resort may experience significant increases in population for a few months of the year. Another community may host an event that greatly increases the population it must protect, and the attendant risk, for only a few days each year. Many smaller communities must augment their overall level of service in anticipation of increased risk and demand for service associated with special events or seasonal activities.

The contours of risk in a community must be overlaid upon one another to provide a complete picture of the level of risk that the community is facing. Most places have only a few types of special risk, although some areas or locations within a community may have a higher level of aggregate risk than others.

Different types of incident risks vary according to different predominant community characteristics. Factors indicating heightened risk for a certain type of incident may have little relation to risk for other types of incidents. Characteristics most important for the following incident types are as follows:

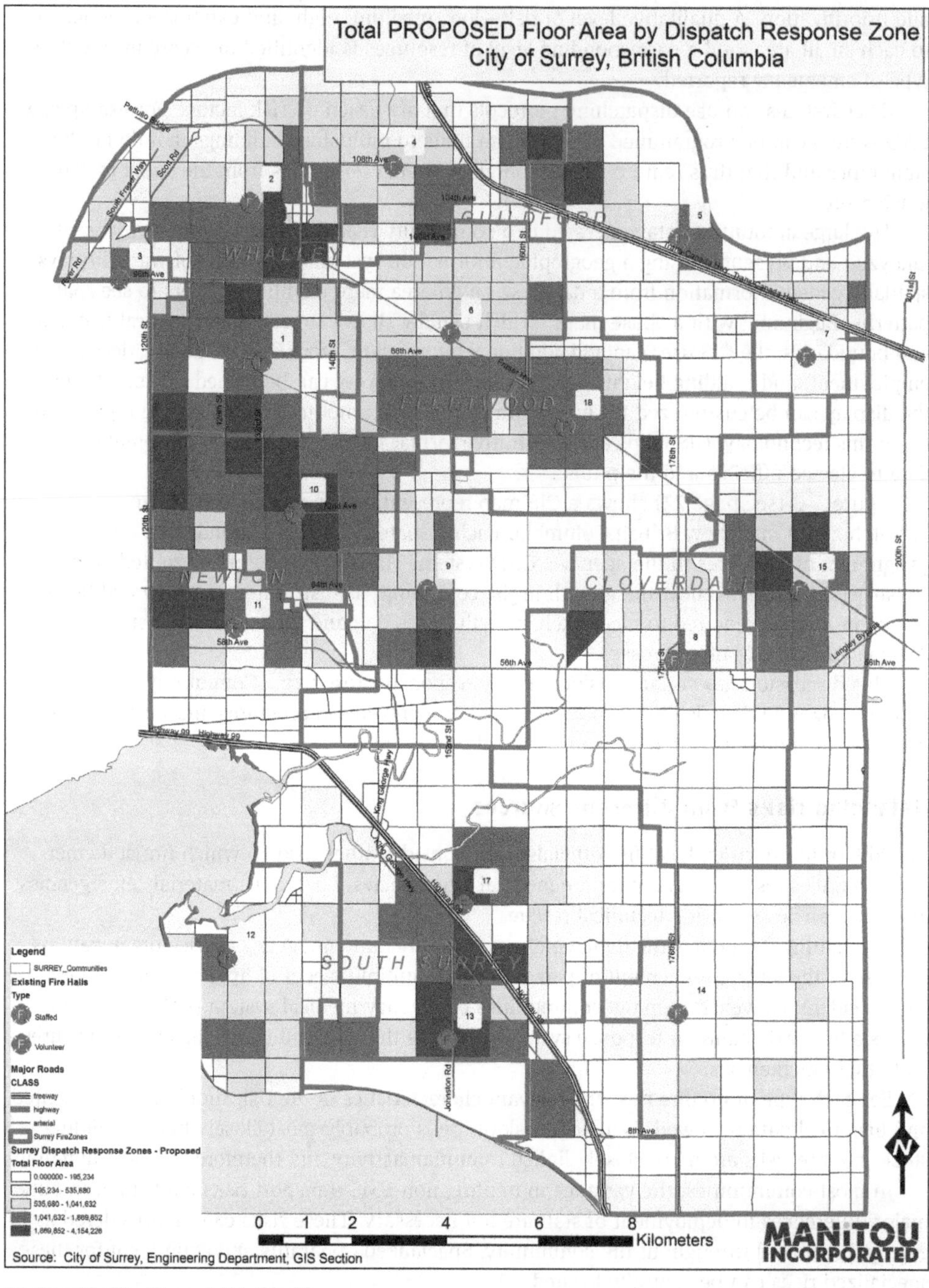

Figure 3-3 The total proposed floor area by dispatch response zone shows the concentration of buildings by geographic area of the community.

Courtesy of the City of Surrey, British Columbia

- *Structural fire:* Risk is fixed to building stock but varies with building use and residential population characteristics.
- *Medical emergencies:* Risk follows population. Temporal variation in risk is associated with employment. Employment centers will experience greater risk during periods when they are in operation. Additionally, heightened risk for higher-risk cohorts that spend most of their time at home is linked to residential concentrations.
- *Incidents requiring technical rescue services:* Risk is tied to natural features, industrial facilities, and specialized installations. There is a general but infrequent risk in times of natural disaster (earthquake, tornado, hurricane, flooding). The particular geographic area will have a unique mix of risks.

Methodologies for measuring community risk

The following discussion of risk measurement focuses on structural fire risk. Emergency medical or other emergency services are considered secondarily. Special risks—for instance, the wildland-urban interface, technical rescue, and hazardous materials—are not included in this overview.

A starting point for managing risk is measuring the level of risk that exists in the community. A number of specific methodologies and standards provide guidance and references for a community seeking to understand its risk profile. In choosing a methodology, fire officials must weigh preparing for "worst-case" events against preparing for events that are more common in their communities. Approaches that target worst-case events tend to be more prescriptive; those that target likely events are based on local experience and may be more flexible. When analysis of local data is not sufficient to determine a level of risk, a more prescriptive approach is appropriate.

Empirical measurement of risk

There is an emerging consensus that actual experience within a community can be an effective and defensible measure of local risk. Traditional approaches to assessing risk have grown out of the insurance industry's early studies on property protection. These approaches, which focus on property risk and the avoidance of conflagrations, emphasize the physical characteristics of buildings or structures, and are concerned with fire flows and the risk of spread to adjoining or adjacent properties.

Today, however, because of widespread demolition of urban centers during the urban renewal programs in the 1960s and 1970s and subsequent redevelopment under improved building codes, the conditions for conflagration are not nearly as prevalent in urban centers as they were over 100 years ago. They are, in fact, exceedingly rare. Rather, today's conflagrations occur mostly at the wildland-urban interface.

Emerging academic studies have shown the importance of examining population-based fire risk. As was noted above, property and life risks are often not distributed equally, and some properties with the highest life risk in a community may have comparatively low property value or economic importance. In addition, preventive activities are typically least intensive in residential occupancies, and most codes do not permit inspection of dwelling units, even though residences are the most common location for fire fatalities.

Resolving this discrepancy between property and life risks raises again the question of how we measure risk. Most existing methodologies emphasize prospective or potential risk: "What would be the expected consequences if a fire occurred on this property?" The other component is actualized risk. Actualized risk is determined by examining the history of fires in the community. But both dimensions must be considered: a community must not ignore a major hazard simply because it hasn't yet experienced a major consequence, but at the same time, it must not ignore or undervalue the real and recurring patterns of risk that may be responsible for the lion's share of incidents, property losses, and casualties. Considerable care must be taken to balance these two sometimes competing approaches. In fire and emergency service departments with a high call volume, the need to improve or maintain response times to actual incidents provides an inherent check on an excessive emphasis on potential risk.

For communities with a sufficient number of incidents (over 500 fire incidents annually) and reliable, complete data, analysis of local data can be a useful component of measuring community risk. Ideally, several years of data will be used to identify patterns in demand for service. Demand can be analyzed by type of incident, location, and time of day. Information on occupancy or resident characteristics can be gathered from small-area census data. For residential fires, these data can provide useful information to correlate demand for service with characteristics of occupants or residents.

Data collected from different municipal agencies, as well as incident information from sources such as the fire and emergency services department's records management system or NFIRS reports, may be used to develop a thorough understanding of both fire and EMS risk, although additional information on patient characteristics may be useful for determining EMS risk.

Prescriptive formulas for measuring risk

Communities without good historical data must rely on prescriptive formulas if they want to evaluate existing patterns of resource deployment to mitigate their risks.

Three formal methodologies that are widely used to address community fire risk are RHAVE, fire flow formulas, and HAZUS. The first two have been used for many years. RHAVE looks at the entire community; fire flow formulas are more widely used in preincident planning and focus on particular scenarios. HAZUS includes nonfire risks and takes a community-wide approach.

RHAVE For years, the Center for Public Safety Excellence (CPSE), which administers the fire service accreditation process, required communities to use a software program called RHAVE (Risk, Hazards, Value Evaluation) to assess their risks. CPSE now relies on a more open, empirical approach to measuring community fire risk (see the accompanying sidebar), but the RHAVE software is still available through a private vendor, and many communities that seek CPSE accreditation continue to use it. CPSE is developing a successor software package that may be available in the near future.

The RHAVE program is a computerized database that uses the Occupancy Vulnerability Assessment Profile (OVAP). The user enters key descriptive and risk-related information for

Center for Public Safety Excellence: Accreditation and risk assessment

The Center for Public Safety Excellence (CPSE) administers an accreditation process for fire and emergency service departments. To be accredited, a department must undertake a risk assessment that will enable it to identify overall service-level objectives, critical tasks, and staffing and other resources needed.

CPSE materials describe physical, economic, and demographic factors that are thought to contribute to the overall level of risk in a community. Physical factors include service-area boundaries, zoning or other development restrictions, and topography, including changes in elevation or barriers that might impede response. Other physical characteristics to be considered are transportation infrastructure, climate, natural or man-made hazards, critical infrastructure, and population growth.

CPSE's accreditation process also advocates using data from the Insurance Services Office on age, size, construction, exposures, fire protection systems, fire flow requirements, and economic value for individual properties. These data can be imported and analyzed using geographic information system (GIS) software.

The CPSE approach to understanding a community's fire risk also uses historical data on the location, nature, and frequency of calls for service. These service data can be expressed as an incident's frequency by unit of time—for example, the number of calls for service per day or per hour. Planners should analyze peaks in workload to ensure efficient provision of service. Demand for service can vary both temporally and by location, so peaks can be expressed in terms of location as well as time and type of incident.

The CPSE accreditation model calls for consideration of both probability and consequence, which correspond to frequency and severity and can be arrayed in a matrix as shown in Figure 3-2 of this chapter. Two methods for deploying resources address probability and consequence: *distribution* of resources refers to the placement of resources in order to provide service for the greatest number of potential incidents, while *concentration* of resources describes a "massing" of resources in proximity to locations with potential for high-consequence events. Fire and emergency service managers must balance these two concepts. At some point, the potential consequences of an event in one location will pull resources away from a location that may have an equally high probability of an event but lower potential consequences.

Risk assessments for individual properties are aggregated to subareas, or fire demand zones, within the fire service district, and these zones are classified according to the predominant risk type (low, moderate, high, etc.) within the area. Nonfire risks are classified using empirical information from call history, land use or development patterns, and nature of complaint.

Risk assessment is a critical component of the accreditation process. As the process continues to be refined and more widely adopted, it will likely become more influential in community fire and emergency risk assessment.

each building in the community, including information on the site, life safety, risk, water demand, and value. Within each of these broad areas, subfields hold detailed information such as property use, number of units in the building, assessed valuation, number of employees, construction type, area of the building, regulatory oversight, frequency of fires, fire load, hazards in the building, fire flow required, and presence of sprinklers. Risk ratings of individual properties are then aggregated into "area" ratings.

Fire flow Fire flow is the amount of water that must be delivered to suppress a fire in a particular structure. Fire flow formulas, derived from experience and testing, can be used to estimate the rate at which water must be pumped according to the percentage of a structure involved in the fire. Fire flow expressed in gallons per minute, together with information on where it is needed, can be translated into personnel and equipment requirements. For example, delivering 250 gallons per minute to the interior of a structure may require more personnel (to manage hose lines) than delivering the same volume of water to the outside of a building.

Three major fire flow formulas are in use: Royer/Nelson, the National Fire Academy (NFA) formula, and the Insurance Services Office (ISO) formula. The first two rely on fairly simple area calculations to estimate gallons per minute. The Royer/Nelson formula, developed at the University of Iowa, calculates the fire flow necessary to fight fire indirectly, from outside the burning building, whereas the NFA formula calculates fire flow for interior firefighting when firefighters are attacking the fire directly. The ISO formula is more involved, requiring more detailed information on the property, including type of construction, occupancy, exposures, and presence of connections (communication) between the structure and adjacent buildings. ISO data on individually rated buildings within a community can be used in prefire planning efforts and integrated into the local risk assessment.

The relevance of fire flow analysis has diminished somewhat over the years. Fire flows were once the primary means of determining the level of response to any particular location, and their use for measuring fire risk was associated with the early emphasis on avoiding urban conflagrations. As the urban fire problem transitioned from "saving the city" to "saving the block" to "saving the building," increased emphasis was placed on the life safety of occupants of these structures. Also, the increasing capacity of modern pumping apparatus has negated some of the relevance of fire flow analysis because the pumping capacity dispatched to most alarms is more than sufficient to meet the demands of a fire in most offensive fire attack operations. Finally, fire flow analysis applies to only one dimension of the overall risk to communities: the risk of fire. Thus, while adequate fire flows are still essential to firefighting and make a real contribution to saving lives, fire flow analysis is mainly a property protection tool.

Nevertheless, fire flow formulas—the earliest quantitative effort to measure the fire risk of a particular structure and match community resources against this risk—remain a valuable component of preincident planning as they identify those properties where additional pumping apparatus may be required to suppress a well-developed fire.

HAZUS The Federal Emergency Management Agency (FEMA) distributes a GIS-based software package known as HAZUS-MH, which uses a standardized methodology to map and display potential losses from a number of natural-hazards scenarios. The estimation and spatial arrangement of losses can be very useful in identifying areas of the community that are particularly vulnerable to hurricanes, floods, or earthquakes. By identifying such areas and providing information on the nature of potential damage, the software can be used to target educational, code enforcement, and other mitigation activities where they are most needed. It can also estimate damage to building stock, essential facilities, transportation facilities, and critical infrastructure; estimate costs of repair and lost income; and identify the population likely to require shelter or other recovery assistance.

Because HAZUS data are GIS based, they can be readily integrated into a jurisdiction-wide tool. The software comes preloaded with basic data from across the United States and is regularly updated using scientific data and research; in addition, detailed local information can be added to further increase the accuracy of estimates.

The HAZUS software can be very useful in assessing the risk from certain natural hazards for which the fire and emergency service departments must prepare. Because it has a wide

Evaluating and managing local risks: Putting it into practice

The city of Surrey, British Columbia (est. 2010 pop. 472,000), is located in the greater Vancouver area and stretches to the U.S. border. Significant growth has brought a large number of high-rise buildings with both residential and office uses. While high-rises had been concentrated in a small part of the community, the plan was to construct more of them throughout the city. The fire and emergency services department realized that such development would create new challenges as more and more alarms occurred in increasingly taller buildings dispersed over a wider area.

Faced with this change in its operating environment, the department conducted a thorough analysis encompassing all facets of its fire and emergency service capabilities. Its analysis also took into account contributions from other entities that had some role in the problem, including building owners and managers, code authorities, and provincial agencies.

It began by studying the literature about the high-rise problem and also did a thorough review of its own incident data to develop a precise understanding of its past experience and the community's potential for large losses. This analysis included calculating the probabilities of fire and estimating the likelihood of a large loss fire.

The department then broke the problem down into various operational components:

- Fire suppression: Water supply
- Standpipe systems
- Selection of proper hose lines and nozzles
- Occupant control
- Public address systems
- Occupant training
- Building and fire code: Need for additional code provisions
- Dispatch: Adding additional units to reported fires in high-rise buildings.

The department analyzed each of these areas and made recommendations where necessary to augment existing resources. It also met with internal stakeholders from all parts of the fire and emergency service to get their perspectives.

The project concluded with action steps and a list of initiatives encompassing staffing, dispatch, protective equipment, and fire codes. The process was defensible and open, and it produced results that could be more effective than any single approach.

Source: Summarized from Charles Jennings, "Handling Highrises: Surrey Uses Systems Approach to Manage Risk," *Fire Fighting in Canada* (May 2009), firefightingincanada.com/index.php?option=com_content&task=view&id=3541&Itemid=210 (accessed May 17, 2011).

community of users, the software also provides a good opportunity for fire and emergency service managers to engage and collaborate with colleagues and other participants in the local government planning process in preparation for large-scale events.

Evaluating service levels and response capability

Side by side with risk assessment, a main component of managing community risk is determining local fire and emergency service levels and capabilities (also addressed in Chapters 4 and 10). The fire and emergency services manager should be able to express the level of service that the local department can provide in operational terms: for example, "The fire and emergency services department can respond with a full complement of personnel in *x* minutes to 90 percent of incidents, and confine *y* percent of fires to the room of origin." The costs of making changes to this service level should be estimated, as should be the cost of alternative approaches to reducing community risk.

There are many approaches to evaluating response capability. Some emphasize fire suppression to the exclusion of other approaches that may be less expensive and equally or more effective. If the fire and emergency services department is not meeting community expectations, a plan should be developed to improve performance. If city management, elected officials, and the public do not provide resources to improve the level of service, the fire and emergency services manager must examine alternative approaches that will reduce the risk or improve capability without added expense.

The most important point to remember is that fire and emergency service capabilities should not be developed in isolation from community risks. While nearly all fire and emergency service departments must have certain fundamental capabilities, communities vary considerably in terms of risk, resources, and demands for service that will affect service levels and program choices.

When evaluating service levels and response capabilities, fire officials should identify specialized services that are needed but not provided by the local fire and emergency services department, and these gaps should be filled through either expansion of local capabilities or identification of available outside resources. Many special services can be obtained through mutual aid agreements or multijurisdictional cooperation to form regional teams. In some cases, those communities that are likely to use such services most often will decide to engage private contractors and assume most of the cost burden themselves.

Basic questions that can be asked about local capabilities include

- Are causes of fires and major risks in the community understood?
- Is a more comprehensive and extensive prevention and code administration program needed?
- Are emerging problems that have been identified through evaluation of local data and preventive programs adjusted accordingly?
- Do trained members, properly equipped, arrive at fire and other emergency incident locations within the recommended time frame and with sufficient staffing?
- Are suppression and emergency management strategies and tactics appropriate, safe, and effective?
- Is a standard risk-benefit assessment part of firefighting and incident management training?
- Do the current training, equipment, and operating practices reflect the community's population and building stock, and the fire and emergency services department's resource levels?

In addition to these basic questions, there are several national industry and consensus standards that have a direct bearing on service levels. These are detailed in the following section.

The ISO Fire Suppression Rating Schedule

Early in the twentieth century, after major fires destroyed the most densely built and valuable parts of several cities, including Baltimore and Toronto, the insurance industry demanded a reliable way of assessing the quality of municipal fire protection. To help fire insurance underwriters, in 1916 the National Board of Fire Underwriters published the first version of what was to become the Fire Suppression Rating Schedule (FSRS). In 1971, when most state rating bureaus were consolidated, the National Board of Fire Underwriters became ISO.

ISO continues to grade communities, and in those of less than 250,000 in population, it periodically carries out physical site inspections. Its representatives visit the community, collect records, and observe the components of the local fire protection system, including such elements as water supplies (hydrants and alternate water sources), equipment (apparatus and tools), staffing (attendance records), training records, and dispatch facilities. Their observations are combined with inspections of selected properties within the community to determine fire flows necessary to suppress a well-developed fire. This information is available to communities doing their own risk assessments.

ISO uses these observations and data to determine a numerical grade for a community's fire protection. The grades range from 1, the highest, to 10, meaning that there is no recognized fire protection provided (see Figure 3–4). In the absence of a public fire protection water supply, the highest grade available is 9. ISO also assigns split grades, giving a separate grade to part of a community that is not provided with a public fire protection water supply. For example, in a grading expressed as 4/9, the 9 might apply to that portion of the community with no hydrants. The importance placed on adequate water supply is evident.

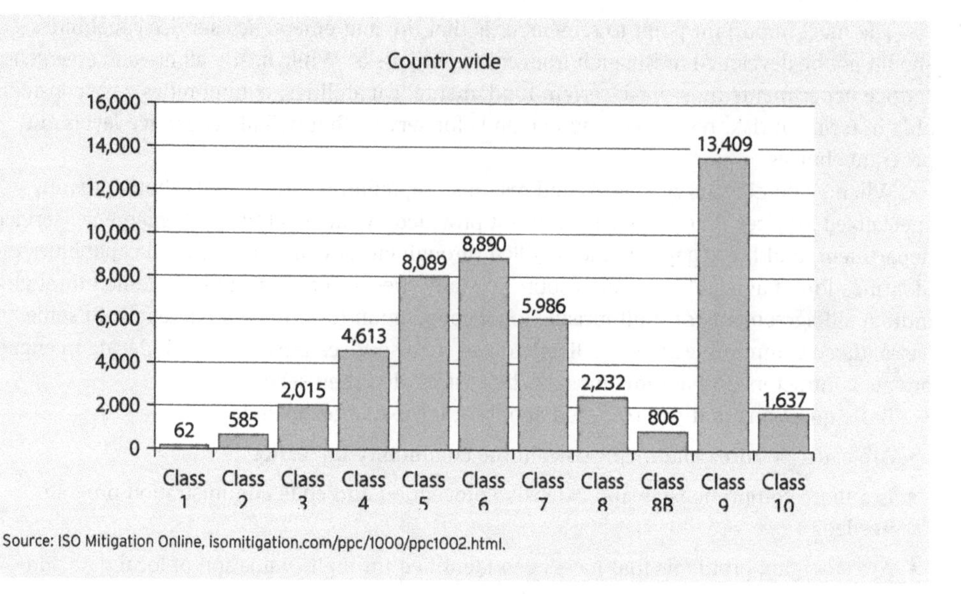

Figure 3-4 This chart depicts the ISO Public Protection Classification distribution of communities across the country.

Although the FSRS is not designed as a management tool for fire services, it has traditionally been extremely influential for establishing equipment, staffing, and deployment levels. It has come under criticism from fire chiefs and advocates for fire prevention because it does not explicitly consider preventive activity and is therefore perceived by some to exert a bias toward fire suppression assets. However, it has exerted a positive influence by providing incentives to communities to improve their water supplies. For example, it allows communities that have areas with no or inadequate fire protection water supplies to install "dry hydrants" and formalize tender (tanker) shuttle arrangements to provide a sustained firefighting water flow in those areas and thereby improve their ISO ratings.

The FSRS is designed to assess fire protection only. It does not provide guidance on emergency medical or other specialized services that may be provided by fire and emergency service departments.

The FSRS is currently under revision. In consultation with stakeholder organizations, ISO has proposed changes in several areas of the schedule, which it reports are currently being reviewed. In the area of community risk-reduction programs, ISO is proposing credit for the adoption and enforcement of a model building code and a model fire prevention code, including fire prevention inspector certification and training.

Also under discussion is a move toward basing credit for fire companies on actual performance data, rather than on strict mileage limits, when good local data are available. This change would rely on time limits used in NFPA 1710 for first-arriving engines and the deployment of a full first-alarm assignment. The fire and emergency services industry is eagerly anticipating the projected release of the schedule in late 2011.

Key ISO requirements for deployment (1980 edition)

Distribution of companies

- Engine companies: 1.5 miles to built-upon areas
- Ladder companies: 2.5 miles to built-upon areas

Response time

Using an assumed travel speed of 35 miles per hour, the above distribution requirements equate to 3.2 minutes for an engine company and 4.9 minutes for a ladder company. The ISO does not use actual response time information but relies on distance in assessing adequacy of stations and apparatus.

Automatic Aid can be recognized under certain criteria.

The ISO Fire Suppression Rating Schedule

The Fire Suppression Rating Schedule (FSRS) is the manual that the ISO uses in reviewing the firefighting capabilities of individual communities. The FSRS measures the major elements of a community's fire suppression system and develops a numerical grading called a Public Protection Classification™ (PPC™) (see Figure 3-4). The grading works as follows:

Fire alarms

Ten percent of the overall grading is based on how well the fire department receives fire alarms and dispatches its firefighting resources. ISO field representatives evaluate the communications center, looking at the number of operators at the center; the telephone service, including the number of telephone lines coming into the center; and the listing of emergency numbers in the telephone book. They also look at the dispatch circuits and at how the center notifies firefighters about the location of the emergency.

Engine companies

Fifty percent of the overall grading is based on the number of engine companies and the amount of water a community needs to fight a fire. ISO reviews the distribution of fire companies throughout the area and checks that the fire department tests its pumps regularly and inventories each engine company's nozzles, hoses, breathing apparatus, and other equipment.

ISO also reviews the fire company records to determine

- Type and extent of training provided to fire company personnel
- Number of people who participate in training
- Firefighter response to emergencies
- Maintenance and testing of the fire department's equipment.

Water supply

Forty percent of the grading is based on the community's water supply. This part of the survey focuses on whether the community has sufficient water supply for fire suppression beyond daily maximum consumption. ISO surveys all components of the water supply system, including pumps, storage, and filtration. To determine the rate of flow that the water mains provide, it observes fire-flow tests at representative locations in the community. Finally, it evaluates the distribution of fire hydrants.

Source: Adapted from Insurance Services Office, "Fire Suppression Rating Schedule," (1980 ed.), iso.com/Products/Public-Protection-Classification-Service/Fire-Suppression-Rating-Schedule-FSRS-manual-for-PPC-grading.html.

The ISO Building Code Effectiveness Grading Schedule

After reviewing hurricane losses, where failure to follow building code requirements, particularly with regard to roofs, is associated with greater loss, ISO produced a Building Code Effectiveness Grading Schedule (BCEGS). The schedule is used to assess building code compliance (a function of building code enforcement) to produce community ratings that can be used in the underwriting process. Each municipality is assigned a Building Code Effectiveness Classification from 1 (exemplary commitment to building code enforcement) to 10 (no recognizable enforcement). The ratings are derived from an assessment of the local codes, enforcement methods, staffing and training of inspectors, and other factors. The schedule is designed to operate as a "credit" only, meaning that communities and properties are not penalized but can only benefit from good performance.

The BCEGS is built around the premise that communities with well-enforced, up-to-date codes should demonstrate better loss experience, which can result in better insurance rates. The prospect of lessening catastrophe-related damage and ultimately lowering insurance costs provides an incentive for communities to enforce their building codes rigorously—especially as those codes relate to windstorm and earthquake damage.

The BCEGS program emphasizes the following key areas pertaining to building codes:

- *Administration of codes:* ISO evaluates the administrative support for code enforcement within the jurisdiction, including the adopted building codes and the modifications of those codes through ordinance, code enforcer qualifications, experience and education, zoning provisions, contractor/builder licensing requirements, public awareness programs, the building department's participation in code development activities, and administrative policies and procedures. This section represents 54 percent of the analysis in the BCEGS program.

- *Plan review:* ISO gives consideration to staffing levels, personnel experience, performance evaluation schedules, and the level of review of construction documents for compliance with the adopted building code in the jurisdiction being graded. This section represents 23 percent of the analysis.
- *Field inspection:* ISO gives consideration to staffing levels, personnel experience, performance evaluation schedules, and the level of the agency's review of building construction. This section also represents 23 percent of the analysis.
- *Building code adoption:* Communities should adopt and enforce the latest code edition of a nationally recognized building code development and publication organization. A community receives fewer points for adopting less current building codes.
- *Building code amendments:* A community receives points on the basis of its adoption of unamended building codes. A community earns fewer points when it amends the code to reduce the structure's ability to withstand natural hazards.

ISO promises that the BCEGS will eventually quantify differences in code enforcement among communities. However, the schedule is being implemented gradually, and ratings currently apply only to properties constructed since in the late 1990s, when the schedule was implemented on a state-by-state basis. For older communities not undergoing significant development, the BCEGS will not play a major role for many years to come.

NFPA 1710 and 1720

NFPA publishes many standards that are relevant to the evaluation of service levels and response capability. Some of these standards are applied to the assessment of risk in individual premises. Others apply to the operation of fire and emergency service departments. Perhaps those that are most directly applicable to measuring community service levels and response capabilities are NFPA 1710, Standard for the Organization and Deployment of Fire Suppression Operations, Emergency Medical Operations, and Special Operations to the Public by Career Fire Departments (2010 ed.), and NFPA 1720, Standard for the Organization and Deployment of Fire Suppression Operations, Emergency Medical Operations, and Special Operations to the Public by Volunteer Fire Departments (2010 ed.).

NFPA 1710 for career departments and NFPA 1720 for volunteer departments both incorporate the notion of a "community-wide risk management model" in their appendixes. Although not part of the requirements of the document, this inclusion reflects a recognition that there should be a connection between the level of risk in a community and the resources required to address that risk.

NFPA 1710 contains clearly defined response time and staffing goals that are based on a 2,000-square-foot, two-story, single-family dwelling without a basement and with no exposures. Structures are classified as high hazard, medium hazard, or low hazard depending primarily on their use and size.

NFPA 1720 includes information on suggested staffing and response time goals that are based on the nature of the community. This standard suggests that risk can be summarized primarily on the basis of the population density, and it sets response time and attendance objectives in accordance with the density of the area being protected.

Empirical evaluation

Many departments look at actual fire loss in order to assess the adequacy of local fire protection. Using NFIRS, many also track key performance data that can be used to assess their ability to confine and suppress fires. Smaller departments and organizations with a small fire problem will have a greater challenge using empirical analysis and must rely instead on other standards. Emergency medical services commonly use experience to assess risk, and performance experience should be reflected in the staffing and deployment of EMS units.

Empirical assessments of service levels and response capabilities allow an organization to measure performance against locally established goals. Performance measures are useful during the budgetary process: they can reinforce the legitimacy of management efforts within the fire and emergency services. Combined with cost analysis, they also help the community understand the connection between desired levels of service and the resources provided to the fire and emergency services department.

Empirical analysis can be especially beneficial when determining the deployment of resources to reduce the response time to emergencies (see sidebar below). While potential risk must be considered, rare events should not necessarily divert resources from potential high-consequence events that happen with regularity. Empirical evidence for fire and emergency service levels should ideally be drawn from local records such as NFIRS reports and CAD data. Tools such as GIS may enable fire and emergency services data to be merged with information on population, building stock characteristics, code compliance, and activities or processes at a given site.

For example, many communities locate ladder companies in proximity to high-rise buildings. While this is generally appropriate, an examination of local historical data may show that there are actually more fires requiring ladder companies in the neighborhoods outside the community's dense center. By locating ladder companies closer to residential areas where fires have occurred most often, the department may be able to improve its response times to a larger number of fires.

Mission statement and response guidelines: Fremont, California

The city of Fremont, California's Standards of Cover report provides an excellent example of a clearly defined performance goal that is translated into resource needs.

Goal of the Fremont Fire Department in Responding to Fire Calls:

Arrive before flashover occurs and confine the fire to the room of origin. Account for and remove all possible victims from inside the involved and exposed structures.

Standard Operating Procedure for Structure Fires—Current System

Effective Response Force for Structure Fires

Resource Type	Number of Firefighters
Engine Company	3 Firefighters
Engine Company	3 Firefighters
Engine Company	3 Firefighters
Truck Company	3 Firefighters
Battalion Commander	1 Firefighter
Battalion Commander	1 Firefighter
Total Personnel	14 Firefighters

Company	Task
1st Engine	Initiate Fire Attack
2nd Engine	Water Supply/Backup Fire Attack
3rd Engine	(RIT [Rapid Intervention Team]) Unless otherwise assigned
1st Truck	Ventilation/Utilities/Forcible Entry
1st Battalion Commander	IC [Incident Commander]
2nd Battalion Commander	Direct Interior Fire Attack/Safety

Note: Search and Rescue is performed by one of the above companies *after* its initial task has been completed.

Source: Adapted from the City of Fremont, "Critical Task Analysis for the Fremont Fire Department," in *Standards of Coverage*, V-5, fremont.gov/DocumentView.aspx?DID=940 (accessed May 18, 2011).

Fire risk management

Once the community's level of risk has been identified and current service levels and capabilities have been evaluated, the fire and emergency services department needs to evaluate the measures at its disposal to influence the level of risk or to mitigate that risk to reduce the severity of incidents that occur. Mitigation of community risks can be undertaken by public or private entities and implemented for individuals, households, organizations, and businesses. The overall risk level can be influenced by long-term changes in the economic or social nature of the community, while specific risks can be mitigated through such actions as improved training or public education to reduce the severity of an event once it occurs.

Risk control

As explained earlier in this chapter, risk control describes those actions taken or influenced by the fire and emergency services to reduce the frequency, severity, and/or consequences of incidents within a community. Two points should be kept in mind: the fire and emergency services department is not the only entity within a community that can implement risk control measures, and it can be useful to distinguish between actions that reduce frequency and those that reduce severity.

Risk control interventions vary in effectiveness, cost, and time required for implementation. To get maximum impact from available resources, the fire and emergency services should measure the impact of various risk control programs. To be able to make valid comparisons among different programs, however, managers must confine their measurement activity to a very narrow set of incident types or loss scenarios. (More information on risk control is found in Chapter 6.)

Reducing fire frequency The incidence of fire can be reduced through a number of approaches and programs. Efforts must be targeted at high-frequency events and may require a behavioral change on the part of the population or certain sectors of it. For example, a

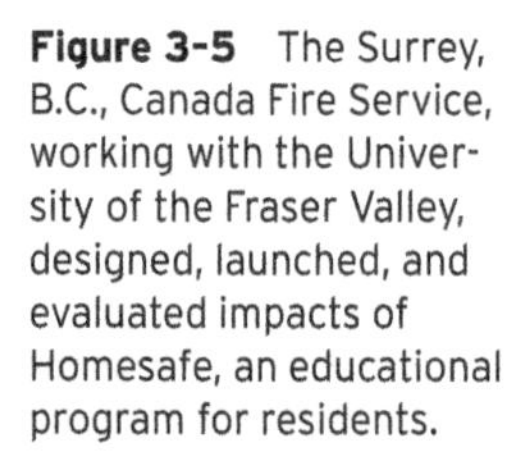
Figure 3-5 The Surrey, B.C., Canada Fire Service, working with the University of the Fraser Valley, designed, launched, and evaluated impacts of Homesafe, an educational program for residents.

Printed with permission from the City of Surrey, British Columbia, Fire Service

department might decide to focus on reducing the frequency of fires caused by fireworks and might thus introduce a program with these components:

- Codes to outlaw fireworks or certain kinds of fireworks
- Public education for the general public on the safe use of fireworks
- Public education directed at businesses to get them to comply with code requirements or to distribute safety information with fireworks they sell.

Some interventions can be undertaken fairly quickly; others (e.g., code changes) take more time. As in the example just given, several strategies for reducing the frequency of a particular type of fire may be undertaken simultaneously, although this approach could complicate the process of evaluating the efficacy of a particular intervention. A partnership with an academic institution or a consultant can help a local department undertake such evaluations (see Figure 3–5).

Reducing fire severity (loss) Programs to reduce the severity of fires are usually directed at high-severity events. The most common approach to reducing severity is to improve or increase the responsive resources of the fire and emergency services. However, a very effective way of reducing the severity of fires in structures is to change the city code to require the installation of fire protection systems, particularly automatic sprinkler systems.

Public fire education on such topics as rapid reporting of emergencies, home escape planning, and the proper use of fire extinguishers can also reduce the severity of events.

In actual practice, most departments work to reduce both the frequency and the severity of fires, but it is important to go beyond a "buckshot" approach and design interventions to target particular results. Usually the first step is to examine the community's own fire loss data gathered from incident reports; collecting supplemental data from special studies can increase an understanding of the community's fire problem and suggest possible solutions.

Preincident planning

Preincident planning is the systematic process of inspecting buildings and complexes, documenting the inspections, and storing the key information in a format that is usable in a timely fashion for managing an incident. Preincident planning activities range in complexity from informal building familiarization programs to comprehensive inspection programs in which all properties that can be inspected (usually small apartments and single-family dwellings are excluded) are divided among companies or shifts, which are responsible for revisiting each property on a regular basis. NFPA 1620, Recommended Practice for Pre-Incident Planning (2003 ed.), provides guidance on the establishment and conduct of a preincident planning program.

Preincident planning is not a fire code compliance inspection, although one inspection can accomplish both purposes. Similarly, while home fire inspection programs are usually designed primarily to assist the resident, information such as the presence of mobility-impaired occupants may be collected by fire personnel in the course of conducting a home fire inspection.

Collecting, storing, retrieving, and acting on information on protection systems, unusual hazards, occupancy, construction features, fire apparatus access, and emergency contacts are the essence of preincident planning. Rudimentary floor diagrams or site plans may also be useful for larger properties or complexes with multiple buildings. Many injuries sustained by fire and emergency services personnel in the course of fire suppression could have been prevented with better knowledge of the construction details and hazards present in buildings.

Information technology has greatly improved departments' ability to store and retrieve this information. To ensure that records stay current, it is important to have in place a process for capturing important information from other agencies, such as building code enforcement, as well as observations from fire suppression personnel. Firefighters on the way to a fire or at the scene can consult the accumulated database of information about the property to learn of hazards and of facility or building conditions. This awareness can not only improve the effectiveness of fire suppression but also increase firefighters' safety by allowing them to avoid or protect themselves from hazards such as stored chemicals and open shafts.

Even if a department does not have a formal preincident planning program, good fire officers will go into the community to learn more about the buildings they protect and the unique features that may present challenges or assist in mitigating a potential emergency. Even informal preincident planning can be effective for controlling a department's operational risk.

Stakeholders in local fire and emergency services

Defining stakeholders in a community risk assessment and identifying their desired service levels for fire and emergency services are critical activities. Organizations tend to focus on their own internal constituencies, and engaging the wider community can be challenging. However, community participation can provide a better understanding of community expectations and also serves to educate the public about fire and emergency services. Once they have made the commitment to include the public, however, fire and emergency service managers must take issues and perspectives raised by the public seriously. Misperceptions and unrealistic expectations may be prevalent. Many citizens may be unaware, for example, that the local fire department has career staff, offers specialized services, or works under training and regulatory requirements placed on it by the state or locality.

A broad-based approach to community participation requires the support of elected officials. Without their explicit support, the fire department's efforts to engage the public could be perceived as an "end-run" around the political process. After all, the purpose of community engagement is not to lobby citizens for their support but to discover their needs. If citizen concerns are incorporated into the planning process, political support will be one outcome, but it should not be the sole purpose of the effort.

Stakeholder groups can be defined as internal or external. The lists presented below are simply illustrations. The selection of representatives from any community should be driven by the community's political culture, economic structure, and existing organizations.

Internal stakeholders

Chief officers
Fire prevention officers
Public educators
Fire suppression personnel
Communications staff
Labor organizations

External stakeholders

Elected officials
Property owners
Neighborhood associations
Chamber of commerce
Major employers
School districts
Hospitals
Local insurance agents
Social service agencies

Working with the public to manage community risk

Fire-related risks can be categorized as internal to the fire and emergency services department (operational risk) or external to it (community risk). The same can be said for stakeholders. Stakeholders in the analysis of risk are defined as those who are involved in or may be affected by decisions regarding risk management. Stakeholders include members of the community as well as fire personnel (see sidebar above). Each stakeholder group should be consulted and involved at some stage of the strategic planning process.

The interests of internal and external stakeholders are sometimes in conflict. For example, the least risk option for internal stakeholders would be to avoid hazardous activity such as interior firefighting. But external stakeholders expect that fires will be extinguished quickly. The community must balance internal against external risks, and the fire and emergency services must set achievable goals for community protection while maintaining an acceptable level of safety for their members. Training, discipline, and strong incident management can reduce operational risk. The operating environment of the fire and emergency services has improved radically over the past twenty to thirty years as improved equipment, higher health and safety standards, and more stringent code requirements for buildings have taken effect.

Information on expectations for service can be solicited from the public using a properly designed survey instrument.[2] General community satisfaction surveys consistently find the fire service to be among the most trusted and highly regarded services within a community. In fact, if the fire and emergency services organization is not ranked in the top one to two positions among local government services, this indicates a problem. Therefore, while such surveys are useful to track performance over time, they should not be used to assess departmental management or operational capabilities or competence. Members of the public are seldom provided with the information to make an informed judgment about the organization.

Using citizen survey data to learn more about community risks

When the fire department in Austin, Texas, studied the causes of fire deaths in the city, it traced some of those deaths to faulty smoke alarms. In 2006, to learn more about this problem, the fire department added two questions about smoke alarms to the city budget office's annual survey of Austin residents. From the survey it learned that older respondents were more likely than other residents to report not having a smoke alarm, and that nearly one-fifth of residents over age 65 who had smoke alarms were unable to report when they had last changed their smoke alarm batteries.

From the survey responses, the fire department identified the need to provide elderly residents with low-maintenance smoke alarms that are easy to test and do not require climbing ladders or chairs to replace batteries (since falls are a major cause of injury to the elderly). The department obtained a grant from the Department of Homeland Security to purchase 2,500 low-maintenance smoke alarms with ten-year batteries; residents are able to test these alarms by remote control. The fire department has been aggressively marketing the program and building partnerships with groups that serve the elderly.

Source: Center for Performance Measurement, "City of Austin, TX," in *What Works: How Local Governments Have Made the Leap from Measurement to Management* (Washington, D.C.: ICMA Press, 2008), 54–57.

At the same time, however, fire managers can use surveys, as well as focus groups and consultation with elected officials, to involve the public in risk management planning. Through surveys they can elicit public feedback to help identify cultural or community heritage assets and to gather information on such topics as smoke detector usage and safety behaviors (see the sidebar above). Internet-based survey instruments and social networking sites can be an aid to this process. The fire and emergency services organization may wish to get some outside assistance to make sure that data collected through such methods are representative of community opinions and behaviors.

Fire and emergency service departments usually confine their interactions with the public (beyond those interactions associated with routine service delivery) to "consulting" and "informing," as defined in Table 3-1. As currently practiced, public consultation often means seeking public support for a favored policy position rather than exploring public preferences for viable alternatives. Or a department may hold public meetings to present its budget, confining the presentation to "informing." Such interactions often become contentious as interested lay parties express opinions in conflict with the positions and expectations of agency "experts."

Table 3-1 IAP2 Spectrum of Public Participation

	Increasing level of public impact				
	Inform	**Consult**	**Involve**	**Collaborate**	**Empower**
Public participation goal	Provide public with balanced, objective information	Obtain public feedback on analysis, alternatives, and decisions	Work directly with public throughout process	Partner with public in each aspect of decision, including developing alternatives and identifying solutions	Place final decision making in the hands of the public
Promise to the public	We will keep you informed	We will keep you informed, listen to and acknowledge your concerns, and provide feedback	We will work with you to ensure that your concerns are directly reflected in alternatives	We will look to you for advice and innovation	We will implement what you decide
Example techniques	• Fact sheets • Websites • Open houses	• Public comment • Focus groups • Surveys • Public meetings	• Workshops • Deliberative polling	• Citizen advisory committees • Consensus building • Participatory decision making	• Citizen juries • Ballots • Delegated decision

Source: Adapted from the International Association for Public Participation (IAP2), "IAP2 Spectrum for Public Participation" (2007), © IAP2, iap2.org/associations/4748/files/IAP2%20Spectrum_vertical.pdf (accessed May 17, 2011).

The UK approach to managing fire risks

In the United Kingdom, where the fire service is considerably more centralized than in the United States and Canada, the standards used to define the level and placement of resources to be provided throughout the country are being revised in response to an ongoing process of risk assessment.

Following a series of national reports challenging the way the fire service operated, the government found that national standards used for deployment of fire apparatus were biased toward property protection and decided to change them. A series of studies was undertaken to develop an alternate approach to evaluating fire services and fire losses—an approach based more on empirical data, such as information on response time, fire losses, and fire characteristics. This strategy was designed to more closely align protection to life risk.

The key tool for assessing risk, plan response, and model consequences is the *Fire Service Emergency Cover Toolkit*, a GIS-based product that is used to simulate various strategies for deploying apparatus. The toolkit can calculate the time of arrival of apparatus and personnel at small geographic locations throughout the service area. The consequences of prospective scenarios can be judged on the basis of

- Lives lost in dwelling fires, special service incidents, and other building fires
- Property loss in other building fires
- Total cost of the resources allocated.

Despite considerable controversy, implementation of local plans based on this work has led to a decrease in fire deaths. The reduction has been attributed to an increased emphasis on fire prevention, including home inspections and smoke detector campaigns.

Subsequent efforts include national legislation that requires planning for emergencies by both emergency services and support organizations through the Civil Contingencies Act. To facilitate this effort, a report produced in 2008 was designed to bridge differences in terminology among emergency services.

Sources: Greenstreet Berman Ltd., *Review of Fire and Rescue Service Response Times*, Fire Research Series 1/2009 (London, England: Communities and Local Government Publications, February 2009), communities.gov.uk/documents/fire/pdf/frsresponsetimes.pdf; International Fire Consultants Ltd., *Risk Terminology*, Fire Research Series 3/2008 (London, England: Communities and Local Government Publications, May 2008), communities.gov.uk/documents/fire/pdf/riskterminology.pdf.

Consequently, many managers are wary of getting the public involved in "technical" discussions. However, a fact-based, clear, and direct presentation of the needs and costs associated with different levels of service can result in better understanding and stronger public support for the fire and emergency service's mission.

Equally important, a department manager must compare the assessment of the department's current capabilities against public expectations or assumptions. The manager should be prepared to suggest alternative approaches to achieving objectives, to enrich public understanding, and to demonstrate that the department is not thinking only of solutions that will increase its budget. For example, the department may have determined during its risk assessment that fighting a fire inside a large factory building in the community would require more fire personnel than are currently available. An alternative to increasing staffing might be to encourage the factory management to install detection and suppression systems to mitigate the level of fire risk.

Framework for public participation The diagram in Figure 3–6 shows the role of public participation in setting objectives and strategies for community fire and emergency services. This framework describes a risk management process that is cyclical and repetitive. Risk assessment and decisions on service levels are not a one-time exercise. As the community, resources, public preferences, and capabilities of the fire and emergency services change, the process is repeated.

The risk management framework has six steps:

Step 1: Objectives and strategies The existing objectives and strategies in use within the community should be documented. Many organizations operate with a number of objectives that

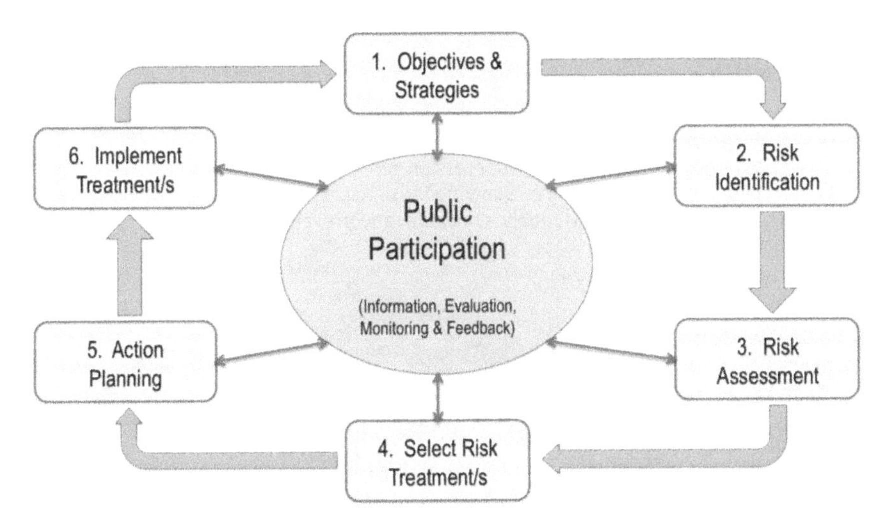

Figure 3-6 The Formative Emergency Planning and Risk Management Framework is also an action-oriented process: risk treatments or interventions that are selected to reduce the frequency and/or severity of events must be put into action, evaluated, and modified or improved.

are well known to members of the department but not formally documented, communicated to elected officials, or even reduced to writing. Basic but very challenging questions about current service levels, intended outcomes of departmental actions, and resource constraints (staffing, equipment, training) that limit fire suppression effectiveness should be answered at the outset of this process.

Step 2: Risk identification The second step is the comprehensive and exhaustive effort described earlier in this chapter to identify the potential and actual risks that face the community. Fire and emergency service managers use actual incident data and information from prefire surveys and other data sources, as well as outside resources such as national standards and planning models, to help identify those risks.

Step 3: Risk assessment In this step, fire and emergency service managers choose those risks that present the greatest likelihood of causing significant loss. Information technology such as GIS is useful in this stage of the analysis. (See earlier sections of this chapter on risk analysis and risk classification.)

Step 4: Selection of risk treatments Risk treatments are approaches to reducing risk—for example, public education and increased enforcement. These treatments can be protective (response oriented) or preventive (aimed at reducing frequency or severity). Public engagement in this step can help identify information that people need to help protect themselves. Citizens and public officials will participate in weighing the costs of alternative interventions—costs measured in terms of budget as well as in cumulative costs to property owners or the public. These treatments should collectively form a coherent strategy for loss reduction.

Step 5: Action planning Action planning is formulating concrete steps to implement the strategy. Defining action steps and exposing them to public scrutiny as well as to the scrutiny of internal customers is very valuable in improving the quality of decisions. Such steps might include securing sufficient large-diameter hose to reach a neighborhood with a poor water supply, or educating residents about kitchen safety as part of a residential inspection program in high-fire incidence neighborhoods. New service-level standards or objectives are developed at this stage of the process.

Step 6: Implement treatments In this step, fire and emergency service managers do what they have said they will do and make additional decisions about how, where, and at what level to enact the action plans developed in Step 5. This stage captures the "give-and-take" of day-to-day management and decision making guided by the strategic priorities set in Step 4. Meetings with affected community groups not only help to ensure that the community understands the complexity of the process but also can build support for continuing action if an initial review of performance results is inconclusive.

Ontario's approach to community fire risk

The Office of the Fire Marshal (OFM) in Ontario, Canada, has systematically reviewed fire services in the province and defined a framework for their use in its municipalities. Ontario requires that each municipality provide fire prevention services but does not mandate fire suppression services. The OFM publishes numerous guidelines for local departments, including a "Simplified Risk Assessment Procedure." Ontario identifies three lines of defense against fire: (1) public education and prevention, (2) fire safety standards and enforcement, and (3) emergency response.

The centerpiece of the province's support for fire services is the provision of a "Comprehensive Fire Safety Effectiveness Model." This model defines an optimum level of protection as "the combination of fire fighting staff and apparatus that delivers a suppression effort commensurate with the fire demand faced, yet representing the most efficient use of resources in a safe and effective manner."[1] The overall model takes a holistic approach and includes eight submodels, or areas of concern: public attitudes, intervention time, detection, suppression capabilities, fire risk, fire prevention effectiveness, impact of fire, and fire-ground effectiveness.[2] The fire-ground effectiveness submodel (see figure) specifies numbers of personnel necessary to accomplish basic tasks for interior structural firefighting and rescue. The numbers are driven by the levels of fire suppression capability, as shown in the figure. Level of service is defined on a continuum ranging from "no fire suppression capability" to "aggressive interior structural firefighting and rescue." The continuum does not apply to rescue services in other situations.[3]

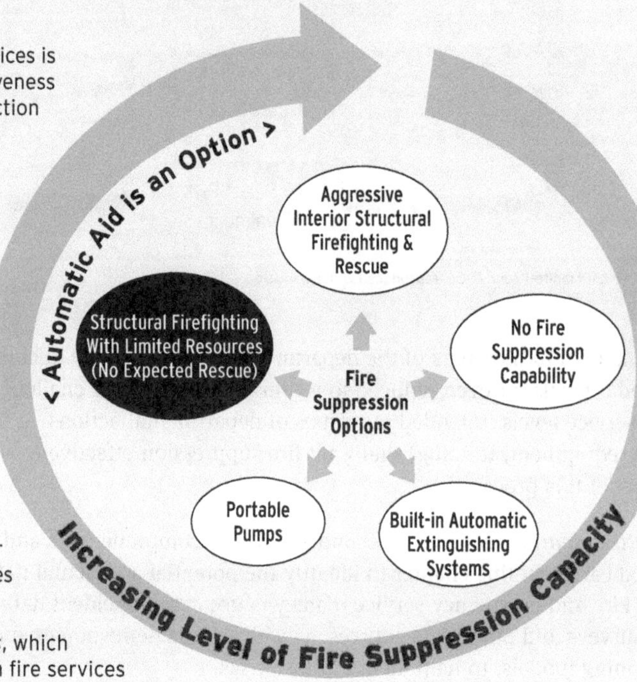

The OFM also publishes *Public Fire Safety Guidelines*, which encompasses the duties and responsibilities for both fire services and elected officials.[4] The guidelines are not mandatory, but individual provisions can become mandatory if adopted by a locality.

In 2002, the OFM undertook a performance benchmarking project in cooperation with other agencies, including the Ministry of Municipal Affairs and Housing and the Ministry of Community Safety and Correctional Services, and is collecting data in a pilot phase. The data will be used to help fire departments and municipalities measure dimensions of their performance that are critical to the province and align their resources more effectively to target those areas.

1 Ontario, Canada, Office of the Fire Marshal (OFM), "Appendix G: Glossary of Terms," in *Essentials of Municipal Fire Protection for Fire Service Leaders* (2007), ofm.gov.on.ca/en/Fire%20Service%20Programs/Municipal%20Fire%20Protection%20Information/Essentials%20of%20Fire%20Protection%20for%20Fire%20Service%20Leaders.asp#Appendix_G.

2 OFM, "Comprehensive Fire Safety Effectiveness Model," ofm.gov.on.ca/en/Fire%20Service%20Resources/Comprehensive%20Fire%20Safety%20Effectiveness%20Model/Comprehensive%20Fire%20Safety%20Effectiveness%20Model.asp.

3 OFM, "Basic Structural Fire Fighting (no Expected Rescue Component)," *Public Fire Safety Guidelines*, ofm.gov.on.ca/en/Fire%20Service%20Resources/Public%20Fire%20Safety%20Guidelines/04-13-12.asp.

4 OFM, *Public Fire Safety Guidelines*, ofm.gov.on.ca/en/Fire%20Service%20Resources/Public%20Fire%20Safety%20Guidelines/default.asp.

Implementing participation Building public trust and confidence in the decisions and actions of public entities in order to improve the government's capacity for service delivery requires agencies to actively involve the public in decision making. It also requires agencies to form coalitions with groups of citizens affected by their actions and with others who can affect the public good.

Public participation in defining meaningful performance objectives will ensure that the objectives developed reflect the unique needs and expectations of the community. If it is involved in the process of developing local plans to address community risk, the public can play a central role in determining what services a community requires and how to measure performance in the delivery of these services. Local conditions, resources, and staff capacity will drive the degree of public participation, and no "one size" will fit all.

Developing information for the public so that it can participate in risk management planning can be a challenging process, but public fire education skills can be effectively applied for this purpose. The important point is to listen to the community's concerns and explain how the department is or is not able to address these needs with its current mix of resources.

Most departments begin at the "consult" or "inform" level and move in the direction of more robust public participation over time (see again Table 3-1 on page 85). There is no optimum level of participation, although it is usually practical to involve the public, and it is possible (and desirable) to collaborate with adequate support from other elements of municipal government. The greater the degree of participation, the broader the set of solutions that can be generated to address community needs.

Smaller departments may begin by informing the public of the services they provide, offering performance indicators such as response times or staffing levels, and defining resources necessary or desired. In small communities, members of the fire and emergency services department are familiar to most citizens, who may already have a good understanding of the services the department provides. Public engagement can be coordinated with other public events, and outreach can be as simple as department members informing their neighbors and co-workers of the need for their input and involvement.

Larger communities may use some of the public engagement strategies shown in Table 3-1 as a component of strategic planning, community risk assessment, or design of loss reduction strategies.

As a way of facilitating local decision making, many jurisdictions have embedded risk management principles in their structure and staffing and attempts to balance preventive and protective resources. The CPSE accreditation model of setting goals on the basis of local needs and resources is a very good example of such an approach.

Creating a strategic plan

A strategic plan is the tangible outcome of the risk management process. A written plan (1) assesses the current environment, (2) defines the department's purpose and mission, (3) describes what the organization wants to look like in three to five years, (4) describes the environment in which the organization operates, (5) defines goals, and (6) charts a course of action to achieve the goals set (see Figure 3-7). The strategic planning process should be linked to the budget so that necessary resources can be directed to make critical changes and sustain effective programs.

A formal planning process for community risk management is important for many reasons. Most important, only by mobilizing stakeholders and top department management can the fire and emergency services department sustain its commitment to change. The planning

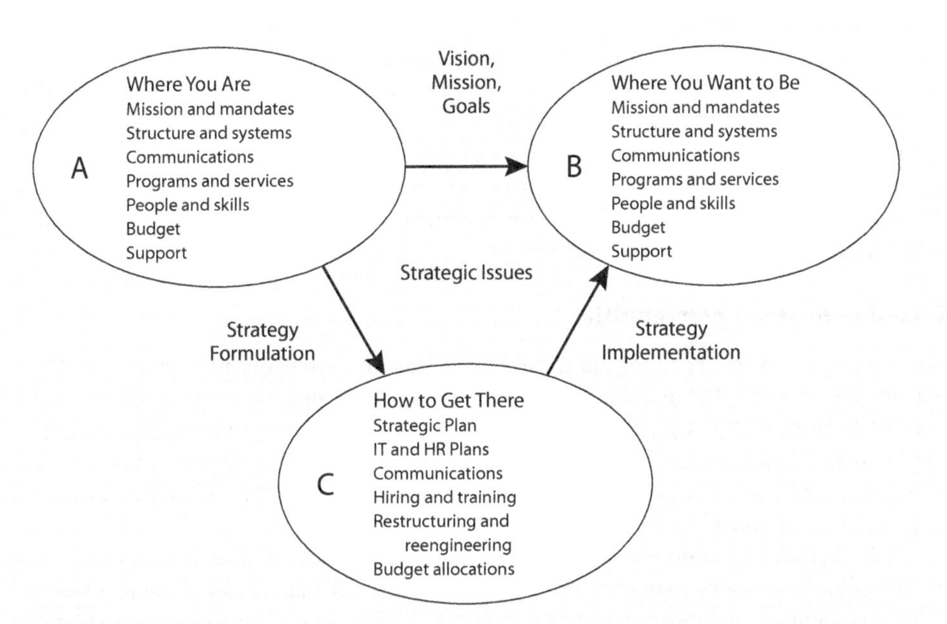

Source: John M. Bryson and Farnum K. Alston, *Creating and Implementing Your Strategic Plan: A Workbook for Public and Nonprofit Organizations*, 2nd ed. (San Francisco: Jossey-Bass, 2004), 5. Reproduced with permission of John Wiley & Sons, Inc.

Figure 3-7 The ABCs of strategic planning are summarized in this chart.

process should engage all internal stakeholders and all representatives of external stakeholders. Without both internal and external support, managers' efforts can be forgotten or stripped of necessary resources when the annual budget is being developed. In a changing environment when citizen expectations are also changing, periodic strategic planning can help fire and emergency services compete more effectively with other organizations for funding.

A written plan can also help a fire and emergency services department better understand the environment and see ways in which its mission can support the broader goals of the community. The plan should be written in clear language that members of the public and elected officials will understand. Specialized terms should be defined, and photographs and diagrams should be chosen to improve communication. A written plan allows other governmental and nongovernmental organizations that partner with fire and emergency services to understand the department's goals as well as the resources and support it needs to achieve them. (See Chapter 12 for more on strategic planning, especially its role in the budgeting process.)

A strategic planning process usually begins with an environmental scan. In the case of fire and emergency services that have conducted a community risk assessment, much of the work of doing an environmental scan has already been completed, but information gathered in the risk assessment will be augmented with information important to the department's ability to acquire and deploy resources.

The purpose of the scan is to identify strengths, weaknesses, opportunities, and threats, so it is referred to as a SWOT analysis. A strength might be that the community is very supportive of the fire and emergency services department. An opportunity might be that a redevelopment plan for an old warehouse district could result in buildings with improved fire safety. A weakness might be that fire prevention personnel do not speak the language of new residents who are having a high incidence of fires. A threat might be that a major manufacturing facility may leave town, resulting in reduced revenues.

The planning process typically includes development of a vision statement. A good vision statement reflects a long-term objective or "end state" for the organization. It should be clear and concise but unique to the community; it should inspire internal stakeholders and be consistent with the highest values of the organization. If it has these qualities, the vision statement can very effectively provide motivation and guidance, particularly for larger organizations. (For more information on vision, mission, and values, see Chapter 12.)

Informed by the SWOT analysis, the strategic plan should list key outcomes that can be used to organize strategic objectives—the concrete goals and performance measures that will be used to assess the effectiveness of the plan's implementation. Each objective should include a realistic target date.

The strategic plan is communicated to all internal stakeholders as well as to key external stakeholders. It is critical that elected officials and the municipality's managers receive copies of the completed plan.

The plan should be monitored and reviewed periodically: the chief or ranking manager should appoint someone to collect key performance data on an ongoing and regular basis. These periodic updates on performance are examined and analyzed to identify trends and areas of success as well as areas where improvement is needed.

Planning in small communities

Undertaking a strategic planning effort can be daunting to a small department, but it is equally important to plan in a small community as in a large one. Given limited data, the smaller department may have to rely more heavily on standards and industry benchmarks, but the planning process and the report itself can be fairly simple. State- or county-level data on fire problems, or information from similar communities, may be useful in identifying and targeting areas for attention.

Risks that are moderate in a larger community may be severe in a small community. Risks for the entire community may be summarized in a few fire demand or management zones. If the community is old, there may be a concentration of properties that pose a considerable risk—for example, a historic downtown or a concentration of closely spaced wood-frame dwellings. The local government may need to emphasize code enforcement, and a true community dialogue may be required to encourage property owners to improve the resistance of major structures to fire.

Smaller communities are likely to have deep citizen engagement with the fire and emergency services, especially if those services are provided by volunteers.

Planning in growing communities

Rapidly growing communities have opportunities to shape their future. Building and fire codes can greatly reduce risk in newly developing areas. Collection and organization of fire incident data and risk-related information can be computerized from the outset. The opportunity to oversee construction allows the fire and emergency services to initiate prefire planning and capture detailed information on new buildings. However, past fire experience may not be a reliable gauge for the future, as the types of structures and households change.

In growing communities, the fire and emergency services department must reach out to new residents to give them safety information and identify their expectations. In semirural areas transitioning to suburbs, new residents may migrate from urban areas with expectations for service that are unrealistic. If they are moving to an area because of its comparatively low taxes, they may oppose any efforts to increase taxes to invest in fire risk reduction.

Planning in large communities

Large communities have the advantage of being able to rely on local experience as a basis for their risk identification and analysis. Where there is a large number of existing structures, it will take considerable effort to gather risk information, particularly if no preincident planning program exists. Legacy data that are not computerized may also pose a challenge to a department undertaking a community risk analysis.

The larger the community and the quantity of resources that must be managed, the greater the need for a sophisticated and well-prepared strategic plan. However, if the budgeting environment is competitive, and if the fire and emergency services department must work with numerous stakeholders, it may be difficult to secure support for the planning initiative. Traditional patterns of deployment may be very difficult to shift. Opposition may arise from people not represented in the planning process, particularly if resources are to be shifted from one part of the community to another.

A large existing building stock means that a large share of the high-risk structures in the community will not change very much in the foreseeable future. Even cities that have experienced major high-rise fires and have instituted sprinkler requirements for old as well as new buildings have typically permitted ten or more years for compliance.

Future trends in community risk analysis and management

Risk management planning in fire and emergency services is going to be more common in the future. Fiscal constraints are growing as pressure from competing needs and increasing costs for just about all aspects of fire and emergency service operations continue to mount. The community risk profile is becoming more complicated as additional services assume a larger role in the overall mix of calls for service. And the conditions that have brought us to this point are not showing any signs of diminishing. Fires and other traditional risks must be balanced against novel but very real high-severity risks, such as terrorism, mass violence, and natural disasters.

The tools available to facilitate risk analysis are becoming more widely used. Codes and standards, as well as third-party processes such as accreditation, are all moving toward a more rigorous analysis of local data as a basis for risk management.

The advent of web-based technologies—in particular, the personalized information-sharing capabilities and web-based computing known as "Web 2.0"—brings vast quantities of information to users. As these consumer-driven technologies find their way into the governmental sphere, data on community risks will become richer and more accessible. The cycle on which such information is updated can begin to approach real time. The mobile computers already in use in many departments have only scratched the surface in terms of their ability to become two-way tools not only for displaying information from central databases, but also for collecting information that can inform risk management on a real-time basis.

Our ability to accurately understand and represent risk will increase rapidly. If we are able to leverage technologies and think creatively, we may be able to combine information from all parts of an organization with community-based and citizen-generated information to provide improved and enhanced services. These services will be based on a better understanding both of stakeholder preferences and of the underlying risks themselves.

Ultimately the fire and emergency services are a community's first line of defense against a host of natural and man-made disasters. Refinements in matching resources to risks will never completely eliminate the need to retain the capacity to respond to rare but extremely demanding events. We must not let our efforts to focus more and more narrowly on the fine details of risks within our communities distract us from meeting our citizens' expectation that we be there when the truly unexpected occurs.

Additionally, we should not let a fixation on emergency response blind us to other, more effective means of mitigating losses within a community. Ultimately, the results of our risk analysis should be used to better direct resources to address those risks, and these efforts should be measured and refined over time.

Notes

1. Federal Emergency Management Agency (FEMA), U.S. Fire Administration, *Risk Management Practices in the Fire Service* (FA-166) (Washington, D.C.: U.S. Fire Administration, FEMA, December 1996), 38–41, usfa .dhs.gov/downloads/pdf/publications/FA-166.pdf.
2. See Thomas I Miller, Michelle Miller Kobayashi, and Shannon Elissa Hayden, *Citizen Surveys for Local Government: A Comprehensive Guide to Making Them Matter,* 3rd ed. (Washington, D.C.: ICMA Press, 2009).

CHAPTER 4

Organizing and Deploying Resources

Sally Young

This chapter provides an understanding of

- The elements of effective departmental organization
- Alternatives for staffing a local fire and emergency service department
- The kinds and types of local fire and emergency service departments
- The pros and cons of various organizational models for local fire and emergency service departments
- Major management choices regarding mission, scope, and resource deployment.

In the twenty-first century, fire and emergency service organizations generally fall into five types, based on the employer-employee relationship, and seven kinds, based on their location within the governmental framework. Large or small, they tend to have a similar basic organizational structure. To fulfill the mission of protecting their communities from fires and other emergencies arising from all hazards, they deploy the resources of personnel, fire stations, fire-rescue apparatus, and other vehicles and equipment. This chapter covers all these topics. In addition, it briefly surveys the array of expanded services provided by many contemporary fire and emergency service departments. Some of these services are responses to emergencies; others represent proactive approaches to making communities safer.

Types of fire and emergency service departments

The type of fire and emergency service department is a function of the employment relationship between the firefighters and the parent organization. There are five basic types: volunteer, career, combination, paid call, and public safety consolidation.

Volunteer departments

A volunteer fire and emergency service department is one in which firefighters are not paid by the department and do not work full time as firefighters. In the United States, volunteer fire departments are the most numerous type; the National Fire Protection Association (NFPA) estimated in 2010 that more than two-thirds of fire departments in the United States in 2009 were volunteer (see sidebar). Volunteer departments depend on the personal commitment of civic-minded members to deliver fire protection and other services. Even in some private fire brigades, the firefighting duties of the firm's employees may be carried out voluntarily and would classify the brigade as being volunteer in type albeit private in kind.

Volunteer fire departments, which protect about 80 percent of the land area of the United States but less than 40 percent of the nation's population, are typically found in communities with populations under 25,000 people.[1] There are some exceptions, however. For example, the volunteer fire department in Pasadena, Texas, operates nine fire stations, and its 200 firefighters serve a population of 140,000 within a city of fifty-two square miles.[2]

Over the past two decades, the trend in the United States has been toward increasing training for firefighters and emergency medical service (EMS) personnel, who may be required

U.S. fire department profile, 2009

- Of the 1,148,100 firefighters who protected the United States in 2009, 335,950 (29 percent) were career firefighters and 812,150 (71 percent) were volunteer firefighters.
- Most career firefighters (73 percent) are in departments that protect 25,000 or more people.
- Most volunteer firefighters (95 percent) are in departments that protect fewer than 25,000 people, and more than half are located in small, rural departments that protect fewer than 2,500 people.
- There are an estimated 30,165 fire departments in the United States. These fire departments have an estimated 52,050 fire stations, 68,400 pumpers, 6,750 aerial apparatus, and 74,250 other suppression vehicles.
- Medical aid calls have more than tripled since 1980.
- A fire department responds to a fire every 23 seconds.
- Departments protecting larger communities tend to have higher proportions of firefighters in the age groups 30–39 and 40–49 than smaller communities.
- In 2009, an estimated 15,100 collisions occurred involving fire department emergency vehicles either responding to or returning from incidents.

Source: Reproduced with permission from Michael J. Karter Jr. and Gary P. Stein, *U.S. Fire Department Profile through 2009* (Quincy, Mass.: National Fire Protection Association [NFPA], October 2010). Copyright © 2010, NFPA.

This chapter is a revised and updated version of Chapter 4, "Organizing and Deploying Resources," by P. Michael Freeman, in the 2002 edition of this volume.

to pass state certification exams before being allowed to provide fire and emergency services. State EMS offices and some state fire certification agencies also require periodic recertification. These requirements have improved knowledge, skills, and professionalism among firefighters but also require a substantial time commitment. Therefore, a critical challenge in many volunteer fire departments is recruiting and retaining enough people who are willing to volunteer their time and service. Many factors affect people's ability to volunteer, but communities in need of volunteer firefighters are primarily residential, with most residents commuting some distance to their jobs. Thus, during the day, few residents are at home or near enough to respond to emergency calls; and at night many are tired, unwilling, or unable to devote the time needed for training and other duties required of active volunteer firefighters.

Although many volunteer fire departments are independent organizations, some are sponsored by colleges and universities. One such department is St. Michael's College Fire and Rescue, located in Colchester, Vermont. This student-run and student-staffed department was established in the wake of a death on campus in 1969. Students who volunteer meet state certification requirements to become emergency medical technicians (EMTs) and firefighters and provide emergency services to the college and surrounding area. A college-based program is an excellent way to provide dependable fire and emergency services in college communities.[3]

Whether independent or affiliated with a parent organization, some volunteer fire and emergency departments require their members to sleep in the stations on an assigned schedule to ensure that the units they staff can respond quickly when an emergency occurs. Other departments that rely on volunteers to respond from their homes create duty rotations to ensure that a sufficient number of personnel can be on scene at any time they are needed, day or night.

Because of their numbers, it is likely that volunteer firefighters will always play a meaningful role in providing fire protection and related services to their communities. The commitment and community spirit that motivate people to prepare themselves to be volunteer firefighters are a tribute to them and to the fire and emergency services at large.

Career (fully paid) departments

In a career fire and emergency service department, all firefighters are full- or part-time employees and are paid a salary for their services. Federal, state, county, and local government fire departments employ career firefighters. Their employment is usually governed by a civil service system, department work schedule, and in many cases a labor contract or similar agreement.

Civil service Federal career firefighters are employed through the federal civil service system. Human resource (HR) issues, such as hiring, promotions, salary advancements, and pensions, are administered according to the civil service rules. The rank of each firefighter position is based on government pay ratings and categories, applicable throughout the federal fire service regardless of the assignment location. The civil service structure is intended to provide order and fairness in these important matters.

Many local career fire and emergency service departments also take a civil service approach to firefighter HR issues. In some cases, a state civil service system handles certain aspects of firefighter hiring, promotional examinations, and other matters. Local fire and emergency service departments generally work in concert with state civil service administrators (if applicable) and with their local government HR agencies. Some local departments, especially municipal fire districts or authorities, have their own in-house or contracted HR specialists to address all personnel-related matters.

Work schedules Once career firefighters complete their basic training—usually provided in a fire academy setting—and achieve the required certifications, they are assigned to fire station duty. Many career departments use a 24-hour rotating shift so that firefighters are on duty one day and then off for the next one to two days. The first priority for on-duty firefighters is to respond to emergencies, but they are allowed to prepare and eat meals and sleep at appropriate times. They will also be involved in many other activities, including in-service training, physical fitness, and proactive community service. Although a 24-hour shift can be mentally and physically taxing, many firefighters prefer it, and local governments find it cost-effective and workable.

A schedule of 24 hours on duty and 48 hours off duty means that firefighters work an average of 56 hours a week. This schedule requires three platoons of firefighters, one on duty and two off duty at any given time. The average number of hours worked weekly is lowered if several extra 24-hour shifts (sometimes called "Kelly days") are allowed off during the year. Firefighters work holidays, so they are usually granted equivalent vacation time instead. Some departments have altered the 24/48 schedule so that firefighters work three shifts out of nine, with four days off in a row every cycle. This is a benefit to the firefighters that does not increase salary costs to the local government.

Another common shift schedule consists of a 10-hour day and a 14-hour night so that two shifts of firefighters cover a 24-hour period. This schedule produces a 42-hour average workweek and generally requires a fourth platoon of firefighters. The added platoon makes this shift arrangement more expensive for the local government because it requires 25 percent more personnel.

Labor relations Firefighters in most career fire and emergency departments have formed associations or labor unions to represent their collective interests. Many of these associations are affiliated with national labor groups, such as the International Association of Fire Fighters (IAFF). Some states prohibit collective bargaining by public employees, although public employees, including firefighters, may join unions. In other localities, there may be formally adopted labor contracts between the local government and the firefighters' union, establishing pay, benefits, and agreed-upon working conditions during the term of the contract. In the interest of public safety, these contracts usually contain provisions that forbid firefighters to strike, often in exchange for binding arbitration to settle contract disputes.

Combination departments

In some communities, fire and emergency services are provided by a department that relies on both career and volunteer firefighters. Both groups respond to emergencies, where they function as a team. The career firefighters provide full-time staffing and usually drive fire-rescue apparatus to the reported incident. Volunteers respond in their own vehicles, augmenting the on-duty career staff at the emergency scene to achieve an effective firefighting force. In some combination departments, volunteers stay at the fire stations for scheduled tours of duty and respond on the fire-rescue apparatus with career personnel. Other departments deploy career personnel to some fire stations and staff other fire stations with volunteers.

Combination departments have evolved in communities where volunteers cannot provide adequate daytime coverage because many of them are employed far away from their homes or because quicker response times are desired. Although they are less common than fully volunteer departments, combination departments offer some communities an economical way to have full-time fire protection, rapid emergency response, and the benefits provided by civic-minded volunteer firefighters. Particularly important in these departments is the need for regular joint training and drilling, with career and volunteer firefighters participating together so that their skill levels are well coordinated for emergency services.

Paid-call departments

Another arrangement for staffing fire departments is to use paid-call personnel. These are essentially part-time employees who are paid on a per-call basis, or per hour for time spent in training and at alarms. Although relatively infrequent, such arrangements offer advantages of greater control over personnel and an incentive for members to participate.

Because the amount of money earned by paid-call personnel is usually not very high, there is still a significant degree of civic-mindedness motivating these members. In fact, many organizations that use paid-call personnel may refer to them as "volunteers or auxiliaries," even though these personnel receive compensation for their service. Paid-call members can also be found in combination departments.

Public safety consolidations

Public safety consolidations refer to a continuum of service delivery arrangements in which some element of service provision is shared among the traditional disciplines of law enforcement, fire, and emergency medical services. While there are many variations, some arrangements, such as a shared public safety communications capability, are so common and long-standing that they are not commonly considered to be consolidations.

There are five basic forms of public safety consolidation:

- *Administrative:* Both departments maintain separate operations, but administrative functions, such as budgeting and human resources, are combined.
- *Functional:* The departments may or may not be administratively consolidated, but some operational functions, such as communications, are combined.
- *Area:* Joint operations are performed in certain areas, such as residential neighborhoods, where demand is relatively low; separate operations are performed in areas with higher service demands, such as the central business district of a city.
- *Partial:* The fire and police departments are administratively consolidated, and most of their operations are integrated. This type of consolidation model uses a combination of public safety officers, firefighters, and police officers.
- *Full:* All administrative and operational functions are integrated into a single department of public safety. Cross-trained public safety officers perform fire and police services, primarily suppression and patrol, while other public safety officers perform specialized services, such as fire and crime prevention and fire and crime investigation.

The most common form of consolidation is the functional type, followed in descending order by full, administrative, partial, and area.

The more common consolidations are mergers of previously separate fire and EMS departments; this is because fire apparatus staffed by firefighters and ambulances staffed by EMTs and paramedics often respond to the same emergencies and work together to provide needed service.[4] In the most advanced form of consolidation, law enforcement, fire, and EMS functions are delivered by the same pool of cross-trained personnel. Public safety consolidations are most common in smaller communities; they are also common in newer communities, where most structures have built-in fire protection features and policing demands are relatively low, allowing police officers the time to fight fires and provide other services typically handled by the fire and emergency services department. Larger cities operating a public safety form of organization include Kalamazoo, Michigan, and Sunnyvale, California.

In concept, public safety consolidations depend on having on-duty law enforcement officers respond in their police vehicles to fires, where they assist in fire suppression activities. Police officers are cross-trained in basic firefighting techniques and carry personal protective equipment in their vehicles. They basically enhance the firefighting capabilities of firefighters responding on fire-rescue apparatus. While organizations transitioning to the fully consolidated public safety form of organization may retain single-role personnel, they usually hire only dual-role personnel going forward.

Some local governments have adopted consolidated public safety operations in order to reduce operating costs by having a smaller cadre of firefighters on duty, augmented by the on-duty law enforcement staff. But despite its benefits, such an approach is usually controversial because law enforcement and fire protection are two distinct disciplines, each with heavy training and certification demands. Moves toward considering consolidation are often fiercely opposed by labor organizations, as well as by senior staff who are not necessarily comfortable operating in both law enforcement and fire/EMS roles.

Kinds of fire departments

Although the need to protect people and property from fires and other emergencies—the basic reason for fire departments—is universal, local circumstances influence how a fire and emergency service department is structured to accomplish its mission. Thus, there are different kinds of fire departments, depending on the source of the department's authority and the entity that provides overall funding and policy direction. In the United States, there are seven basic kinds of fire departments: military, federal, state, local government, county, intergovernmental, and private.

Military fire departments

At U.S. military installations, where the firefighting is highly specialized or where there are overriding defense concerns, uniformed members of the armed services may function as the fire and emergency services department. The trend in the military is toward civilianizing these functions, using civilian military employees or personnel employed by private contractors.

Federal fire departments

At other military posts, bases, and federal installations, fire protection is routinely handled by federal firefighters—nonmilitary personnel employed by the federal civil service system and trained to provide all fire protection services. Federal firefighters serve in all fifty states and Puerto Rico, staffing conventional fire stations and fire apparatus, as well as using specialized equipment. They protect naval shipyards, restricted military installations, training centers, and military housing complexes. In many areas they interact and respond with their military counterparts, as well as with local government firefighters from communities that adjoin federal facilities.

The number of federal civil service firefighters fluctuates with changes in U.S. defense budget appropriations: as dollars are diverted from military and defense programs, military facilities are closed. When this occurs, fire protection of the base facilities often becomes the responsibility of the local civilian fire and emergency services department. Sometimes federal firefighters who would have been laid off or transferred across the country are hired by the local fire department.

The U.S. Department of the Interior and the U.S. Department of Agriculture also maintain firefighting forces. Under the former, the agencies that employ firefighters include the National Park Service, Bureau of Land Management, and Bureau of Indian Affairs. Under the latter, the U.S. Forest Service has firefighters trained to fight forest and wildland fires in the national forests.

State fire departments

Certain regions of the United States and Canada maintain provincial or state-level fire and emergency departments, usually to address widespread fire risks that clearly extend beyond the jurisdiction of local governments. These risks are generally related to forests, logging concerns, or highly flammable natural fuels that pose serious threats to life, property, and the economy of a particular region if fires occur and are not controlled.

In Canada, the Ministry of Public Security in the province of Quebec cooperates with local fire departments and operates an extensive firefighting air force, using Canadian-built SuperScooper aircraft, to combat the annually occurring forest fires. In the United States, the California Department of Forestry and Fire Protection (CAL FIRE) employs full-time career and seasonal firefighters to conserve and protect state-owned lands. Much of the land that CAL FIRE protects is sparsely populated, but abundant volatile vegetation makes it susceptible to large-scale wildland fires; in other areas, residential and commercial development has extended into lands with highly flammable vegetation that poses a serious threat to the structures. (The presence of structures adjacent to or within wildland areas is referred to as the wildland-urban interface or intermix.) CAL FIRE also contracts with a number of California cities to provide their fire protection services.

Other states, including New York, North Carolina, Texas, Virginia, and Washington, also provide wildland fire protection services through their departments of forestry; these services are provided primarily in rural areas where protection and conservation are equally important objectives. The suppression of fires by state-level fire agencies conserves state resources, such as wildlife and forests, while also protecting water resources and ecosystems that would be disrupted by large wildfires.

Courtesy of City of White Plains (New York) Department of Public Safety

Figure 4-1 Many fire departments are organized to protect a specific government.

Local government fire departments

In the United States and Canada, local government fire departments employ the vast majority of firefighters and fire equipment (Figure 4–1). These departments may be operated by cities, towns, counties, districts, authorities, and other municipalities, or, if fully volunteer, they may be independent nonprofit corporations serving particular areas. Local fire departments provide fire protection and usually some level of emergency medical services, and many of them respond to emergencies arising from a variety of hazards.

Funding for combination and career departments usually comes from the local government's general fund and is allocated to the fire and emergency services department in the annual or biannual budgeting process. Some jurisdictions levy a fire tax to support the department. The fire chief prepares the budget request within guidelines established by the local government manager. (Preparation of operating budgets is discussed in detail in Chapter 12.) The local government includes the fire department's request in the overall budget request for all departments, which it then submits to the elected officials, who have final approval authority. In general, 85 percent or more of a career fire and emergency services department's budget may go to salaries and benefits. The percentage varies slightly depending on the size of the community and on staffing practices. According to the International City/County Management Association's *Municipal Year Book 2010,* for cities greater than 100,000, those cities responding to the survey averaged 85.6 percent of their total budget for personnel.[5]

Volunteer fire departments, whose firefighters receive no pay or nominal stipends, depend on a variety of funding sources. Some receive direct support from the local governments they serve to cover operating costs—utilities and fuel, for example. Many hold fundraising events to cover the cost of new and specialized equipment. In many areas, volunteer and combination fire departments are independent, nonprofit corporations governed by boards of directors.

County fire departments

In some places in the United States, local fire protection services are provided by county-level agencies rather than municipalities, and funding and policy direction are provided by county elected or appointed officials. Virginia, for example, gives counties the same powers as municipalities, and there are a number of county fire departments in that state.

Usually a county fire and emergency services department is formed when there is a local need that cannot be met by just one local fire and emergency services department. That was the case in Los Angeles County, California, where much of the unincorporated area of the county's 4,400 square miles is covered in highly flammable brush. Wildland fires are driven by steep gradients and seasonal Santa Ana winds, with the result that thousands of acres burn, threatening populated areas of the county. After wildfires, there is the threat of mudslides from the denuded hills. Wildfires also lead to imbalances in the water percolation cycles. Accordingly, in 1923 the County Board of Supervisors formed the Department of County Forester and Fire Warden to conserve the wildland areas by performing fire prevention and fire suppression activities. Over the years the department's responsibilities have broadened; as of 2010, what is now called the Los Angeles County Fire Department (LACoFD) provides contractual fire services to fifty-eight incorporated cities within Los Angeles and Orange Counties.

There are numerous county fire departments in operation across the United States, ranging from predominantly rural, all-volunteer departments to metropolitan, urbanized departments serving large populations with predominantly career staffing. County fire departments are found throughout California, Georgia, Maryland, Virginia, and other states. Generally, the emergency response services they provide are similar to those provided by many local fire departments, but because of their size, they are often able to provide specialized services or equipment that is beyond the capability of many smaller organizations.

Intergovernmental fire protection

The desire to contain costs, improve the level of service, solve problems innovatively, or accomplish all three objectives has led some localities to develop intergovernmental agreements for providing fire protection. Basically, two or more jurisdictional bodies form a separate governmental unit to carry out the functions of fire protection. In some states, these units may be created through a joint powers agreement; in others, a fire protection district may be created. With either approach, provision must be made for funding, decision making, and overall control. The collective power that is created when jurisdictions pool their firefighting resources and personnel can benefit citizens by eliminating some duplication and spreading the costs over a wider base.

In a joint powers agreement, local jurisdictions form a special authority to deliver fire services. In the Orange County Fire Authority (OCFA) in Southern California, for example, a board consisting of an elected official from each city served and two officials from Orange County sets policy, establishes the budget, and governs the OCFA. Where permitted by state law, a fire authority enables local jurisdictions to pool their tax dollars so that all may benefit from a wider range of services with greater efficiencies.

A fire protection district is typically governed by a board of directors elected from the area to be protected. Funding for the district may come from a portion of local taxes, special fees, or some type of assessment. The laws of each state establish the limits within which special fire districts must function.

A local governing body may also contract for fire protection with another agency. For example, a town or community may contract with a state-run fire and emergency services department for local services, or one jurisdiction may contract with another for fire protection. Usually, such contracts reflect a desire to contain costs while maintaining service levels.

Private sector fire protection organizations

Some large, complex industrial plants organize their own fire brigades to provide fire protection services (and possibly a wide range of other services) to the plant and its employees. Private fire brigades may call for assistance from the local fire and emergency services department when emergencies occur at the plant; some private fire brigades routinely respond with the local fire and emergency services department in areas adjacent to the industrial complex, especially when the private brigade has specialized equipment or supplies for hazardous materials (HAZMAT) incidents. (For information on NFPA standards for private fire brigades, see Chapter 10.)

There are also companies that market fire protection and emergency medical services to communities, industrial complexes, and governmental facilities. These companies' employees deliver the same services as would the local fire and emergency services department. The private company is accountable to the local elected body for the quality and efficiency of its service delivery. Rural Metro Corporation, located in Scottsdale, Arizona, provides fire protection and emergency medical services, including ambulance transport, to a large number of cities and towns. Wackenhut Services, Inc., provides fire, emergency medical response, and rescue protection primarily to industrial corporations and federal governmental facilities.

In some cases, local jurisdictions contract with private firms for fire services instead of providing the services as a direct local governmental function. In other cases, the local government fire department enters into a limited partnership with a private firm to deliver emergency ambulance service; contractual terms address all aspects of the operation, including how revenue and costs are shared. At some airports in the United States and in other countries, private sector companies provide aircraft rescue and firefighting (ARFF) (discussed more fully further on under "Expanding the Services Delivered"), a specialized fire protection service. Federal agencies also may contract with private fire protection service organizations to protect their facilities.

Organizational structures in fire departments

Like any organization, a fire and emergency services department must have an efficient structure that divides responsibility for critical functions and distributes authority so that services are delivered in a timely, orderly, and safe manner. Given the nature of emergency services, many fire departments use a paramilitary model for operations, regardless of the organizational structure.

Traditional approaches

Traditionally, the organizational structure of a fire and emergency services department starts at the top with the fire chief. The chief—or the highest-ranking officer, whatever the title—is the chief administrator as well as the chief firefighter.

In a small department with only one or two stations, the fire chief is responsible for most administrative and operational functions, including incident command at large incidents, budgeting, policy development, and HR functions such as hiring and discipline. If there is an assistant-level chief officer, that person is often responsible for fire prevention as well as emergency operations. This structure is normal for volunteer, combination, and small career departments.

A basic workable approach in a medium-sized department divides authority and responsibility between operational service delivery (line) functions and administrative support (staff) functions (see Figure 4-2).

Although in large career fire departments the fire chief responds only to the largest emergency incidents, he or she is still responsible for firefighting as well as for fire preven-

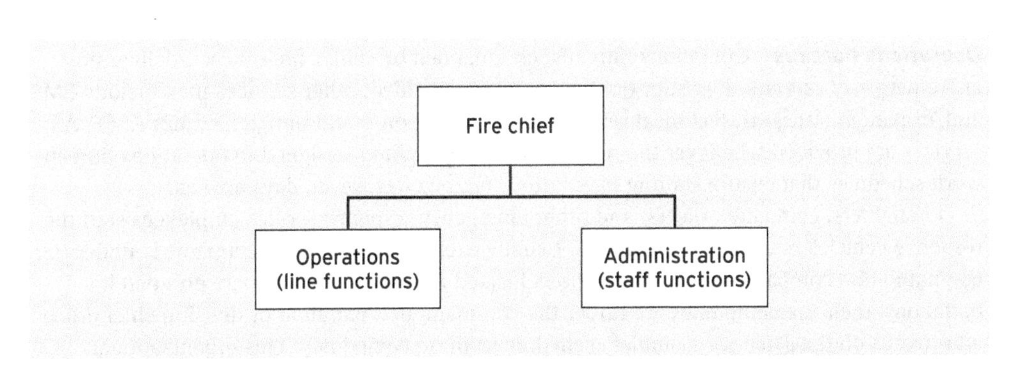

Figure 4-2 A basic organizational approach that works in medium-sized departments is shown here.

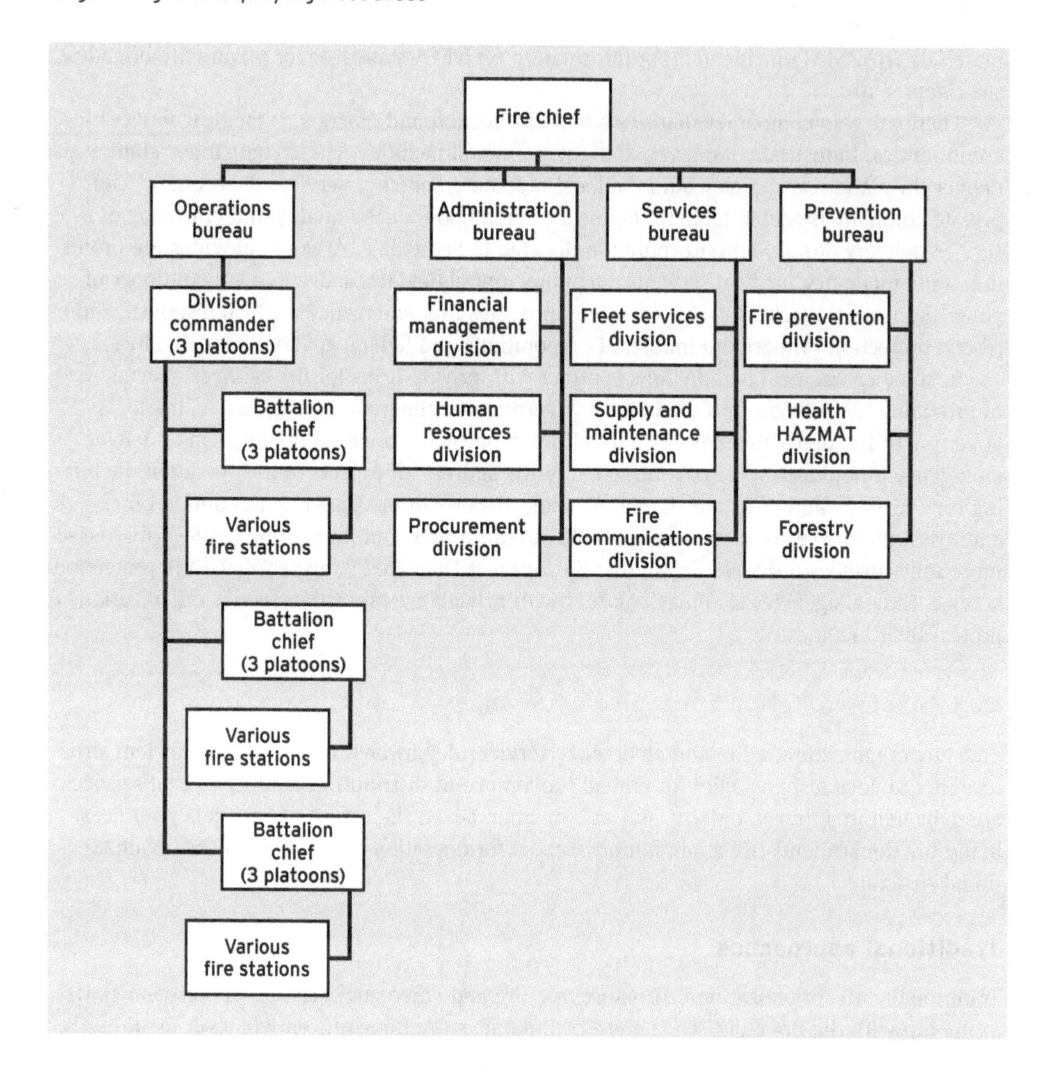

Figure 4-3 This chart shows the traditional division of responsibility among bureaus and the divisions under them in larger fire departments.

tion, budgeting, and human resources. The magnitude of these responsibilities leads to the traditional division of functions among bureau or division chiefs, who command bureaus or divisions that are assigned specific areas of responsibility. Given the need for expertise in critical support functions and the range of emergency services delivered, even fire departments of modest size often use more complex organizational designs to accomplish their missions.

Typically, a department's major areas of responsibility include operations (fire suppression and other emergency services), administration, services or support, and fire prevention. Each area is headed and managed by a bureau or division chief, who reports to the fire chief (as shown in Figure 4-3). When workload or complexity requires a broader organizational structure, bureaus may be divided into divisions and divisions into sections. Section managers are generally on the same organizational level as platoon battalion chiefs, although nonuniformed employees may have a slightly lower pay status.

Operations bureaus Operations bureaus, commanded by senior fire officers, deliver fire and emergency services. Fire suppression is always provided; other services may include EMS and/or patient transport, technical rescue, HAZMAT response and mitigation, and ARFF. All services are provided whenever the need arises, so firefighters assigned to operations bureaus work schedules that ensure staffing twenty-four hours a day, seven days a week.

Firefighters, company officers, and other emergency response service employees staff the response vehicles housed in fire stations. Usually each fire unit, or fire company, is under the command of a company officer. Fire stations located in contiguous areas are grouped into battalions; their fire companies are under the command of a battalion or division chief officer who works on the same (or a similar) schedule as these companies. This organizational arrangement provides consistent managerial presence and oversight for both routine matters and emergencies, regardless of the time of day. In addition to addressing routine administrative matters, the division or battalion chief is also available to respond to large-scale emergencies when incident command-and-control requirements are complex.

At the upper levels, the organization of operations bureaus varies widely from community to community. In communities where large-scale emergencies are infrequent, the battalion chief may be the highest-ranking officer assigned to shift work. Where major emergencies occur more often, the shift work schedule is often extended to include a division-level fire officer. This is generally the case in large cities with high population densities, aged and complex building stock, and frequent large fires.

In most fire departments, each fire station is under the supervision or command of a station officer. If the department is fully paid, the station officers generally work the shift schedule, with a station officer on each shift. Station officers report directly to battalion chiefs and are responsible for all employees assigned to their stations and shifts, including paramedics when emergency medical services are provided from that station. When more than one fire company is assigned to a station, the most common practice is for a fire captain to be in charge of the fire station (as station commander) and a single fire company; additional fire companies assigned to the station are commanded by a captain with less seniority or by a fire lieutenant. In some departments, two companies in the same station are commanded by company officers of equal rank and authority.

The sequence of fire officer ranks in many career departments is battalion chief, captain, lieutenant, and engineer/driver. In smaller volunteer and combination departments, there may not be battalion chiefs or lieutenants in the sequence.

When a fire and emergency services department provides prehospital emergency medical response, a division or section—usually within the operations bureau—has responsibility for it. This division provides for the coordination of medical training and the administrative oversight for firefighter paramedics and the services they provide. (The provision of emergency medical services is discussed briefly below and in greater detail in Chapter 5.)

Fire prevention bureaus A fire prevention bureau, headed by a manager who is usually called the fire marshal, is responsible for preventing fires by enforcing the fire code in existing structures, reviewing construction plans for buildings to be built, and interacting with other local code enforcement agencies. Many prevention bureaus also have responsibility for fire investigation, in which specially trained investigators determine the cause and origin of fires and document cases of arson for prosecution in the courts. Fire and life safety education is another function commonly assigned to the fire prevention bureau. (These areas are discussed in greater detail later in this chapter and in Chapter 6.)

Administrative bureaus Working under the management of a bureau chief, an administrative bureau is generally responsible for budgeting, financial management, human resources, planning, and procurement. Authority and responsibility for these functions are delegated to division managers, who may be civilians with expertise in the relevant administrative fields and not uniformed fire officers.

Most local career fire departments function as part of a larger local governmental entity that has departments for purchasing, human resources, and financial management. Even then, there is usually need for these functions within the fire and emergency services department itself in order to provide expertise unique to the department and also to coordinate with other local government administrative departments.

In smaller departments, administrative functions can be carried out by a subordinate unit of the fire chief's office. In these cases, the fire and emergency services department is more likely to depend on other local government departments because it lacks sufficient personnel and expertise to provide full administrative services itself.

Services bureaus For effective operations, fire and emergency service departments require a wide range of specialized support services, including fleet purchasing and maintenance; facility design, construction, and maintenance; purchase and maintenance of tools and equipment; and stocking and distribution of personal protective equipment and supplies of all

Figure 4-4 A service technician refills the self-contained breathing apparatus bottle for a firefighter at the scene of a fire.

Courtesy of the Charlotte (North Carolina) Fire Department

kinds (see Figure 4-4). These critical and highly technical functions are handled by a services bureau, which may be under a bureau chief, or by the local government's fleet maintenance and facilities management departments.

Routine duties require services bureau employees to prepare contracts with vendors and maintain sufficient quantities of parts and supplies for distribution on demand in support of the department's mission. Divisions within the bureau employ mechanics who repair vehicles and fire apparatus, technicians who maintain self-contained breathing apparatus and other specialized tools, and crafts personnel who maintain and repair fire stations and facilities.

Communications is a critical function that is provided in a variety of ways. Communications employees, who may or may not be uniformed employees, work a shift schedule and are responsible for receiving calls for emergency services, dispatching appropriate fire units, and tracking and coordinating units and personnel needed to respond to incidents. Communications is generally responsible for maintaining computer-aided dispatching components, global positioning systems for emergency response vehicles, and telecommunications systems of various types. Because of the number and complexity of computer systems in emergency and routine communications, many fire and emergency service department communications sections have an information technology support staff. (For more detail on electronics and other communications, see Chapters 15 and 16.)

Other functions Other functions that fire and emergency service departments may need include training, research and planning, community services, disaster services, emergency preparedness, information management, public information, employee relations, and internal affairs. These may be designated divisions or sections placed under different bureaus, depending on local needs and management practices in the given local government.

Beyond traditional approaches

In specific communities, special circumstances have resulted in organizational structures that are different from the more traditional approaches to organizing a fire and emergency service department.

As mentioned, the LACoFD protects fifty-eight incorporated cities, many of which are contiguous to one another, as well as all unincorporated areas, including urban and

Kalamazoo, Michigan's Department of Public Safety

Kalamazoo, Michigan (2009 pop. 72,825), operates a fully integrated public safety department consisting of dual-role, cross-trained officers who perform both police and firefighting functions. New personnel are also trained at the medical first-responder level. The department has operated in this form for over twenty years.

The department's mission statement (taken from its 2008 annual report) shows the effective integration of policing and fire and emergency services functions.

> The mission of Kalamazoo [Department] of Public Safety is to provide for the safety and welfare of all citizens and visitors to the City of Kalamazoo and to protect them from the loss of life and property from the ravages of fire or crime. This mission includes, but is not limited to, the maintenance of order, the promotion of crime and fire prevention programs, the investigation of crimes leading to the apprehension of perpetrators, recovery of property, and the providing of emergency medical life support services. The exploration of new ideas and concepts leading to improved services which optimize resources will be a high priority for department personnel. The promotion of good will, community respect, and confidence in Kalamazoo Public Safety will continue to be of the highest priority for all employees. Mission priorities are:
>
> - Public Safety patrols which maintain order and provide optimal response to criminal offenses and citizen calls for service.
> - Fire suppression capabilities which minimize potential fire hazards and loss of life and property.
> - Criminal and special investigations to apprehend serious criminal violators, recover stolen property, and deter vice and drug offenders.
> - Crime and fire prevention and community education programs which reduce personal and property loss from crime and fire incidents.
> - Communications, records, and data management provide an efficient means of dispatching service calls, and allow for the evaluation of all services.
> - Training of personnel to ensure professional performance of duties and enhance department appreciation of community and organizational diversity.[1]

Public safety officers can be assigned to patrol or other specialized law enforcement functions, or to operate a piece of fire apparatus. Fire apparatus are normally staffed with one or two personnel who operate from a fire station. When a call comes in, additional personnel are dispatched as needed from patrol functions on a geographic basis. Patrol officers don firefighting equipment and operate in firefighting roles. Supervisors assume command functions using the incident command system. First-line supervision is provided by sergeants, with higher ranks providing supervision of larger incidents.

In addition to specialized police functions, such as investigations, special weapons and tactics (SWAT), a bomb squad, a fire marshal's office, crime scene investigation, training, and an office of professional standards, the department also has a robust community outreach program, including a senior citizens academy, child car seat inspections, and an explorer post (for high school students and other young adults interested in pursuing a career in law enforcement or fire services). (For more information on explorer posts, see learningforlife.org/exploring/index.html).

In a casual comparison, the number of employees in Kalamazoo Public Safety versus the number in cities with separate fire and police departments indicates that Kalamazoo has fewer employees, on average, than similar-sized communities with separate police and career fire departments.[2]

Fiscal pressure and the continued emphasis on homeland security-related issues in the public safety realm may bring this rare organizational form back into the spotlight in coming years. Additional research into the benefits and potential drawbacks of this method of organization is warranted.

1 *Kalamazoo Public Safety Annual Report 2008* (Kalamazoo, Mich., 2008), 4, kalamazoocity.org/publicsafety/2008%20Annual%20Report.pdf.

2 *The Municipal Year Book 2010* (Washington, D.C.: ICMA, 2010), Tables 3-16 and 3-17; *Comparative Performance Measurement: FY 2005 Data Report* (Washington, D.C.: ICMA Press, 2006); and phone calls to agencies.

wildland areas. Covering 4,400 square miles with fire and paramedic services, as well as with helicopter-supported fire attack and air squads, bulldozer operations, ocean lifeguard services, and brush firefighting hand crews, requires a departure from the traditional approach to organizational structure.

To address the diverse needs of the large geographic area it serves, the LACoFD has created three regional operations bureaus. A deputy chief commands each region and is accountable for all emergency and nonemergency service delivery in it. (The region that covers the oceanfront includes the ocean lifeguard services in addition to all other services.) The bureau chiefs and their support staffs are housed within their respective regions, ensuring that executive management is close to the actual point of service delivery.

Deployment concepts

The primary mission of fire and emergency service departments is to protect life and property from fire. All aspects of department operations—from the location of stations, to the choice of vehicles and equipment used, to staffing practices—should be designed with the characteristics of hostile fire and the department's mission to mitigate its impact in mind.

Hostile fire grows with amazing speed. It takes only six to eight minutes after an object in a room is ignited for the entire room and its contents to erupt into flame in a phenomenon known as "flashover." At flashover, life inside the structure is highly endangered because the fire's further spread is inevitable. Time is the critical difference between a small, easily controlled fire and a large fire that threatens to destroy an entire building. Time is also critical in saving lives: four to six minutes are as long as a human being can go without breathing or without an effective heartbeat before brain damage and death occur.

Response time, then, is a critical component of a fire department's success in fulfilling its mission. As usually measured, response time counts the minutes and seconds from the exact moment that an emergency call is received in the dispatch center until the first emergency unit arrives on scene. Given that call processing and dispatching may take up to a minute, the reaction time and the travel time of the firefighters are tremendously important. (Neither firefighters nor telecommunicators have control over the time elapsed between ignition and discovery of a fire and the call to 911. This is why response time is only one of several components critical to minimizing fire losses; other critically important components include fire prevention efforts, code enforcement, and public fire education.)

A recent innovation brought over from the EMS field (where it is part of a more comprehensive practice known as "system status management") is the concept of mobile deployment (see sidebar on page 107). In mobile deployment, emergency apparatus is posted with its crew at a certain location—a street corner or a parking lot or some other convenient place—during times of the day when past experience shows that it will be needed for rapid response to emergencies. Mobile deployment has the advantage of not requiring the maintenance of a facility with recurring costs; however, the human needs of the personnel staffing the apparatus must be taken into account. To provide coverage for long periods, crews may be rotated or, more often, deployed during only limited peak hours.

Ideally, a fire and emergency service organization will prepare a deployment plan that looks at least ten years into the future and serves as the basis for the organization's long-range resource planning. This plan should include needs for stations and other facilities as well as for apparatus and staffing. Key considerations should include condition, size, and serviceability of existing stations; number, age, and mix of apparatus; and future growth or changes in development or population patterns within the community. (More on deployment planning can be found in Chapter 13; specific concerns for locating a fire station are detailed in the next section.)

Locating fire stations

A fire station is a major investment, and its construction involves decisions that should be made with care and the involvement of the community that the station will protect. Since a station is a visible and enduring statement of the community's commitment to the safety and

System status management and mobile deployment

Mobile deployment is generally defined as the process of basing vehicles and personnel away from fixed stations or facilities for part of the working day or shift. Some fire and emergency service organizations use some form of this activity, particularly that of pre-positioning resources in areas where there is a high likelihood of an event. For example, brush units may be assigned to patrol activity during periods of high fire danger in wildland areas. The principal advantages of mobile deployment are (1) reduced response times because units are placed close to calls that may be remote from an existing fire station and (2) reduced turnout time because the unit is already staffed and in the field.

The more formal term, *system status management (SSM)*, was coined by Jack Stout, a noted emergency medical service (EMS) innovator and consultant. Arrangements that can be classified as SSM include peak-hour staffing and the movement of units in response to changes in temporal and spatial demands for service—for example, the relocation of a company from the center city during the day to a residential area at night.

SSM is usually supported by a statistical analysis of demand and system response times, with adjustments made regularly to maintain or improve response time performance. Units are placed at predefined "posts" that can vary in sophistication from a street corner to a major venue or another public facility, such as a police station. Where emergency medical services are provided through a private contract, use of SSM is more common as such services must meet stringent performance criteria and often struggle to contain costs.

Studies of EMS systems using SSM show that gains in response time are possible, and many of the largest and best-performing EMS systems use SSM because they typically place a high emphasis on quality of service and sound management.

A focus on response time must be monitored in conjunction with quality-of-service measures to make sure that the toll on employees and equipment does not diminish service. Such a toll may include long periods of sitting in a vehicle and frequent moves from post to post in response to the system's dispatch model. In one study, such practices have been linked to lower morale and higher dissatisfaction among employees. This suggests that SSM must be implemented as part of an overall management strategy.

For fire and emergency service organizations, periods away from stations or facilities with crew amenities should be weighed against gains in response time. The higher operating costs of fire apparatus versus ambulances must also be considered and included in any analysis. Limited use of SSM techniques is an established part of some organizations' operations and will likely become more popular as organizations increasingly measure their response-time performance.

Source: Summarized from S. Dean, "The Origins of System Status Management," *Emergency Medical Services* 33 (June 2004): 116–118.

well-being of its citizens, it should be designed not only to be highly functional but also to fit into the community. This is just as true for a one-station volunteer department as it is for a large urban department with dozens of stations.

Locating a fire station is like playing chess without a board. It is a complex game complicated by political realities. The ancient cliché is correct: the two most difficult things for a fire and emergency services department to do are to put a fire station in a neighborhood and to take a fire station out of a neighborhood. Selection of a station site is one of the most potentially controversial decisions the department can make. To be successful, the department must have good working relationships with the community and its elected leaders, and it should use siting methodologies, including analyses of past and future calls for service and of drive time. The obsolescence or expansion needs of neighboring facilities may create opportunities for repositioning more than one station.

It will also help to remember that there are no perfect sites. The goal should be to agree on a site that facilitates the effective provision of emergency services. No one should expect perfection in a station site, but the best location possible should be chosen.

Before a fire and emergency services department can locate—or relocate—a station, it must decide what is important. Is response time a problem? What emergency services does the department offer, and how is it organized to provide them? What does the community need and expect from the department? The answers to these questions should be written in a clear and logical document that members can refer to at any time. The department must be prepared to justify and defend its criteria, both in conversations and in writing.

Justifying the need for a station For many years, fire chiefs used the Insurance Services Office Public Protection Classification (ISO PPC™) rating schedule as the major justification for station location (see sidebar on page 79 in Chapter 3). The schedule is still useful, especially in smaller communities, but it should not override the fire and emergency services department's assessment of local needs. Departments are advised to check NFPA's two deployment standards: NFPA 1710, which covers career departments, and NFPA 1720, which covers volunteer departments. The response time and resource requirements of these standards will assist the department in assessing and clarifying its needs.

Basically, there are two methods for justifying the need for a new station or a relocation.

Time and distance The first method is to select a response benchmark that is based on a realistic assessment of the service area, resources, and community desires. As it is unrealistic to expect to be able to service all areas of a rural community within a set response-time goal, a more sensitive measure of service provided could be based on response-time objectives in terms of percentile performance (90 percent of incidents within *x* minutes). The use of average response times, while common, is not preferred because the average can be affected by extremely small or large values and would therefore not reflect the actual level of service being delivered. Any response-time objectives must include a clear, written definition of response time to permit comparisons among communities and to identify areas for improving service. Using response-time data, the department can identify areas in the community where it cannot meet its objectives and might need an additional station. (For more information on response-time performance measures, see Chapter 14.)

There are several software packages on the market that can measure and show response distances on maps; such packages, which vary from general and relatively inexpensive to very specific and expensive simulation software, will integrate with existing geographic information system (GIS) software to create customized maps. Street speeds and results of time and distance analyses should be checked against actual drive times. GIS staff from local planning or other departments can be a resource in doing these analyses. However, no software can substitute for fire officials' knowledge of their own jurisdictions.

Number of calls The second method is to establish a criterion for the number of calls that the department responds to in an area within a given time. For example, a community might decide that a station is required in an area that generates more than two calls per day. However, the number of calls does not reflect the actual workload posed by long responses into a remote area. Often response times and workload will be balanced when the decision is made to build a new station. One way of determining the minimum number of responses for a station is to ascertain the number of responses made by the least active station in the department. If the least active station makes 500 responses per year, for example, that would be a de facto minimum for that community.

Choosing a site for the station Effective response to fires and other hazards depends on the specific risk to life and property that fires and hazards represent in different properties. Therefore, there are several factors to consider in deciding on a station site.

Property use What are the hazards faced in the area to be protected? For example, the risk that fire represents in a hospital, where there are many nonambulatory people and pure oxygen is present, is much higher than in a single-family detached dwelling, where four active people live.

Questions to ask concerning property use in the area under consideration include the following: Is the area built out, or will there be further development? What is the population density? For example, apartment complexes are big customers for emergency medical services and the site of frequent fires, especially minor ones like car fires and dumpster fires.

Street network What are the roads like? Are there major thoroughfares? Can fire apparatus navigate neighborhood streets? Are there many cul-de-sacs? What is traffic like? Are there barriers, such as barricades, railroad crossings, one-way streets, or bridges that fire trucks cannot cross? Are there plans to modify the street network significantly? The fire and emergency services department should stay in close communication with the transportation department to ensure that there are no surprises.

If a fire station is located on a congested thoroughfare, traffic preemption devices may be installed to ensure that firefighters can control traffic to allow apparatus to respond quickly and safely. At a minimum, traffic control devices should be considered in front of the station to permit emergency vehicles to exit the station without having to "fight" traffic. In addition, the station should be set back far enough from the street to allow approaching traffic to see emerging fire vehicles.

Location of other fire stations Where are adjacent fire stations in relation to the area under consideration? What fire companies are in those stations? How will the new station fit into the existing matrix? That is, how can it help support existing stations, and how will existing stations support it? Given that some areas will require more responses or resources than others, depending on the nature of the emergencies, the goal is to ensure appropriate spacing among fire and emergency services department resources. This is where locating stations is like playing chess without a board. The second and third fire companies dispatched to a fire (known as the second and third due) in the area served by the new station may have to come from other stations, and their response times must be acceptable. Defining the community's response standards is essential, as noted above.

When considering the availability of department resources to a proposed site, volunteer and combination fire departments must also consider where their members live and how long it will take them to respond to the station to retrieve apparatus and equipment needed for emergency operations. Ideally, some members will live close to the station while those who are dispersed throughout the community will be able to respond quickly from home. Volunteer and combination departments should also consider the location of neighboring departments in choosing sites for their own stations. The goal of neighboring departments should be to site stations near the center of their districts while allowing for apparatus to respond quickly to other districts when needed.

Property availability Is there a parcel in the area under consideration that is big enough for a fire station? How far from the ideal spot is that property? Are water and sewer mains available, or must they be extended—and at what expense? Are the property owners willing to negotiate with the fire and emergency services department, or will the department have to condemn property? Condemnations are expensive: there are court costs, relocation costs, and lost business reimbursement costs in addition to the cost of the land itself. In many cases, governments cannot avoid paying more than the assessed valuation of a property without some special effort. However, the added costs of acquiring a good parcel should be balanced against the long service life of the station and the cumulative benefits of improved services over time.

Fire and emergency service departments should be wary of land offered by developers. These "gifts" may be at the back of a housing tract, for example, providing great response to that tract but not so great response to anywhere else. Departments should also avoid historic properties, if possible. Finally, there may be costs for the demolition of existing buildings, remediation costs if the property is a brownfield, and other local fees such as impact fees. All these costs should be considered in the decision to purchase a particular site.

Attributes of the site The site should be an acre and a half to two acres to allow enough room for on-site rainwater detention, parking for employees and visitors, and a turning radius for drive-through bays. Topography is important; it is not good to be at the bottom of a valley and have to respond uphill to all calls, nor is it good to have a station in a floodplain. Departments should check in with the appropriate planning or land use agency to identify any restrictions or undesirable property characteristics.

A related issue is how nearby property is being used. If possible, communities should avoid locating a station next to a HAZMAT occupancy: if there is a major HAZMAT emergency, the station may have to be taken out of service. Stations should also be away from uses that pose barriers to quick response, such as railroad tracks, light rail, and freeways. It makes no sense to put a fire station close to a beach or a lake, where half the response area is under water. If the station is sited close to an airport, the Federal Aviation Administration (FAA) must be consulted to ensure that antenna installations are not a problem. The FAA will also be involved if the department plans a helicopter facility at the station.

Future needs Fire stations should be located where they will be needed for the long term, not the short term. That means that fire departments must balance an area's current needs against its future needs. How will the area develop—or redevelop—in the future? What will the road network look like? Will the predominant land uses change? How will they change? Answers to these questions will help departments find the balance that is needed.

The future needs of the fire and emergency services department itself are also important. The station should be large enough to accommodate all the apparatus and personnel that might reasonably be needed over its life. One-bay stations allow no space for growth. If possible, fire departments should use a generic station design with at least two bays that will accommodate an aerial vehicle as well as auxiliary vehicles, in addition to a pumper.

Politics Finally, since political realities will make or break a station site, fire and emergency service departments must be professional in their request and justification for a new station and their selection of a site. They must also keep elected officials and the public apprised of their plans and progress. In order to "sell" the need for a new station at a particular location, a department should make sure that its relationships with its stakeholders are in good shape. An attractive, well-designed fire station in the right place will serve the community and be a visible symbol of the community's commitment to the emergency needs of its citizens. Any enhancements to the facility should be justifiable on the basis of increased usability, savings in maintenance or operating costs, or aesthetic appeal. (For further discussion of fire station transitions, see Chapter 13.)

Vehicles and equipment

Regardless of its range of services, every fire and emergency services department relies on a fire engine, or pumper, to transport firefighters and necessary equipment to the scene of a reported fire. This is because of the vehicle's versatility and flexibility. Every fire engine has a pump to increase pressure on water taken from hydrants or other sources so that effective, powerful fire streams can be developed in fire hoses. Many engines also carry 300–500 gallons of water for use on small fires where a hydrant hookup is unnecessary. With a crew of trained firefighters, an engine company can handle or begin to make a difference at almost any emergency.

In most communities, the engine company is supported by a truck or ladder company and its crew of firefighters. Ladder companies carry ladders of various lengths, including extension ladders. Most commonly, a ladder truck will also have a hydraulically operated aerial ladder that may extend from 75 to 135 feet. Aerial ladders are common in urbanized areas where building heights exceed three stories.

At structure fires, engine company firefighters lay and advance hose lines and use directed streams of water to confine and extinguish the fire. Ladder company firefighters search for lost or trapped occupants, use specialized tools to gain entry into locked buildings, and use ladders to access rooftops, where they cut holes to allow superheated fire gases and smoke to escape. They may also effect cross ventilation by opening doors and windows, taking advantage of prevailing winds or forced air from large fans that these companies carry (see Figures 4–5 and 4–6).

All firefighters are trained to accomplish specific objectives at fires (see the sidebar at the top of page 112). In communities that do not have ladder companies, engine company firefighters will perform the tasks necessary for each particular incident.

Courtesy of the Charlotte (North Carolina) Fire Department

Figure 4-5 Ladder company firefighters perform ventilation.

To maximize flexibility, some departments use quints. A quint is a piece of apparatus that performs five firefighting functions: it carries water, has a pump, is loaded with hose, carries various ground ladders, and has a hydraulically operated aerial ladder. The St. Louis, Missouri, fire department has placed quints in every fire station to reduce costs (by not having engines and ladders) and increase versatility (by having a quint respond from every station). Many departments equip their ladders with pumps, hose, and water for versatility, but these vehicles are not referred to as quints because they accompany engines and typically perform ladder company operations. Quints continue to grow in popularity, especially for departments with limited staffing or in areas where the demand for service may not justify a separate pumper (engine) and ladder company. Because they are large vehicles and are not particularly suited to medical first-responder calls, quints should be used with deliberation.

In addition to the basic engines and ladders, other ancillary fire vehicles that are housed in fire stations to respond to emergencies include HAZMAT units, rescue trucks, ambulances, battalion chief vehicles, and mobile command posts (see the sidebar on specialized equipment on the next page). In rural and suburban areas where there is no central water system, volunteer and combination departments will also have tenders (tankers) to ensure an adequate water supply for fire suppression. (For more information on fire vehicles and equipment, see Chapter 13.)

Photo by Charles R. Jennings

Figure 4-6 Specialized equipment may be necessary to deal with unusual hazards, such as this warehouse fire located adjacent to railroad tank cars.

Staffing fire companies

Having functional fire stations in the right locations is important. So, too, is having technologically up-to-date vehicles and equipment. But most important of all is having the appropriate level of staffing. Firefighters,

Fire-ground objectives

The specific objectives to be accomplished at the scene of a fire (i.e., on the fire ground) are as follows:

- *Rescue* is the highest priority and encompasses all necessary fire-ground commitments of firefighters to search for and remove victims endangered by fire.
- *Exposure protection* is the second-highest priority and encompasses all efforts to contain the fire to the building of origin if at all possible.
- *Confinement* is the objective of holding the fire to the smallest area possible, with an emphasis on preventing the fire from traversing any other avenues.
- *Extinguishment* is the process of extinguishing the flames and cooling the fuels involved to below-ignition temperature.
- *Ventilation,* performed at any point in the firefighting effort, involves the planned, systematic removal of smoke, fire gases, and heat from the involved structure.
- *Salvage,* the conservation of property, includes all actions to conserve property and contents from heat, smoke, and water.
- *Overhaul* ensures the complete extinguishment of the fire and the safety of the structure, and establishes at least a probable cause of the fire's ignition.

career or volunteer, make the difference in whether lives are saved and property is protected and conserved. The issue of firefighter staffing can be, and has been, contentious. But at bottom, staffing levels depend on the ability of the local community to fund them. Building stations and buying apparatus and equipment are not cheap, but those costs do not compare with the recurring costs of paying salaries and benefits.

The most important concept in staffing—whether for fire or nonfire emergencies—is the assembly of an effective firefighting force (see Figure 4–7). According to NFPA 1710, to increase the chance for a positive outcome, the first responding effective force (often a single company) should be on scene with a fire officer, an engineer/driver, and two firefighters to begin mitigation efforts within six minutes of receiving a call. Within ten minutes after call receipt, the effective firefighting force should be in place, consisting of at least two engines, a ladder, twelve firefighters and officers, and a battalion chief with an aide. These are the basic response criteria set forth in NFPA 1710, Standard for the Organization and Deployment of Fire Suppression Operations, Emergency Medical Operations, and Special Operations to the Public by Career Fire Departments.

Specialized equipment

To handle a wide range of emergencies effectively, many fire departments have developed specialized apparatus. Such apparatus includes heavy rescue or urban search and rescue units, water tenders and fuel tenders (which carry water or fuel to incidents), food dispensers, deicing units, mobile air compressors, hazardous materials (HAZMAT) response units, command posts, and watercraft.

HAZMAT units are designed to carry tools for those firefighters certified as HAZMAT technicians to use in controlling spills and leaks at HAZMAT emergencies. The units are often staffed like regular fire companies, with cross-trained firefighters who respond on pumpers to fires and on the HAZMAT unit to other emergencies. In some departments, HAZMAT units are staffed continuously by dedicated firefighter-HAZMAT technicians.

Mobile command posts are designed to accommodate radios, communications equipment, maps, and support supplies for incident command staff. They can range in size and sophistication from a modified van or ambulance up through custom-built units on a recreational vehicle or bus chassis. Whenever a fire or other large-scale emergency warrants its use, the mobile command post is set up to facilitate on-scene command and control of the incident. When an emergency involves other responding agencies in addition to the fire and emergency services department, their mobile command posts can be positioned near that of the fire department to ensure on-scene coordination.

Figure 4-7 Assembly of an effective firefighting force is essential to successful fire suppression.

Courtesy of the Charlotte (North Carolina) Fire Department

How best to assemble an effective firefighting force is the decision of the individual fire department and its community. There is wide consensus among fire service analysts that this effective force must be assembled in a timely fashion for effective interior structural firefighting. In 1984, the Dallas, Texas, fire department conducted a landmark study in which it measured the time necessary to complete essential fire-ground tasks with crews composed of different numbers of firefighters. Basically, the smaller the crew, the longer it took to accomplish a task and the more exhausted the firefighters were.[6]

The IAFF, the International Association of Fire Chiefs, the National Institute of Standards and Technology (NIST), Worcester Polytechnic Institute, and the Center for Public Safety Excellence are working together to reevaluate the relationship between response times, staffing levels, and fire-ground performance (see the sidebar on page 114).

Also influencing staffing decisions are regulations issued by the U.S. Occupational Safety and Health Administration in 1998. While these regulations do not specify company staffing levels, they do require that when firefighters enter an atmosphere immediately dangerous to health and life, at least two must enter together and two more must be available outside to assist if the first two require help. The "two-in/two-out" rule affects fire-ground operations in that initial fire attack decisions must consider the number of firefighters on scene as interior operations begin. Similar concerns are addressed in Canadian provincial standards.

Handling emergency calls

Rapid and accurate transmission of information is essential for any emergency response to be effective. The technology of emergency communications is evolving rapidly, and the impact on emergency service delivery is positive. Computer-aided dispatching systems tied to 911 systems identify the location of an incident and the appropriate resources to dispatch. Global positioning systems tell dispatchers where all fire resources are and help firefighters find the most effective response routes. Mobile data computers give firefighters the information they need about buildings and hazardous materials they may encounter, and automatically notify dispatchers of the firefighters' arrival at incidents. Improved radio systems enable firefighters to communicate more quickly.

Technology has become essential to emergency response, but even more essential is a properly staffed and trained dispatching center to receive calls for emergency service and dispatch the appropriate resources. No technology can replace the dispatcher who knows the community, the available resources, and the best way to send firefighters quickly to those in need. In the United States, the most common arrangement for handling emergency calls

Firefighter Safety and Deployment Study

The Firefighter Safety and Deployment Study is a multiphase effort currently under way through the work of a joint partnership of the National Institute of Standards and Technology, the International Association of Fire Fighters, the International Association of Fire Chiefs, the Commission on Fire Accreditation International, and Worcester Polytechnic Institute (see firereporting.org).[1] The goal of the study, which is funded by grants from the Assistance to Firefighters Grant program, is to create a scientifically based community risk assessment and resource deployment model and performance evaluation tools to assess how well fire departments match resources to the risk events to which they are deployed. In addition to collecting and analyzing actual incident data from more than 400 U.S. fire departments, the study conducts field experiments to assess resource deployment and response time to low-hazard residential structure fires—specifically, the fire-ground time-to-task of various crew sizes on a low-hazard, 2,000-square-foot, two-story occupancy. The experiments also assess the size of the fire and the toxicity of the atmosphere facing firefighters who enter the structure and occupants who may be trapped or unable to facilitate their own rescue.

When complete, this study will help fire departments and local government managers optimize their fire service operations so as to ensure the safety of both the firefighters and the public. Good management requires the effective and safe use of expensive, life-saving resources–fire stations, apparatus and equipment, and firefighters. Decisions about crew size and how much apparatus to deploy in a specific community depend on a number of variables, including population density, distribution of structures, age and type of construction, size of a fire station's first-due coverage area, and resources available to the jurisdiction. Effective use of available resources, in turn, requires that deployment strategies be revisited periodically and reevaluated in the context of changing community needs and local circumstances. Any system deployment changes should also consider local fire prevention and fire and life safety education efforts.

1 The complete study, *Report on Residential Fireground Field Experiments, NIST Technical Note 1661, April 2010,* can be found at nist.gov/cgi-bin//get_pdf.cgi?pub_id=904607 or iaff.org/10News/PDFs/NISTReport.pdf.

for fire protection or emergency medical response is to have the local police agency serve as the public safety answering point for 911 calls. If the fire and emergency services department has its own communications center, the 911 call will be transferred immediately from police communications for processing. In many jurisdictions, one communications center handles all calls (see Figure 4–8), with dispatchers handling fire and police calls separately. (See Chapter 16 for detailed information on communications systems and emergency response centers.)

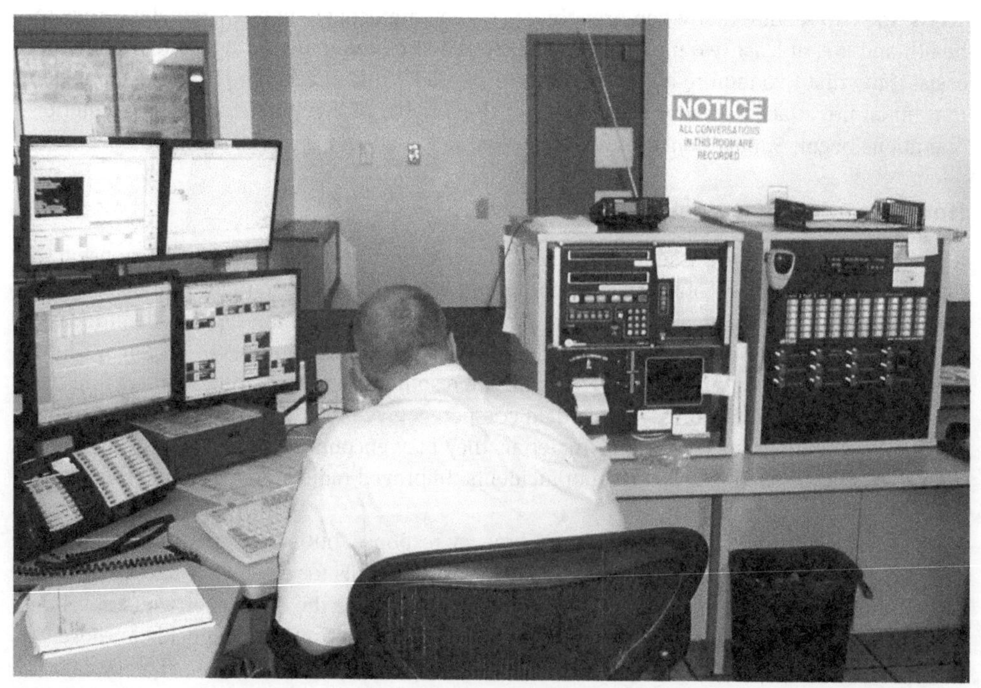

Figure 4-8 A typical communications center handles public safety services for a smaller community (the town of Andover, Massachusetts).

Photo by Charles R. Jennings

Expanding the services delivered

The role of the fire and emergency services department varies from community to community. In some jurisdictions, fire suppression is all that is required. As long as the department responds quickly and competently when called, the community is content with its service.

In other communities, department managers have identified services beyond fire suppression that firefighters, with appropriate training and equipment, can provide to contribute to the safety and well-being of the people they serve. Some services are responses to nonfire emergencies and are reactive in nature, as is fire suppression. Other services are proactive, intended to prevent emergencies and make the community a safer and more pleasant place to live and work. The more services that a fire and emergency services department can competently provide at reasonable cost, the greater the benefit to the community and the greater the improvement to public safety. As the department assumes a greater role in improving the quality of life in the community, it also gains public support.

Fire prevention and plan review

Firefighters early recognized that many fires are caused by dangerous activities and human carelessness; thus, fire prevention services were born. National fire codes were developed to eliminate building practices that contribute to catastrophic fire losses. Fire codes, as well as building, electrical, plumbing, and mechanical codes, aim to ensure that buildings are safe to occupy and easy to escape from, and provide firefighters with safe ways to deal with emergencies.

In many jurisdictions, firefighters routinely inspect most properties for fire hazards while certified fire inspectors inspect specialized and hazardous occupancies, such as chemical plants, schools, and hospitals, on a quarterly or annual basis. In other places, fire prevention inspectors are responsible for all inspections. North Carolina, for example, requires that all inspectors be trained and pass certification examinations in their areas of expertise before they may conduct inspections. Any firefighter may sit for certification as a fire code inspector and then perform inspections, and although it is difficult to provide the training for all firefighters, many departments do provide basic inspection training for all members or certify all officers in basic inspection capabilities.

Reviewing construction plans for compliance with the fire code is another important aspect of fire code enforcement. Plan review is an integral part of the building permitting process, and inspectors also check buildings as they are being constructed to ensure that construction is in compliance with approved plans.

A vital part of fire inspections is engaging business owners in the process of creating safe environments. The inspector must consider the needs of the business and present him- or herself as a friend of the business owner, explaining code requirements and assisting with compliance. Recognizing the costs of code compliance should not deter a fire and emergency services department from enforcing the code, but it should lead inspectors to promote the business value of code compliance.

The goal of fire code enforcement should always be to improve public safety. In communities undergoing urban revitalization that requires significant changes to structures in older areas, inspectors are on the cutting edge. They must be careful not to appear to obstruct progress, but they also must work proactively with developers to ensure that updates meet code and that new construction and new neighborhoods are safe. Fire departments can influence the ways in which communities are allowed to grow by insisting that safety be a part of the planning process. (See Chapter 6 for an in-depth explanation of fire prevention programming.)

Public fire and life safety education

Many fire departments, career and volunteer, are extensively involved in public fire and life safety education programs. Some of these programs are designed by fire and emergency service department educators and delivered at local schools and community events and in the news media. Fully engaged fire departments use all available means to conduct public education, including the Internet (see Figure 4–9). Public service announcements are used on radio and television to promote fire safety tips. Public access cable channels are excellent vehicles for fire departments to broadcast safety messages.

Figure 4-9 The New York City Fire Department makes safety brochures available in ten different languages; pictured is a detail from a smoking safety brochure in Korean.

Courtesy of the New York City Fire Department, "Fire Safety Information"

Many fire departments tie their safety messages to the seasons, promoting Christmas tree safety during the winter holidays and outdoor grilling safety in the summer, for example. Fire safety becomes a year-round topic for the community. (See Chapter 6 for discussion of public education programs.)

Fire investigation

Usually, firefighters have little difficulty in determining how and where fires begin. When an unattended pot on a stove catches fire or an electrical outlet shorts and ignites, fire origin and cause are obvious. When the origin and cause are not so obvious, however, a fire investigator is called. If arson is suspected, the investigator will not only determine origin and cause but also treat the scene as a crime scene, collecting evidence and working with law enforcement to identify suspects and develop a case to take to the district attorney for prosecution. (See Chapter 6 for more discussion of fire investigation programs.)

Emergency medical services

Firefighters have always rendered first aid to injured people, but in the 1970s the field of pre-hospital care developed as the third emergency service (fire, police, and emergency medical) in the United States. Many fire and emergency service departments expanded the role of firefighters to include provision of basic life support (BLS) and/or advanced life support (ALS). The models for providing emergency medical services vary widely. Some departments provide all services, including ambulance transportation, at the ALS level; others train firefighters to the EMT level and act as first responders, with another agency providing transport services (see Figure 4-10). While some governmental EMS agencies exist, many communities rely on the private sector to perform transport or some other aspect of emergency medical services. As EMS call volumes increase, many communities have turned to alternative organizational forms to provide this service.

Usually, fire departments that provide emergency medical services rely on the expertise of a medical doctor who specializes in emergency medicine and functions as both medical

Courtesy of the Charlotte (North Carolina) Fire Department

Figure 4-10 Firefighters and paramedics work together to free and treat a patient at an automobile wreck.

director, responsible for overall medical control issues, and liaison with local medical authorities. The requirements for medical supervision vary by state. Any agency providing emergency medical services should be aware of the chain of supervision for medical care and approval of protocols, equipment, and practices.

Some fire departments, although comparatively few, provide emergency medical services using personnel other than cross-trained firefighter paramedics; however, most departments use firefighters who have been trained and certified to provide BLS and ALS services. (See Chapter 5 for a discussion of fire department emergency medical services.)

Hazardous materials response

In the 1980s fire departments in the United States recognized the need for response to emergencies involving hazardous materials. Fire and emergency service departments have since become the first line of defense against and control of chemical emergencies caused by industrial accidents, illegal drug laboratories, and clandestine dumping of hazardous waste (see Figure 4–11). Departments with HAZMAT response teams work in partnership with local industry to prepare for potential HAZMAT incidents, developing mitigation as well as response plans. In many communities, the fire and emergency services department is the lead agency in planning, writing, and updating local emergency disaster plans. And with the advent of concerns about terrorism and weapons of mass destruction, HAZMAT expertise is fundamental to preparation for these events as well. This proactive role benefits both the community and the fire and emergency services department by preparing all responding agencies and hospitals to cooperate during response to a HAZMAT incident (see Chapter 2).

Technical rescue services

Technical rescue services fall into a number of categories. Perhaps the most common is the extrication of people trapped in wrecked vehicles. High-angle rescue is the rescue of people trapped in high places—on the sides of buildings, for example. Swift-water rescue involves plucking people from rapidly moving water, such as rivers in flood conditions. Urban search and rescue, or USAR, is the rescue of people trapped in collapsed buildings or in situations where their exact location is unknown.

Normally, teams of firefighters are given specialized training to perform technical rescues. In some communities, fire companies with rescue training and equipment are routinely on

Figure 4-11 Firefighters put down foam at the scene of a tanker rollover.

Courtesy of the Charlotte (North Carolina) Fire Department

duty; in others, a team of on- and off-duty firefighters is assembled to respond to calls for service. The rise of large-scale terrorism has highlighted the need for departments to prepare for such events, and technical rescue is a fundamental component of that preparation.

Aircraft rescue and firefighting

Aircraft rescue and firefighting (ARFF) is the discipline of response to aircraft emergencies (see Figure 4–12). Aircraft crashes are complex incidents involving fire, HAZMAT spills, extrication and rescue, and trauma and death; and ARFF firefighters receive highly specialized and

Figure 4-12 A European rescue firefighting vehicle on display at Interschutz, Hannover, Germany, June 2005.

Photo by Sally Young

technical training to respond to these situations. The FAA requires that ARFF personnel be on duty at commercial airports before aircraft can take off or land. They may be employees of the local fire department or of the airport itself, or they may be contract employees.

Community partner and customer-oriented services

Firefighters are members of the communities they serve, and fire stations, as public facilities, belong to the people they serve. Many fire departments encourage their firefighters to be active participants in their communities and to open their fire stations to community events, such as blood pressure checks and safety inspections for child car seats. Fire stations also serve as polling places for elections and host voter registration, and they are distribution points for residential smoke detectors. Some communities use standardized signage to let children and their parents know that the fire station is a safe place for a child who needs help (see the sidebar below).

The use of fire stations and firefighters for community services and the forging of partnerships are becoming more common as local government managers and fire chiefs realize the convenience of an existing network of fire stations located throughout a community. The community-focused approach has had a pervasive, positive impact on the fire service, leading firefighters to see members of the public as "customers" rather than "victims."

Customer service involves positive engagement with the person being served so that the person's needs are discovered and cared for. For example, a medically stable patient may be transported to the hospital of his or her health care provider, even if it is not the nearest hospital. The result is greater user satisfaction for the patient and the hospital, as time and money are saved by eliminating the need for costly hospital transfers (see Chapter 5).

Other customer-related programs cover all aspects of what fire and emergency service departments do. Pamphlets aimed at preventing fires and injuries outline home and business

Safe Place program

Some local fire and emergency service departments have joined with youth shelters to collaborate with school districts, police departments, businesses, parents, and community members to establish the Safe Place program. Participants in the program accept responsibility for the well-being of young people living in their communities.

A "safe place" is a fire station, business, public building, police station, or other place where a young person can receive support and assistance during a crisis. Safe Place locations are marked with a distinctive diamond-shaped yellow sign or decal for easy identification.

Participating fire departments display the Safe Place sign at each fire station and ensure that all personnel know how to contact the sponsoring youth shelter for the proper assistance. Because of the fire station's visibility in the community, it can be the first stop for a child who needs to escape from a potentially violent situation or deal with some other crisis. If the firefighters are out of the station, young people can easily access emergency telephones installed outside the station to call the Safe Place number or to contact dispatchers.

Firefighters provide assistance to children by

1. Placing their fire company out of service while providing assistance
2. Telephoning the Safe Place number to connect with professional help and transportation for the youth
3. Reassuring frightened, lost, or endangered children
4. Initiating response of emergency medical personnel for children who have medical problems or calling appropriate law enforcement authorities for immediate safety concerns
5. Assisting children who fear that they will imminently become victims of crime, intimidation, or abuse
6. Reporting crimes to law enforcement officials and providing descriptions of vehicles and suspects when possible.

Source: Adapted from information provided by the National Safe Place Office, YMCA National Safe Place, Louisville, Kentucky, safeplaceservices.org.

fire safety tips. Many fire departments have relationships with the American Red Cross and the Salvation Army, among other charitable agencies, so that they can call for assistance for people who need it. They also provide detailed guidance to people who have experienced fires, enabling them to take immediate steps to limit further damage, preserve unaffected possessions, establish security, and initiate recovery efforts.

Gone forever are the days when a fire and emergency services department, career or volunteer, only suppressed fires. Firefighters, fire chiefs, local government managers, elected officials, and the citizens they serve have all seen how much a proactive, community-based, customer-oriented department can accomplish when it looks beyond fighting fires and considers the range of services that it delivers to the community.

Raising revenue and controlling costs

Fire and emergency protection is financially beneficial to a community, whether it is provided by a local fire and emergency services department or through a multijurisdictional arrangement. Although fire and emergency services are not exempt from the budget pressures that affect all local government services, the fire department, unlike many other services, has some options for both raising revenue and controlling costs.

Raising revenue

Career and combination fire departments in the United States are generally supported by local taxes. Although there is usually no charge for a basic emergency response, some jurisdictions levy fees for extraordinary service provided by their fire departments; some assess fees for permits for welding, firework stands, firework shows, oil wells, or other activities; some require reimbursement for HAZMAT responses; some charge for plan reviews, inspections, and reinspections; and many charge for repeat fire code violations that have not been corrected within reasonable times. Such revenue usually flows into the local government's general operating fund.

In communities where the fire and emergency service departments provide ambulance service, a fee is usually charged for transportation to a hospital and for medical supplies used for the patient's care. Many of these charges are paid by third-party providers of health care insurance or by Medicare or Medicaid. Often transportation services are provided to those who cannot afford the fee or do not have insurance. When costs exceed income for emergency medical and transportation services, the local government will face budgetary challenges. To generate a more predictable revenue stream, some communities have instituted ambulance subscription fee programs; such programs enlarge the number of payers by encouraging all citizens to pay a small subscription fee that will ensure them a "free" ambulance ride to the hospital, should they need one during the subscription year. Residents who do not subscribe and visitors to the community pay a higher ambulance transport fee if they require the service. To make the subscription system work, a fire and emergency services department must evaluate the actual cost of ambulance transport.

From the basic fire suppression and prevention services to specialized fire and rescue programs, communities benefit from fire department services. Quality of life and community safety are closely related, so the more ways that a fire and emergency services department serves its residents, especially when user fees generate revenue, the greater the returns.

Controlling costs

As personnel account for the largest share of the budget in career and many combination departments, efforts to obtain greater efficiency in the use of personnel can help to control costs. Of course, as in all sectors of government employment, benefit and pension costs are a major concern.

Seeking to control costs, particularly on high-value items such as fire apparatus, fire hose, or personal protective equipment, some fire departments have cooperated to form joint purchasing consortia. Similar consortia have achieved control over costs for joint services such as firefighter recruit testing, basic firefighter training, and dispatching services. Where response

A shared training facility

The Glendale Regional Public Safety Training Center in Arizona is the product of an intergovernmental agreement among the cities of Avondale, Glendale, Peoria, and Surprise and the Maricopa County Community College District. Completed in 2007, the center, which is tasked with delivering fair, objective training related to job requirements, is built on sixty-seven acres and comprises over 94,000 square feet of space, including

- Seven classrooms
- A large lecture hall
- A five-story fire training tower
- A driving track with a 75,000-square-foot skid pad
- A physical fitness workout room
- A physical agility test room
- A law enforcement firing range and classroom.

Among the numerous amenities on the site are a prop area, which includes anchor points for technical rescue training; a single-family home simulator; natural gas prop training; a railroad tanker; a confined space simulator; an auto extrication area; a flashover simulator; and a simulated fire station with a "dirty" classroom.

Some of the center's facilities are used by fire and emergency services as well as by law enforcement and the private sector. The center is also used by the Maricopa County Community College's public safety training programs. The center's governance calls for each participating jurisdiction to pay according to its share of use of the facilities.

The flexible management structure within the partnership agreement allows for administrative and fiscal review of the center's financing and operation. An executive board approves capital plans, annual operating budgets, and legal actions. The center's director is appointed by the executive board and evaluated by the board and participating fire chiefs.

Scheduling for the center allows a maximum of 80 percent coverage for scheduled classes, leaving 20 percent capacity for discretionary purposes. There is a priority established for access to the facility, with emphasis on basic and advanced training for participating agencies. The lowest priority is for private agencies with public safety-related training needs.

Source: Summarized from Chris DeChant and Jim Higgins, "Study Group," *Fire Chief*, December 1, 2007, firechief.com/training/ar/arizona-departments-public-safety-training-facility/; see also goglendaleaz.com/government/fire_protection.html (both accessed May 25, 2010).

areas in different communities can be served from a common station, some departments have also entered into arrangements to share such facilities as vehicle maintenance shops, training centers, and even fire stations.

Another practice that benefits both service recipient and taxpayer is the creation of automatic aid agreements between fire departments, in which the departments agree to dispatch the closest unit to an emergency, regardless of the jurisdiction in which the emergency occurs. Such arrangements have to be equally advantageous for both parties and usually require prior formal approval of the governing body of each locality. When automatic aid is in effect, a fire and emergency services department may be able to avoid the cost of an additional fire station or fire company with the associated firefighters.

In the Washington, D.C., metropolitan area, suburban jurisdictions use the concept of automatic aid—for example, dispatching apparatus from more than one jurisdiction on the initial alarm—and closest station response to deliver services more effectively. Because the closest station is selected to respond, a call may be answered exclusively with units from a neighboring jurisdiction. This practice has evolved into common policies, procedures, and radio designations in many operational areas.

Automatic aid agreements are also growing in popularity in volunteer and combination departments, where response levels, particularly at certain times of the day, are not sufficient to produce a timely response from an effective firefighting force. These agreements are helping to deliver a higher level of service without adding considerably to costs.

Organizational changes, including consolidation and shared services, are the most effective way to reduce the overall costs of fire protection. Per capita costs can often be reduced by providing services to a larger population base. Achieving such efficiencies requires the leadership of fire chiefs and the support of elected officials.

The Assistance to Firefighters Grant program, administered by the U.S. Fire Administration, has had a positive impact on the nation's fire service. For volunteer and combination departments, it provides an opportunity to win funding for needed apparatus, equipment, and even facilities and staffing. Departments that develop grant-writing expertise can use grants to provide significant upgrades to their response capabilities at little or no cost to their communities. Truly innovative departments of any size can leverage this expertise by seeking out local foundations that may be interested in providing funds for needs that cannot be met through normal budget processes.

New challenges for a new millennium

Whatever the approach to providing fire protection and emergency medical services, the local government manager, fire chief, and elected officials face an array of challenges. On the one hand, the need for properly trained firefighters; dependable tools, equipment, and apparatus; and adequate infrastructure of stations and communication capabilities will always place economic demands on the community. On the other hand, a deficiency in any of these critical elements will put human life and valuable property at greater risk in case of fire, accident, illness, or other emergency.

Rapid changes in technology and societal norms and expectations will affect how fire and emergency service departments conduct their business. Among the high priorities for fire and local government managers are adapting to changes in the health care system, preparing for natural and man-made disasters, using technology effectively and efficiently, and ensuring diversity and fairness in hiring and promotions—all while trying to control costs and maintain basic fire and emergency services. The need for fire and emergency service providers to take an incisive look at their operations has never been greater.

Notes

1. Michael J. Karter Jr. and Gary P. Stein, *U.S. Fire Department Profile through 2009* (Quincy, Mass.: National Fire Protection Association, October 2010), ii and 17, firecompany4.com/wp-content/uploads/2010/07/National-Volunteer-Firefighters-Profile-2009.pdf.
2. Pasadena Volunteer Fire Department, pasadenavfd.com/.
3. Saint Michael's Fire & Rescue, www2.smcvt.edu/firerescue/.
4. International Association of Fire Fighters and International Association of Fire Chiefs, *Police and Fire Consolidation: An Ineffective Use of Resources* (Washington, D.C., and Fairfax, Va., n.d.), iaff.org/09News/PDFs/PSOSystems.pdf.
5. Evelina R. Moulder, "Police and Fire Personnel, Salaries, and Expenditures for 2009," in *The Municipal Year Book 2010* (Washington, D.C.: ICMA, 2010), Table 3–17.
6. McManis Associates and John T. O'Hagan and Associates, "Dallas Fire Department Staffing Level Study," June 1984.

CHAPTER 5

Emergency Medical Services

Jennie L. Collins

This chapter provides an understanding of

- The role of emergency medical services in the continuum of patient care
- The fundamental infrastructure needs in an emergency medical service (EMS) delivery agency
- The various deployment models used in EMS delivery agencies
- The impact that external factors at the national, state, and regional levels have on EMS delivery agencies
- The importance of establishing and maintaining collaborative relationships with other health care system providers.

Emergency medical services function at the crossroads of three different realms: public safety, health care, and public health. Emergency medical service (EMS) delivery agencies are diverse and dynamic, often born out of local needs, influenced by regional coordination, and affected by state regulations. Direction and oversight of this multidimensional activity demand attention to operational, clinical, educational, and administrative needs. There is tremendous variability across the nation's EMS delivery agencies, as this chapter will show.

History of emergency medical services

While the roots of prehospital care may not run deep, emergency medical services have grown and flourished over the last half century. The nation's first organized rescue squad was created in 1928 in Roanoke, Virginia. Over the next couple of decades, a few hospitals located in large cities began to offer ambulance services but struggled with staffing shortages as military conflicts overseas affected workforce availability. Many funeral homes operated their vehicles as hearses or ambulances, depending on the need.

After World War II, civilian rescue squads began to develop, but their ambulances lacked equipment, and there were no training programs or standards for service. It was not until the 1960s that the modern EMS industry began to emerge. In 1966 the National Academy of Sciences published *Accidental Death and Disability: The Neglected Disease of Modern Society*,[1] which brought attention to the need to address the traffic-related injuries and deaths that were occurring on the nation's highways (Figure 5–1). The report highlighted deficits in training, the inadequate equipping of ambulances, and the lack of a coordinated system for the care of the injured.

As a result of the report's recommendations, President Lyndon Johnson signed into law the National Traffic and Motor Vehicle Safety Act of 1966. While this act focused on highway accident victims, it became the cornerstone legislation for EMS system development. Another

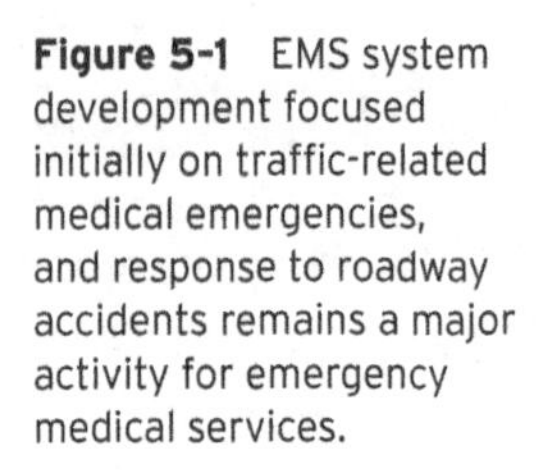

Figure 5-1 EMS system development focused initially on traffic-related medical emergencies, and response to roadway accidents remains a major activity for emergency medical services.

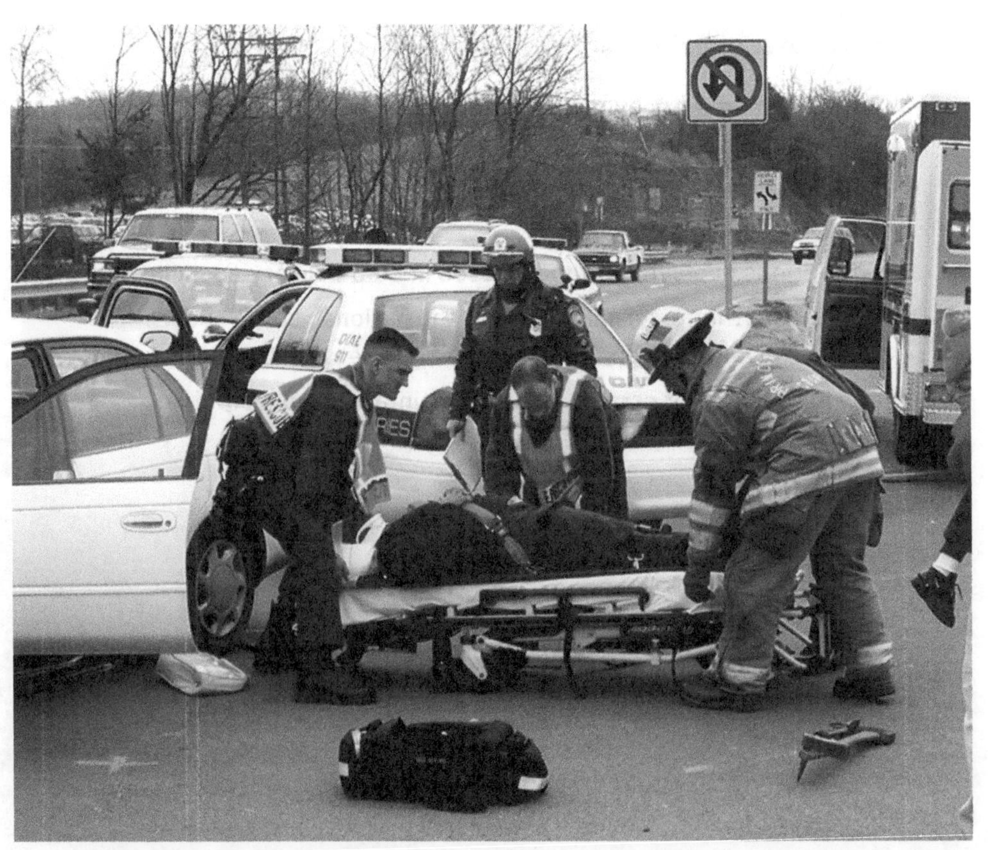

Courtesy of Prince William County (Virginia) Department of Fire and Rescue

Bruce Evans, EMS chief, city of North Las Vegas, assisted in the initial planning and writing of this chapter.

act established the U.S. Department of Transportation, which was given the responsibility to develop and implement EMS education and training standards. The National Highway Safety Bureau, the predecessor of the National Highway Traffic Safety Administration (NHTSA), was created in the following year.

The National Registry of Emergency Medical Technicians (NREMT), created in 1970, provided a national certification agency for EMS providers. However, EMS systems developed as a patchwork of agencies and support systems across the nation. Because of inadequate funding at all levels of government, system development was inconsistent. Then a television show titled *Emergency!*, about Los Angeles County Fire Department's paramedics, debuted in 1972; becoming an instant hit, the program ran for five years and set the bar for widespread public expectations of community EMS capabilities. Congress passed the EMS Systems Act of 1973, creating a federal grant program for the development of regional EMS systems and, for the first time, defining the components of an EMS system:

- Staffing
- Training
- Communications
- Transportation
- Facilities
- Critical care units
- Public safety agencies
- Consumer participation
- Access to care
- Patient transfer
- Coordinated patient record keeping
- Public information and education
- Review and evaluation
- Disaster plan
- Mutual aid.[2]

While national EMS organizations and professional associations, including several physician groups, grew in the 1980s, federal funding for emergency medical services declined. State oversight over regional and local EMS agency and system development varied, and the growth of local EMS agencies was strongly influenced by local needs, demographics (rural, suburban, urban), and resource availability.

In the 1990s, NHTSA, along with the Health Resources and Services Administration, released another landmark publication, *Emergency Medical Services Agenda for the Future*, which articulates a vision of an integrated EMS and health care system.[3] NHTSA followed up that publication with implementation guides. One of these, the *Emergency Medical Services Education Agenda for the Future: A Systems Approach*, released in 2000, contains five major components developed to achieve national consistency among entry-level EMS providers.[4] (In this chapter, the term *provider* refers to frontline personnel who provide hands-on emergency medical services.) The five components are the National EMS Core Content, National EMS Scope of Practice Model, National EMS Education Standards, National EMS Certification, and National EMS Education Program Accreditation.

Despite all these national efforts, emergency medical services continue to be underfunded and fragmented. In 2006, the Institute of Medicine (IOM) published a report titled *Emergency Medical Services at the Crossroads*, which dissected a variety of issues hampering the delivery of emergency medical services and the maturation of the nation's EMS system.[5] The fundamental issues at the national level—insufficient coordination, disparity in response times, uncertain quality of care, lack of readiness for disasters, divided professional identity, and limited evidence base—were found to have the same proportional impacts at the local level.

Mandates for local emergency medical services

While there have been federal initiatives to improve emergency medical services across the nation, there are no federal mandates that require localities to deliver these services. Local emergency medical service (EMS) systems are typically influenced by federal initiatives and state legislation. In the majority of states, state law defines the extent and operation of these local systems. As a result, EMS systems typically develop and operate to suit local needs, and service delivery remains variable and highly fragmented.

EMS stakeholders from the early years could probably not envision the diversity of barriers (real or perceived) or the challenges and opportunities that would confront the EMS system during its relatively short history and rapid growth. The traditional paradigm of EMS delivery—reacting to individual patient needs at the time of an emergency—is challenged now by a proactive, community health care, service-based model.

Overview of emergency medical services

No two EMS agencies are exactly alike. Local systems are designed to manage a wide spectrum of community needs. Some employ only volunteers, some have only career personnel, and some have a combination of career and volunteer personnel.

Community expectations

Today, emergency medical services are available to virtually every citizen across the nation who dials 911 from any telephone. Only small, isolated pockets of the country lack 911 coverage. Citizens expect to be able to report an illness or injury and receive emergency medical care for their specific need. Through public education efforts, media depiction of the industry, and the actual witnessing of EMS care being delivered, citizens have high expectations that their calls will be met with rapid and appropriate response and that lives can be saved.

However, not all EMS agencies are equipped or trained to handle every medical situation that arises. Most focus on serious medical or trauma patients where intervention is time critical, even though the majority of EMS patients have relatively minor complaints that do not require immediate intervention. EMS agencies will deliver services to special-needs populations, such as the very young and the elderly, bariatric (severely obese) patients, and patients in home health care settings with specialized life-preserving equipment (e.g., ventilators or implanted cardiac

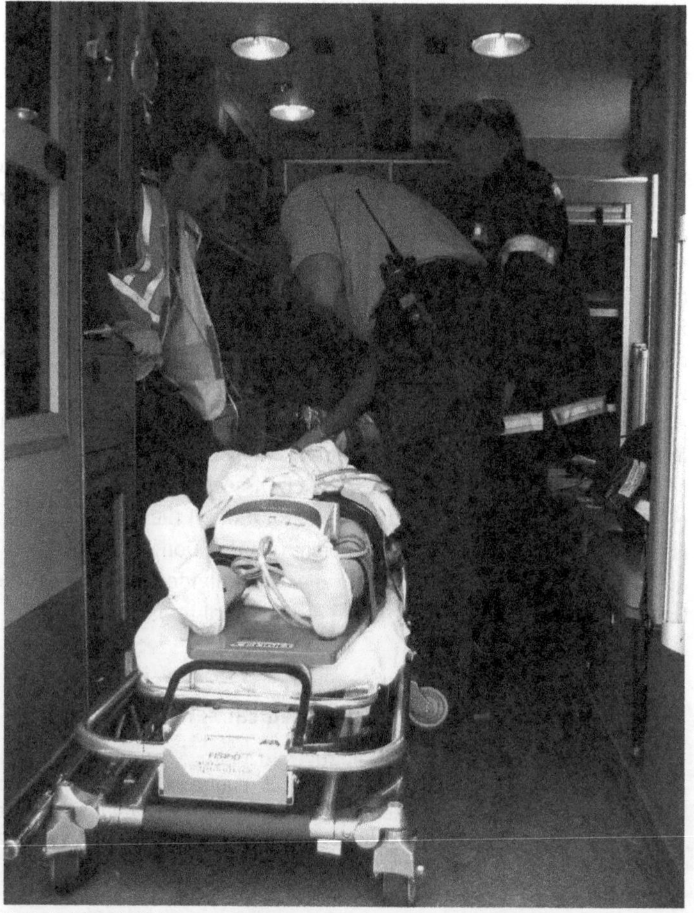

Figure 5-2 Reducing mortality associated with cardiac arrest events depends on early access to EMS care.

Photo by Adam K. Thiel

assist devices). Although typically infrequent, special-needs service requests present significant challenges that require intensive and focused training for providers. EMS systems that serve ethnically diverse communities must address cultural and language barriers.

Continuum of care

Emergency medical services entail a coordinated arrangement of personnel, equipment, and facilities organized to respond to any type of medical emergency. In the delivery of these services, public safety, health care, and public health overlap. Stakeholders include providers who are directly involved in delivering emergency medical services, EMS agency leaders, governmental and private entities, physicians in multiple specialties, nurses, hospitals, educators, elected officials, and numerous professional organizations and associations. Beginning with the agency's public education and prevention efforts and continuing through the call for service, the response to the call for service, the movement of the patient to a medical facility, and subsequent transport back home or to an extended care facility, the entire EMS system is integral to a patient's continuum of care.

One important element of the continuum of care is what is known as the "chain of survival," a series of actions with the shared goal of reducing mortality associated with cardiac arrest events (Figure 5–2). The chain of survival components are early recognition of symptoms (public education), early access (911), bystander care (cardiopulmonary resuscitation [CPR]), early defibrillation, and early access to advanced life support (ALS).

Agency types

Most EMS agencies develop and are organized to fit local needs and available resources. In developing, organizing, and maintaining an EMS agency, a multidimensional approach and consideration of numerous variables are needed. Managers must objectively identify the community's needs and vision, the resources available, the infrastructure components that exist or can be put into place, and system stakeholders.

The various delivery models should be examined with an understanding that they are not "cookie-cutter" pieces that can easily transfer from one locality to another. The needs in urban areas are different from those in rural areas. There is much debate on what is required for system effectiveness and what constitutes best practices. For many localities, it may be best to establish a vision and then follow a building-block approach, using a consistent plan-implement-evaluate-revise methodology.

Provider roles

One of the variables to consider when organizing EMS delivery is the role of EMS providers—those personnel (whether volunteer or career) who provide hands-on medical services to patients.

Single-role providers provide only emergency medical services. Unlike dual- or multiple-role providers, they are not cross-trained to provide any other services, such as firefighting or

Local emergency medical service systems

When a local government decides to provide emergency medical services, agency leaders, elected officials, and citizens need to express their expectations for service delivery. According to the Institute of Medicine, health care delivery must be safe, effective, patient centered, timely, efficient, and equitable.[1] Using a building-block approach, the locality may first address safety by initiating emergency medical services with volunteer resources operating on call. In time, through system monitoring, if the locality finds that there is too much variability and a lack of continuity in staffing, the plan may need to be adjusted, with career personnel integrated into the service model to ensure sustainable and consistent staffing. If provider fatigue is identified as an issue, alternative shift schedules may be considered as potential solutions. Localities will often find that early solutions to their service delivery model will be challenged and may need to be modified as the environment, expectations, and needs change.

1 Institute of Medicine, Committee on the Future of Emergency Care in the United States Health Agency, *Emergency Medical Services at the Crossroads* (Washington, D.C.: National Academies Press, 2007).

technical rescue. Factors to be considered in deciding whether to use single- or multiple-role providers are as follows:

- *Recruitment and retention:* Work conditions (hours, pay, benefits, etc.), training requirements, and advancement opportunities all affect recruitment and retention. Some potential and existing EMS providers, in both the volunteer and the career workforces, do not want to become cross-trained in other service delivery skills. Others *do* want a dual role and opportunities to perform other skills (e.g., firefighting). Dual-role organizations can give providers the opportunity to transition out of EMS positions to other roles in order to move up in the agency's hierarchy. Although transition to other roles won't appeal to all EMS providers, it may help others avoid burnout.
- *Medical screening:* If National Fire Protection Association (NFPA) standards are voluntarily adopted by the authority having jurisdiction, they are applicable to those EMS providers who are cross-trained as firefighters. However, there are no national industry standards for occupational medical programs for single-role EMS providers, and this can create inequity in the health, safety, and welfare of first responders.
- *Salary and Fair Labor Standards Act (FLSA) impacts:* Typically, career personnel who have cross-trained as firefighters have higher pay than single-role, EMS-only career providers. Additionally, cross-trained career providers may fall into exempt categories of FLSA that permit them to work more hours than single-role EMS providers before triggering overtime compensation.
- *Existing infrastructure:* Preexisting infrastructure such as emergency personnel, facilities, and vehicles will influence the decision to pursue a dual-role deployment model. For example, a fire station may have space for an ambulance as well as for existing firefighters who can be cross-trained as EMS providers.

The cumulative effects of workplace stress, shifts, assignment locations, and exposure to safety threats all must be considered when evaluating deployment models. Regardless of the model chosen, the safety, health, and welfare of the provider must be the highest priority.

It is difficult to compare the relative effectiveness and efficiency of the various agency types and delivery models because of deficiencies in objective and consistent performance measures and data. As mentioned, most agencies reflect what the community can support according to local perceptions of quality care delivery. The most common types of agencies delivering emergency medical services across the United States are described below. Single- and multiple-role providers can be found in any of these types.

Fire-based agencies

Approximately 60 percent of the nation's fire departments integrate emergency medical services into the operations of the fire department.[6] In fire-based EMS agencies, fire personnel are generally cross-trained as emergency medical technicians (EMTs) or paramedics. Fire station facilities are typically located strategically throughout a community, and co-locating EMS resources can be an efficient and logical approach to providing adequate coverage.

The organizational structure of fire-based EMS agencies varies: some departments maintain their emergency medical services in a separate division and command structure; others fully integrate all aspects of their medical services and fire operations throughout the department's hierarchy.

Third-service agencies

Rather than incorporate EMS capabilities into their fire departments, some localities maintain a separate EMS division, which cooperates with the fire and law enforcement public safety agencies. Some of these local governments have a fire agency, a law enforcement agency, and an EMS agency (third service). Other local governments, such as Charleston County, South Carolina, and Wake County, North Carolina, contract with a private entity to be the third-service provider. For many of these localities, the fire department provides the immediate response (first responders) and relies on the separate EMS agency to provide patient transport.

State emergency medical service agencies

Each state and territory in the United States has a lead emergency medical service (EMS) agency. This agency is usually part of the state health department, but in some states it is part of the public safety department or is an independent state agency.

State EMS agencies are responsible for the overall planning, coordination, and regulation of the state's EMS system as well as for licensing or certifying EMS providers. These agencies typically, but not universally,

- Serve as the lead agency for statewide trauma systems or other specialty care systems
- Collect data from local EMS agencies, hospitals, and trauma centers and monitor system performance and outcome
- Promulgate statewide medical protocols for EMS providers, or otherwise establish the scope of EMS practice within the state
- Operate or coordinate a statewide communications system that connects EMS providers in the field with hospitals as well as with trauma and specialty centers
- Coordinate the distribution of federal EMS grants or administer state EMS grant programs
- Plan for and coordinate the medical response to disasters and mass casualty incidents and, since September 11, 2001, homeland security medical initiatives
- Administer or coordinate regional EMS programs.

Source: National Association of State EMS Officials, nasemsd.org/About/StateEMSAgencies/.

Public utility agencies Public utility agencies, often referred to as quasi-governmental agencies, are the product of a specific arrangement between a local government and another entity to provide EMS response to a community. In this situation, the local government maintains overall authority for the emergency medical services and may own the physical infrastructure (e.g., ambulances and equipment), but it contracts with the outside entity to provide the EMS personnel.

Examples of public utility models include MedStar, which operates ALS services in Fort Worth and surrounding cities in Texas, and the Richmond Ambulance Authority, which provides EMS response to the Richmond, Virginia, area. The MedStar agency covers a 421-square-mile area with more than 880,000 residents. Its fleet of fifty-four ambulances responds to about 100,000 emergency calls a year. The Richmond Ambulance Authority covers 63 square miles with a population of more than 200,000, and its fleet of thirty ambulances responds to over 50,000 calls annually.

Private agencies Private EMS agencies may be locally owned, or they may be operated by a national company in either a for-profit or not-for-profit business model. They contract with federal, state, and local governmental units, as well as with private companies and individuals, to provide services in both nonemergent and emergent settings. For example, a private EMS agency might offer emergency response services as well as transportation services to nonambulatory individuals who need to get to medical appointments or move between medical facilities (e.g., from hospital discharge to a rehabilitation facility). Some localities may not offer nonemergent services, leaving this market to private agencies in the area. Localities may also find it attractive to contract for their EMS delivery needs with a private EMS agency instead of investing in developing their own resources.

If a local government contracts with a private agency, it can establish specific measures, such as response time parameters, that the contractor must meet, and can make the contractor responsible for providing the amount of resources required to meet the performance measures. Another option is for the locality to require the contractor to provide a set amount of resources placed at specified locations—for example, ten ambulances distributed among the locality's fire stations.

As part of any contractual arrangement, the locality will need to specify the party responsible for providing the vehicles (e.g., ambulances), medical direction, supervision, and oversight of personnel, training, patient billing, and financial administration.

Hospital-based agencies Hospital-based EMS agencies operate under the oversight of a hospital to provide EMS coverage either independently or cooperatively with public services (e.g., the fire department). Depending on the hospital's agreement with the local government and the evolution of the service (e.g., as a stand-alone service or in cooperation with the local government), the hospital-based resources can be dispatched by the locality's 911 center, or calls can be transferred from the 911 center to a secondary dispatch center for the hospital-based EMS agency. As is the case for any agency type, optimum resource placement will be influenced by the locality's size, geography, traffic patterns, and service needs. Location at the hospital's facility alone may not be adequate. The local government may need to contract with multiple hospital-based services or develop a cooperative agreement to co-locate hospital resources in public facilities to ensure adequate service-area coverage.

Scope of services

Today's EMS systems are a community's safety net for emergency care in response to an array of issues.

Many local government EMS agencies take an "all-hazards" approach, meaning that the agency will respond to all types of incidents. While the all-hazards approach requires specialized skills and training for providers, it does make efficient use of personnel resources for multiple roles. Examples of an all-hazards scope of services are

- Hazardous materials response
- Law enforcement EMS tactical integration
- Urban search and rescue
- Mass gatherings
- Wildland firefighting
- Rural/frontier public health.

In many places, no single agency can respond to all these types of events, and the EMS agency must work in concert with other public safety agencies to provide effective service. See the "Challenges" section near the end of this chapter for descriptions of these special services. Below is an overview of common functions that most EMS agencies perform on a daily basis.

Emergency medical dispatch

The entry point into an EMS system is the call to 911 for help. Public safety answering points (PSAPs) are local government–operated 911 centers. Primary PSAPs take all types of emergency calls (medical service, fire, or law enforcement) and dispatch resources to respond. In some primary PSAPs, personnel are crossed-trained to handle all types of calls; in others, incoming calls are triaged to separate sections or to secondary PSAPs for handling according to their nature and urgency.

Secondary PSAPs take subsets of calls (e.g., medical, fire) transferred from a primary PSAP for further questioning and resource dispatch. Typically, PSAPs are operated by the locality's fire or law enforcement entity or may be jointly controlled by those organizations.

It is important to realize that first responders may not be the first resource handling a medical emergency. Personnel trained in emergency medical dispatch (EMD) can begin life-saving procedures as soon as phone contact is made with the patient or with those at the patient's side.

All PSAPs need to integrate an EMD program into their operations. EMD programs, which are scripted protocols for dispatchers and may use flip cards or be part of the center's computer system, have three major components:

- *Answering and triage of incoming emergency calls:* The call taker identifies the nature of the emergency call as well as the level and type of resources needed in response. Included in this step is the determination of how responding resources should travel to the scene—whether using emergency driving (lights and sirens) or normal driving.
- *Provision of prearrival instructions:* The PSAP should use a systematic process for questioning the caller about the emergency and providing instructions for medical intervention (e.g., for hemorrhage control, childbirth, CPR) to be performed prior to the arrival of emergency responders. It is vital that there be a seamless transition between prearrival instructions and EMS expectations and protocols.

Dynamic deployment: Richmond Ambulance Authority

The Richmond Ambulance Authority (Virginia) uses sophisticated software programs to analyze emergency incident volume by hour of the day and day of the week, and it places ambulances in locations predicted to optimize response times for the expected incoming emergency calls. In addition to predicting the locations of future emergency incidents, the computerized algorithms guide the redeployment of available resources to ensure that the system efficiently maintains desired service levels during periods of emergency response.

- *Quality improvement activities:* Once processes are implemented, the PSAP must perform oversight, coordination, and continuous monitoring to ensure that program information is accurate and compliance is maintained.

An EMS agency can choose one of numerous commercial EMD programs or develop its own. An EMD program requires the active involvement of a medical director, most often the EMS agency's medical director.

Prehospital service

Two broad EMS response levels are found in most localities: basic life support (BLS) and advanced life support (ALS). BLS units are equipped to provide initial patient care with such items as oxygen, bandaging materials, splinting devices, and automated external defibrillators and are staffed by basic-level certified EMS providers. ALS units are equipped with such additional patient care items as medications, intravenous fluids, advanced airway devices, and cardiac monitors capable of defibrillation, cardioversion, 12-lead electrocardiography, and transcutaneous pacing and are staffed by highly trained and certified EMS providers.

Single-tier and tiered EMS agencies An EMS agency is considered single tier if it provides the same level of service regardless of the nature of the request. Single-tier agencies may be all BLS or all ALS.

A tiered EMS agency provides different levels of response. For example, BLS-certified firefighters may provide first response and ALS ambulances may provide patient transports, or vice versa. EMD call triage for determining the level and type of resources required for dispatch is an especially critical component for a tiered agency in order to ensure that the resources sent are matched to the caller's needs.

Fixed and dynamic deployment EMS response vehicles can either be deployed from established locations or moved to posts in accordance with expected call volume. These two deployment models are termed "fixed" and "dynamic." Fixed deployment usually means housing EMS resources at fire or EMS stations, which are strategically located to provide response coverage across a community. Many fixed deployment systems include the backfilling of resources that are committed to emergency incidents when systemwide resource levels drop below levels necessary for expected incident demand. Localities may also use "flex" units that are deployed only during expected peak demand periods.

Dynamic deployment (see sidebar above) means that resources are posted to various locations within a geographic area on the basis of retrospective analysis of emergency call–volume data, which are used to predict where emergency calls are most likely to occur in the future. For example, ambulances may be parked along streets or in parking lots, and posting sites may change during the day according to incident trend analysis or real-time factors such as major traffic disruptions or weather.

Operational medical director

EMS providers are certified or licensed by the state EMS office. However, that certification or licensure does not authorize the EMS provider to use his or her skills without being supervised by a qualified physician. Supervising EMS providers is the role of the agency's operational medical director (OMD). The OMD also works with the agency's leadership to set policies and procedures related to medical care, to provide oversight of all activities related to patient care, and to ensure that EMS providers are properly credentialed and operate within their scope of practice.

In the clinical setting, EMS providers have dual accountability: to the agency's chain-of-command structure as well as to the OMD. For effective, efficient, and cohesive operations, the agency's leadership and OMD must collaborate and work cooperatively. The OMD is the ultimate authority for the EMS agency's clinical patient care and for determining the appropriateness of EMS providers' clinical practice activities.

All states require EMS agencies that provide ALS services to have an OMD. However, not all states require medical director oversight for BLS agencies. EMS agency leaders must research their individual state's requirements on this issue.

Medical director qualifications

All states require that OMDs have an unrestricted state license to practice medicine or osteopathy. Typically, the state's EMS office requires that OMDs complete a training course designed to orient them to their responsibilities and level of authority. If the OMD is Board Certified in Emergency Medicine, the completion of the state's training program for medical directors may be the only additional requirement necessary for endorsement as an OMD. If the physician is not Board Certified in Emergency Medicine, he or she may be required to take training to obtain certification in Advanced Cardiac Life Support, Advanced Trauma Life Support, and Pediatric Advanced Life Support. The local government should contact the state EMS office for its specific training and continuing education requirements for medical directors.

The following professional associations publish materials regarding OMD qualifications and position descriptions on their websites:

- National Association of EMS Physicians (NAEMSP), naemsp.org
- National Association of State EMS Officials (NASEMSO), nasemso.org
- American College of Emergency Physicians (ACEP), acep.org.

Forms of agreements

The most typical types of affiliation between a local EMS agency and its OMD are the following:

- *Employer/employee arrangement:* The OMD may become an employee of the EMS agency. Depending on the size and expectations of the EMS agency, the OMD may be hired as either a full-time or a part-time employee. Compensation varies. Prospective OMDs may like this form of relationship if a benefit package is offered and payroll deductions (e.g., taxes) are automatically withdrawn. Potential disadvantages for the OMD may be restrictions on political advocacy without prior employer approval. Also, while differences over the direction of the organization may not diminish the OMD's authority, they may affect the supervisor-subordinate hierarchical relationship.
- *Contract:* An agency may contract with a physician to be its OMD. The contract must identify the director's role and responsibilities, the compensation or resources that have been agreed upon, the amount of work effort expected (e.g., number of hours per week), and the dissolution process.
- *Memorandum of understanding/agreement:* A memorandum of understanding or agreement is not typically considered to be as binding on the involved parties as a contract.

The EMS agency needs a formal written agreement with its OMD, and it must seek legal counsel in developing that agreement. The agency leadership should contact the state EMS office to identify any requirements related to the scope and authority of the OMD position as a starting point for determining the content of the written agreement.

Items that need to be addressed in the written agreement are duties and responsibilities, compensation (e.g., volunteer position, hourly compensation, or salary), number of expected hours of commitment, and insurance coverage (e.g., liability, workers' compensation). The agency should also identify what support it will provide the OMD, such as administrative assistance, training, continuing education (e.g., periodical subscriptions, conference attendance), and outfitting (e.g., uniform, personal protective equipment). Depending on the size and scope of the EMS agency, resources available to support the OMD will vary.

Position description and performance requirements

Before it develops a formal agreement with the OMD, the EMS agency must clearly articulate the duties and responsibilities of the medical director's position. The written agreement should not only include the position description but also document specific expectations—for example, hours of commitment. To clarify expectations, the written agreement should contain or reference performance measures that are specific, achievable, and outcome focused.

Performance measures can be provided as a companion document to the OMD's position description. They will identify how the medical director is expected to carry out the role and responsibilities identified in the position description—for example, "The operational medical director will participate in the training of EMS providers." Contained within that responsibility might be

- The OMD will function as the physician course director for all agency EMT courses.
- The OMD will instruct a minimum of one continuing education course on a quarterly basis. Each continuing education session will be a minimum of four hours in length.

Liability coverage issues

The OMD must be protected from liability whether or not the position is compensated. A physician's standard liability policy is insufficient for a medical director; since the role of the OMD is multifaceted, a combination of liability protections is required. Agency leaders should consult with their legal and risk management offices, and medical directors should seek independent counsel to review liability coverage. Listed below are liability coverage considerations:

- *Indemnification:* The EMS agency should indemnify its medical director, meaning that it will assume responsibility for financial awards to prevailing individuals in any lawsuit related to the medical director's duties.
- *General liability coverage:* The OMD makes decisions and renders actions regarding an EMS provider's ability to perform clinical skills. When the OMD restricts or withdraws the provider's ability to practice, a general liability exposure can arise.
- *Medical malpractice coverage:* The OMD has liability exposure related to the patient care rendered by the EMS providers within the agency. Medical malpractice coverage is designed for situations in which a patient was injured or died because providers rendered care that deviated from accepted practice.
- *Errors and omissions coverage:* The medical director provides oversight of clinical and administrative activities (e.g., training). Errors and omissions coverage provides for defense costs and damage expenses that may be incurred from professional liability claims.
- *Directors and officers coverage:* The medical director is a leader in the EMS delivery agency. Coverage for directors and officers is designed to provide for defense costs for claims against directors or officers for wrongful acts or internal mismanagement.

Workforce

Among the challenges that the Institute of Medicine (IOM) identified for emergency medical services are two related to the EMS workforce: (1) shortages in the EMS workforce due to inadequate compensation or difficult working conditions, such as extended shift periods and high incident volumes; and (2) variation of training requirements due to states not uniformly adopting NHTSA's *National EMS Scope of Practice Model.*[7] The second challenge leads to fragmentation and variation in the delivery of emergency medical services across the nation. It also makes it difficult for providers to move among different localities, regions, and states.

These and other EMS workforce issues are complex and interrelated. This section discusses the composition of the workforce; provider scope of practice levels and education standards; recruitment; selection; training; and health, wellness, and safety.

Volunteer or career?

In most communities, EMS agencies have evolved over time, influenced by population densities and geography (rural, suburban, urban), fiscal resources, and community expectations. Urban-area agencies are typically staffed with career personnel. Many of these career agencies are fire-based configurations or are private agencies that contract with the local government to provide service. Advantages to career-staffed agencies are that staffing levels can be managed through employer relationships and the ability to mandate activities. However, compensation and benefits can account for up to 90 percent of the total budgetary expenses in career organizations.

Although some urban EMS agencies rely on volunteer personnel, the preponderance of volunteer agencies are located in suburban and rural settings. Volunteer staffing is considered less costly to the organization, but there are costs for the outfitting, initial training, and continuing education of all personnel, regardless of whether they are career or volunteer. There can also be considerable attrition among volunteer EMS personnel. New personnel come into the organization and are trained, only to leave in a relatively short time for other opportunities, especially after they earn ALS qualifications. Many individuals interested in emergency medical services complete training in a volunteer organization and then move to a career organization or to other health care professions. Some members remain for the long term, but in general, a volunteer EMS agency experiences a great deal of variability in staffing levels and must balance competing time commitments for training, staffing needs, and personal issues.

Combination agencies use volunteer and career staff, reducing the overall amount of career staffing needed. However, these agencies still face some of the issues described above, as well as other issues that arise when career and volunteer members work together.

The viability of volunteer and combination systems largely depends on two major factors. First is the community's ability to sustain a pool of interested and engaged volunteers. Second is the agency's ability to adapt to changes in the community that increase or change the demand for services. In growing communities, the demand for services will grow exponentially, and socioeconomic, political, and financial issues may require different service delivery

Emergency medical service field experiments

Emergency medical service (EMS) calls consume the majority of time for many fire departments that provide the service. However, little research has been done to identify the outcomes of existing response models. One challenge is that emergency medical services remains dispersed at the federal level among transportation, health and human services, and homeland security. Thus, a concerted effort to determine effectiveness is made increasingly difficult. In 2010, a study—published as the *Report of EMS Field Experiments*—began to quantify, for the first time, elements of a strategic advanced life support (ALS) deployment model.[1] Other models exist that are routinely used by both fire department-based emergency medical services as well as by private ambulance services, and evaluating each model would have been impossible within the confines of the first-ever research proposal.

This 2010 study was conducted by a research partnership among the Center for Public Safety Excellence, the International Association of Fire Chiefs, the International Association of Firefighters, the National Institute of Standards and Technology, and Worcester Polytechnic Institute. The Department of Homeland Security funded the efforts through the Assistance to Firefighters Grant Program. The study identified the time required to perform a number of events related to ALS calls for service and evaluated time-to-task interventions. It focused on patient access and removal and on treatment of the trauma and cardiac patient. Extrapolating the time-to-task produced a method for completing specified elements found on ALS calls for service.

This study was the first time such research had been conducted, and it highlighted the need for much more evaluation and analysis.

1 Lori Moore-Merrell et al., *Report on EMS Field Experiments* (EMW-2008-FP-01603) (2010), iaff.org/tech/PDF/EMS%20Nist%20Report_LORES.pdf.

models. If the community's demand for services has increased, its level of expectations will also increase, placing pressure on the EMS agency to maintain consistent staffing levels to improve response times. Often, as communities transition from rural to suburban to urban, the pool of volunteers declines. When this happens, the EMS agency may have to transition from a full volunteer service to a combination service, and then to a full career service.

Provider scope of practice and education standards

NHTSA's *National EMS Scope of Practice Model* (included in *Emergency Medical Services Education Agenda for the Future: A Systems Approach*)[8] identifies four EMS provider levels and indicates the minimum knowledge and skills for each level (see Table 5–1).

Not all states have adopted the *Scope of Practice Model*, and some state EMS offices have established different provider titles and skill sets. Those states that establish their own scope-of-practice and certification or licensure levels either use certification exams provided by the NREMT or develop their own testing tools. This situation contributes to the variability found in emergency medical services across the nation, a situation that is compounded by the fact that some states give regions the authority to provide training and establish EMS provider levels.

Local agencies typically augment national, state, or regional training requirements to reflect local community needs. For example, an agency might add or increase training hours for special-needs populations (e.g., pediatric patients). Its medical director must oversee and approve all locally developed training or skill requirements and ensure that providers do not operate beyond their certification or licensure scope-of-practice level.

NHTSA's *National Emergency Medical Services Education Standards*[9] define the knowledge, skills, and abilities that entry-level EMS providers must obtain to meet the *Scope of Practice Model*. However, with the exception of paramedic training (see sidebar at the top of page 136), EMS training programs are not subject to national standards for accreditation. Local agencies can develop their own training or use training developed by the state EMS office, national organizations, or private companies. Agency leaders should check with their state's EMS office to determine whether it has any particular requirements regarding training accreditation. This is another area where agency leaders and their OMDs need to collaborate.

Table 5-1 *National EMS Scope of Practice Model* provider levels

Title	Description
Emergency medical responder (EMR)	Has basic knowledge and skills and can perform basic patient care procedures, such as obtain chief complaints, make general patient assessments, administer oxygen, and apply bandaging and splinting (including spinal immobilization). All care is performed with minimal equipment.
Emergency medical technician (EMT)	Builds on the EMR's knowledge and skills but training includes additional basic-level knowledge and skills, such as patient assessments, operation of ambulances and all their basic equipment, and the performance of clinical rotations. In some states, EMTs may monitor previously established intravenous (IV) fluids, may assist the patient with the patient's self-administered medications, or may administer certain medications as specified in their agency's protocols.
Advanced emergency medical technician (AEMT)	Builds on the EMT's knowledge and skills but training includes additional clinical rotations. The AEMT is capable of performing such skills as initiation of IV or intraosseous fluids, administration of specific medications, and placement of certain advanced airway adjuncts.
Paramedic	Receives complex knowledge and skills training with about 1,000 additional hours of clinical and didactic education above an EMT to provide an advanced level of patient care. The paramedic can perform an array of advanced procedures, including endotracheal intubation, surgical airways, administration of numerous medications, and performance of cardiac monitoring and advanced cardiac therapies.

Source: Drawn from the National Highway Traffic Safety Administration, *National EMS Scope of Practice Model* (Washington, D.C.: Department of Transportation, 2005), ems.gov/pdf/EMSScope.pdf.

Paramedic training accreditation

In 2007, the National Registry of Emergency Medical Technicians (NREMT) established a new accreditation requirement for paramedic-level training programs. This requirement, to be effective January 1, 2013, will mandate that all paramedic applicants graduate from an accredited program in order to take the NREMT test.

Some states have established their own accreditation programs for paramedic training, and one national organization, the Commission on Accreditation of Allied Health Education Programs, as part of the Committee on Accreditation of Educational Programs for the Emergency Medical Services Professions, offers EMS paramedic education program accreditation.

Recruitment

It has become increasingly difficult to recruit EMS workers, especially in areas with poor working conditions and low pay. In particular, finding enough paramedics will only become more difficult as aging baby boomers place a higher demand on the medical system. Paramedics are in high demand in the EMS job market and often change employers to find better pay, improved working conditions, or promotional opportunities. Many agency leaders are now using hiring preferences for ALS-trained individuals (e.g., certified paramedics in the candidate pool will be the first to receive employment offers), as well as certification or licensure incentives and retention bonuses (e.g., additional compensation above base salary). Agencies may want to review promotional possibilities for EMS providers and consider offering them opportunities for higher levels of responsibility and pay without forcing them out of their EMS career track.

Selection

Selection of personnel, whether volunteer or career, is one of the most important tasks that an EMS leader or manager can perform. Selecting the right people reduces risk to the organization and allows management to focus on supporting and helping personnel improve the organization and enhance their skills.

Agency leaders need to be familiar with NREMT certification requirements as well as with state EMS regulations. Certification requirements for criminal and background checks should be incorporated into an agency's hiring process. Additional components of the process may include résumé and credentialing review, physical ability assessments, medical and psychological screenings, a polygraph assessment, and interviews. The depth and breadth of hiring practices will vary among the types of EMS agencies. For example, a hospital-based agency may require only satisfaction of criminal and background checks and a résumé, credential review, and interview for a hiring decision to be made, but a fire-based agency may require all the components listed above.

Initial training

The agency's OMD is responsible for reviewing and approving all educational content used in training to ensure that it is appropriate and accurate and meets all applicable requirements (e.g., national, state, or local). Most EMS training courses require the involvement of a physician course director. For some courses (e.g., those offered by the American Heart Association), specific training requirements are identified by the course's administrative manual. It is the responsibility of the physician course director to oversee the delivery of the educational content in order to meet these requirements. The agency's OMD may function as the physician course director, as is often the case for locally offered classes. Sometimes, a separate physician course director may be needed (e.g., for large regional courses).

Once EMS provider candidates complete their training, they may attempt certification or licensure testing. Initial testing consists of written and practical examinations. NREMT provides tests for all EMS provider levels in the *Scope of Practice Model*, and most states use NREMT

Virginia Beach EMS Recruitment and Retention Program

The Virginia Beach Department of Emergency Medical Services (VBEMS) is a third-service EMS system providing 911 emergency medical and rescue services to Virginia's most populated city, primarily through hundreds of certified volunteers. VBEMS staff have worked with the ten volunteer rescue squads of Virginia Beach, the Virginia Beach Volunteer Rescue Squad Foundation, the Council of Virginia Beach Volunteer Rescue Squads, and individual members of the system to increase the number of volunteers in VBEMS to record levels.

The approach to implementing a new recruitment and retention program was multipronged. VBEMS expanded the use of its social networking program for recruiting efforts. The VBEMS recruiter collaborated with a new recruiter funded by the Virginia Beach Volunteer Rescue Squad Foundation and with the city's other public safety partners, two regional EMS councils, and the state's public safety and health partners. The regional EMS councils received a Virginia Office of EMS, Rescue Squad Assistance Fund grant for improving EMS recruiting locally and regionally. Cooperatively, the agencies established a website (BecomeEMS.org) to attract interested citizens and provide information for local agency contacts.

VBEMS partnered with the city's Multimedia Services Division to create a video describing how a person without experience may join the organization, train to be a volunteer emergency medical technician (EMT), and continue his or her education to become a paramedic. Additional videos will be released highlighting the Air Medic Program and Lifeguard Services Division to encourage professional development of current members into other areas of VBEMS.

In its retention efforts, VBEMS attempts to reduce barriers to volunteering, especially as those barriers relate to competing time pressures. The department expanded the number and frequency of orientation and training sessions, refined the new-member intake and credentialing processes, enhanced new-member transition among its divisions, and used technology to improve communications. This has resulted in a record number of recruits entering EMT classes and an increase in the number of previous members rejoining the system.

The graph below illustrates volunteer staffing growth over a three-year period. Since these figures were compiled, the department has increased its staffing to over 1,000 members.

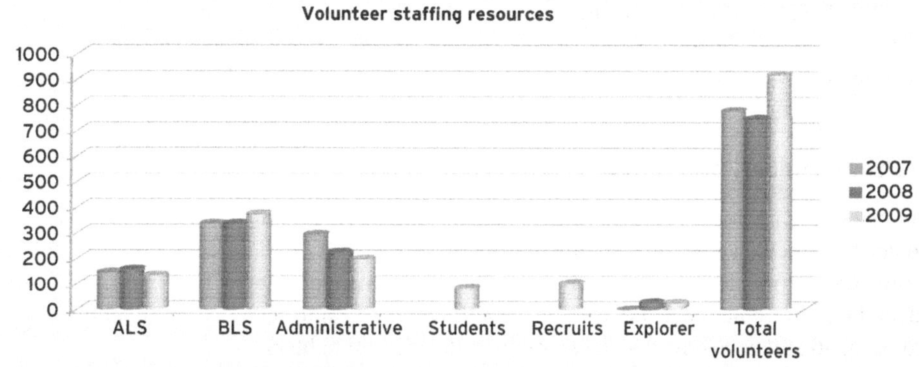

Graph courtesy of Virginia Beach (Virginia) EMS

Photo courtesy of Virginia Beach (Virginia) EMS

testing, but as with all other aspects of emergency medical services, there is variability among the states. EMS providers in states that do not use NREMT testing may find that their certificates or licenses are not recognized by other states, so if they move to a new state, they may have to take additional testing to gain recognition as EMS providers.

Continuing education training programs

The NREMT and all states require all levels of EMS providers to complete continuing education credits, with the amount varying among states. The NREMT recertification cycle is two years; state requirements for frequency of recertification vary.

An agency's continuing education program should support all EMS providers' recertification requirements. The agency's OMD must be involved in program development to ensure accuracy of medical content. The program should reflect patient care trends and results of the agency's continuous quality improvement activities, and should provide training in assessments and skills needed for high-risk incidents that occur infrequently. For example, EMS agencies have made great strides to ensure that they develop pediatric-specific protocols, provide pediatric-related training, and have appropriately sized equipment for pediatric care. However, the lack of routine exposure to the pediatric patient population makes it difficult for EMS providers to maintain skills in this area. Concentrated and continuing training is needed to offset a lack of routine exposure.

An agency's leaders need to work in concert with the agency's OMD to ensure that the state's EMS office requirements for continuing education programs are satisfied and are appropriate to the provider's scope of practice. The Continuing Education Coordinating Board for Emergency Medical Services, a national organization, will verify that continuing education program content meets national education standards, and its endorsement is typically accepted by the NREMT.

A component of all continuing education programs is verification of providers' competencies. The agency's OMD is responsible for this verification and must attest to the providers' skill assessments during recertification of their credentials with either their state EMS office or the NREMT. This verification ensures that providers' knowledge and skill sets are adequately maintained, especially skills used in low-frequency but high-risk situations. OMDs may work in conjunction with the agency's chain of command, especially those in the training section, to assist with knowledge and skill verification assessments.

Health, wellness, and safety

National standards for firefighters' fitness, health, and safety provide for annual medical screenings, fitness evaluations, comprehensive lab screenings, audiometry testing, behavioral health support, vaccines/inoculations, and rehabilitation support (see Chapter 11). EMS providers do not have national standards for health, wellness, and safety, but some of their risks and occupational exposures are comparable to those of firefighters.

Barriers to implementing a wellness program for EMS providers can be external or internal to an agency and may range from member apprehension, organizational culture, and budget constraints to infrastructure challenges. To achieve a comprehensive wellness and fitness program, it is imperative that EMS agencies institute best practices and address organizational barriers.

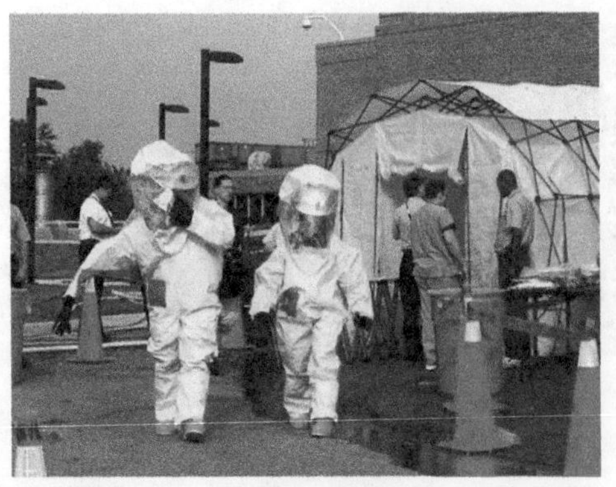

Figure 5-3 EMS providers wear full protective gear during a training drill.

Courtesy of Prince William County (Virginia) Department of Fire and Rescue

The prehospital setting can be physically and mentally demanding on EMS providers, who often leave the profession because of occupational stress and injuries. Back injuries and other musculoskeletal sprains, strains, and tears are especially common. Often uncontrolled and unpredictable, the EMS environment also includes the threat of infectious and contagious diseases, violence,

Leading causes of EMS personnel injuries and fatalities

Emergency vehicle crashes

Ambulance crash data indicate that the rear patient-care compartment is more hazardous to emergency medical service (EMS) personnel than the driver's compartment. Agency leaders must maintain a vehicle safety program that includes seat belt-wearing policies and must incorporate engineering practices to improve vehicle safety and reduce EMS provider injuries.

Cardiovascular

There is a lack of specific cardiovascular health and fitness studies among EMS personnel; however, firefighter cardiovascular health issues are well documented, and since many firefighters also perform as EMS providers, their statistics could be extrapolated for similarities. EMS providers experience comparable predictors for increased cardiovascular risks, such as weight gain, high cholesterol and blood glucose levels, and hypertension. Agency leaders need to ensure that comprehensive health, safety, and wellness programs are in place within their organizations.

Violence and assault

EMS personnel are exposed to threats of violence and can become victims of violence-induced injuries, including intentional assaults. Agency leaders need to provide training for personnel with a focus on how to recognize and neutralize potentially violent situations.

Musculoskeletal injuries

The nature of patient care and emergency response poses risks for musculoskeletal injuries, especially involving the provider's back: such injuries often occur when providers have to lift patients while in an awkward body position or must repetitively lift heavy objects. Training programs for EMS providers need to review proper lifting techniques, and an appropriate fitness program can assist in reducing musculoskeletal sprains and strains.

Exposure to infectious diseases

Exposures to blood and other bodily fluids are a risk for EMS providers. EMS providers can be exposed to blood through needle sticks and other puncture injuries; they are also vulnerable to splash and spatter exposures to mucous membranes and openings in skin. The pathogens of primary concern are the human immunodeficiency virus (HIV), hepatitis B virus (HBV), and hepatitis C virus (HCV); the risk for contracting infections such as methicillin-resistant *Staphylococcus aureus* (MRSA) is also high. A well-designed and comprehensive infection control program incorporating engineering controls and work practices is a must for EMS agencies.

Stress and mental health

EMS providers are exposed to psychological trauma and may develop occupational stress, burnout, and other mental health conditions, such as post-traumatic stress disorder. A comprehensive health, safety, and wellness program also needs to address the behavioral health needs of personnel.

Source: Drawn from Les R. Becker and Rebecca Spicer, *Feasibility for an EMS Workforce Safety and Health Surveillance System* (Washington, D.C.: National Highway Traffic Safety Administration, February 2007), nhtsa.gov/DOT/NHTSA/Traffic%20Injury%20Control/Articles/Associated%20Files/EMSWorkforceFeasibility3.pdf.

and vehicle crashes. EMS providers are at particular risk when operating in the back of a moving ambulance and when providing patient care on roadways.

Like firefighters, EMS providers should have performance-based physical assessments upon hire. EMS agencies need to incorporate an ongoing and comprehensive wellness and fitness program, including a behavioral health component, for the protection and benefit of their personnel and the organization.

EMS providers must be trained and required to use personal safety equipment to protect against injuries and contact with bodily substances (Figure 5–3). Agency leaders should review NFPA 1999, Standard on Protective Clothing for Emergency Medical Operations (2008 ed.).

Provision of patient care

EMS providers supply patient care in the out-of-hospital setting with oversight from the OMD. Providers must perform only those procedures identified for their level of certification or licensure, and within the parameters of their agency's protocols. The *National EMS Scope of Practice Model* identifies the procedures that EMS providers may perform according to their level of certification or licensure. As explained earlier, not all states have adopted the national document, and in states where it has not been adopted, the providers' scope of practice may be defined by the EMS state office, regional authorities, or individual localities, depending on existing regulations.

Protocols

An agency's protocols identify the medical procedures and expectations to be followed by EMS providers. Protocols are designed for the multitude of situations that will be encountered in the field. Some state EMS offices may mandate that state- or regional-level protocols must be used, giving little latitude to agencies in establishing protocols. Other states allow local agencies great latitude to assimilate available state or regional protocols or to develop their own.

If an agency develops its own protocols or modifies state or regionally prescribed protocols, the medical practice activities need to be based on industry-accepted medical literature, national standards, or best practices. Often, medical directors will use a committee of BLS and ALS providers to assist in the development or review of the agency's protocols. Regardless of the process used, as industry standards are revised in accordance with medical evidence, protocols must be routinely reviewed in order to keep the operational environment current.

Standing orders

Standing orders supplement the agency's protocols. Standing orders describe specific activities that providers are authorized to perform without delay when necessary, such as the initiation of oxygen to a patient who is having difficulty breathing, the use of a defibrillator in specific cardiac arrest situations, and the administration of life-saving medications for severe allergic reactions or for cardiac arrest when time is critical.

Medical control

Medical control is the term for consultation between EMS providers and physicians regarding specific patient care situations. There are two types of medical control: online and off-line. Online medical control comes into play when EMS providers on the emergency scene or in transit to a receiving health care facility need orders to perform specific procedures that are not authorized in their standing orders. They use a telephone (landline or cellular) or radio to contact a supervising physician, who may be at a designated health care facility and who does not have to be the agency's OMD.

Off-line medical control refers to the administration of the agency's provider training, protocols, standing orders, and other policies and procedures related to patient care. A key component of off-line medical control is the review of patient care–related activities for quality improvement. Quality improvement requires the monitoring of providers and of the system as a whole as well as the identification of educational program gaps and needed corrective actions.

Transport issues

Some of the issues to be considered in providing care to patients who require transport are outlined below.

Destination determinations EMS deployment models are centered on providing optimum response times as determined by characteristics of the area served (e.g., geography, road systems, and speed limits). EMS agency leaders need to consider how their destination determinations affect their unit-hour usage. Factors such as regionalization of medical facilities and hospital overcrowding may make it necessary to rethink the traditional response time–driven deployment model.

When specialty or regional centers are available, an important part of patient care is providing EMS field triage and determining the appropriate medical facility for each patient. Some states require EMS agencies to comply with state or regional destination determination plans. EMS agencies need to educate their providers on appropriate facility selection and develop protocols or policies to guide EMS providers' choices of destinations.

Courtesy of Prince William County (Virginia) Department of Fire and Rescue

Figure 5-4 Helicopters are used to transport patients to distant treatment facilities when speed is essential.

Aeromedical service

Aeromedical transport agencies have proliferated over the last two decades. Many use helicopters primarily. Helicopters were first used in military conflicts, evacuating critically injured soldiers from the battlefield to field hospitals, which vastly improved the soldiers' chances of survival.

In the civilian application, aeromedical services are provided by governmental agencies such as local or state fire and law enforcement agencies, hospital-based services, and private firms. Local EMS agencies use aeromedical transport when ground transport time to a specialized center is lengthy.

In recent years, safety in the aeromedical industry has received increased scrutiny. The appropriateness of flights is debated with regard to patient conditions, risk and benefit analysis, and patient outcomes. EMS agency managers and leaders need to monitor their agencies' use of aeromedical services and review those activities with their medical directors, receiving facilities, aeromedical service representatives, and EMS providers as part of their ongoing quality improvement activities. Items reviewed should include the amount of aeromedical use, the appropriateness of use, patient outcomes, aeromedical service feedback, and the frequency with which the EMS agency has to contact multiple aeromedical agencies to obtain a single flight.

Regionalization of health care facilities There has been an increased emphasis on regionalizing medical care so that communities can have access to specialty centers to improve outcomes for the sick and injured. With regionalization and strategic identification of specialty care facilities, not every hospital has to make the infrastructure investment to provide every specialty service. For example, regional centers provide pediatric care, trauma care, burn care, cardiac care, and stroke care. Specialty centers make a commitment to provide a higher level of care. A hospital's decision to become a designated specialty center is voluntary. Some areas of the country, particularly rural or frontier areas, do not have ready access to specialty centers.

When the regional center is a long distance away, the local EMS agency will spend a large amount of time transporting patients by ground, or it will rely heavily on alternative patient transfer mechanisms (e.g., aeromedical and interfacility transport resources). The use and safety of aeromedical services (Figure 5-4) has come under increasing scrutiny (see sidebar above). Moreover, aeromedical transport cannot be used during inclement weather. However,

Ambulance diversions

Recognizing that hospital diversion of ambulances can negatively affect EMS systems, several EMS systems and hospitals in the King County, Washington, area are trying to achieve a zero-diversion environment. Included in this project are eighteen hospitals, six fire-based advanced life support (ALS) ground transport agencies, one private ALS aeromedical agency, and seventeen basic life support ground transport agencies (fourteen fire-based and three private agencies). A project manager was hired to coordinate the efforts, and all entities contributed data to clarify the breadth and depth of the issues. About two years after data collection efforts were enhanced and common terminologies were instituted, hospital diversions were significantly reduced. Nine hospitals had achieved zero diversions during a nine-month period, and another five hospitals had achieved zero diversions in one or more months during the same time period.[1]

1 Ed Mund, "Ending Ambulance Diversion," *EMS World* 40 (April 2011): 31-38, emsworld.com/print/EMS-World/Ending-Ambulance-Diversion/1$16596 (accessed May 9, 2011).

transporting a patient to the closest nonspecialty facility may require a subsequent interfacility transport to get the patient to an appropriate specialty care center, delaying definitive care.

Most EMS agencies deploy their resources according to average response times within the jurisdiction. If an agency's units are often engaged in extended transports to distant regional or specialty facilities, the agency will have to analyze the changing usage patterns and develop new unit-usage models. Agencies also need to engage with their local and regional health care facilities in order to stay informed about plans for expansion and possible impacts on EMS resources.

Hospital diversions Emergency room overcrowding is well documented and adversely affects EMS. When the closest appropriate receiving facility cannot receive a patient because the emergency room is full, it may divert the EMS unit to another facility (see sidebar above). The unit must then travel farther to deliver the patient and is not available to respond to other calls for a longer time. Again, agency leaders and medical directors must work with local health care–receiving facilities to reduce the impact of overcrowding on EMS costs and effectiveness. One strategy is to develop a regional plan that places hospitals in zones to control the distances that local EMS units must travel. Another strategy that some EMS agencies have adopted is a no-divert policy, which places the responsibility to manage internal overcrowding on the hospital.

Interfacility service In the continuum of care, patients often need to be moved between health care facilities—for example, from a hospital to a rehabilitation facility, from a skilled nursing center to a hospital, or from a community hospital to a specialized hospital (e.g., regional trauma center, stroke center, cardiac center) for specific care. Often private EMS units perform interfacility transports, but some hospitals negotiate an agreement with the local government to provide this service, especially for emergency patient transfers. Depending on how the agreement is structured, the local government may receive funding from the hospital in exchange for having a unit available for immediate response to the facility when an emergency transport is required.

Agency performance issues

EMS agency leaders, along with the OMD, must ensure that EMS providers are consistently delivering high-quality patient care and that the organization is efficient and effective in supporting and directing that care. A comprehensive performance assessment program can provide the organization with the information it needs to efficiently manage resources, identify its strengths and weaknesses, monitor the effects of change on the EMS system, and scan the environment for opportunities. Policies and procedures should be routinely reviewed to keep the agency's performance consistent with industry best practices.

Quality improvement

Modern EMS quality management approaches look at internal (organizational) processes and external patient care activities prospectively, concurrently, and retrospectively (see Table 5–2). All providers, whether career or volunteer, must be held to the same expectations and standards of patient care.

Table 5-2 Quality improvement methods

Quality improvement activity	Activity examples
Prospective processes	Conducting initial and continuing education training, including clinical rotations.
	Observing training and conducting provider skill reviews.
	Modifying clinical protocols and policies as needed, considering research and literature on medical advances in EMS practice.
Concurrent processes	Directly observing and evaluating EMS providers.
	Riding along with providers to observe crew performance through all aspects of service delivery.
	Providing ongoing input for organizational efforts and educational opportunities.
Retrospective processes	Reviewing cases, tracking patient outcomes, auditing documentation, and conducting customer satisfaction surveys.

Prospective approaches to quality management place quality improvement efforts in the forefront and provide direction for the organization. Prospective activities include training, ongoing review of agency protocols and policies, and monitoring industry advances.

Concurrent activities include observations and evaluations performed by the EMS agency's supervisors, officers, and medical director. Observations should be random and assess provider performance through all aspects of service delivery, including the service delivered to the customer. Frontline supervisors should also make routine observations and have a process for providing ongoing input on organizational efforts and opportunities for education.

Retrospective activities are the more traditional approach to most EMS agency quality improvement efforts, but EMS providers tend to view this approach as looking only for mistakes and view feedback as punitive rather than constructive. EMS agencies need to design their processes so that responsibility for actions is accepted and behavior modifications are viewed as constructive and educational. They can also look at what happens before the provider-patient interaction, and they can closely observe what happens during that interaction, in order to improve the quality of service.

The EMS agency leadership, the OMD, supervisors, educators, and providers must all cooperate to ensure the success of quality improvement activities. There must be accountability at the provider level and all the way up through the chain of command to ensure compliance with policies and procedures. Highly successful quality improvement programs maintain a focus on management's performance and overall system performance, and will implement educational initiatives to address any individual or group performance gaps identified, rather than taking a punitive approach to EMS providers.

Crew resource management (CRM) is an error reduction strategy that many EMS agencies have adopted from the aviation industry to make everyone in the crew responsible for promoting safety and maintaining the highest level of operational efficiency. CRM has five key components: communication, situational awareness, decision making, teamwork, and removal

Using customer feedback to improve service

Henderson, Nevada, uses customer satisfaction to measure and improve EMS performance. The city surveys all EMS customers and tracks results by patient type. Each month, EMS personnel receive personalized summaries of feedback from the customers they served, often accompanied by copies of actual surveys with narrative feedback in the respondents' own handwriting. Monthly summaries also go to the fire chief, battalion chiefs, and medical director.

The fire chief personally conducts the customer service training required for all emergency medical staff, and personally thanks employees who achieve high customer service ratings.

Source: Center for Performance Measurement, "City of Henderson, NV," in *What Works: How Local Governments Have Made the Leap from Measurement to Management* (Washington, D.C.: ICMA Press, 2008), 58-59.

HIPAA impacts on quality improvement activities

The Health Insurance Portability and Accountability Act (HIPAA) of 1996 provides federal protection of personal health information. Under HIPAA, only the minimum amount of information required for quality improvement activities should be disclosed by health care entities involved with the patient's care. Any patient care record used for case review must have all specific patient identifiers (e.g., name, social security number, and address) and nonessential information removed. However, for EMS quality improvement programs to be effective and comprehensive, the patient's movement through the health care system and the patient's outcome must be tracked. Through their liaisons with receiving facilities, operational medical directors can be instrumental in getting emergency medical services recognized as a key component in tracking the patient's movement through the health care system and in getting records linked to provide outcome data.

of barriers. The National Firefighter Near-Miss Reporting System (discussed in Chapter 9) has numerous safety-related resources, including information on CRM and EMS issues, which can be accessed at firefighternearmiss.com/index.php/main-resources.

Performance measures and benchmarking

Establishing performance measures and benchmarking performance are core activities for any agency. Assessing the productivity and efficiency of the agency's operations, and comparing the agency's performance with external industry examples and standards, provide benefits for internal planning and quality improvement activities.

Performance measures should be quantifiable, based on objective evidence, and related to positive patient impacts and outcomes. If there is a lack of evidence-based information to support local decision making, agency leaders should evaluate the industry's best practice performance measurement models for ideas on initiating or improving performance measurement.

Benchmarking means comparing performance with similar internal sections of the EMS agency or with external agencies. Typical items that are benchmarked include work schedules, response times, unit-hour usage, and patient care intervention times. Some EMS agencies find that they do not have the data to make useful comparisons. However, agency leadership should look at the entire agency's functions to determine potential benchmarking activities beyond time-centered data elements—for example, number of patient conditions improved, number of acute coronary syndrome patients receiving 12-lead electrocardiogram monitoring, and other specific treatment modalities.

Performance measurement for emergency medical services

Resources on performance measures and best practices for emergency medical services are provided by the following organizations:

- International Association of Fire Chiefs and International Association of Fire Fighters: *EMS System Performance Measurement* (2002), iaff.org/tech/PDF/EMSSystemPerformanceMeasurement.pdf, which specifies fifteen EMS-related quality indicators, defines each measure, and identifies data collection needs to support each measure.
- National Fire Protection Association (NFPA): NFPA 450, Guide for Emergency Medical Services and Systems (2009 ed.).
- National Highway Transportation Safety Administration: *Emergency Medical Services Performance Measures: Recommended Attributes and Indicators for System and Service Performance* (December 2009), ems.gov/pdf/811211.pdf.
- American Society for Testing and Materials (ASTM) International: ASTM F1339-92, Standard Guide for Organization and Operation of Emergency Medical Services Systems (2008), astm.org/Standards/F1339.htm.
- ICMA Center for Performance Measurement, *Comparative Performance Measurement: FY 2009 Data Report,* available at bookstore.icma.org/Comparative_Performance_Measur_P2125C29.cfm.

Benchmarking an agency can be a catalyst for infusing new ideas and improving processes and services. (See Chapter 14 for more information on performance measurement and benchmarking.)

Emergency medical and ambulance service accreditation

Accreditation acknowledges the efforts and accomplishments of an EMS agency. The process includes an independent external review that validates the organization's commitment to quality of service and operational efficiency. The initial step of an accreditation process is to perform a self-assessment, which in itself can be an important catalyst for positive agency change. The decision to pursue accreditation will require the commitment of the entire organization. Industry organizations that offer accreditation are the Commission on Accreditation of Ambulance Services, the Center for Public Safety Excellence, and the American Ambulance Association.

EMS research

Emergency medical services as a specialty and a profession have been in place now for more than forty years. Despite years of dedicated service, there are significant gaps in data collection and performance documentation, gaps that have contributed to deficient industry outcome tracking and continuing fragmentation. The profession has been slow to engage in evidence-based research. Few agencies are actively involved in applying the scientific method to EMS operations, and even fewer have allied themselves with credible research institutions. Very little scientific research on EMS management procedures has been produced, and there is no journal devoted to the science of managing emergency medical services. EMS treatment modalities are more often products of tradition and the assimilation of emergency medical care into conventional medical practice rather than the adaptation of conventional medical practice to the EMS environment. This has led to some prehospital practices that have questionable benefit for patient outcomes.

As the EMS profession continues to evolve and local resources are constrained, it will be critical for the industry to demonstrate its efficiencies, effectiveness, and positive impact on patient survivability beyond anecdotal evidence. Issues such as inadequate information management systems, difficulty in assimilating patient-related data, inadequate resources (e.g., investigators, funding, infrastructure capacity, and support), regulatory issues, and a lack of strategy and approach are examples of barriers to good EMS research.

Several initiatives have begun to review prehospital equipment and treatment modalities. In 2002, the National EMS Research Agenda Implementation Project identified priority topics for clinical and systemic research topics. The 2007 IOM report *Emergency Medical Services at the Crossroads*, cited previously, is an excellent reference document for understanding the need for EMS research, the details on the National EMS Research Agenda Implementation Project, and the recommendations for federal support made by both these initiatives.

Agency functional needs

In addition to staff, EMS agencies rely on infrastructure that supports effective and efficient patient care, including vehicles in good working condition, adequate storage and training facilities, and the right equipment and computer programs. Ongoing maintenance as well as major system upgrades and large capital item replacements require planning and management.

Fleet issues

Vehicles are among the most expensive items in an EMS agency's budget. The purchase and routine replacement of ambulances should be included in the agency's capital budget. If the local government contracts with a private ambulance company, the vehicle fleet that is provided should be closely monitored to ensure that apparatus are safe, available, and appropriate.

Most agencies reference the federal KKK-A-1822 standard and the National Truck Equipment Association Ambulance Manufacturers Division Standards (2007 version) for the purchase and design of ambulances.[10] When NFPA's new design standard for ambulances, NFPA 1917, Standard for Automotive Ambulances, is published (target date 2012), the federal KKK standards will no longer be revised.

Washington Metropolitan Council of Governments' regional preparedness effort

The Metropolitan Washington Council of Governments (MWCOG) initiated a Cooperative Purchasing Program in 1971 to reduce costs using economies of scale created through volume buying. In 2005, MWCOG obtained Urban Area Security Initiative grant funding to purchase seven mass casualty support units (MCSUs) and seven ambulance buses. The MCSUs were designed to treat 100 patients, and the ambulance buses can transport twenty littered (nonambulatory) patients.

The purchase of these vehicles makes possible joint training between neighboring jurisdictions, increases the region's capacity to respond to mass casualty events, and ensures interoperability during these events. The vehicles, which were purchased using a standard set of vehicle specifications, are housed throughout the region and are available for emergency response to any location in the National Capital area.

Photos courtesy of Montgomery County (Maryland) Fire and Rescue Service

Many EMS agencies routinely replace ambulances at specific mileages or when repair costs become excessive. Agencies need to budget for projected fuel and maintenance costs and any state licensing requirements. Grant assistance, cooperative purchasing with other agencies, and purchasing under existing state or local contracts can all help reduce the fiscal impact of large acquisitions.

Medication storage requirements

EMS agencies must stay informed about regulations related to the supply and storage of medications. Depending on the agency, medication exchange agreements, and state and federal regulations, the process of medical supply and storage will vary. Some agencies have an agreement with the local hospital pharmacy to supply and exchange medications used during the delivery of patient care. Other agencies handle the purchase and storage of medications themselves.

If the EMS agency elects to purchase and store medications, its OMD must be closely involved. Permits must be obtained from the state pharmacy board and the Drug Enforcement Administration (DEA) to store the medications. To comply with state and federal regulations, the agency must have in place several administrative and operational policies and must follow specific security- and temperature-regulating practices.

The DEA number that the agency's OMD uses in his or her primary practice is the number used for prescribing medications to agency patients. It is recommended that the OMD obtain a separate DEA number for ordering medications and related supplies for the EMS agency. Obtaining a separate DEA number for agency duties can help the OMD avoid potential conflicts with his or her private practice.

Equipment

States typically specify the minimum amount of equipment required for all levels of transport vehicles. EMS equipment is classified into two types: consumable and durable. Consumable equipment items, such as oxygen masks, bandages, and intravenous fluids, are disposable and meant for single-patient use. Durable equipment items, such as cardiac monitors, stretchers, and long back boards, are meant for repeated use and can be used on multiple patients. For

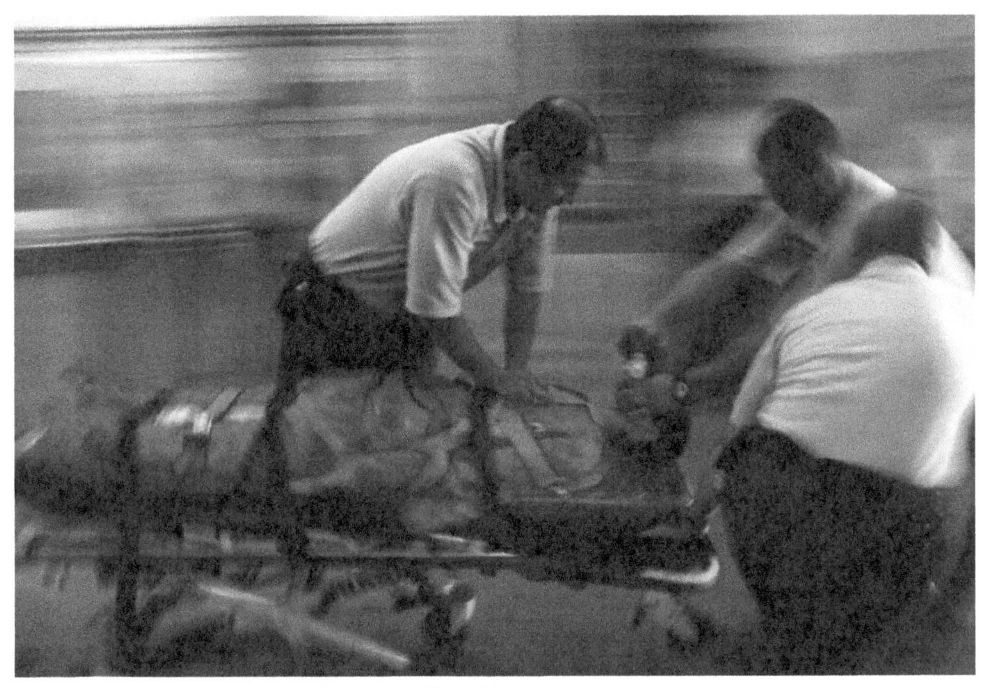

Courtesy of Prince William County (Virginia) Department of Fire and Rescue

Figure 5-5 EMS training can use manikins to simulate CPR.

expensive durable equipment items, agencies should explore both purchasing and leasing options, especially if the EMS system is large, to determine the fiscal benefits of each.

Equipment is also needed for training and education. It is important that training settings, especially those for low-frequency, high-risk incidents, be as realistic as possible. Realistic manikins are available in adult and pediatric sizes; the instructor can program these manikins to simulate reactions to treatment modalities (Figure 5-5). However, these manikins can cost thousands of dollars.

Electronic patient care records

An electronic patient care reporting (e-PCR) system can improve consistent data capture and enable real-time reporting.

NHTSA and the Health Resources and Services Administration have developed the National EMS Information System (NEMSIS). NEMSIS standardizes definitions of data elements so that databases at the local, regional, state, and federal levels can exchange information. (No patient identifiers are included in the NEMSIS database.) EMS services and hospitals can be linked with local, state, and national databases and the trauma registry to enable data to flow both ways. Even the smallest EMS agency can report data by phone or with Internet access. This system can be integrated with EMS patient care records, and integrated data can be used to assist in clinical evaluation and care provided to patients as well as for performance measurement and research. NEMSIS captures performance indicators defined in NHTSA's *Emergency Medical Services Performance Measures: Recommended Attributes and Indicators for System and Service Performance,*[11] which is based on the NEMSIS Uniform Prehospital Dataset definitions.

To date, forty-eight states and two territories have agreements to promote and implement the NEMSIS system. While NEMSIS has standardized the prehospital dataset, future efforts are still needed to address full integration of EMS data with receiving facilities for data element sharing related to the continuum of care and outcome-focused research.

System finance and revenue recovery issues

While the public may see emergency medical services as essential to public safety, along with fire and law enforcement, this provision has not received governmental funding at the same

Special taxes

- **Idaho:** Idaho levies an annual $1 fee on each driver's license issued. Revenues go into a dedicated EMS fund, which has assisted Idaho's EMS programs with funding for equipment, ambulances, and communication tools for rural programs.
- **Maryland:** The state created a dedicated EMS fund in the late 1980s by assessing a fee on all vehicle registrations. The fund is for EMS and trauma systems, including the state police EMS helicopters.
- **Virginia:** In 1983 Virginia instituted "One-for-Life" legislation, adding a $1 fee on motor vehicle registrations to support EMS. Incremental fee increases have brought the current fee to $6.25 (now called "6.25-for-Life"). Of this, $0.25 is earmarked for training and continuing education, and $2 is earmarked for the state police helicopter program. Of the remaining $4, $1 is returned to the locality where the registered vehicle is housed in order to support local EMS agencies. The rest supports statewide EMS needs, such as the Office of EMS, regional EMS councils, statewide EMS organizations, an EMS grant program, basic and advanced life support training programs, EMS system development and initiatives, emergency operations, and technology and radio communications enhancements. The EMS fee generates approximately $32.5 million statewide, but over the last few years, some of these revenues have been diverted from local emergency medical services to support shortfalls in the state's general fund.

level as its public safety partners, nor has it received federal funding for infrastructure comparable to that received by the transportation and public utility systems. Sustainable financing for EMS system costs will require that several governmental funding and reimbursement models currently in use be restructured, such as having Medicare and Medicaid reimburse EMS agencies for responding to calls that require treatment but not transport to a medical facility.

Tax support

Most local governments are funded by taxes (see sidebar above). Typical tax sources are property taxes, local income taxes, and the general sales tax. Some localities levy special taxes that can be used to help fund fire and emergency medical services; these might include impact fees assessed on developers of new construction or new business owners to establish infrastructure in the district or community. Each state legislates how local governments can assess fees to support various expenses.

Revenue recovery

EMS agencies can bill third-party payers such as Medicare, Medicaid, and independent health insurance companies to recover some costs. All health care insurance companies include EMS costs in their actuarial models, and policy premiums reflect this fact. Compared to health care costs in total, EMS charges are minuscule.

Under current regulations, the cost of treatment without patient transport to a hospital is not reimbursed by Medicare or Medicaid. However, this cost may be reimbursed by many commercial insurers, and it can be billed directly to patients. For this reason, an EMS billing program will not collect enough to pay for all the costs of a locality's EMS system, but it can certainly provide a predictable and stable revenue source that will relieve the total tax burden on the citizens for their EMS services.

While there are numerous options for structuring an EMS billing program, it is imperative that such a program be administered consistently and in compliance with all applicable regulations. The federal Office of Inspector General has rendered opinions that permit local governments to bill the appropriate third-party payor for EMS services and also to consider any portion of the service bill not covered by the insurance carrier (e.g., copayment or deductible) as satisfied by the resident's local tax payments. The local government may also consider tax payments made by residents without health insurance coverage as satisfying their financial obligation for local emergency medical services.

Billing and payment in the insurance industry are frequently performed through electronic exchange of required information and electronic fund transfers. EMS billing can be performed by trained staff in the finance department or fire department, or it can be outsourced.

Medicare is the single largest third-party payor in EMS billing programs, and it has the most stringent reimbursement regulations. Severe penalties are exacted on EMS agencies that mismanage or defraud Medicare billing practices. Navigating a changing landscape of regulations and requirements puts legitimate and well-intentioned providers at risk. One way to reduce risk is to outsource this function to a commercial billing company with demonstrated expertise. Commercial billing companies normally demand 4–12 percent of collected revenues.

To implement an EMS billing program, the local government must work with legal counsel to develop a comprehensive billing compliance plan. If a commercial billing company is used, the local government must ensure that it also has a comprehensive compliance plan. The local government must demonstrate compliance with federal anti-kickback statutes, especially those related to ambulance restocking. The Safe Harbor Rule for restocking issues, the "Red Flag Rules," and HIPAA requirements must be addressed.

When an EMS billing program is first introduced and implemented, some opposition should be expected. Opposition is often based on unfounded assumptions and misconceptions, and a proactive, factual, and targeted campaign to educate internal and external customers will often resolve concerns.

Grants

The Federal Emergency Management Agency administers several federal grant programs, but only a small percentage of direct and dedicated funding goes for emergency medical services. Federal programs for targeted patient populations or needs, such as emergency medical services for children and poison control centers, have been cut or are consistently being threatened with reduced budgetary support. Competition for state funding for emergency medical services and public safety education is intense, and the level of funding is insufficient to meet all the needs.

Foundations

Local EMS leaders may develop a not-for-profit foundation or association to help cover the costs of special initiatives. Many research grants, estate gifts, and endowments from other nonprofit organizations require that funds provided by such a foundation stay outside the government budget. The local not-for-profit foundation allows other service groups or private individuals to advance a program or an aspect of EMS care that may not be a priority or may not be affordable for the EMS agency's government or funding agency.

A foundation or nonprofit association must have a board of directors to qualify for federal tax-exempt status under 501(c)(3) of the Internal Revenue Code. To qualify for such status as a nonprofit under a different section of the code, a corporation must comply with the requirements of that federal tax code section. The business purpose of the nonprofit must be listed in the articles of incorporation, and if the organization is applying for tax-exempt status, it is very important that its purpose be well described in the articles.

Challenges and trends

The methods and nuances of service delivery are multifaceted and a dynamic aspect of any EMS agency. Emergency medical care remains unique in the delivery of health care services as its providers are exposed to dangers that other health professions do not typically encounter.

Nationally, demand on EMS agencies is increasing as calls for service rise and the population ages. The workforce is shrinking and financial resources are declining. Community growth demands a variety of planning activities, including transitional planning to span periods or phases of development. Similarly, there are challenges and trends ahead that will require new approaches to EMS delivery.

Patient demographic challenges

EMS providers treat nearly 20 million patients a year, many of whom have experienced complicated medical or traumatic events.[12] In only 14 percent of emergency room visits have patients been transported by ambulance, but that patient demographic accounts for 40 percent of subsequent hospital admissions.[13] EMS providers care for patients with more severe conditions than patients who self-admit to the emergency room.

Seniors often account for the greatest number of patient transports. Many seniors have chronic illnesses that cause difficulties in their care. As life expectancies increase and the baby boomer generation ages, the demand on the medical system, including emergency medical services, will increase. EMS agencies, especially in areas where active adult developments and assisted living facilities are present, must plan ahead for higher incident volume and patient care complexity.

Bariatric (morbidly obese) patients also present challenges for EMS agencies. Treatment and transport of this patient population may require equipment with an increased weight capacity rating and wider widths, and additional personnel are often needed to safely move the patient.

Since EMS providers are on the front line of health care, they can expect to encounter situations involving infectious and contagious diseases. Patients with chickenpox, measles, pertussis, or a disease caused by bioterrorism are potential EMS patients, and EMS providers must be diligent in using universal precautions (body substance isolation) and proper hand washing to protect themselves and the general population. Providers must rate the likely risk posed by presenting signs and symptoms and must record patients' medical history, including vaccinations, and recent travel.

Resource deployment and capacity issues

Maintaining an EMS agency in a state of constant readiness has high associated costs. The typical EMS system is designed for the worst-case scenario and to meet the needs of the most complex incidents. While EMS patients can have severe sicknesses or injuries, many have low acuity conditions. There is industry debate on the best model for deploying EMS resources so that the qualifications of responding personnel match patient needs, and even more attention is being centered on having EMS care that is based on contemporary medical evidence.

Additional challenges face EMS systems in rural areas. Rural areas are geographically large and have low population densities. For EMS agencies, this means delays in emergency notification due to lower frequency of bystanders, variation in available staffing because most rural EMS agencies are staffed by volunteers, extended response and transport times, and limited availability of formal training programs. Strategies for addressing the specific needs in rural areas are strategic deployment of ambulances; resource-sharing agreements among towns, cities, or counties; public education in programs such as CPR and first aid; and partnerships with other EMS agencies and hospitals to increase educational outreach.

Special services

Local government–based EMS agencies often take an all-hazards approach to service delivery. Such an approach encompasses the following specific situations:

Disasters or multiple and mass casualty incidents EMS providers, along with other public safety agencies, respond to an array of emergency incidents including disaster and terrorism incidents (Figure 5–6). However, while EMS personnel represent one-third of first responders, the EMS system has not received nearly that share of federal funding for emergency preparedness activities.

EMS agency leaders need to engage with their local emergency planning committees and emergency management staff to ensure that the EMS role and needs are adequately included in disaster planning efforts. When plans are exercised, either in a tabletop or full-scale functional format, emergency medical services must be included.

Hazardous materials (HAZMAT) EMS agencies may respond to a hazardous materials (HAZMAT) incident. Specialty HAZMAT teams will have specific medical support needs that

Photo by Charles R. Jennings

Figure 5-6 Emergency medical services are a critical component of disaster management.

require additional training for EMS providers. NFPA has several standards related to provider protective clothing and EMS provider competencies for HAZMAT responses that agency leaders need to be familiar with (see Chapter 10).

Technical rescue EMS responses to incidents such as building collapses or those involving trench rescues, confined space rescues, rope rescues, swift-water rescues, or other types of technical rescue require specialized skills beyond routine rescue techniques. EMS agencies may be requested to provide patient care to the technical rescue team members as well as to the victims.

Medical search and rescue Search-and-rescue incidents involve the systematic search for individuals who are in distress or lost, and often occur in recreational areas such as waterways, ski areas, wilderness areas, and caves. In such cases, EMS resources are often integrated with those of the search-and-rescue team.

Law Enforcement Emergency Medical Service At times EMS providers support high-hazard law enforcement situations. Several different models in the industry address the integration of emergency medical services with tactical law enforcement teams. The Law Enforcement Emergency Medical Service is an innovative concept that integrates multiple public safety resources. In situations such as active shooter incidents, law enforcement will perform a dynamic scene entry and begin to secure segments of the scene. An EMS team and the fire department will move into those secured areas to assess and immediately evacuate victims to a casualty collection point for subsequent movement from the scene. This is a transitional and highly dynamic environment that requires close coordination among all involved responders.

Another specialized program designed to train tactical medics is Counter Narcotics and Terrorism Operational Medical Support (CONTOMS). Established by the Department of Health and Human Services, Department of Homeland Security, and the U.S. Park Police, CONTOMS is nationally recognized and operates in specific tactical environments for law enforcement and military operations.

Wildland Many wilderness areas, national forests, national parks, and other undeveloped areas border urban areas. Responses to large events that occur in these wildland-urban interface areas often use a base camp concept, from which teams are deployed out into the affected areas. Often other departments or even other states will request resources. Agency leaders and medical directors need to be familiar with how responding to an emergency situation in another state's jurisdiction or on federal property may affect an EMS provider's ability to provide patient care.

Mass gathering events For community events that must be planned in advance, such as entertainment and sports events, rallies, and parades, it is essential that emergency medical services be included in all event planning to ensure that resources are available to provide medical support for the large crowd. Interagency collaboration and coordination are needed for pre-event analysis and prediction modeling for the various types of expected medical situations.

Public education

As health care costs increase, EMS agencies can reduce their service delivery costs by investing resources in public education and training to prevent injuries and thereby avoid expensive treatment responses. EMS agency leaders need to integrate injury prevention into their strategic and operational plans (see Figure 5–7).

Figure 5-7 EMS providers will give child safety seat training and also install child safety seats.

Courtesy of Prince William County (Virginia) Department of Fire and Rescue

Public education resources

Several organizations are involved in a national movement for injury and violence prevention, and they offer templates to agencies to encourage and assist in the development of community-based programs. The National Highway Transportation Safety Administration (NHTSA) has a program titled Public Information, Education, and Relations for Emergency Medical Services Curriculum: Injury Prevention Modules (PIER).[1] The National Training Initiative for Injury and Violence Prevention focuses on developing essential skills for injury prevention professionals.[2] The State and Territorial Injury Prevention Directors Association, in partnership with the National Association of State EMS Officials and NHTSA, offers a multiagency injury prevention grant program.

1 NHTSA, *Public Information, Education, and Relations for Emergency Medical Services Curriculum: Injury Prevention Modules*, DOT HS 809 520 (Washington, D.C.: NHTSA, October 2002), ems.gov/vgn-ext-templating/ems/docs/PIER.pdf.
2 University of North Carolina, Injury Prevention Research Center, iprc.unc.edu.

EMS agency leaders recognize the vital importance of preventing the 911 call, but budgetary reductions often force them to sacrifice public education in order to keep response units in service. Grant programs are available (see sidebar above), but it is difficult to sustain long-term efforts with grant funding.

Technology advancements

EMS agencies are challenged to keep pace with increasingly sophisticated technology while balancing their needs against budgetary impacts. Agency leaders are often asked to meet with equipment vendors to review new market devices, many of which are introduced without any evidence-based data or outcome results.

An objective and performance-based evaluation process should be a part of any organization's technology-related research and development efforts. A committee can be designated to identify positive innovations as well as novelties to avoid.

One new commercial technology has emerged within the last decade that presents opportunities and new challenges for emergency medical services. Vehicle telematics (the integrated use of telecommunications and information science) and Advanced Automatic Crash Notification (AACN) combine telecommunications with automated sensors and predictive computer programming to help improve response to vehicle crashes. Commercial vendors such as OnStar, ATX, SYNC, 911 Assist, and Hughes Telematics now equip passenger and commercial vehicles with this technology.

Vehicle telematics can notify 911 without relying on the involved individual or bystanders. This is especially beneficial when the vehicle occupants are incapacitated or the incident occurs in a remote area. AACN systems are the second generation of telematics systems and can predict crash severity. Crash data are collected from multiple vehicle sensors that indicate vehicle speed, seat belt use, air bag deployment, number and direction of impacts, and vehicle rollover, and can predict injury severity on the basis of these elements. The system integrates the vehicle's electrical sensors, cellular capabilities, and global positioning system (GPS) to send data to an AACN monitoring center, where advisers contact the PSAP in the area of the accident and relay information that allows PSAP personnel to determine the amount and type of emergency response resources to dispatch.

According to the Centers for Disease Control and Prevention (CDC), the capability for faster notifications, initial victim triage, and the appropriate dispatching of resources to the incident scene indicates that AACN has the potential to improve patient outcomes in the severely injured crash victim.[14] The CDC has partnered with OnStar to investigate and develop evidence-based protocols in response to this technology. However, not all AACN vendors use the same prediction software; not all systems notify a staffed vehicle monitoring center; data systems are not linked into current national injury data systems; and the AACN center serving as the intermediate link between the vehicle and the PSAP delays immediate PSAP notification. Finally, the ability of the current 911 infrastructure to support the current multimedia-capable cellular phones and continued technology advancements is as yet unknown.

Resources for emergency medical services

American College of Emergency Physicians (ACEP), acep.org
American Heart Association (AHA), heart.org/HEARTORG/
American Red Cross (ARC), redcross.org
Center for Domestic Preparedness (CDP), cdp.dhs.gov
Centers for Disease Control and Prevention (CDC), cdc.gov/
Commission on Accreditation of Ambulance Services (CAAS), caas.org
Department of Health and Human Services (DHHS), dhhs.gov
Department of Transportation (DOT), dot.gov
EMS for Children (EMSC)[1]
Federal Emergency Management Agency (FEMA), fema.gov
Federal Interagency Committee on Emergency Medical Services (FICEMS), ems.gov/ficems/index.html
Health Resources and Services Administration (HRSA), hrsa.gov
International Association of Fire Chiefs (IAFC), iafc.org
International Association of Fire Fighters (IAFF), iaff.org
National Association of Emergency Medical Technicians (NAEMT), naemt.org
National Association of EMS Physicians (NAEMSP), naemsp.org
National Center for Injury Prevention and Control (NCIPC), cdc.gov/injury/index.html
National Fire Protection Association (NFPA), nfpa.org
National Highway Traffic Safety Administration (NHTSA), nhtsa.gov
National Institute for Occupational Safety and Health (NIOSH), cdc.gov/niosh/
National Institutes of Health (NIH), nih.gov
National Registry of Emergency Medical Technicians (NREMT), nremt.org
Occupational Safety and Health Administration (OSHA), osha.gov

1 While the EMSC has branches in different states, nationally it is part of the ACEP.

Summary

In a relatively short period of time, the field of emergency medical services has provided an arena for the professional development of countless dedicated and passionate individuals committed to health care delivery in a unique environment. The development of this field has seen many successes, and as the field continues to evolve, there will certainly be twists and turns that current and future EMS providers and agency leadership will have to navigate.

Challenges will emerge from a multitude of directions as emergency medical systems continue to function at the crossroads for public safety, health care, and public health. Health care reform at the national level will undoubtedly affect local EMS agencies, whose leaders need to increase their collaboration and networking with various regional, state, and national governmental agencies and national professional organizations to decrease fragmentation and advance knowledge. EMS stakeholders share many values that must be kept in focus as they cooperate to refine this valuable community service.

Notes

1. Committee on Trauma and Committee on Shock, *Accidental Death and Disability: The Neglected Disease of Modern Society* (Washington, D.C.: National Academy of Sciences, National Research Council, September 1966).
2. Institute of Medicine (IOM), Committee on the Future of Emergency Care in the United States Health Agency, *Emergency Medical Services at the Crossroads* (Washington, D.C.: National Academies Press, 2007).
3. National Highway Traffic Safety Administration (NHTSA), *Emergency Medical Services Agenda for the Future,* DOT HS 808 441 (Washington, D.C.: Department of Transportation [DOT], August 1996), nremt.org/nremt/downloads/EMS%20Agenda%20for%20the%20Future.pdf.
4. NHTSA, *Emergency Medical Services Education Agenda for the Future: A Systems Approach* (Washington, D.C.: DOT, 2000), nhtsa.gov/people/injury/ems/FinalEducationAgenda.pdf.
5. IOM, Committee on the Future of Emergency Care, *Emergency Medical Services at the Crossroads.*
6. Michael J. Karter Jr. and Gary P. Stein, *U.S. Fire Department Profile through 2009* (Quincy, Mass.: National Fire Protection Association [NFPA], October 2010), ii, firecompany4.com/wp-content/uploads/2010/07/National-Volunteer-Firefighters-Profile-2009.pdf.
7. NHTSA, *National EMS Scope of Practice Model* (Washington, D.C.: DOT, 2005), ems.gov/pdf/EMSScope.pdf.
8. Ibid.
9. NHTSA, *National Emergency Medical Services Education Standards,* DOT HS 811 077A (Washington, D.C.: NHTSA, DOT, January 2009), ems.gov/pdf/811077a.pdf.
10. See National Truck Equipment Association, Ambulance Manufacturers Division (AMD), ntea.com/content.aspx?id=3620.
11. NHTSA, *Emergency Medical Services Performance Measures: Recommended Attributes and Indicators for System and Service Performance* (December 2009), ems.gov/pdf/811211.pdf.
12. NHTSA, *National EMS Scope of Practice Model.*
13. IOM, Committee on the Future of Emergency Care, *Emergency Medical Services at the Crossroads.*
14. Centers for Disease Control and Prevention (CDC), *Recommendations from the Expert Panel: Advanced Automatic Collision Notification and Triage of the Injured Patient* (Atlanta, Ga.: CDC, Department of Health and Human Services, 2008), cdc.gov/injuryresponse/pdf/AACN%20Report_FINAL-a.pdf.

CHAPTER 6

Comprehensive Prevention Programs

Jim Crawford

This chapter will provide an understanding of

- The political, business, and other stakeholders influencing the code development and enforcement process
- Local, regional, and national sources of data to support the implementation of a comprehensive prevention program
- The need for comprehensive prevention programs to include a robust fire and life safety education component
- The applications and interrelationships between fire prevention–related codes, standards, laws, and regulations
- The reasons for reviewing fire protection plans, the impact of such a procedure, and ways in which plan review enhances comprehensive prevention
- Fire investigation as a means of improving the overall efficacy of a comprehensive prevention program.

Reinventing Government, written by David Osborne and Ted Gaebler in 1992, identified a lack of competition as one of the problems preventing innovation in government services.[1] Actually, in a tight economy, government services compete for tax dollars with other services and with other programs within each service. Every local government must decide how much to pay for parks, police, sewers, water, transportation, and fire and emergency services. And within the fire and emergency services, how much to pay for prevention programs is a never-ending dilemma that forces competition for limited dollars among emergency operations, hazardous materials (HAZMAT) programs, and prevention.

What then are local managers to do? The more enlightened might subscribe to the old adage that "an ounce of prevention is worth a pound of cure." But they will want to know what they are getting for their money, and they have a right to expect that the prevention professionals in their employ understand the basics of an effective prevention program.

This chapter covers the basic components of a comprehensive prevention program for modern fire and emergency service departments: engineering, enforcement, education, and investigation. These are functions that fire departments should address if they wish their prevention efforts to be effective. This chapter also describes two other components of effective prevention programs: establishing community coalitions to support the prevention effort, and expanding the prevention effort to cover losses and injuries from causes other than fire (e.g., falls by elderly people, bicycle mishaps, drownings). Finally, the chapter includes a section on evaluating prevention programs and a section on staffing and funding options.

Comprehensive prevention: An overview

The term *comprehensive prevention* may be unfamiliar to many within the fire and emergency services or to other local decision makers with an interest in prevention. The term *prevention* is itself almost a misnomer. Typically it means preventing a problem before it occurs, but for the fire service it has traditionally described not only efforts to prevent fires from occurring but also efforts to mitigate them after the fact with built-in protection. For example, fire sprinkler systems do not prevent fires, nor do fire alarms, but they can mitigate the damage by alerting people early enough to escape a fire—or by suppressing the fire until firefighters can arrive.

Traditionally, all these prevention efforts have been limited to code enforcement and public education activities, with the emphasis usually placed on code enforcement programs. The broader term *comprehensive prevention* has evolved to mean the prevention of loss—not only from fire but also from a variety of emergencies. Because most calls handled by a modern fire and emergency services department (for some departments, the figure is as high as 70 percent) are medical emergencies, preventing other losses can mean preventing a medical incident (like a fall) before it occurs or mitigating its effect after it happens, and comprehensive prevention efforts contain elements of both strategies.

Other emergencies to which fire and emergency services respond are a variety of HAZMAT incidents that are a threat to public health or the environment or both. Drowning incidents, auto accidents, trench accidents, terrorist actions, and numerous other emergencies may also result in a call to the local fire department for help. Consequently, the prevention efforts in most fire departments are really efforts to control property damage and losses in human life from a variety of causes.

The building blocks for prevention

For each type of emergency, the building blocks for prevention (including mitigation) are essentially the same: engineering, enforcement, education, and investigation designed to reduce risk or actual loss. In practice, these four concepts are generally embodied in specific functional areas. For example, engineering principles are used in the function of reviewing plans of new construction so that fires or fire spread can be prevented: the review ensures that building features meet code requirements or that alternatives, such as fixed fire protection features, are identified and included in the design before construction begins.

This chapter is a revised and updated version of Chapter 12, "Comprehensive Prevention Programs," by Jim Crawford, in the 2002 edition of this volume.

The enforcement function assumes a need for laws and regulations that govern construction and behavior, and reduce risk or loss. Fire codes apply not only to new building construction or remodeling, but also to existing buildings that must *maintain* their building and fire protection features in accordance with adopted fire codes.

However, the world is a complex place, and not every emergency situation can be regulated with construction practices or laws. Many fire departments are finding that their most significant problems occur in family dwellings, where efforts to design or regulate safety clash with cultural values that give priority to personal privacy and rights. Thus, public education necessarily becomes a principal tool in ensuring safe behaviors that will reduce risk and loss.

Underlying these loss control tools is the assumption that active investigation of the causes of emergencies will lead to better prevention efforts. The causes of fire must be determined if fires are to be prevented. Virtually every major fire code requirement can be traced to the lessons learned through investigations of disasters. Most departments pursue some type of investigation activity as part of their comprehensive prevention efforts. And many are also actively involved in preventing or prosecuting arson-caused fires, so investigation programs usually address that issue as well.

Many refer to evaluation as the fourth "E" of prevention programs. Fire investigations are part of the evaluation process because investigation of cause is, in a sense, also an evaluation of past prevention efforts. But more will be said later in the chapter specifically about evaluation of comprehensive prevention efforts.

Obstacles to prevention

Comprehensive prevention efforts are made more challenging by a number of factors: a shortage of resources, cultural biases, an increase in the size and cultural diversity of the population served, and an increase in potentially hazardous new technologies. Ignorance of how to go about setting up fire prevention programs is still a significant factor for many fire departments. Passing out fire hats, badges, and coloring books is no substitute for identifying community risks, preparing prevention efforts designed to manage those risks, and evaluating prevention efforts over time for modification, elimination, or continuance.

For the many fire and emergency service departments that lack the resources to conduct prevention efforts on a large scale, the best way to control losses effectively is to involve the community in planning and executing prevention programs. Establishing coalitions with business and community groups has become more common and has proven to be very effective in inducing a local community to take charge of its own emergency problems.

Cultural biases also complicate the fire and emergency service's ability to establish comprehensive prevention programs. According to Dr. John Hall of the National Fire Protection Association (NFPA), the United States and Canada are still among the worst of the industrialized nations at controlling fire losses.[2] A number of studies (many of them conducted by TriData Corporation) have examined why some other nations generally perform better (with regard to fire losses) than the United States.[3] These studies found that in Europe and Asia, a long history with fire has produced a strong behavioral emphasis on safety and hence more emphasis on prevention, whereas the United States and Canada (and some other industrialized nations) still emphasize technology and believe that nature (and fire) can be controlled by external means. That belief, combined with a consumer culture that uses materials and discards them, may make U.S. and Canadian populations relatively apathetic about prevention, to which they might assign a low priority. More recent studies from the United Kingdom and Australia are indicating that targeted use of integrated risk management principles (see sidebar on page 174) by individual fire stations are very successful at reducing fire losses—far more so than in the United States.

Another challenge to a comprehensive prevention effort is rapid population growth, which puts greater demands on services of all types, including those provided by a fire and emergency services department. Population growth means greater density of housing; and where fire can spread more quickly from one housing unit to others, greater prevention efforts are required. In addition, the stacking of living or working space in high-rise buildings creates problems that a traditional fire department response normally cannot meet (see Figure 6–1).

Figure 6-1 Extinguishing fires in high-rise structures requires appropriate staffing, equipment, and procedures. Without the timely arrival of the necessary resources, these fires can cause extensive property damage and loss of life.

Photo by Adam K. Thiel

As the population grows not only in number but also in cultural diversity, behavioral differences can further increase the demands on a fire and emergency services department's resources. For example, immigrants who are unfamiliar with U.S. heating or cooking appliances may misuse them. In the home countries of some immigrants, the fire and emergency service is viewed as a governmental authority and is feared rather than trusted. Prevention efforts for diverse populations require multicultural and multilingual programs. Fire and emergency services must develop relationships to reach audiences that may not be able to read.

Fire departments must also stay abreast of the hazards that new technologies represent. The use of exotic chemicals and products increases the potential for HAZMAT emergencies that can threaten large portions of any community.

Generally speaking, the more complex (culturally and technologically) a community is, the more challenges it will face in establishing comprehensive prevention efforts because the scope of programs will necessarily be broad. But the increased demands on emergency services alone will compete for every available dollar, and prevention programs often suffer as a result of that competition.

High-risk high-rises

As communities continue to grow up rather than out, the fire service is facing a stark reality borne out by some studies of the past. In one case, the Louisville (Kentucky) Fire Department realized that parking a full complement of firefighting equipment and personnel at the base of a high-rise would still not allow firefighters to get to a fire floor in time to prevent flashover and extremely dangerous situations. The answer for some time has been to provide fire sprinklers in high-rise buildings, but there are still many high-rises in the nation—most often, apartments, condominiums, and, in once case (Vancouver, Washington), a building that houses elderly low-income residents—without the protection of fire sprinklers. Owners of these high-rises have successfully resisted retrofitting fire sprinkler systems because of the inconvenience and expense of doing so. Consequently, these buildings represent one of the most significant potential risks and a challenge for firefighting forces anywhere they exist.

Finally, a major obstacle for many fire departments focused exclusively on emergency response is that they confuse public relations activities—such as passing out foil junior fire marshal badges—with prevention. Good comprehensive prevention programs are based on sound planning: research and the purchase of materials that work or the development of specialized materials when they are needed.

Whether small or large, communities must meet these challenges, and the way to do so effectively is to use the four basic loss control tools of engineering, enforcement, education, and investigation.

Engineering: Plan review

A department that includes a plan review component in its prevention program is taking advantage of engineering concepts to help ensure a safe level of construction and use. The department makes sure that construction and development plans are reviewed with an eye to fire and life safety issues. This review allows the department to engineer safety designs into the community, thus reducing the occurrence of fires (as well as the expense of providing fire protection after the fact) and improving public safety. For example, a way to increase cost-effective protection during the construction plan review process is to promote the installation of fire sprinkler systems. The fire department's active involvement in the plan review process can ensure continuity between the construction and the use of a building, and can give the department a different (and more cost-effective) view of protecting the public.

Plan review requires time, specialized training, and expertise in the fire, building, and mechanical codes. It also requires some understanding of the construction process and of the way in which issues (e.g., placement of fire department connections for building suppression systems) translate from a piece of paper to actual construction in the field. New construction plan review requires coordinating the fire code with building, planning, transportation, and environmental codes, and provides an opportunity to solve problems before they appear during construction.

Those who review plans must also pay special attention when alternative materials and methods are proposed to satisfy performance-based safety objectives instead of prescriptive requirements. Performance-based codes are discussed later in this chapter.

Fire and life safety issues in relation to new construction

Before the plans are reviewed for fire and life safety issues, the use of the building and its construction type must be reviewed for compliance with the building and applicable fire codes. The building department usually determines compliance, but because the interrelationship between building use and construction type bears heavily on safety, the participation of the fire department at this stage is valuable. There must at least be very close coordination between the building department and the fire department.

It is important for plan reviewers and decision makers (elected officials, city and county managers, and fire chiefs) to understand that buildings are approved and constructed for certain uses and that no one set of construction requirements will suit all types of use or occupancy. For example, the construction requirements for a public assembly occupancy (e.g., a concert hall) usually include more exits than do those for a warehouse structure of the same square footage. Obviously, the reason for the difference is that the number of people per square foot is far greater in a structure where the public will assemble than in a warehouse, and all those people must be able to exit quickly in an emergency.

The interrelationship between occupancy type (or building use) and construction requirements is at the root of many fire disasters that have shaped the fire codes. The fire and emergency services must acknowledge this interrelationship at the plan review stage so that problems may be resolved before construction is completed. Parenthetically, the relationship between the building's construction and its occupancy (use) can be affected when new businesses try to locate in a building that was not designed to handle their safety needs. The incompatibility between the original construction and the new use is usually discovered by a fire inspector making regular rounds of his or her inspection district. Most businesspeople, after all, are focused on their own operational needs and either lack the expertise required for assessing their safety needs or overlook the matter in their haste to do business. If inspectors do not understand the interrelationship between the building's construction and its use, they can miss unsafe situations that should be corrected.

In addition to proper emergency exiting, other fire and life safety features that typically concern fire departments in connection with new construction include fire department access, water supply for firefighting, and fixed fire protection features (e.g., fire sprinklers and alarms). The plan review process is an opportunity to ensure that fire department vehicles can respond and position themselves effectively during an emergency, that water supply is adequate for handling a fire (see the discussion of fire flow in Chapter 3), and that the number and placement of fire hydrants are adequate.

Because fire sprinklers have proven effective in extinguishing or at least controlling fires until the fire department can respond, the fire department must take an active interest in their installation. Sprinklers are now required in many types of buildings, and building officials usually review plans to make sure they are provided for. However, different types of buildings require different sprinkler systems, and some types of systems have special applications. For example, dry sprinkler systems are used in areas where water pipes might freeze; other systems are specially designed for use in homes. Sometimes fire sprinklers must be retrofitted when older buildings are remodeled and brought into compliance with current codes. It is often valuable, therefore, to have fire professionals who understand the construction and hydraulics of sprinkler systems be the ones to review plans in order to properly focus attention on these critical fire protection features—important details can be missed in a review that is too broad.

Currently, the International Residential Code produced by the International Code Council (ICC) requires fire sprinklers in every one- and two-family dwelling in communities where the code is adopted. However, business interests (primarily homebuilders) are fighting that requirement at the national, state, and local levels, so in many communities it has not yet been adopted.

As mentioned previously, exiting requirements are very important to the fire and emergency services because of incidents in the past when it was impossible to rescue large numbers of people who were trapped inside a burning building. The tragedy at the World Trade Center on September 11, 2001, caused another surge of study and debate about adequate exiting. Even the use of elevators for fire exiting, a concept widely viewed as impractical in the past, is being considered again.

These and other fire and life safety issues are often reviewed by fire and emergency services personnel, or by another agency such as the building department, during the construction process. Whichever agency does the review, the fire service must understand—and other local decision makers should recognize—that the fire service has an active interest in building construction and therefore in having the plans reviewed from the perspective of fire and life safety issues. Whether the plans are actually reviewed by fire service personnel or not, these construction issues always enter into a fire department's consideration of the entire fire protection and loss control package that constitutes its fire protection capabilities.

Engineered wood products

Engineered wood products pose a critical concern for the fire and emergency services. High construction and material costs for new buildings and homes in recent decades have created an intense demand for wood products that are inexpensive, can meet a specific construction need, and are lighter and easier to use than traditional wood products. The problem with these products is that in a fire scenario, they often fail far earlier than traditional construction materials do. The dangers of lightweight roof construction are well known, but lightweight flooring and other construction features may give way much faster than ordinary wood, presenting a serious threat to firefighters who are not aware that engineered products are in place. There is a great deal of information on engineered wood products available at the National Fire Protection Association website (nfpa.org), and studies are under way to determine how best to mitigate the problems associated with these products.

Many fire departments have found it valuable to contract with (or hire) fire protection engineers to help them with plan review. Staying abreast of the changes in construction code requirements and new technologies is challenging and often requires special expertise. In addition, because many private firms in the development industry are hiring their own engineers to provide technical reviews of the construction plans or to assist in design, a fire department has to be prepared to meet a technical review with an equal measure of expertise. If it does not, it may fail to note technical flaws and may miss important safety items during the review process.

Plan reviewers must be able to handle specific problems associated with certain types of construction or of occupancy. One occupancy type of concern is hospitals; another is construction in wildland areas, which will be discussed shortly.

Interrelationships and competition among codes

Because of the relationship between construction requirements and the intended use of a building, the codes relevant to each portion of a building's construction should be developed and managed in a coordinated fashion (a change to one code may affect another code), and conflicting interests should be kept in balance. These codes are building (including mechanical and electrical), planning, transportation, environmental, and fire.

Building codes Building codes generally establish the prescriptive requirements in building construction for safety purposes. Building codes generally include separate code requirements (and separate codes) for mechanical systems (heating and ventilation), plumbing, seismic stability, structural stability, and electrical safety. Mechanical systems are often of strategic value for smoke control, and electrical safety is obviously a major factor in fire prevention. Structural stability, exiting, and occupancy types are all issues dealt with in a typical building code.

Planning codes Planning codes usually delineate density and zoning requirements—issues that can directly affect the need for fire department emergency response capabilities. For example, the planning department will usually be the agency that decides whether housing can be built in a wildland area. It also determines housing densities and the location of business or manufacturing operations, both of which require specific fire department response capabilities.

Planning codes can be the subject of intense community conflict: developers may want increased density within the codes to allow for more development, and local decision makers may want increased density to prevent urban sprawl (a goal that has a natural citizen constituency within many communities), yet local property owners may want more green space and may resist increases in density for construction, particularly for housing.

Transportation codes Transportation codes cover road construction requirements. Road construction practices sometimes conflict with fire department goals for quick emergency response, so planning and transportation codes are where the requirements for adequate fire department access are sometimes addressed. Access in wildland-urban areas is one area of concern, as explained in the sidebar on page 162. Another is the introduction of measures, such as speed bumps and narrower roads, to reduce traffic accidents that can delay emergency response. Both goals (reducing accidents and facilitating emergency access) are legitimate but are usually supported by different sectors of a community concerned about different types of problems.

Environmental codes Environmental codes may exist separately or be contained within broader codes that deal with sewage disposal, water supply, and water drainage. Environmental codes that affect water supply—for example, a restriction on flowing water from fire hydrants because of water quality issues—may conflict with the fire department's need to test fire hydrants to make sure that water for firefighting purposes is available when needed. Conflicts can also arise over vegetation in wildland areas. Trees and vegetation protect water and air quality, but they also increase fuel load and the risk of wildfires, which can devastate communities, even in urban areas (see Figure 6-2). Consequently, some fire departments participate in environmental impact reviews to determine how fire hazards may be mitigated while environmental issues are being addressed.

Problems posed by wildland-urban interface and intermix

One situation that puts particular pressure on fire departments is the expansion of urban areas into surrounding wildland areas with highly flammable vegetation (this expansion is called *wildland-urban interface* or *intermix*). Many urban departments are simply not prepared to fight wildland fires on a large scale. Under these circumstances, a fire department must identify ways to control fire losses in wildland-urban areas other than by fighting the fires: it must consider vegetation control and roofing material requirements.

Wildland-urban areas also require wider roads into and out of the community so that people can escape while fire agencies are responding to the scene. Where people escaping in automobiles meet responding fire crews, the streets should be wide enough to handle the extra traffic load. The fire department may want to prohibit on-street parking unless adequate off-street parking is not available.

But these various requirements are not neutral in their effects. They tend to generate conflicts between the needs of the fire department and the needs of other groups in the community.

Photo by Adam K. Thiel

Figure 6-2 Fires in the wildland-urban interface can be extremely resource intensive and demand the skillful coordination of assets from multiple jurisdictions and disciplines. This 2005 fire in Goodyear, Arizona, required mutual aid from surrounding jurisdictions and the State of Arizona.

Fire codes Fire codes are generally designed to prevent fires from occurring and to minimize their effects once they have begun. Model fire codes are developed both for new construction and for current building maintenance, all with the goal of preventing fires or mitigating their damage if they do occur. Currently, the two most comprehensive fire codes in use throughout the United States are produced by ICC and NFPA. NFPA also publishes more than 200 related standards that provide additional requirements for many specific fire safety issues. (For a discussion of standards, codes, and regulations pertinent to the fire and emergency services, see Chapter 10.)

Requirements for fire sprinklers, fire alarms, fire department access, and fire water supply are all typically found in fire codes. But the individual issues addressed in the model fire codes and accompanying NFPA standards cover such a large scope of potential fire problems and are so complicated that developing expertise in the field takes considerable training and time.

Many codes allow alternative materials and methods to achieve a result equivalent to prescriptive code requirements. For example, when a developer wishes to reduce requirements for fire flow from hydrants or for fire department access, some codes accept fire sprinklers as an alternative method of providing adequate water for suppression. New efforts to substitute performance objectives for prescriptive code requirements provide even more opportunities for creatively crafted local solutions to construction problems (see the section on "Performance-based Codes"). It is advantageous to have fire department personnel involved in the plan review process, devising engineering solutions that can be balanced against emergency response capabilities.

Coordination and advocacy

Decision makers must understand the interrelationships among these various codes if plan review is to take place not in isolation but in relation to the larger development context. In addition, decision makers should not forget that codes and ordinances for construction are usually in place for a reason. Under pressure to streamline development procedures, local decision makers often conclude that a one-size-fits-all plan review process will benefit the community's economic vitality. They attempt to lump codes and ordinances together in a quick review process that can miss vital safety issues. Consistency and efficiency are certainly legitimate goals, but those who are designing a municipal or county system for reviewing construction and development plans should approach their task cautiously.

As for the fire and emergency services department, it needs to pay attention to its part in the larger community development process—a process in which competing interests within the community seek to use the codes to support their own values and goals. As the various interests are balanced for the collective good, a lack of advocacy for fire safety issues could lead to disasters that capture the attention of the community, which will want to know why such a situation was not prevented.

Consequently, one of the challenges for fire departments in the plan review process is to be advocates for public safety while coordinating their efforts with the requirements of the other codes. Such a challenge requires the fire department's plan reviewers to know the other, related codes and to be committed to working as a team to resolve problems when all the conflicting interests have legitimate points of view.

Performance-based codes

An important issue affecting plan review is the effort to streamline the development process by replacing prescriptive requirements with performance goals. Performance goals can often be met by more than one design solution for construction and development. Performance-based codes allow flexibility in construction practices and are supposed to do so without reducing the level of safety for building inhabitants.

But substituting performance goals for prescriptive requirements can be taken to extremes. Some developers of buildings that would normally require fire sprinklers, for example, have sought to save time and money by offering design features that they claim will provide the same level of life safety protection without the installation of sprinklers; however, these claims are often difficult or impossible to prospectively substantiate. Model fire and building codes already incorporate a degree of performance design. Although these codes require certain specific safety features (e.g., fire sprinklers, smoke and fire separation between the floors of a building, and specific requirements for earthquake/seismic stability), they also allow alternative materials and methods that will achieve the same level of safety that prescriptive code requirements achieve. In essence, fire and emergency service departments have used performance goals for many years.

Since many fire departments already have experience exchanging some protection features for others, performance codes could represent an opportunity to be more creative in crafting local solutions. However, the movement toward more formalized performance-based codes presents fire officials and local decision makers with additional challenges.

Performance-based design requires a level of expertise in engineering and computer modeling that most fire and emergency service departments do not yet have. Fire officials and local decision makers will therefore have to ensure that they can provide adequate scientific and engineering analysis to properly evaluate performance goals in the plan review process.

Legal issues in plan review

Whenever a government agency establishes requirements of any kind, legal issues invariably arise. It is impossible to totally protect an agency from the threat of a lawsuit, for people may file suit in court as they wish. Each agency responsible for fire protection should therefore be prepared to conduct its operations in a fashion that minimizes legal liability and protects itself in court. (For a discussion of fire department liability for negligence, see Chapter 10.)

The most important thing that local decision makers can do is obtain expert legal advice to determine how they are affected by federal, state, and local statutes applicable to adoption and management of fire codes. Usually a municipal, county, or special fire district's legal counsel can provide such advice.

The legal issues most commonly connected with plan review concern the competence of the review itself and the justification for the government's requirements. Taking an individual's property rights by means of code requirements, without due process, can expose the jurisdiction to legal liability. For example, limiting someone's ability to build a structure without providing notification or an appeals process could be considered a "taking" of value from the developer or property owner.

Jurisdictions that perform plan review should make sure that the employees who conduct the review are qualified to do so. Any legal challenge to the accuracy of the work will ultimately come down to the ability of plan reviewers to perform their jobs skillfully. Technical training and certification are becoming more prevalent and in some jurisdictions are required. In addition, problems may arise if reviewers provide inadequate information. For example, a reviewer may approve a developer's plans but overlook some code requirements. If the overlooked requirements are caught later and the developer is required to comply at a later stage of the development process, at extra expense, the developer could sue for damages.

If plans are approved that do not comply with the applicable code, almost certainly there will be some liability. There may be legal challenges if the person performing the plan review tries to require features that are not included in applicable codes. Builders who find out they have added safety features that are not actually required are usually upset, and justifiably so. Conversely, when safety features are clearly overlooked in the plan review process, an unsafe building may result, and if that building later burns and someone is injured in the fire, liability could exist for the jurisdiction that approved substandard construction practices.

Fire officials and local decision makers who are responsible for the plan review process must understand the limits within which they are allowed to operate. The best and most appropriate way to understand these limits is to obtain legal counsel from attorneys with expertise in fire and building codes and familiarity with plan review.

Enforcement: Code adoption and administration

The second principal function of a comprehensive prevention program is enforcing fire and life safety codes (and helping to develop model codes). Enforcement is the mechanism used to obtain compliance with codes and laws during the construction process and afterward, when buildings are occupied. Enforcement after construction means regulating people's behavior.

Laws and codes developed with the best of intentions accomplish nothing if they are not followed. Most people will comply with laws and codes if they understand the need, but nowadays not everyone sees the same need for fire safety codes, even though each of the model codes is rooted in fire disasters, such as the fire on May 28, 1977, at the Beverly Hills Supper Club in Southgate, Kentucky, which killed 165 people, and the one at the MGM Grand Hotel in Las Vegas, Nevada, in 1980, which killed 85 people and injured another 600. Most people never hear about the Rhythm Nightclub Fire that occurred in April of 1940 in Natchez, Mississippi. That fire, which started when flammable decorations were ignited, killed 209 African Americans and still ranks as the second worst nightclub fire in U.S. history. More recently, in 2003 the Station Nightclub Fire in West Warwick, Rhode Island, occurred when a rock band set off fireworks indoors without a permit, and the fireworks ignited flammable foam installed on the walls and ceiling to help with sound acoustics. That fire killed 100 people.

All these fires, and others before and since, have taught lessons about fire safety that have been incorporated into modern fire and building codes. As mentioned above, laws requiring smoke detectors and codes requiring fire sprinklers and adequate exiting in case of emergencies stem from these lessons. It is important, therefore, to ensure that everyone complies with the codes.

Codes are often paired with standards that provide more detail and regulations. For example, a code may require that fire sprinklers be provided in an occupancy, but the specific installation and hydraulic requirements necessary to make sure that the sprinklers will function properly will be in the accompanying standards. Thus, not only fire codes but also accompanying standards must be enforced as part of a comprehensive prevention program.

Code development: Model codes and globalization

Adopting codes and standards governing building construction and use implies not only that these policies will be administered effectively but also that the people involved in administering them will ensure that they are up-to-date and in accord with modern fire safety practices. To meet this responsibility, decision makers at the local level must participate in the development of codes and standards. No one is a better advocate for high-quality codes, and no one better understands their effect on the community, than the people who administer them daily.

Not all fire departments can afford to participate in the development of model fire and life safety codes, but those that can afford to usually do. And their role is important: they help ensure that model codes are based on actual field experience in firefighting and inspection activities.

Participation in the model code process usually involves becoming a member of the code development organization, traveling to its code development meetings, and voting on the language of the model code. Some code development organizations allow input and proposals via the Internet, but in most cases, voting still has to be done in person.

As fire officials or other decision makers participate in code development, they are exposed to an emerging trend that affects the process used by each of the model code organizations. Trade has become global, and trade agreements between nations have opened up economic opportunities for international companies, which desire consistency of code applications across international boundaries. Thus, there is a need for codes and standards (in all areas) that can be used in more than one nation. The first areas to feel this pressure have been product standards and construction practices, but other codes and standards are following suit.

As the demand for uniform codes and standards increases, the participants in the process of adopting model language become more numerous and represent a wider range of national perspectives, histories regarding fire and life safety, scientific analyses, and views about how codes should be written. Many of these participants are from nations that cannot afford the protections taken for granted by people in more industrialized nations. Accordingly, views vary widely about how many safety features should be provided and what constitutes an acceptable level of risk. For example, Mexico allows the storage of propane gas on rooftops of buildings; the United States does not.

To meet this challenge and to influence the code development process in an international arena, participants will have to bring to bear active participation, sound knowledge of scientific and engineering techniques, and accurate data.

Enforcing codes and standards means adopting them and administering them, and fire officials and local decision makers must understand the limits and the foundation of their authority to do precisely that. Administering codes requires identifying and drawing up an inventory of properties to be inspected, maintaining a database and a record-keeping system, training and selecting personnel, and managing the appeals process. (Evaluating the performance of enforcement personnel and the enforcement program is also necessary and is discussed near the end of this chapter in the section titled "Using Performance Measures to Evaluate Prevention Programs.") To understand the legal issues involved in adopting and managing a code enforcement program, those who administer the codes should obtain legal guidance about the extent of their authority, and about their liability, when enforcing fire codes.

Local and state codes are usually based on the model codes produced by ICC (iccsafe.org) or NFPA (nfpa.org). Fire officials should participate in the development of these model codes as much as possible to help ensure that the codes are in alignment with local needs. In doing so, however, they must recognize that the globalization of codes and standards (concomitant with the globalization of trade and commerce) will challenge U.S. practices and their ability to influence code development (see the sidebar above).

The authority to adopt and enforce laws, codes, and standards

Usually local authority to adopt and enforce laws, codes, and their underlying standards is passed down from the state. That is, the laws and codes relating to fire safety adopted by local jurisdiction are usually taken from a model fire code that has been adopted in a statewide version or from specific state statutes.

Model codes are produced nationally and internationally to provide a minimum level of public safety. In addition to passing laws relating to fire reporting, smoke detectors, fire sprinklers, and fireworks, many states adopt a statewide version of a national model fire code—typically that of ICC or NFPA, as mentioned earlier. But model fire code language is useless to a local jurisdiction unless the community adopts it as law. Once the state permits the local jurisdiction to adopt certain code provisions, the jurisdiction must adopt the provisions that it wants to enforce, in accordance with state law.

Fire officials and other decision makers must understand which level of authority belongs to the federal government, which to the state, and which to the local jurisdiction. Most local codes have been in place for many years, so the underlying authority is taken for granted. But legal challenges may nonetheless arise; and for newly formed fire departments, the foundation of legal authority may not be clear. It is most important that fire officials obtain proper legal advice locally so that they will fully understand both the legal authority of the jurisdiction's code enforcement efforts and the limits of that authority.

Scope of model codes

ICC and NFPA both produce a family of model codes (e.g., building, fire, mechanical, etc.) appropriate for use anywhere in the nation. Although it is better for a jurisdiction to adopt codes produced in one setting, some jurisdictions do mix the codes, adopting those they find most desirable and working out points of conflict they encounter among the codes adopted.

Some statewide model codes represent the minimum standards for fire and life safety; local jurisdictions may exceed these minimums depending on the community's specific needs or desires. For example, some jurisdictions have adopted local ordinances that exceed their statewide requirements, as is the case with the fire sprinkler ordinance of Louisville, Kentucky. Kentucky's state code, like most state codes, applies to new construction only, but Louisville was able to demonstrate its inability to control high-rise fires with traditional firefighting means and was therefore able to adopt into law a requirement that fire sprinklers be placed in all commercial high-rise buildings. The requirement was retroactive, and it superseded previous building codes. Another example of exceeding a minimum standard occurs when a community requires that sprinklers be installed in all residential properties, not just in commercial structures or in one- and two-family homes. That has been the case in Scottsdale, Arizona, for many years, and the results have been well documented.[4]

Other codes, primarily building codes, are mini-max in their scope: they specify both the minimum and the maximum fire and life safety requirements and cannot be changed except by specific appeal or an amendment process, usually at the state level.

Administration of the code enforcement process

Adopting the laws necessary to administer codes and standards is only the beginning of code enforcement. Administering the enforcement process effectively is critical, and it is an art that requires sound judgment and open communication between those responsible for enforcement and those who are legally required to comply.

Not every fire departments has been given the authority to administer its jurisdiction's code enforcement activities. Philadelphia, for example, at one time assigned fire hazard inspections to the city's division of licenses and inspections.

Fire departments that do administer code enforcement need policies to guide the various personnel who are responsible for enforcement at different levels of the organization (e.g., fire marshal versus inspector) (Figure 6-3).

The distinction between law and policy for code officials is that laws and codes

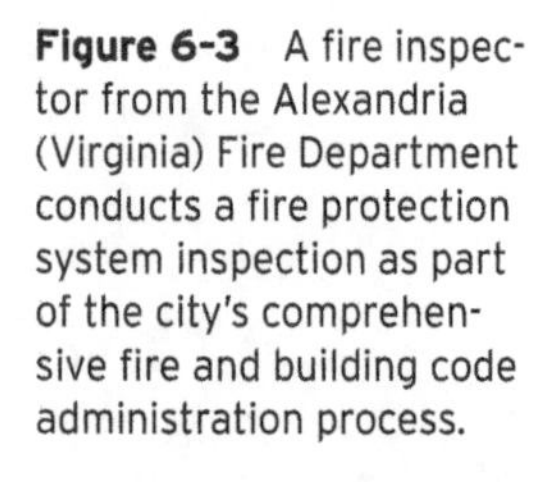

Figure 6-3 A fire inspector from the Alexandria (Virginia) Fire Department conducts a fire protection system inspection as part of the city's comprehensive fire and building code administration process.

Courtesy of the Alexandria (Virginia) Fire Department

usually state the prescriptive requirements (e.g., what kinds of structures are required to have smoke alarms), whereas policies—much like standards—deal with the more specific how-to questions that arise during the daily administration of codes. For example, a law may state that a smoke alarm is required in every home; the standard may say what type of alarm is appropriate and where in the home it should be placed; and the policy describes how the law and standard will be enforced—such as through the issuance of some kind of citation or penalty. The policy may also address how often inspections should be held or how building occupants should conduct and report a self-inspection.

Policies establishing code administration practices help to ensure consistency and equity in enforcement. Many codes require some interpretation as to their exact meaning, and some codes leave decisions about specific issues up to the local fire official. For example, the Uniform Fire Code (a model code) stipulates that the fire chief may determine what constitutes an imminent fire hazard requiring drastic enforcement measures. Such discretionary authority is very broad in theory but is rarely exercised in practice because of practical political concerns. Any fire administrator who thinks that he or she has the final word in code enforcement is naive about the pressures that concerned citizens can bring to bear if they perceive what they believe to be an abuse of power by fire officials or decision makers. Given the occasional need for interpretation and for the exercise of discretion, clear policies establishing code administration practices can be very advantageous.

Policies may or may not have the same force as law; again, local jurisdictions should obtain legal advice about their authority to enforce policies as well as laws. The two may have different enforcement procedures—or legal weight.

The steps in administering the code enforcement process are outlined in several publications, including the International Fire Service Training Association's manual *Fire Inspection and Code Enforcement*[5] and inspection manuals produced by NFPA and ICC. Among the activities described in these manuals are identifying and inventorying properties to be inspected, maintaining a database and a record-keeping system, training and selecting inspectors, and managing appeals.

Identifying and inventorying properties to be inspected The goal of a code enforcement inspection program is to ensure that business properties comply with appropriate fire safety codes, although inspections also provide an opportunity to make nonbinding fire and life safety recommendations. Ideally, every commercial property in a jurisdiction receives regular, systematic fire safety inspections. However, many jurisdictions are not able to put the ideal into practice, and local decision makers may be forced to prioritize their inspections. They may base their priorities on a statistical history of fire problems and on a list of occupancies, such as hospitals and schools, where the risk of death or loss is great although the likelihood of fires is small. Consequently, a prioritized inspection list may include properties where fires are frequent as well as properties where fires are infrequent but the risk of death or loss is great.

Usually, hazards that have been identified are abated through some type of administrative or quasi-judicial system of code compliance. In some cases, jurisdictions seek a court order to obtain compliance. Most jurisdictions order immediate code corrections to correct simple hazards—those that do not pose an imminent threat to life safety—but set the date for reinspection about thirty days later to give the building owner/operator time to comply. Providing notice that the hazard exists—and is not allowed by code at any time—helps limit liability for the jurisdiction during the period actually allowed for compliance.

Most codes define an imminent threat loosely, and the judgment of local decision makers is required. An imminent threat usually exists when a fundamental fire safety feature has broken down and the breakdown threatens the safety of a structure's occupants. Typical examples include locked exits, shut-off fire sprinkler or alarm systems, and people placed in a hazardous area that was not designed for them. Finding people living in a building that was not designed for their safe exiting is most threatening to fire officials, who are concerned about residents' safety and about their own liability if they allow an unsafe practice to remain unabated. In these kinds of circumstances, a much shorter time to gain compliance is usually given. In extreme cases, a business may be closed until compliance is obtained.

Some hazards involve structural or mechanical problems that may require longer periods of time to be corrected. Under those circumstances, it is up to fire officials to determine an acceptable timetable for correcting the hazards.

Maintaining a database and a record-keeping system A database and a record-keeping system are very important aids in prioritizing inspections; they provide information on where fires are occurring and how often buildings are inspected. When a fire occurs, decision makers usually want to know when the building was last inspected and what the inspector found, to see if there is a relationship between the hazards noted in the inspection and the cause of the fire. A good record-keeping system can therefore help improve prevention efforts by allowing officials to pinpoint the businesses that most commonly have fires and the hazards that most commonly lead to fires. A good record-keeping system is also important for legal purposes, as discussed in a later section of this chapter.

Selecting and training inspectors A major issue in administering code inspections is the need to ensure consistency. This need is partly addressed by policies and partly by careful selection and training of inspectors.

Selecting the right kinds of people to work in a code enforcement program is important and can be difficult to do. Choosing enforcement personnel from among firefighters may be desirable: firefighters are usually dedicated to fire safety and, because of their own experience, can be effective advocates for code enforcement and compliance. (Persuasion is often effective in gaining willing compliance before enforcement is necessary.) Unfortunately, many firefighters are reluctant to become enforcers because the role requires them to push people to do something that the people may not want to do—in strong contrast to the role that firefighters usually play of being present to help in the event of an emergency. Consequently, many departments use nonfirefighting personnel, and some even use volunteers, to conduct inspections.

Staffing patterns are discussed in more detail in the section on staffing and funding options for prevention programs, but decision makers should pay particular attention when selecting their code enforcement personnel. No one can cause problems for a fire official or local decision maker more quickly than a fire code inspector who is either inept or overly attracted to the role of enforcer.

The codes can be complex, and inspectors who are more experienced are often better able to identify code violations. When an experienced inspector identifies hazards that previous (less experienced) inspectors missed, occupants sometimes complain that the (more experienced) inspector is "harassing" them. Consequently, inspector training is critical for the effective management of code enforcement activities, aiding consistency in identifying hazards.

A variety of training programs for code enforcement personnel are available, as is certification for both familiarity with the code and experience doing inspections. Each of the model code organizations offers some type of training and certification program. And many jurisdictions are finding value in "certifying" their inspections by certifying their personnel and carefully administering their inspection process. For example, many jurisdictions include a check sheet for their inspectors in order to provide more consistency during the inspection (see Figure 6–4). And some use preinspection letters to notify businesses as to what common hazards will be looked for during an inspection so that the business owners may prepare and become partners in creating a safe environment, rather than being merely passive targets of enforcement actions that are imposed on them (see Figure 6–5 on page 170).

Managing the appeals process The final authority for fire code administration is usually an appeals board. Boards do not generally have the authority to eliminate code requirements, but they do have broad authority to determine equivalent forms of protection or to interpret code where it is not clear. A board may be created at the state level, as is the Massachusetts Fire Safety Commission, or at the local level. Members of appeals boards are usually architects, engineers, and design professionals from the community who have a working knowledge of the code but are not directly connected with the fire and emergency services. The purpose of these boards is to act as the final arbiter when the code requirements are subject to interpretation, or when alternative materials and methods are being suggested for equivalent levels of fire and life safety protection. (The obvious example is when fire sprinklers are offered in lieu of other fire suppression water supplies.) However, appeals boards do not supplant the judicial system when the issue is one of legal interpretation or legal challenge.

PALM BEACH GARDENS FIRE DEPARTMENT
10500 N. Military Trail, Palm Beach Gardens, FL 33410 Phone (561) 775-8260 Fax (561) 775-8269
FIRE SAFETY INSPECTION REPORT

Occupant:__________ Date:__________
Address:__________ Suite:__________ Phone No.:__________
Emergency Contact:__________ Title:__________ Phone No.:__________

( )	Means of Egress: ( ) obstructed ( ) locked ( ) improper locking device. Location(s):
( )	Emergency Lighting: ( ) inoperative ( ) not provided. Location(s):
( )	Illuminated Exit Sign: ( ) inoperative ( ) not provided ( ) battery back-up inoperative. Location(s):
( )	Fire Sprinkler System: ( ) required clearance (18 inches) not maintained for fire sprinkler heads ( ) not monitored by fire alarm system ( ) no maintenance contract *NFPA 25* Fire Department Connection: ( ) obstructed ( ) damaged ( ) missing caps Fire Sprinkler Riser: ( ) valves not chained and/or locked ( ) spare heads not provided
( )	Fire Alarm System: ( ) non-functional ( ) no current inspection tag ( ) no central station monitoring
( )	Dangerous accumulation of waste or combustible material. Location(s):
( )	Fire Extinguisher(s): ( ) not provided ( ) not accessible ( ) not mounted ( ) requires maintenance *Minimum classification is 2A-10BC rated extinguisher inspected and tagged by a licensed technician* Location(s):
( )	Electrical Hazards: ( ) improper use of extension cord ( ) missing blanks in electrical panel ( ) use of outlet multiplier ( ) combustible material too close to a heat producing appliance ( ) electrical panel obstructed – *minimum 30" clearance* ( ) circuits not marked Location(s):
( )	Address not visible from the roadway: ( ) front ( ) rear
( )	Knox Box: ( ) requires maintenance ( ) missing/improper keys
( )	
( )	
( )	
( )	

Authority: Chapter 38, Code of Ordinances, City of Palm Beach Gardens

( ) NO VIOLATIONS NOTED THIS DATE	**( ) FORWARD TO FIRE MARSHAL**
( ) ALL VIOLATIONS CORRECTED	**( ) FORWARD TO CODE ENFORCEMENT**

Your immediate attention is required on the above listed items. You have (14) days to correct any and all violations unless otherwise noted. Failure to correct violations on or before the re-inspection date will result in further action by the Fire Marshals office. Please contact the Fire Prevention Division of the Palm Beach Gardens Fire Department if you have any questions. (561) 775-8260.

Inspected by:__________, I.D. No.____, Date:_____ Occupant:__________
Re-inspected by:__________, I.D. No.____, Date:_____ Occupant:__________
Remarks:__________

White copy – Occupant Yellow copy – Occupant after violations corrected Pink copy – Fire Prevention

Figure 6-4 The Palm Beach Gardens (Florida) Fire Department's check sheet for inspections lists common hazards that inspectors should check for.

Managing the appeals process means establishing some kind of review board (i.e., the appeals board itself) with specific authority for the task. It means processing appeals in a timely fashion and preparing board members and code management personnel to deal with decisions professionally and within the scope of their authority.

Many jurisdictions also set up an administrative appeals process to deal with smaller issues regarding code enforcement that may arise frequently. Handled by senior managers in the prevention field, an administrative appeals process may provide a quick remedy for code interpretations—a responsibility that individual inspectors may not even wish to have.

Legal issues in code enforcement

Like the plan review process, enforcement strategies may raise legal issues. Fire officials should take several precautions to avoid legal liability.

First, maintaining records and ensuring the completion of hazard abatement are important. In numerous court cases, local jurisdictions have been found liable because they failed to abate hazards that either had been or should have been identified.[6] Consequently, having an accurate record of inspections and hazard abatement may very well provide some protection from legal liability. Second, local authorities should be aware that entry to inspect a property is not granted automatically and may require an administrative warrant from an appropriate court. Third, local jurisdictions may have some protection from liability for failing to inspect if they lack the resources to inspect. But that is a very difficult outcome to determine in advance of a lawsuit. To determine what level of protection from liability they may enjoy, fire officials and decision makers should obtain expert local legal counsel.

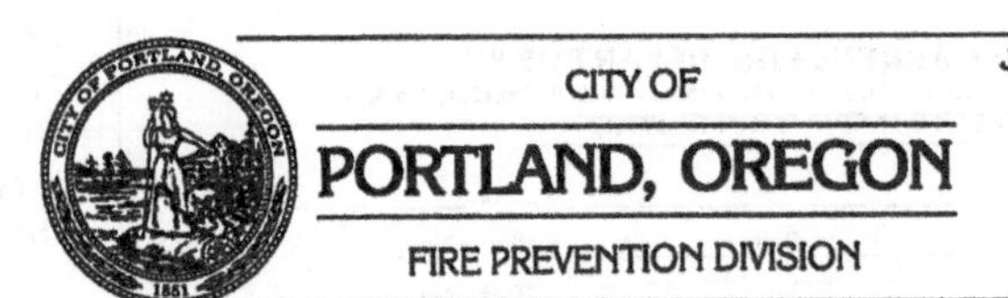
CITY OF
PORTLAND, OREGON
FIRE PREVENTION DIVISION

Jim Francesconi, Commissioner of Public Utilities
Robert Wall, Chief
Jim Crawford, Fire Marshal
55 S.W. Ash Street
Portland, Oregon 97204-3590
(503) 823-3700
FAX (503) 823-3710

"YOUR SAFETY IS YOUR RESPONSIBILITY"

Dear Business Owner/Manager:

We're sending this letter to let you know that an Inspector will visit your occupancy soon to perform a regular routine fire prevention inspection. While the Inspector will look for compliance with all parts of the Fire Code, he/she will pay special attention to hazards/violations that are most common and that are most likely to cause fire damage to your business. A list of these hazards (and detailed explanation of each) is enclosed. We encourage you to correct these hazards and any other violations before the inspection. **Any hazards from this list that we find during the initial inspection will result in a fee of $10 per violation category.**

It is the Fire Marshal's responsibility to inspect all commercial structures in the City except one- and two-family residential units. The objective of these inspections is to reduce fire damage and loss of life. **The Fire Marshal's Office seeks willing compliance with the Fire Code.**

Upon completion of the inspection, our data base will be updated and **a bill for the inspection mailed to you.** There is a fee for each occupancy as listed on the enclosed "Fee Schedule." Most businesses can expect the initial bill after the first inspection. There are also fees that will be billed after a re-inspection if code violations are not corrected in a timely manner.

The fee-for-service aspect of this fire prevention program is new. It is the result of decisions by the City to recover costs of services that include private benefits. See "Background Information" for an explanation of this new program and information about your right to appeal.

If you have any questions before the inspection, or if you would find it convenient to schedule an appointment for the inspection, call 823-3700. Your call will be directed to the appropriate District Inspector.

Figure 6-5 Some jurisdictions (e.g., Portland, Oregon) are now sending out preinspection letters to allow building owners and managers to comply *before* an inspection is actually done. The idea is to achieve willing compliance from businesses that are otherwise ignorant of what is required by proper fire and life safety regulations.

Educating the public about fire and life safety

A basic precept in the United States is that a person's home is his or her castle. Accordingly, fire and life safety codes have traditionally been lenient with regard to personal living space. One- and two-family dwellings and even individual apartment units enjoy protection from code enforcement activities. But most fire-related deaths and injuries occur in residential properties, so public fire and life safety education should be one of the more important strategies of a comprehensive prevention program.

Many jurisdictions say that public education is a priority but in fact give it little support. However, more fire departments are coming to understand the value of public education and the effect that it can have on their total protection and prevention effort. They are increasing their resources for this vital function and are seeing positive results.

A modern public education program that strives to reach the general public and change behavior to improve safety consists of two approaches: bringing education into the schools and taking it directly to the public. Bringing fire education into the schools reflects the long-held belief that the way to produce lasting results in safety attitudes and behaviors is to reach young children, who will grow up to be safer adults. Going directly to the public with a variety of methods has the same basic goal: to increase knowledge and change behavior so that people are safer. Another decision is whether to deliver the public education program as a stand-alone message or whether to deliver it in partnership with other agencies (and their respective messages).

Conducting a comprehensive public fire and life safety education program means providing true educational opportunities in a variety of settings. Whether in schools, at community meetings, or through marketing outlets, high-quality education must be age appropriate and in a form that will capture interest. It raises the public's level of consciousness about safety. But to be effective, education efforts must ultimately do more than raise consciousness: they must change the behavior of targeted populations to reduce the risk of, and the losses from, fire and various injuries.

Courtesy of the Portland (Oregon) Fire and Rescue Department

Figure 6-6 A Portland, Oregon, firefighter teaches school-age children about fire and life safety.

Courtesy of the Alexandria (Virginia) Fire Department

Figure 6-7 The Alexandria (Virginia) Fire Department's fire safety house is mounted on a trailer for movement to events across the city.

Education in the schools

Schools are generally recognized as a critical part of any public education program. To be effective, however, fire and life safety education for children must go beyond simple presentations of what a firefighter looks like in protective gear. Showing schoolchildren what firefighters do has good public relations value but does not teach them anything about their own safety. School presentations should include well-designed educational activities to teach children directly, involving them in decision-making and learning exercises (Figure 6–6). Research indicates that students who are actively involved in making decisions are more likely to remember educational messages and change their safety behaviors. A video is fine, but active participation—even physical participation—has proven to be a longer-lasting educational tool.

Because teachers are sometimes the best source of safety education, fire and life safety education in the schools also includes preparing teachers' curricula to serve as technical guides for the teachers' lessons. Even when supplemented by fire department presentations, teachers are always the best resource for providing education in the schools. The fire service accomplishes its prevention goals more effectively by helping teachers than by trying to replicate their role.

The fire department's role in school programs is to support solid educational curricula with presentations that reinforce the safety consciousness achieved by children who have been exposed to a well-structured educational program. For example, presentations such as clown programs or puppet shows as well as other age-appropriate educational offerings can reinforce the proper messages for children (see Figure 6–7). And a simple visit from the local firefighters can serve as a positive reinforcement mechanism for teachers to help them motivate children's learning, for children usually enjoy a visit from the fire department.

Well-designed safety curricula may achieve a level of sophistication that truly teaches students proper messages and behaviors, and involves solid educational activities in which the students practice decision-making and learning exercises. These educational "products" must also be well tested, and there must be documented evidence that the resources invested are actually producing something of value for the children and for the departments expending the resources. High-quality products such as NFPA's *Risk Watch®* or *Learn Not to Burn®* have been tested, and their educational value has been documented. Anything developed at the local or state level must not only meet the same standard of testing but also be in a form that teachers will find useful; otherwise, the materials will sit on the shelf.

Risk Watch® and *Learn Not to Burn®* are registered trademarks of the National Fire Protection Association (NFPA), Quincy, Mass.

Children's fire safety house

Firefighters in Clark County, Washington, (as in many communities) have built a down-sized mobile replica of a two-story house featuring a bedroom and a hallway on each floor. Their purpose is to teach fire safety to elementary school children. Firefighters and volunteers conduct fire exit drills with the children inside the fire safety house using electronically operated smoke detectors, a nontoxic smoke machine, and red strobe lights to simulate a real house fire. A control room operated by one person is located inside the fire safety house, which also contains the controls for the smoke machine as well as the piping system used in directing the smoke. These homes are a great tool for learning because they involve physical activity—but they are labor-intensive.

Schools are under increasing pressure to improve their performance in core areas while reducing costs, so fire safety alone may not receive the priority it once did. Thus, many fire departments are expanding their public education efforts in schools to cover the prevention of other injuries besides those related to fires. The underlying concept of the *Risk Watch®* curriculum is that safety for schoolchildren is best promoted by a coalition approach:[7] the fire service, law enforcement, public health, and other agencies with an interest in public safety must cooperate to maximize their effect in schools already pressed for time and resources. While NFPA no longer provides support for *Risk Watch®*, it does provide support for its basic fire safety curriculum, *Learn Not to Burn®*.

Those pursuing effective educational strategies in schools will find that there are two national trends—one toward preventing all the injuries encountered by a modern fire and emergency services department, the other toward establishing coalitions between the fire service and other organizations. The purpose of these coalitions is to raise the public's consciousness of, and level of concern for, safety by doing so *collectively*. And some states, like Oregon, are developing their own multihazard safety curricula with assistance from other partners.

Targeted public education programs

Educating children is only one major part of a comprehensive public education strategy. The other is taking the message directly to the general public, usually using one or more of the media. Because public education programs are usually not well funded, the effort to reach the public outside the school system must be prioritized and targeted. A large (purchased) advertising campaign that works for private sector products is not within the budget of most fire departments.

A fire department needs to analyze its data about the community's fire or injury problem and then target audiences most at risk for fire loss (see Figure 6–8). Taking this approach usually leads to the conclusion that there are several target audiences besides schoolchildren. National data published by NFPA and the U.S. Fire Administration (USFA) suggest that other groups at high risk for fire loss are elderly people, young children, ethnic minorities, and low-income residents. In fact, the strongest correlating factor for fire loss is usually the income level of victims.[8]

Public education programs are most effective when they are developed specifically for each target audience or target message. And for maximum effect, they are often combined with other prevention strategies. Portland, Oregon, for example, has a combination program designed specifically for elderly (mobility-impaired) people that couples fire safety education with a low-cost program to prevent falls. The fire department cooperates with a nonprofit organization (Unlimited Choices) to provide fall prevention hardware (e.g., nonskid rugs, elevated toilet seats, bed rails) as well as smoke alarms, fire safety materials, and even some new technology that is designed to regulate kitchen stovetop cooking temperatures (see Figure 6–9).

Radio, television, and newspapers all play a role in the public marketing effort. Specialized displays and home fire safety trailers that demonstrate the value of fire sprinklers are a popular way to provide education to certain segments of the community. And many departments still make specialized presentations to businesses or civic organizations, and participate in such large events as home and garden shows, to disseminate the fire and life safety message.

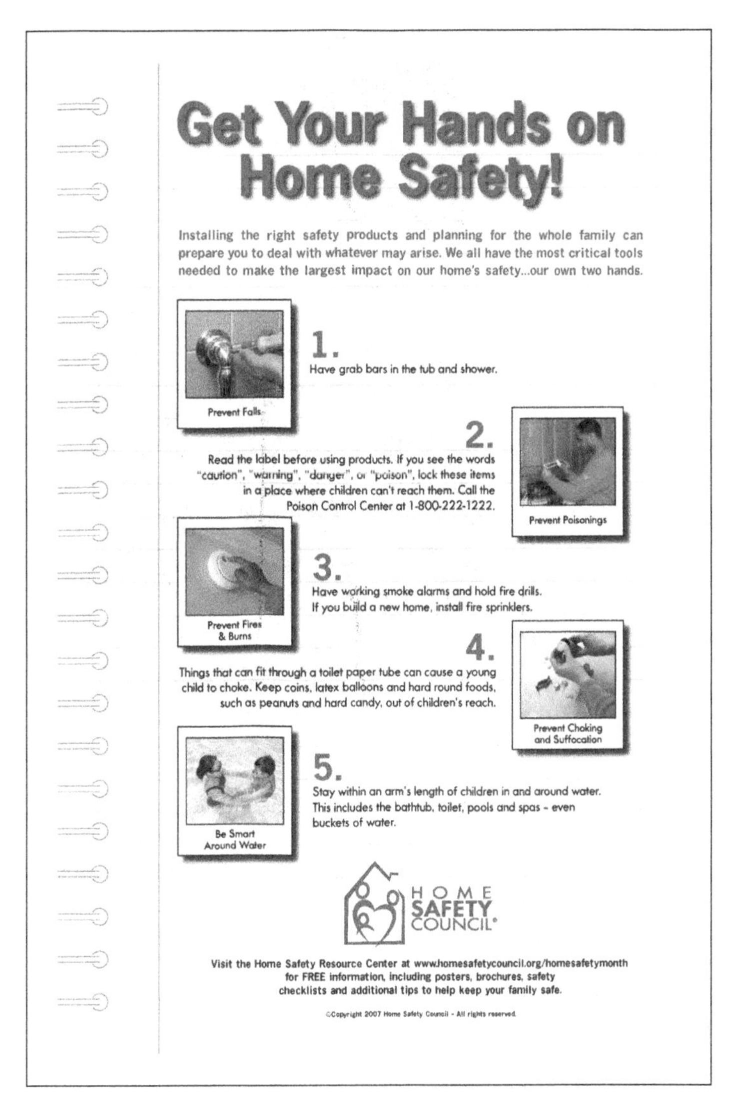

Courtesy of the Home Safety Council®

Figure 6-8 Safety posters, such as this example from the Home Safety Council®, can help convey fire and injury prevention messages to a wide audience.

WHAT IS SAFE-T-ELEMENT®?

The **Safe-T-element®** cooking system is a patented product upgrade for electric coiled stovetops, engineered to help prevent cooking fires before they start while reducing the amount of electricity required to cook.

An element on high, red hot and unattended for even a short period of time is one that has reached a dangerously high temperature and is out of control. That amount of heat is never necessary. No one needs 700°C/1291°F when oil ignites at as low as 370°C/698°F.

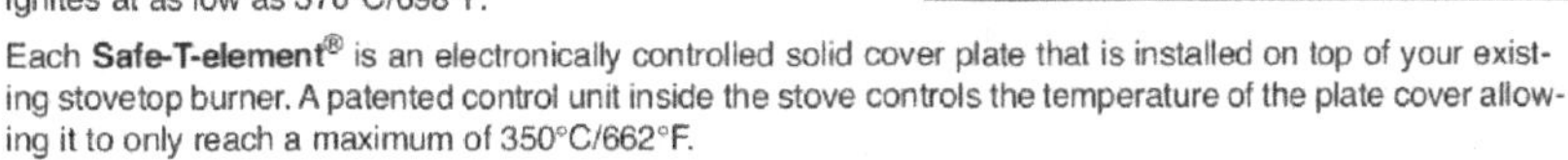

Each **Safe-T-element®** is an electronically controlled solid cover plate that is installed on top of your existing stovetop burner. A patented control unit inside the stove controls the temperature of the plate cover allowing it to only reach a maximum of 350°C/662°F.

When the plate reaches a temperature of 350°C/662°F, it automatically shuts the stove off and conversely as it cools to just below 350°C/662°F the stovetop is turned on again. In this way the burner plate maintains a temperature of 350°C/662°F, more than enough for efficient and effective cooking, while not allowing household materials to ignite.

Courtesy of Pioneering Technology Corporation

Figure 6-9 Technology, such as the Pioneering Technology Safe-T-element® shown here, holds great promise for helping to reduce residential fires.

Figure 6-10 Alexandria, Virginia, firefighters speak with a resident during a door-to-door fire and life safety campaign.

Courtesy of the Alexandria (Virginia) Fire Department

Door-to-door visits in high-risk areas (see Figure 6–10) are providing documented results in the United Kingdom and elsewhere in the world and are beginning to make a resurgence in popularity in the United States. Many fire departments (like that in Dallas, Texas) are finding value in having firefighters be more actively involved with their communities. The solid educational value of station-based prevention efforts is substantiated by greatly reduced fire incident rates (by 40 percent in some areas of the United Kingdom)[9] (see sidebar below on integrated risk management). Some departments may also find community involvement helpful in developing relationships that can lead to political and community support during budget deliberations.

Other fire departments have targeted specific audiences or problems in connection with other issues. For example, juvenile fire setting is a specific fire problem that requires a multi-disciplinary approach. Education is needed, of course, but families of fire setters need screening to determine the level of fire-setting activity of the children; and sometimes psychological intervention is needed to keep the fire-setting behavior from recurring (see sidebar on facing page).

Integrated risk management

Global studies in fire prevention conducted by TriData and the Centers for Disease Control and Prevention (sysplan.com/index.html#capabilities) point out a growing trend in places like Australia, New Zealand, and the United Kingdom for a perspective on modern-day fire departments. Called integrated risk management (IRM), the concept combines elements of emergency response with the traditional elements of fire prevention (e.g., engineering, enforcement, and education) for integration into fire department operations at the station level.

IRM requires identifying risks for specific areas of a local jurisdiction, usually by station response area, and developing proactive strategies to minimize those risks while maintaining a focus on emergency response capabilities. Integrating the two activities (response and prevention) is a challenge, but it has provided impressive results in these nations—achieving up to 40 percent reductions in fire loss statistics. Commonly, IRM involves reaching out to high-risk areas—usually housing—and making sure that home safety surveys teach people how to be more safe, ensuring that smoke alarms are in working order and that home escape plans are created and practiced.

The concept of IRM is catching on in the United States and is being explored in a number of jurisdictions, including Dallas, Texas; Portland, Oregon; Vancouver, Washington; and Wilmington, North Carolina.

Program to control juvenile fire setting

Many fire departments around the nation still conduct programs designed to identify and appropriately aid juvenile fire setters—with a goal of preventing them in the first place or preventing repeat behaviors. The main components include educational programs that teach parents and sometimes even small children about the dangers of fire and that stress the importance of keeping matches and lighters out of the hands of curious children. Another important tool, however, is a screening questionnaire developed over many years by the U.S. Fire Administration (USFA) to help identify the motivation for juvenile fire setters. In most cases, small children are merely curious; having no idea about how dangerous fire can be, they sometimes cause disastrous results—even death—with no intention of doing so. The screening survey can also help to identify children with emotional disturbances who may be acting out with fire, and children with more deeply rooted psychological problems that manifest themselves in deliberate fire setting.

A partnership with mental health professionals properly trained to deal with serious fire-setting behaviors is critical. Fire departments should confine their role to providing educational interventions for fire setters (and their families) who are motivated by normal curiosity, have had a scare, have learned their lesson, and are not apt to repeat their mistake. Emotionally disturbed children need professional help not normally provided by the fire service.

A wealth of resources on the topic is found at the USFA website (usfa.dhs.gov) to point local fire departments in a productive direction.

Seasonal programs are designed to educate the community about fire problems just before the problems normally begin. Examples include programs that deal with heating fires or Christmas tree safety in the winter. Summer problems usually include outdoor cooking, fireworks around the Fourth of July, or wildfire hazards for wildland-urban interface zones.

For example, the Orange County Fire Authority has developed a very comprehensive approach to wildfire safety called "Ready, Set, Go" (ocfa.org). It stresses creating defensible spaces, preparing for wildfires in advance, and leaving the area at an appropriate time to avoid risk of injury or death.

Some departments increase their prevention efforts around Halloween, when destructive activities traditionally increase. Many departments also take advantage of National Fire Prevention Week (always around October 9, the day of the Great Chicago Fire), when school and community attention is drawn to the subject, by increasing their education and other prevention efforts to coincide with the increase in public interest.

Some seasonal programs are oriented toward local problems that are not fire related. The Phoenix (Arizona) Fire Department, for example, has a program aimed at preventing drowning incidents, which are a particular problem in the Phoenix area.

Opportunities for targeted educational programs are numerous, and excellent resources are available to local jurisdictions, which can produce their own programs or buy ready-made ones. The USFA maintains a resource guide on its web page, and NFPA has an active education department, including its Center for High-Risk Outreach.[10]

Before local materials are developed, the fire department must research target audience needs and preferences. It must make sure that the educational materials being developed are age and culturally appropriate. Professional help should be sought because developing effective educational materials requires special knowledge and skill.

Investigating fires

Fire investigation—the fourth major component of a comprehensive prevention program—is the base on which the engineering and educational components are built. It is also a direct part of the enforcement component in the many fire departments where the fire investigation unit is responsible for arson determination and assistance in the prosecution of arson cases. Data from investigations also underpins program evaluation efforts.

Most fire departments investigate fires to identify the area of origin and determine the probable cause so that similar fires can be prevented. Sometimes the cause is readily evident, and responding fire officers can successfully conclude how a fire originated. Sometimes the cause is not so clear.

If arson is suspected, the nature of the investigation changes: its scope usually increases dramatically, law enforcement officials (the police and public prosecutors) become partners in the investigation, and interviewing witnesses becomes more difficult. (Arson investigations are discussed in more detail in the next section.)

But even if a crime is not suspected, an investigation may still involve outside interests. For example, most insurance companies routinely hire their own investigators to determine the cause of a fire. They do so to protect themselves from probable civil actions, such as subrogation suits between insurance companies or with product manufacturers over who is responsible for paying for the damage. For example, if an electrical appliance caused a fire, the insurance carrier may sue the manufacturer of the appliance to recover expenses for both the damages and the cost of the investigation. Private investigators hired by insurance companies may or may not agree with local authorities about the cause of a fire. And when a very expensive fire loss occurs, there are usually enough special interests with a stake in the financial loss to make the investigation complex and subject to scrutiny by many outside sources.

These circumstances demand a high level of proficiency on the part of fire investigators, who must make a solid presentation, with scientific evidence, to support claims about cause. Accordingly, many fire departments are increasing their proficiency in fire investigation, recognizing that technical expertise and training are critical for the validity of their investigative efforts.

The causes of fire, of course, vary widely. Principal causes include electrical malfunction, carelessly discarded cigarettes, and unsafe kitchen practices, such as leaving cooking unattended. Whatever the specific cause, the general cause is always that a source of heat comes into contact with something that will burn. And human behavior, whether deliberate or not, is almost always a significant factor in a fire's start or spread.

Collecting data

Whether a fire is unintentional or is purposely set, certain investigative activities are basic. First is the physical investigation of the fire scene, beginning with observations about fire conditions made by those who arrive at the scene first: certain characteristics of smoke or flame color, for example, can indicate causal factors. Second, during fire suppression, firefighters must preserve the scene of the fire as much as possible so that critical physical evidence will not be destroyed: examination of burn patterns can lead investigators to the area of origin, even in a badly damaged structure, and understanding how physical items in a structure react during a fire can lead to a determination of probable cause. For example, burn patterns of ordinary wood may help indicate whether accelerants were used to start a fire, and multiple points of origin indicate that a fire was deliberately set. Third, narrowing the cause further requires a good deal more scientific analysis and sophistication: providing evidence that a fire occurred in a particular appliance, for example, may require an understanding of how the unit operates and possibly a scientific analysis by a private laboratory.

Fire investigators must be well trained in recognizing fire burn patterns and applying the science of investigative techniques to the physical characteristics of the many materials inside a fire scene. Investigators must also be trained how to interview witnesses to the fire to help recreate the fire scenario. But training is not enough. Effective fire investigation efforts also require equipment and other resources to identify causes and to aid in the prosecution of crimes. For example, laboratory analysis may be needed to corroborate the conclusion of a fire scene investigation. Many departments use dogs trained to detect accelerants to help pinpoint cause and identify cases of suspected arson (see Figure 6–11).

Interviewing witnesses is particularly important when arson is suspected. When a crime is suspected that involves the entire criminal prosecution system, from police officers to prosecutors and judges, the investigator enters another realm of investigation technique. He or she must preserve all evidence and establish a chain of its possession so that the evidence can be used in any future court proceedings. The investigator must use special interviewing procedures and documentation so that the conclusion will withstand legal scrutiny.

During arson investigations the relationship among investigators, the local police, and prosecutors is critical. A report prepared for the USFA by TriData Corporation concluded that because the activities of determining cause, investigating whether arson was involved, and

Photo by Adam K. Thiel

Figure 6-11 The federal Bureau of Alcohol, Tobacco, Firearms and Explosives (ATF) National Response Team is a potential resource for local fire and emergency service agencies addressing complex investigations of certain types of fires.

developing a criminal or civil case intermingle, close coordination between fire and police agencies is particularly important.[11] Some large fire departments train and certify their fire investigators as law enforcement officers in order to control the investigation sequence in criminal cases more effectively.

Nationally produced guidelines for fire investigation—such as NFPA 921, Guide for Fire and Explosion Investigations (2011 edition); the International Fire Service Training Association's

Fire investigation

As the science of fire investigation has improved, once-common beliefs about fire patterns and what they reveal about fire cause have been debunked. Modern guides on the practice of fire investigation, including NFPA 921 produced by the National Fire Protection Association, have helped advance professionalism in the field.

But past mistakes in fire cause investigation have highlighted the need for specialized training in this area and for caution when drawing conclusions. For example, a report written for *The New Yorker* about the case of Cameron Todd Willingham, who was convicted and put to death for starting a fire in which his children died, is a riveting study of how fire investigators either deliberately ignored clues or misinterpreted commonly held beliefs about fire patterns on glass. Later studies found that they had incorrectly concluded that the fire was deliberately set and that the father of the victims in the fire was the arsonist responsible.[1]

Subsequent investigations called into question the investigation techniques and the credibility of the forensic science used in fire investigations. One study, commissioned by the State of Texas (where Willingham was convicted and put to death), concluded that there was no scientific basis for a determination of arson, that evidence contradicting conclusions of arson was ignored, and that discredited "folklore" about fire patterns was used, leading to what one scientist described as a process more "characteristic of mystics or psychics."

The point for local decision and policy makers is that fire investigation is a very serious challenge that requires specialized and thorough training and constant diligence as scientific knowledge and the level of professionalism in the field improve.

1 David Grann, "Trial by Fire," *New Yorker*, September 7, 2009, newyorker.com/reporting/2009/09/07/090907fa_fact_grann (accessed December 4, 2010).

manuals on fire investigation; and the *Pocket Guide to Arson and Fire Investigation*, produced by the Factory Mutual System—can all help local decision makers design an investigation program that will sustain legal challenges and provide accurate information.[12]

The use of data from fire investigations

Another part of the fire investigation effort is compiling and analyzing data. This function can be conducted by investigators or analysts, and the data can be either statistical or anecdotal. Similarly, the analysis can be done either statistically on a large scale, with databases built over time, or anecdotally on specific fires. Both kinds of data and analysis are valuable to officials who design proactive prevention strategies.

Anecdotal evidence about human behavior and other contributing factors can be especially revealing. For example, investigation of a single fire might reveal that papers were left too near a portable heater, doors were left open (thereby allowing air to feed the fire), and wall coverings were flammable. Specific observations like these provide valuable information that lay people can readily understand about contributing factors that helped start the fire or aided its rapid spread.

Evaluation of long-range data on loss should be another goal of a fire investigation program. Prevention strategies benefit from the historical perspective provided by a good investigation process that produces detailed and relevant data over an extended period of time. Consequently, a record-keeping system for fire investigations is a critical tool of comprehensive prevention efforts. More is said about the evaluation of fire investigation data in the section below on performance measures.

Legal liability in investigation

Conducting investigations produces its own set of potential legal liabilities, which involve standard police rights and responsibilities regarding the conduct of criminal investigations. In the investigation of an unintentional fire, the right of entry can become an issue. To protect themselves from legal challenges, local decision makers should be sure that investigators receive proper training and should establish clear-cut policies and procedures. And they should have local legal experts review their practices to ensure compliance with appropriate local, state, and federal requirements.

Using performance measures to evaluate prevention programs

The major parts of a comprehensive prevention program are the engineering, enforcement, education, and investigation activities that help reduce risk and loss within a community. This section addresses a basic management issue underlying all these components. Even though most people accept the concept that preventing an incident is cheaper than dealing with it after the fact, local decision makers must justify expenditures for every type of government service. Concerned taxpayers want to know what their tax dollars are producing and whether the services are managed efficiently.

Prevention programs are often the most difficult to evaluate because so many variables affect the loss data. However, some model performance measures are available that may help show whether prevention programs are producing the desired results and are doing so efficiently.

The Governmental Accounting Standards Board has developed evaluation measures that can be applied to fire department activities, although the board stipulates that comparing one jurisdiction with another is very difficult because the variables in jurisdictions are hard to match. The USFA, in conjunction with the California Polytechnic Institute, has also produced some model evaluation measures. The International City/County Management Association, too, through its Center for Performance Measurement, has developed performance measures for prevention that include indicators connected with fire inspections, community risk reduction, and educational programs. Generally speaking, these indicators can be categorized as measures of workload, efficiency, and effectiveness, and as steps toward the identification of best practices. (Chapter 14 discusses performance measurement in detail.)

Evaluation measures

In the course of developing strategies for fire loss prevention, the collaborative effort known as Vision 20/20 (see sidebar at the top of page 180) also developed model performance and evaluation measures for fire prevention. The workload, efficiency, and effectiveness measures most often requested by those who monitor the performance of government programs have been married to the more substantive evaluation techniques used by public health organizations for specific prevention efforts. Formative, process, impact, and outcome measures are all different ways of evaluating the results that specific programs achieve.

Formative evaluation is the research that is done before programs are implemented; its purpose is to determine why problems exist and how they relate to particular target audiences and their behaviors and attitudes. This part of an evaluation will help local practitioners effectively design and target their efforts.

Process evaluation is monitoring and documenting the process steps in program design, development, and implementation. Process evaluation helps demonstrate how programs were created and implemented so that they can be repeated elsewhere or improved upon.

Impact and outcome evaluation measures in this context usually refer to how behaviors relate to risk and how loss data over time are actually changed by specific program efforts. It is important to look at such measures over time to avoid conclusions stemming from normal fluctuations and variations that are due to random chance.

Much more detail on model measures, as well as links to other efforts for assistance—including ICMA, the Center for Public Safety Excellence, and the National Fire Academy—can be found on Vision 20/20's web page (strategicfire.org). (See Chapter 14 for a full discussion of performance management.)

Workload measures are those that document the amount of work performed—for example, the number of code enforcement inspections done per inspector. Efficiency measures are those that demonstrate whether something is done quickly and at the lowest possible cost. They cover the cost per inspection or per public education presentation. Workload measures will demonstrate that employees are doing an adequate amount of work, and efficiency measures will provide some indication of how quickly things are being done and what they cost in relation to similar services. However, it is effectiveness measures that produce the most solid results for local decision makers who are evaluating their department's prevention efforts.

Effectiveness measures show the impacts or outcomes of specific prevention efforts, and the relationship between these outcomes and the stated goals and objectives of the efforts. Effectiveness measures get at the heart of the question usually asked by concerned taxpayers: Why is this service in place, and what results is it producing?

Public health and medical communities have been measuring the results of their prevention (injury control) efforts for many years. They commonly refer to formative, process, impact, and outcome evaluation measures to describe the results that prevention programs are measured against (see sidebar above). They share with the governmental accounting interests the term *results.* And there are many common measures that are used to reflect both impact and outcome.

The most commonly used effectiveness indicators measure educational gain, risk reduction, and loss reduction. Measuring educational gain means providing evidence that public fire and life safety education activities are (or are not) producing a desired learning result. A questionnaire asking about the practices of the recipients of an educational program before and after the program can document whether the recipients are actually learning or are merely sitting through a presentation they will forget the next day.

One of the basic reasons for having a comprehensive prevention program is to reduce risk. Measuring risk reduction (or changes in risk) means documenting an increase (or lack of increase) in safety behaviors or a decrease (or its lack) in hazard-producing behaviors. For example, national statistics indicate that smoke detectors are effective in saving lives; therefore, documentation that the number of working smoke detectors in a community has increased can be evidence that the risk of dying in a fire is reduced. A compilation of hazards abated during fire inspections can also provide evidence that risks have been reduced.

Vision 20/20

In 2006 a group of fire prevention professionals from around the nation met in Orlando, Florida, to discuss how fire prevention efforts in the United States could be improved without "reinventing the wheel."

They obtained funding from the Department of Homeland Security under the Assistance to Firefighters Grant program and brought together over 500 people in webinars and town hall-style meetings, which then led to a national planning meeting where 170 national leaders and practitioners met in Washington, D.C., to develop a strategic plan. Titled "Vision 20/20," the resulting report laid out five strategic directions for fire prevention that needed additional emphasis.

Not in order of importance, the five strategies are

- Advocacy of fire prevention programs, including a tool kit for use locally that is designed to demonstrate to policy makers the need for fire prevention programs.
- A national public education/social marketing campaign designed to produce a national unifying theme for fire prevention, similar to "Only You Can Prevent Forest Fires." Concurrently, the national campaign should focus on working smoke alarms for every home in the United States.
- An effort to increase the level of importance of fire prevention *within* the fire service, where emergency response is predominant.
- An effort to identify and increase the use of technologies that would prevent fires or mitigate their damage.
- An effort to improve collaboration on the development, adoption, and use of model fire and building codes, which would in turn improve public safety relative to fire.

Updates on the specific activities to implement these strategies can be found on Vision 20/20's web page at strategicfire.org.

Measuring risk reduction is a valuable part of a strategy for evaluating prevention programs because the indicators provided can be used to quantify the overall effectiveness of a prevention program. For example, a random sample survey of citizens in a community might indicate *how many* are practicing safe behaviors that lead toward a reduction in fire deaths or property loss: *how many* people have working smoke detectors, and *how many* practice fire escape planning. Local decision makers can also quantify *how many* community fire hazards have been abated in a code enforcement inspection program. However, documenting changes that reduce risk does not necessarily mean that there will be fewer fires.

Consequently, the ultimate effectiveness measures may be those that document loss reduction. Measuring the loss reduction that is due to prevention programs will provide the

The responsibilities of a fire marshal

The responsibilities of a fire marshal have expanded over the past decade and will expand still more with the need to manage comprehensive prevention efforts. Traditionally, the fire marshal in most fire departments has been responsible for supervising the efforts of fire inspectors to make certain that businesses are complying with the fire code. In some departments, the fire marshal is also responsible for fire investigation activities; in others, the person is involved in reviewing plans for new construction to ensure fire code compliance; and in still others, the fire marshal has responsibility for the fire department's public education activities.

However, the role of fire marshal is expanding to include coordinating all these components of a comprehensive prevention effort. The position of fire marshal can be extremely sensitive to the politics of local government. The fire code is subject to some interpretation, and the person responsible for its administration must have good judgment and tact. Pressure from the business community to lessen standards can be intense, and elected officials are often the first to hear complaints about a fire marshal who is—or is perceived to be—abusing his or her authority. These complaints put constant pressure on the person holding the position to perform in a consistent and tactful manner. Accordingly, it can be a high-pressure job with a great deal of responsibility, requiring technical expertise, the ability to manage diverse job functions, and the ability to perform well under pressure.

The National Fire Protection Association now produces NFPA 1037, a model professional qualification standard that outlines the job performance requirements (knowledge, skills, and abilities) for fire marshals.

best evidence of positive results. That is the ultimate performance (or outcome) measure that, if favorable, justifies the expense of conducting prevention programs. However, local decision makers should be warned against leaping to conclusions based on short-term analyses of loss data. A change in activity can be caused by normal variations that show up in any statistical analysis, so all the performance measures that look at effectiveness should be evaluated over a period of at least five years. Looking at loss reduction over a period of time can provide the best picture of whether a local jurisdiction's losses from fire are decreasing. And it is statistically more accurate to compare any jurisdiction's performance with its own performance in the past than to compare it with another jurisdiction's performance.

Staffing and funding options for prevention programs

Local decision makers will always want to know how many people it takes to do certain tasks—hence, the need to evaluate workload measures. However, a wide variety of staffing options are used in the fire and emergency services, and comparative data are as yet inadequate to identify a truly "best practice" model.

Looking at prevention programs in other jurisdictions will provide some ideas for improvements to the local prevention effort. Sometimes the best ideas come from a jurisdiction that is much smaller or much larger, so it is best not to restrict a survey to only jurisdictions of comparable size or population.

Local decision makers should also understand that not every idea can work effectively in their own jurisdictions. Local politics, agreements with professional unions, reliance on volunteers, and the needs of the local community are all relevant factors when departments are deciding on the most appropriate mix of services and staffing for their own areas.

And finally, local decision makers should be cautioned against expecting too much of any one staff position. Expecting one person to conduct plan reviews for new construction, enforce the fire code, make public fire and life safety presentations, and investigate fires may be unrealistic. If one person is given responsibility for all these tasks, the result may be inadequate expertise or attention—either of which can create legal liabilities. If a community's resources are limited, the type and scope of prevention programs conducted in that community will necessarily also be limited.

Staffing

As mentioned, there are a variety of staffing options for performing prevention activities. Many jurisdictions, such as Seattle, Washington, use emergency response personnel to conduct all or some of their routine fire code inspections. These inspections are commonly called "company inspections" because they are conducted by fire and medical emergency crews (called "companies"). Many jurisdictions that use company inspections also certify their firefighting personnel through model code development organizations to ensure that those personnel are knowledgeable enough to conduct thorough inspections. Training and adequate supervision are critical to ensure that major hazards are not missed during inspections.

Many departments train firefighters as inspectors, public educators, or investigators and move them into a specialized unit to conduct their respective fire prevention programs. Other jurisdictions hire personnel from outside the fire department, recruiting for employees with specialized education and experience relevant to the tasks they will be assigned. Some volunteer departments (e.g., some departments in Nassau County, New York) also use volunteer inspectors. Whether a volunteer or a career professional is used, training of personnel is critical.

Some fire departments have managed their code enforcement options with self-inspection programs: they ask businesses to identify their own hazards and to abate them voluntarily. Self-inspections are often the only option when a department lacks the resources to inspect commercial occupancies on a regular schedule.

Many businesses are inspected by a variety of local and federal safety agencies, including the Occupational Safety and Health Administration, and the lack of coordination among these various code enforcement organizations is a common subject of complaint by businesses.

To achieve their own prevention goals, therefore, some fire departments try to coordinate their inspections with other agencies.

The performance of prevention personnel will be determined largely by the quality of their training. NFPA produces professional qualification standards for each of the prevention disciplines: NFPA 1031 is for code enforcement and plan review personnel; NFPA 1033 is for fire investigators; NFPA 1035 is for fire educators, including those who manage juvenile fire-setting programs; and NFPA 1037 is for fire marshals and focuses on management of prevention programs.

Funding

Funding options for prevention programs are somewhat limited. Most prevention programs are supported by local tax dollars, but many supplement their budgets with funding from other sources. The three major supplemental funding sources are fees, grants, and fundraising.

Some departments charge fees for inspections, reasoning that business occupancies receive (and require) a higher level of fire protection inasmuch as they are inspected, while private homes are not usually covered by the fire code and are not inspected. This mix of public and private benefit usually leads to a fee schedule that recovers part but usually not all of the costs associated with fire code enforcement. Because new development is usually expected to pay for itself, it is fairly common for fire departments to support the costs of plan review almost exclusively with fees. Fee structures vary widely, but usually the size of the fee is related to the amount of work done. Plan review for complex buildings will often have a higher fee than that for simpler buildings.

Many jurisdictions use grants to supplement their prevention funds. The Department of Homeland Security offers fire prevention grants as part of its Assistance to Firefighters Grant program (firegrantsupport.com/afg). These funds are limited, and the awards are usually targeted to high-risk problems and audiences. Various other grants are available throughout the nation, but there must be a connection between the interests of the grantor and the needs of the grantee. Grant writing has become a special art in a world where competition for available dollars is extreme, so professional help is sometimes employed.

Fundraising for prevention programs can include a variety of activities, from pancake feeds to standing on street corners with fire boots in order to collect donations from passing motorists. More organized fundraising targets community or business interest donations, which are not formal grants but can be sizeable. Fire and emergency service departments must proceed with caution when fundraising to ensure that relationships that produce donations do not also produce conflicts of interest. For example, a local construction company may want to partner with the fire department to produce brochures to give to citizens who have experienced a fire, but their competitors may view such a partnership as giving the partnering company an unfair advertising advantage. Still, developing relationships in the community, demonstrating need, and obtaining supplemental funds has become common practice for fire prevention practitioners across the nation.

Summary

Comprehensive prevention programs are a combination of four strategies designed to reduce risk or loss in any given community. The first strategy consists of engineered safety solutions: the jurisdiction reviews plans for new construction for fire department access, adequate water supply, and fixed fire protection systems. The second consists of enforcement efforts: fire inspections ensure compliance with a properly adopted and administered code enforcement program. The third consists of education activities that are designed to reach schoolchildren or other targeted groups (see Figure 6–12). The fourth consists of an adequate fire investigation program that provides the information necessary for targeting prevention efforts appropriately and controlling the problem of arson in the community. Evaluation, referred to by some as the fourth "E" of prevention, includes activities to measure the effectiveness and efficiency of prevention activities.

Courtesy of the Alexandria (Virginia) Fire Department

Figure 6-12 A firefighter visits a local elementary school classroom in Alexandria, Virginia, to speak with children about smoke alarms during Fire Prevention Week.

Comprehensive prevention programs can be conducted by specially trained personnel, emergency response personnel, or even volunteers. These programs can involve any activity in which the public takes an active role to protect itself (e.g., self-inspection programs for code enforcement, or neighborhood coalitions that go door-to-door with appropriate fire and life safety materials). But however they are conducted, comprehensive prevention programs are multifaceted, using the full variety of prevention strategies to work toward the common goal of prevention: fewer deaths and less loss.

The technological and legal issues that prevention personnel must deal with will become more complex in the future. Emerging trends in prevention include greater emphasis on performance codes, the movement toward all-injury control, and the establishment of coalitions to promote fire and life safety. Planning and partnerships with the community will be needed, as will increases in professional development opportunities for fire prevention personnel.

Shrinking resources could require the fire and emergency services department to put ever-greater emphasis on prevention. Thus, prevention programs should be a vital part of any fire department's total fire and life safety protection package for its community. Comprehensive prevention programs will be among the innovative and competitive strategies that local jurisdictions undertake during tough economic times.

Notes

1. David Osborne and Ted Gaebler, *Reinventing Government: How the Entrepreneurial Spirit Is Transforming the Public Sector* (Reading, Mass. Addison-Wesley, 1992).
2. John R. Hall Jr., *The Total Cost of Fire in the United States* (Quincy, Mass.: National Fire Protection Association [NFPA], 2010), 24.
3. Philip S. Schaenman, *International Concepts in Fire Protection: New Ideas from Europe* (Arlington, Va.: TriData Corporation, 1993), *International Concepts in Fire Protection: Practices from Japan, Hong Kong, Australia and New Zealand* (Arlington, Va.: TriData Corporation, 1985), and *Proving Public Fire Education Works* (Arlington, Va.: TriData Corporation, 1990); see sysplan/tridata.com for more current studies on global concepts of fire prevention.
4. The Home Fire Sprinkler Coalition has several documents on Scottsdale's experience at homefiresprinkler .org/FS/Scottsdale15.html.
5. International Fire Service Training Association (IFSTA), *Fire Inspection and Code Enforcement,* 7th ed. (Sunrise, Fla.: IFSTA, January 2009).

6. *Adams v. State (of Alaska)*, 555 P. 2nd 235 (1976); *Coffey v. City of Milwaukee (Wisconsin)*, 74 Wis. 2d 526, 247 N.W. 2d 132 (1976). See Appendix A of NFPA, *Fire Inspection Management Guidelines* (Quincy, Mass.: NFPA, December 1982).
7. See NFPA, "Risk Watch®," nfpa.org/categoryList.asp ?categoryID=1050&cookie_test=1.
8. Reports on the relationship between fire loss and demographic characteristics are available for download on U.S. Fire Administration (USFA) and NFPA websites (usfa.dhs.gov and nfpa.org). See, for example, "Socio-economic Factors and the Incidence of Fire" at usfa .dhs.gov/downloads/pdf/publications/socio.pdf.
9. See System Planning Corporation, "Fire Prevention Week: Best Prevention Practices Identified from Abroad May Help U.S. Fire Safety," sysplan.com/ documents/news/2008/SPC_NEWS_RELEASE_ October_3.pdf. Full reports on the effectiveness of station-based prevention efforts are available for free downloading at TriData's website, sysplan.com/ tridata/international_studies.
10. See USFA at usfa.fema.gov; see NFPA at nfpa.org (mailing address: 1 Batterymarch Park, Quincy, MA 02269-9101) for programs; and Center for High-Risk Outreach, at nfpa.org/categoryList.asp?categoryID= 201&URL=Learning/Public%20education/Center%20 for%20High-Risk%20Outreach.
11. USFA, *A View of Management in Fire Investigation Units: Issues & Trends for the 90's*, vols. 1 and 2 (Washington, D.C.: Federal Emergency Management Agency, USFA, 1990 and 1992), at usfa.dhs.gov/ downloads/pdf/publications/fa-093.pdf and usfa .dhs.gov/downloads/pdf/publications/fa-116.pdf.
12. FM Global, *Pocket Guide to Arson and Fire Investigation*, 5th ed. (Johnston, R.I.: FM Global, 1990).

PART TWO

Organizational Leadership

CHAPTER 7

Leading and Managing

I. David Daniels

This chapter provides an understanding of

- Leadership and management, their interrelationship, and the importance of organizational settings
- How leadership and management relate to the work of a fire and emergency services executive or chief officer
- The challenges facing fire and emergency services management and leadership
- Organizational culture and its importance to fire and emergency service organizations
- The elements needed for successful change.

Effective leadership and management are critical to the success of fire and emergency services. Most failures and adverse outcomes for these organizations, particularly outcomes involving scandal, failure to perform, erosion of public esteem, and loss of confidence from elected officials and jurisdiction managers, can be traced to deficiencies in leadership and management.

Although leadership and management are important at the emergency scene, they are equally important (and more challenging) in daily department operations. Fire and emergency service leaders and managers are generally at their best in complex emergencies. However, the ongoing *organizational* challenges facing fire and emergency services are just as real and just as dynamic. And although many of those challenges are not new, they have grown more complex. The downturn in the national economy has constrained resources available even for basic government services. In career fire and emergency service departments, wages and fringe benefits have escalated ahead of inflation; in volunteer departments, membership is decreasing as lifestyles change, financial pressures force residents to take on two jobs, and training requirements rise. Additionally, the public and the media have become more aggressive in demanding to know why and how adverse outcomes and failures occur in public safety organizations. Indeed, these times are challenging for fire and emergency services, and leadership and management are critical to determining how these organizations will fare in the future.

Doing "what we've always done" is seldom adequate to secure organizational success. Such success requires satisfying internal stakeholders as well as the community and the governmental oversight structure—be it a city council, fire district, or board of commissioners. Thus, the fire chief is faced with the challenges of achieving success as defined by his or her own organization, by the government, and by the community at large.

Historically, many people, including local government managers, perceived fire and emergency service leaders as working in silos, interested primarily in fire suppression, and lacking clear systems for succession planning as well as the professionalism, education, and policy skills needed to be effective public sector leaders. These criticisms reflected deficiencies in the leadership and managerial preparation of fire and emergency service chiefs and administrators. Although traditional fire services have approached both leadership and management as a quest for "how to," leaders now need to focus on "why, where, and when?" while managers focus on "how, in this case?" The future of fire and emergency services will likely rise or fall on the ability of organizations and their leaders and managers to demonstrate that they provide value above and beyond their ability to respond to emergencies.

Too many in the fire and emergency service assume that leadership and management concepts developed and practiced outside the service are only partly applicable to our industry. This perspective is limiting for those who lead fire departments as well as for those being led, those who manage, and the activities being managed. The fundamental leadership skills that cause a firefighter to follow his or her company officer into a raging inferno or to rescue a trapped victim are, in fact, similar to the skills necessary to lead a work group in a conversation about cultural competency or to implement a new organizational safety culture. The skills needed to successfully manage command and general staff functions at a major emergency are similar to those needed to manage an organization's performance management systems, including the evaluation of personnel and program effectiveness in achieving the strategic goals of the project or program. Indeed, all these skills are equally important.

While a fire and emergency services department may successfully resolve emergency incidents, it must also succeed in acquiring the necessary resources of money, staff, facilities, and equipment to be effective in the long term. Many in the department are charged with managing emergency incidents, but only the chief is responsible for these "big picture" objectives.

Who leads, who manages?

Fire and emergency services are in no way monolithic from an organizational perspective. There are many variations in titles, job descriptions, and expectations for personnel at the various levels of service delivery, and it is difficult to use specific terms without appearing to leave out some organizational element or segment of the industry. This chapter addresses services provided to a public sector customer by a public sector provider, but the discussion is not restricted to those examples. The following terms are used:

- *Jurisdiction* indicates the local government or political subdivision that has the overall responsibility for delivering emergency services. The term includes counties, cities, boroughs, hamlets, towns, villages, districts, subdistricts, authorities, and similar entities.
- *Jurisdiction executive* describes the person at the highest organizational level of a jurisdiction. This could be either an elected or an appointed position, depending on the form of government. The term includes county executive, county manager, commission chair, board chair, mayor, city administrator, city manager, and similar positions.
- *Organization* means the entity or agency that provides direct service to the customer. The term includes departments, districts, and authorities. For the most part, the term *agency* is used as a synonym for *organization.*
- *Organization (or agency) executive* describes the person at the highest level of the organization. The term includes the fire chief, administrator, chief engineer, and director. Organization executives also serve as jurisdiction managers.
- *Organization (or agency) manager* describes a person in a primarily managerial role within an organization. The term includes the chief officer (deputy, assistant, battalion, division, etc.), fire marshal, assistant fire marshal, medical services officer, company officer (captain, lieutenant, sergeant, etc.), manager, and supervisor. It is assumed that all organization managers must have leadership qualities to be effective in the long term.

The terms *management* and *leadership* often coexist in the same position or same person. While management is associated more closely with position or title within an organization, leadership can be exercised independent of these distinctions; indeed, informal "leaders" are important at all levels of an organization. However, if an organization is to be successful, its officer corps must have both management and leadership skills. The chief in particular must exercise both kinds of skills effectively. One can argue that these two distinct skill sets should be used in varying proportions throughout the course of a fire officer's professional life.

To suggest that either leading or managing is more important than the other is a simplistic approach to a complex relationship. Fire and emergency services are complex, and the processes of leading and managing them are equally, if not more, complex.

Management

Management is considered a science whereas leadership is seen as an art. Most early research on the subject of organizational effectiveness was conducted in the field of management. One of the first major examinations of management was the twentieth-century work of Frederick Winslow Taylor. In his book *The Principles of Scientific Management,*[1] Taylor postulated that there was "one best way" to accomplish any job, and many succeeding theories have agreed that managing is a much more objective endeavor than leading. Those who reject absolutes might have an argument, but for this discussion of management, we will assume that Warren Bennis was accurate in his assessment: "Leaders are people who do the right thing; managers are people who do things right."[2]

Often practiced in extremely challenging circumstances, good management ensures that service is efficient, effective, consistent, and of relatively high quality. Additionally, good management provides the nonbiased, consistent, nonjudgmental environment that strengthens the department's ability to be effective overall. The various definitions of the term *management* can be applied in concert with the principles of management.

John Kotter defines management as follows, contrasting it with leadership:

> Management is a set of processes that can keep a complicated system of people and technology running smoothly. The most important aspects of management include planning, budgeting, organizing, staffing, controlling, and problem solving. Leadership is a set of processes that creates organizations in the first place or adapts them to significantly changing circumstances.[3]

Many who, on the basis of Taylor's work, consider management a scientific endeavor also think that good management rests on principles that have the authority of natural law. One of the first to define management principles and encourage management training was Henri Fayol, who drew on his experience as a successful industrialist at the beginning of the twentieth century. His "14 Principles of Management," which represent the kind of long-standing, time-tested, widely accepted concepts that most fire and emergency services use as a basis for decision making, are still considered sound and wise. They concern the general management of an organization rather than departmental supervision or the activities of an individual manager. They emphasize "discipline" and "command," concepts that are familiar in the fire and emergency services but perhaps less accepted elsewhere. While other thinkers have described slightly different management models, Fayol's principles provide a solid place to start in describing the work of management in any organization:[4]

1. *Division of work:* High levels of competence make employees more efficient. Division of work allows individuals to increase their competence at specialized functions that contribute to the completion of the organization's strategic goals.
2. *Authority and responsibility:* To be effective, managers must be able to compel action by others. The principle of authority and responsibility provides the formal means to accomplish this while enabling the organization to ensure that the actions of the manager are consistent with the needs of the organization itself.
3. *Discipline:* People are more effective when they discipline themselves. Managerial culture is more effective when self-control is combined with a set of clearly documented and consistent corrective actions that the organization can take in response to activities that do not support its strategic goals.
4. *Unity of command:* An employee should receive orders from one superior only. Only one manager can be held ultimately responsible for a specific set of activities at a time (see Figure 7–1).
5. *Unity of direction:* There should be one head and one plan for a group of activities having the same objective. Everyone engaged in a given activity should work under the same direction to be effective (see Figure 7–1).
6. *Subordination of individual interest to the general interest:* Managers must be able to take an objective view of the goals of the organization and subjugate their personal interest and their group's interest to those goals. Managers must understand the overall goals of both the organization and the specific work program, and the safety of all personnel should be an organizational goal.
7. *Remuneration:* To the extent that workers see personal benefit, they will support the goals of the organization. Not all workers are motivated by personal benefit, but it is unrealistic to expect individuals to work against what they perceive as their own interest for the good of the organization.
8. *Centralization:* Centralization is effective only as it contributes to achieving the strategic goal. Depending on the issue and the systems of accountability in the organization, more or less centralization may be appropriate. Centralization may be important for oversight and ensuring consistency, but central offices cannot have authority over or be accountable for services delivered in far-flung locations by numerous personnel. No degree of centralized expertise can supplant the importance and primacy of field supervision.
9. *Scalar chain:* The clearer the lines of authority—the "chain of command"—from top management to the entry levels of an organization, the greater the likelihood that an organization will achieve its strategic goals. However,

Figure 7-1 Complex incidents, such as this train derailment with hazardous materials, show the importance of such classic management concepts as unity of command and unity of direction.

Courtesy of the Fulton County (Georgia) Fire Department

respect for the chain of command must be reconciled with the need for swift action: employees at each level must have appropriate authority to work outside the chain of command to serve organizational goals.

10. *Order:* Resources should be expended in the right places at the right times. Recognizing, clarifying, and reinforcing "doing things right" in the organization is one of the most important roles of management.
11. *Equity:* The maintenance of a culture and of systems of equity is of critical importance both inside and outside the organization. Equity is a business decision, not an emotional one. Equity based on freedom from bias should not be confused with fairness, which is often superficially pleasing but not necessarily free of bias.
12. *Stability:* Stability in the tenure of personnel should not be based on the amount of time the person has been a part of the organization, but on the function that the person fulfills, the level of competence the person brings to that function, and the degree to which the person helps the organization to fulfill its goals. This principle is particularly applicable to the management of more traditional fire services, where there is strong belief in the role of empiricism (often expressed, for example, in "objective," easily measured personnel selection criteria) in the development of its leaders and managers.
13. *Initiative:* Notwithstanding the need to have unity of command and direction, it is important for members of an organization to understand clearly the extent to which they can be involved in the organization's success. Managers should ensure that opportunities for member initiative are regular parts of the job. Members who are allowed to create and see their ideas implemented will give the organization more over the long run than those who feel that they are simply "cogs in the machine."
14. *Esprit de corps:* Effective managers must be able to promote team spirit, unity, and harmony within the organization. This concept recognizes that people contribute more toward the goals of the organization when they feel a part of the team and when there is an environment of harmony and unity within the work group as opposed to one of unnecessary competition. This is one of the many areas where strong management and leadership skills will overlap.

Essential management concepts for fire and emergency services

Modern fire and emergency services grew out of a "quasi-military" approach to firefighting that had its roots in ancient Rome, where the military took responsibility for suppressing fires as an extension of its responsibility to protect cities from attack. As fire services developed around the world, they adopted military terminology, uniforms, and rank structures.

Periods of major expansion in the fire services have usually coincided with the end of wars or conflicts, providing opportunities for the employment of military veterans. Many firefighters in the early fire services had military backgrounds, and jurisdictions often gave "veteran's preference" to applicants with such backgrounds. As these firefighters rose to management roles, they shaped the management perspectives of the industry, often by applying concepts that they learned in the military.

Military concepts of management provide important tools for fire and emergency service managers when they must move groups of people from one location to another with multiple pieces of equipment, or apply standardized strategies and tactics, or deal with the sometimes extreme carnage found at emergency scenes. However, some managers tend to apply the "battlefield management approach" to all situations, emergency or not. A classic description of a poor manager in the fire and emergency services is someone who is "great at a fire but. . . ." The truth of the matter is that some managers do fairly well where battlefield management is applicable but poorly in many other circumstances.

The reason is that fire and emergency services have evolved over the years into much more than fire departments. Most, if not all, local fire departments function as more than simply "war machines" during emergencies. To be effective on the modern fire ground and in the modern organizational environment, fire and emergency service managers have to employ two important managerial concepts: objectivity and control.

Objectivity To be ultimately successful, fire and emergency service managers require "dispassionate objectivity." As discussed, they are expected and needed to "do things right"—to "handle or direct with a degree of skill . . . to make and keep compliant . . . to treat with care . . . [and] to succeed in accomplishing."[5] The challenge for the manager is that people perceive "doing things right" very differently, depending on how they think the "things" will affect them. This is where objectivity becomes so important. The manager's role is to "do the right things right" and not to focus on how others react. Personal relationships, preconceived notions, and biases are just some of the obstacles that a manager must overcome to make objective, fact-based, and goal-oriented decisions.

Being objective should not be mistaken for being cold, heartless, or hard. A manager's ability to accomplish a strategic goal is connected to his or her ability to use all available resources, including people and their skills and abilities, and to do so in a way that achieves the current goal without damaging the long-term relationships that must remain in place to accomplish future goals.

Control The concept of control is important to a manager because control ensures that activities support the overall strategic goals of the organization. However, a manager should exercise control appropriately, increasing and relaxing it as circumstances require.

Managers who use too much control and those who use too little stand at opposite ends of a spectrum. At one extreme are the micromanagers—those managers who exercise extreme control over the resources placed in their circles of influence. Micromanaging can occur at any level of the emergency service delivery system, from appointed city or county managers through organizational-level managers. Used as a primary management tool, micromanaging can have an extremely negative impact on motivated and creative members of an organization. It undermines accountability and often suggests that the manager is focusing undue resources on the task at hand and neglecting longer-term concerns. However, micromanaging can be an effective tool in situations where human or other resources are not meeting the manager's goals.

At the other extreme are the "anything goes" managers—those managers who demonstrate no control whatsoever over the resources in their charge. Their primary concern is the happiness of their personnel. Few studies have been done on this type of manager, generally because those who exhibit this quality do not remain in place for very long. They may be popular with the members of their units, but they are poorly regarded by management because they fail to achieve goals, and by peers because they undermine the standards and norms of the organization.

Modern management practices

For the fire and emergency services, four current management practices are important for focusing management attention and setting objectives for the organization.

Quality management/continuous improvement Total Quality Management (TQM) is a method of management closely associated with W. Edwards Deming, who introduced it to Japanese industry after World War II. At its heart is the use of statistical measurement and comparison to monitor and improve performance. TQM was applied originally to the manufacture of industrial products such as automobiles and equipment, where its focus was on "error" rates, with the goal of minimizing waste and improving profitability. In the 1980s TQM began to be considered an overall management philosophy that could be applied to services as well. Continuous Quality Improvement (CQI) brings TQM principles to a particular product or service. CQI is widely adopted in the medical field, in emergency medical services, and in dispatch functions. Both TQM and CQI are processes as opposed to static practices. Current performance is never "good enough" and is always subject to further improvement.

Customer service focus The customer service management model requires an agency to engage with the customer. This model goes beyond merely measuring customer satisfaction to providing services that the public values. This may include extension into areas viewed as outside the core mission of the department, such as injury prevention activities, the provision of community services, and even the performance of nonemergency services. Encompassed

The Phoenix customer service model

The Phoenix Fire Department (PFD) "Customer Service Management Policy" goes far beyond customer service, defining culture and values throughout the organization. The PFD defines customers broadly to include not just direct recipients of service but also their families, friends, and neighbors, as well as other organizations and even people who observe the fire department's daily operations. The PFD defines customer service as "the ability to give the customer what they want."

The department's mission statement includes this language:

> Membership in the Phoenix Fire Department Family carries with it a host of responsibilities and expectations. The awareness and commitment to meeting all of them will ensure the fulfillment of our mission.

The policy calls for striving for "added value" in interactions with customers. The PFD achieves added value by exceeding expectations and leaving the customer with a perception that the department "care[s] and is nice."

Internally, the customer service management policy includes recognizing the important role played by support functions (such as dispatch, training, and administration) within the department. Externally, the policy requires quick and skillful response to customer needs.

Key to this effort is the notion that members of the PFD are empowered "to operate between the lines to provide caring service with both quality and value." The PFD lists a series of questions that an employee can ask before providing added value service:

- Is it the right thing for the customer?
- Is it the right thing for the department?
- Is it legal, ethical, and nice?
- Is it safe?
- Is it on your organizational level?
- Is it something you are willing to be accountable for?
- Is it consistent with our department's values and policies?

If the answer to these questions is yes, then the employee does not need to ask permission, and should feel empowered to provide the added value service.

Guidelines to create a positive public impression include the following: "follow SOPs [standard operating procedures], mission statement, organizational values; be professional; give the customer your undivided attention; take a moment to educate the community about what we do." At incident scenes, this includes providing "services necessary to assist customers in reconnecting their lives."

Management's responsibilities include integrating customer service into the human resource process.

The policy includes an awards and recognition program with flexibility that allows an employee or crew being recognized to choose among a graduated scale of awards that range from memos, letters, and certificates through time off.

Source: This sidebar, which summarizes the Phoenix Fire Department's customer service management policy, is drawn from Phoenix Fire Department MP 201.00, 03/09-R, pueblogrande.com/FIRE/20100.pdf.

within the customer service model are elements of continuous improvement, internal cultural development, and community engagement. This model is credited to the Phoenix (Arizona) Fire Department under Chief Alan Brunacini.[6]

Performance management Performance management is the integration of performance measurement into the management structure of the organization. In some ways, it is an attempt to define management success in quantitative terms in accordance with the organization's overall goals and objectives. Examples of performance management systems include various versions of "stat" programs, modeled after New York City's well-regarded COMPSTAT program, which is credited with helping to achieve major reductions in crime.[7] Performance measurement systems require managers to pay considerable attention to setting overall goals and monitoring their achievement. Systems for improving performance (such as TQM and CQI) are implicit in performance management. Buy-in is critical to a true performance management system, which requires support from the jurisdiction executive as well as from fire and emergency service officers and members. For more information on and examples of performance management, see Chapter 14.

Change management Change management focuses on helping an organization succeed in a changing environment. Recognized as a need partly in response to the difficulties encountered by organizations attempting to adopt a TQM approach to management, change management explicitly addresses the human dimensions of organizational improvement. The approach puts great emphasis on the cultural and psychological dimensions and on organization theory; it encourages employees to ask questions; and it explicitly recognizes the resistance to change that can come from organization members. As it gives attention both to efficiency and profitability as well as to cultural change, it is a holistic approach that is revolutionary for most fire and emergency service organizations. Change management is discussed in more depth later in this chapter.

Leadership

In the delivery of emergency services in the public sector, leadership can be defined in several ways:

- To take somebody somewhere: "We expect our chief to lead us through this situation."
- To assume a position of authority (especially in the phrase "take the lead"): "She takes the lead in any group"; "We were just waiting for someone to take the lead"; "They didn't follow our lead."
- To travel in front of; to go in advance of others: "The procession was headed by the fire chief."
- To cause a certain result: "Their aggressive smoke detector campaign has led to a significant reduction in home fires."

In their book *Leadership on the Line,* Ronald Heifetz and Marty Linsky argue that to lead—to "raise important questions, speak to higher values, and surface unresolved conflicts, . . . [to] lead people through difficult change [and] challenge what people hold dear"—is "to live dangerously."[8] Kotter says leadership defines "what the future should look like, aligns people with that vision, and inspires them to make that happen despite the obstacles."[9]

A leader has the responsibility to identify the destination, while a manager has the responsibility to identify the road that should be taken to get there. The difference between the two is the classic difference between strategic and tactical thought. Because the right road to the wrong destination is useless, many perceived management failures are actually leadership failures.

In his book *The Seven Habits of Highly Effective People,* Stephen Covey defines the second habit as "begin with the end in mind."[10] This "habit" supports the notion that leading is about accomplishment. One of the most important products of leading is movement from one place, position, status, or perspective to another. The overall effectiveness of leadership is generally closely connected to the ability of leaders to take a group from one place to another, but the first challenge for the leader is to decide where they are going.

The popular fire service quote "100 years of tradition, unimpeded by progress" is directly opposed to the concept of leadership. To continue to fight fires as we did 100 years ago would be rejected out of hand by all but the most hidebound organizations. Yet in many organizations well regarded for their firefighting prowess, administrative functions resemble something out of the 1970s. The advancement of the organization in this area as in all others is the responsibility of the leader.

Those who would lead should do so from the front of the organization and the front of the issues. In nearly every area of endeavor, there is an expectation that leaders are those who thrive on being "at the front of the line" and "at the head of the pack." Leading from the front means being an example of the organization's values and a compass for followers trying to move toward the organization's goals. Leading is about being the first to do the tough work and the last to give up the goal. Additionally, leading from the front makes it easier for followers to find the leader.

More important than the leader's position is the leader's philosophy. Those who see themselves as leaders in fire and emergency service departments and the jurisdictions they serve must focus on the issues that the departments value as much as or more than they focus on the organizational positions in which they may find themselves. They must also focus on the issues that their jurisdictions value. To lead, the leader must think, plan, and act strategically and with the forward movement (going somewhere) of the department and jurisdiction in mind.

Leadership is considered an art because it is extremely situational; no single set of principles is universally accepted in the fire and emergency services or in any other industry, culture, or institution. However, Fayol's principles of management are broad enough to accommodate the diversity that exists within (and outside) the industry and can be adapted to guide leadership in the fire and emergency services.

1. *Work design:* While managers are responsible for dividing blocks of work into discernable blocks for completion, leaders must be able to design work that is clear and consistent with the goals and purposes of the organization.
2. *Motivation:* A leader must be able to cause others to do things that they might not necessarily do and go places where they might not otherwise go absent the leader's involvement. This is with or without the authority or responsibility to compel the follower in a formal sense.
3. *Model for discipline:* The ability to model the behavior, attitudes, and traits consistent with a clearly articulated vision, mission, and statement of values and goals is an important tool in establishing the overall tone and strengthening the relationship between the leader and the follower.
4. *Focus of command:* Effective leaders know their limitations. They limit the degree to which they attempt to directly lead large numbers of followers; they share and delegate command so that their efforts can be sustained over an extended period and so that other leaders and managers with consistent goals are not hindered from being successful.
5. *Clarity of direction:* Leaders must be able to clearly identify overall direction, connecting that direction with specific goals and the work that it will take to get there.
6. *Coordination of interest:* The interests of a leader must be coordinated to the extent that "self-sacrifice" begins to resemble synchronicity. A leader whose self-interest is not served by the journey may not stay on the path long term.
7. *Incentives to lead:* Whether it be pay, status, or the satisfaction of achievement, every leader needs to pick personal incentives that can motivate his or her efforts, especially when success seems protracted.
8. *Singular focus:* To lead, a leader needs to focus on the goal to be achieved and the road toward that goal. The past serves only as a reference point.
9. *Respect for the chain of command:* Simple compliance with a chain of command can be difficult for leaders. It is important that the leader respect the value of the chain and how its use serves the goals and purposes of the organization.
10. *Loyalty:* Effective leaders are able to inspire at least a modicum of loyalty, especially among those who follow the leader most closely.
11. *Consistency:* For leaders to maintain the support of followers, their reactions and responses must be consistent with the goals of the organization and with their own reactions and responses in similar circumstances.
12. *Right people for the work:* Effective leaders focus on placing the right people in the right positions to do the work necessary to accomplish the vision, mission, and goals of the organization.
13. *Openness:* Effective leaders are open to possibilities for more efficient, more effective, or safer methods of achieving the goals of the organization.
14. *Anticipation:* Great leaders are able to foster a sense of anticipation about the future on the basis of the achievements and positive environment of the organization itself.

Essential leadership concepts for fire and emergency services

Modern approaches recognize the importance of leadership not only at the top of an organization but also distributed throughout it. In a decentralized, dispersed organization such as the fire and emergency services, there is a need for leadership throughout the organization twenty-four hours a day, not just when the chief is present. A distribution of leadership skills can help an organization be more resilient and more likely to succeed. Training programs should foster and develop leadership at all levels of the organization. Leadership does not start with promotion.

The essentials of good leadership are more dependent on the relationship between the leader and the follower than are the essentials of good management. Where managers base their perception of management on an inventory of experiences from within the organization or group, leadership is more closely tied to the life experiences of both the leader and the follower. For example, a person who has had first-hand experience in a major emergency incident may have informal leadership authority over another person with the same seniority and rank but without that experience.

Just as objectivity and control are important concepts for the manager to understand, subjectivity and influence are important concepts for the leader to understand.

Subjectivity As emphasized previously, the core responsibility of a leader is to "do the right thing." This entails subjectivity. Subjectivity—living with ambiguity—may be difficult for leaders who have been effective as managers and who thrive in an environment of well-defined "objective" policies, regulations, and scientific constraints.

As a leadership concept, subjectivity refers to a leader's ability to use personal experiences and perceptions to form a course of action in situations that are not well-defined or are outside normal circumstances. The specific rules of leadership are sometimes unwritten, and the leader must have the courage to do what he or she believes is right—without a clear rule to follow and sometime in the face of opposition. Subjectivity requires taking risks and knowing at the same time how to avoid risks that would damage the organization or the people in it. The key to the concept of subjectivity as a tool for a leader is staying open to possibilities.

Influence Once the leader has embarked on a course of action, he or she must cause people to follow along that course. Thus the leader must use influence. This means convincing followers that the course meets not only the needs of the organization but also their personal needs. The leader can use two human tendencies to influence followers: conformity and obedience.

Psychologists use three factors to explain why people conform.[11] The first is normative social influence, or the group pressure that people feel based on their need for approval and acceptance. The next is informal social influence, which causes people to conform to group pressure out of a need for direction and information. The last factor is people's admiration for and desire to resemble certain reference groups or people. In addition, in the organizational context, a position in and of itself creates a degree of influence by virtue of people's belief that the position can have an impact on those around and associated with it.

The second major form of influence relies on followers' obedience, their tendency to go along with authority. People obey for a variety of reasons, including the perceived power of a position or the person in it, the amount of responsibility that they believe they have for a particular action, and the degree to which they observe the actions of people with whom they identify.

Leadership and management styles

Style refers to the manner and methods that a leader or manager uses to interact with other people, especially those whom they lead and especially when making decisions. In a classic study of leadership styles, Kurt Lewin and colleagues identify three basic styles that can be used to describe both management and leadership: autocratic, participative, and delegative.[12] As with so many leadership and management concepts, though, there are other labels that can be placed on these styles; the foundation of each style is the amount of participation that followers have in the decision-making process—or, defined another way, the amount of control that the leader or manager retains.

Decision-making styles in a fire and emergency services organization fall along the continuum of control. At one end, the autocratic style (also known as authoritative or directing) centralizes decision making at the top of the organization, typically reserving to those who have the rank, position, or perceived authority almost exclusive control over decisions. Autocratic

Participative decision making

In an industry generally viewed as "quasi-military," the prospect of participatory decision making may be viewed by some as a sign of lack of leadership or managerial prowess. However, for a leader, the participation of followers is essential. While this is not necessarily the case for a manager, participation of those being managed is certainly preferred and may produce more effective outcomes. The degree of participation desired depends on both the organizational level and the style of leadership or management, as well as on the goals and objectives to be achieved.

For example, the acquisition of an emergency services vehicle is an activity that has both strategic and tactical value, can be the product of goals and objectives established by both leaders and managers, and requires participative decision making for the best possible outcome. Elected and appointed leaders of a jurisdiction are interested in the design, construction, and purchase of a technical rescue vehicle for a variety of strategic reasons. They see the purchase strategically as a tool to provide the types of services that the jurisdiction requires, as an example of the jurisdiction's fiscal management practices, and as a source of community pride. Managers of the jurisdiction see the same purchase as the tactical fulfillment of these same strategies. Leaders and managers of the department see the vehicle as a tool that brings pride to the workforce because of its uniqueness in the area, increased effectiveness because of its design, and increased efficiency.

To meet all these goals, the organization will require involvement and participation from both jurisdiction and department leaders and managers. Department leaders must participate in the policy-level discussion about the timing of the purchase, vendor approval, and purchase price. Department managers must focus on how the vehicle will affect the response area's risks, how it will be designed and equipped, and how and where it will be deployed. No one leader or manager will be able to address all the issues involved in such a complex undertaking—not because of a lack of dedication to the organization, but because everyone has a limited perspective on any given situation.

The process of placing a new rescue vehicle will entail ranges of participative decision making that again depend on the goal or objective. For strategic goals, the range of participation is inherently wider in that the ultimate goal is much broader. The range of participation will also depend on the level of the leader or manager who is ultimately responsible for the decision and on that person's degree of technical expertise in the subject area. Leaders at the jurisdiction level will generally not have the requisite technical expertise in design, construction, and purchasing and thus will generally rely on the jurisdiction's managerial staff; they may also want to involve those with more in-depth levels of expertise—that is, consultants or contractors—to determine whether a particular decision will fulfill the goal that they are attempting to achieve.

decision making can be effective for time-sensitive decisions and when knowledge of the organization's strategic goals and relationships is critical to the outcome.

The participative (also known as permissive or democratic) style places decision making at lower levels of the organization, regardless of rank, position, or perceived authority. This style is very effective when managers or leaders are attempting to establish "buy-in" with the regular members in the organization. It gives those who generally have limited legitimate authority an opportunity to make decisions of impact and importance to the entire organization.

The delegative style moves further out along the control continuum, passing the decision-making process to the followers. The leader or manager agrees to follow the collective will of the group.

In the fire and emergency services, the effectiveness of the participative and delegative styles is closely tied to the amount of discretion that the manager or leader has with which to accomplish the strategic goal. The greater the amount of discretion, the more involvement in decisions can be allowed. Decisions under this mode are most effective when the stakeholders are the primary group affected by the decision and time is not a particular concern. For example, stipulating the details of fire apparatus specifications is often delegated to a committee with representatives of end users.

However, members may perceive invitations to participate in decision making as a manager's or leader's attempt to shift responsibility (and/or blame) for a decision to lower levels of the organization. Such a perception weakens the overall effectiveness of the manager or leader. It is critical to involve others in decisions to the extent that they know and understand the impacts of their involvement, but overreliance on consultation may weaken the manager or leader, not only by giving the impression that he or she is managing by committee and evading responsibility, but also by overtaxing members' willingness to offer advice and participate in decision making. Those who do not clearly understand the implications of a decision to be made should not participate in making it but can and often should be consulted as part of the process.

Each of the aforementioned styles—autocratic, participative, and delegative—has strengths and weaknesses depending on the situation. An effective leader or manager will use all three styles to accomplish strategic goals. In each situation, he or she must differentiate between the importance of achieving the goal and the importance of maintaining a relationship. Being involved in decision making often bolsters people's perception that their interests are being represented; however, there are occasions when autocratic, authoritative decisions accomplish the same end, especially when followers feel threatened by circumstances outside the leader's or manager's circle of influence.

In 1969, Paul Hersey and Kenneth Blanchard published the life cycle theory of leadership.[13] This widely used model of situational leadership balances the leader's task orientation against

Figure 7-2 This figure represents Paul Hersey's Situational Leadership® Model.

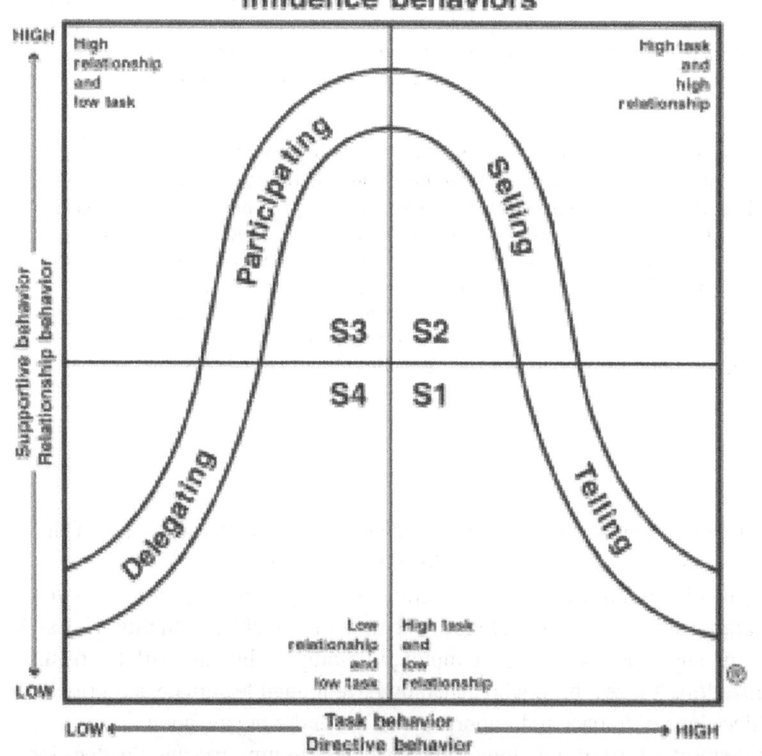

Performance Readiness®

HIGH	MODERATE		LOW
R4	R3	R2	R1
Able and confident and willing ↔	Able but insecure or unwilling	Unable but confident or willing ↔	Unable and insecure or unwilling

Source: Paul Hersey, Kenneth H. Blanchard, and Dewey E. Johnson, *Management of Organizational Behavior: Leading Human Resources*, 8th ed. (Upper Saddle River, N.J.: Prentice-Hall, 2001), 118. © Copyright 2006. Reprinted with permission of the Center for Leadership Studies, Escondido, CA 92025, situational.com. All rights reserved.

the nature of the leader's relationship with other members of the organization to determine the appropriate leadership technique to be used. The techniques include telling (high task orientation and low relationship), selling (high task orientation and high relationship), participating (low task orientation and high relationship), and delegating (low task orientation and low relationship) (Figure 7–2). The orientation on this scale would be different for each person supervised, as well as for the task assigned and the person's competence in that task.[14] The key variable in determining which method to use was based on *maturity*, defined as the ability of the people being supervised to act independently, their desire for achievement, their willingness to accept responsibility, and their experience and ability in performing the task. The emphasis of life cycle leadership is primarily on the development of team members.

This theory was subsequently refined and renamed the Situational Leadership® Model by the Center for Leadership Studies. In Situational Leadership®, the key variable of maturity is further refined to task-specific *readiness*. Readiness is composed of two dimensions: willingness and ability. *Willingness* is defined as a combination of confidence, commitment, and motivation. Understanding willingness requires that these three traits be evaluated individually. That is, someone may be highly motivated to undertake a task but be lacking in confidence. *Ability* is determined by the amount of knowledge, experience, and demonstrated skill the individual or team member brings to the task. Ability must be demonstrated to be valid.

The Situational Leadership® Model has continued to be refined over the years. Hersey's collaborator Blanchard has a version of the model known as Situational Leadership® II. In Blanchard's version, the four leadership styles of telling (S1), selling (S2), participating (S3), and delegating (S4) are renamed directing, coaching, supporting, and delegating, respectively.

Connecting theory and practice

Like leadership and management at the scene of an emergency, leading and managing an organization require strategic, tactical, and task-related decision making. Fire service officers tend to excel at tactical decision making. Strategic leadership and management are often more difficult.

Strategic leadership and management

Lack of strategic leadership and management is the greatest challenge in fire and emergency services across the board. Strategic leadership must focus on the "what," the ultimate goal, rather than on the "how," the details of how things get done. Strategic thinking is important at every level, beginning with internal and external customers; extending up through middle, upper, and executive levels of the organization; and reaching the appointed and elected leadership of the jurisdiction itself. Leading and managing strategically is of primary importance because it is the foundation for tactics and tasks. Effective leaders and managers must always be strategic, working at the tactical or task level only to support—and ensure that resources expended also support—the strategy.

Representative competencies for strategic leaders are presented in Table 7–1. These competencies are adapted from a U.S. Fish and Wildlife Service training manual. That they apply so effectively to the fire and emergency services speaks to the universal nature of high-level strategy within public organizations.[15]

Prominent among the competencies in Table 7–1 are situational awareness and risk assessment in the broad sense, collaboration, innovation, and use of objectives and performance measures. These competencies are aspirational for most chief officers: achieving them would be a sign of a very effective executive and an effective organization.

Leading a fire and emergency services department through a master planning process is an example of strategic leadership. The cornerstone of a master plan for emergency services must be a clear vision of the future of the emergency services delivery system. The more closely the vision of that system aligns with the community's vision of itself, the more support is likely to be generated in the community. Depending on the strength of this alignment and the power of the vision, the organization executive may step into a strategic leadership or management role for the jurisdiction itself if no elected or appointed leader takes that role.

Table 7-1 Elements of strategic leadership competence

Element	Distinguishing behaviors
Understands the organization, its mission, its customers, and its evolving environment.	Influences the organization's strategy to achieve its goals by taking all internal and external factors into account that affect the ability to accomplish the mission. Demonstrates a keen understanding of the complementary and competing impacts that other governmental agencies have on the ability of the organization to accomplish its goals. Develops and implements collaborative strategies that leverage the interdependent interests of diverse partners in accomplishing goals. Adapts strategies to preserve important partnering relationships on the basis of changes in organizational capability and capacity.
Plans and works toward long-term success, affordability, and sustainability, employing systems thinking and other analytical forecasting tools to assess risks and prioritize among options, programs, and initiatives.	Discerns implications of the changing environment on the organization's ability to accomplish its goals, and proactively adapts strategies to adjust priorities and address change pressures. Conceives of and implements strategies that integrate program areas and leverages internal resources to identify and achieve shared priorities and objectives. Measures strategy effectiveness and identifies proactive measures to adapt program initiatives to overcome obstacles. Implements a human capital management strategy that identifies gaps, develops new competencies in the workforce, and establishes a culture supporting innovation, creativity, and risk taking.
Plans strategic direction for the organization that is consistent with its fundamental purpose/mission and is based on a holistic view of interdependent internal and external variable factors.	Plans a strategic direction for the organization that is based on a holistic view of agency priorities and limited resources. Develops strategies to support the administration's policy direction and works with the legislative branch to accomplish the administration's goals.
Establishes and values the importance of objectives and performance measures consistent with organization goals.	Develops and implements budget and performance integration strategies. Works with partners to achieve success measures through collaborative initiatives. Identifies opportunities for organizational reengineering, builds support for organizational change, and restructures assets to align with identified priorities and improve organizational effectiveness.
Communicates strategies and obtains support for them.	Articulates the strategic direction of the organization. Works with stakeholders to gain support.

Source: Adapted from U.S. Fish and Wildlife Service, *USFWS Leadership Competency Development Model: A Tool for Developing the Service's Leaders* (March 2008), 136–137, training.fws.gov/LED/competencymodel/USFWS_Leadership_Competency_Development_Model.pdf.

Many fire chiefs and administrators find themselves reporting to an elected or appointed policy-making body that focuses not on strategies for the jurisdiction but instead on tactics for the department. Jurisdiction executives and legislators serve the delivery system much more effectively when they function as policy makers and strategic thinkers, focusing on strategic issues such as overall service levels, resource allocation, qualitative measures, and indicators of success. Issues such as numbers of fire stations, response time goals, levels of staffing, and sizes of budgets are popular areas of interest, but these are, from a jurisdictional perspective, tactical issues. Executives and legislators make the ultimate decisions about these issues, but they should be guided by the technical expertise of department chiefs.

The administrator of the organization must work consistently to keep elected and appointed leaders and managers focused on strategy without "crossing the line" and losing the support and respect of their bosses. An organization executive who finds that elected or appointed officials consistently override technically sound recommendations on tactical matters should increase efforts to educate those officials—or consider other career opportunities.

Department chiefs should also strive to function mainly at the strategic level. If they neglect strategy, there is no one else in the organization responsible for this function. However, the size of the department and the composition of the workforce will play a major role in determining how a chief can split time between strategic and tactical concerns. In smaller departments, these concerns can be very closely related, and the chief may fulfill both functions simultaneously. Fire chiefs of larger career departments will likely not have the time to be involved in equipment specification or firefighter training, whereas those in smaller departments may be directly involved in these activities.

Sometimes a department's strategic goals may be "tactical" from the perspective of the jurisdiction as a whole. For example, a city might set a strategic goal of "a safe and livable community," and it may operationalize that goal by setting a specific objective for the fire and emergency services department: "achieve a response time for the first unit of five minutes, 90 percent of the time, to all emergency calls." The department might then consider this objective to be a strategic goal and develop numerous tactical objectives to support it.

Tactical leadership and management

Tactical leadership and management both involve converting strategy into smaller segments (objectives) that are more concrete and measurable and build toward a strategic goal. Each tactical objective will generally involve a combination of tasks. To reach the emergency response time goal cited above, different elements of the organization perform numerous tasks. A specific tactical objective might be to answer and dispatch all emergency calls within sixty seconds; to support this objective, a task for Fleet Maintenance might be to perform preventive maintenance on all apparatus to ensure reliability.

Another example would be a jurisdiction's strategic goal to ensure that each department's workforce reflects the community that the department serves. The department must translate this goal into tactical objectives for recruitment, selection, training, and development programs.

Effective tactics always support a strategy. If a tactical objective does not support a strategy, it should not be implemented. Some organization activities may not support any of the organization's strategic objectives. For example, they may be remnants of the organization's past or reflect the interests of a group or a stakeholder no longer considered important by the jurisdiction.

Tactical leadership requires the executive to be involved personally in establishing and designing programs that support strategic goals. Tactical management may involve allocation of funding and establishing parameters for policies that govern these programs.

Task leadership and management

Generally, task-level leaders and managers can be found at every rank below the executive head of the organization. They work to accomplish objectives that support the goals of the organization, which in turn should support and be consistent with the goals of the jurisdiction.

Management (and leadership) successes or failures are connected to the manager's (or leader's) ability to get things done. Whether these are the "right" or "wrong" things to do depends on how closely they are perceived as supporting the objectives or goals of the person evaluating "success." This fact presents a challenge for task-level leaders and managers. Nearly everyone above the task level has an idea of how the "down line" tasks should be accomplished, but not all those who set organizational goals and objectives understand how to translate goals and objectives into tasks. Thus, the task-level leader or manager must exercise discretion in deciding how tasks are accomplished, but must also make sure that tasks support objectives of the organization, not personal goals and objectives.

The extent to which a chief must function at the task level depends almost exclusively on the resources available. Even in a very large organization, resource limitations may require the chief's participation at the task level in support of some goals or objectives. At the same time, even a small organization may have sufficient resources to accomplish a particular goal or objective without the chief's participation at the task level, thus allowing the leader or manager to function in a strategic role.

While hiring decisions may be based on one's record or potential for functioning at the strategic and tactical levels, firing decisions tend to be based on task-level success or failure. A fire chief may be hired for his or her prowess as a fiscal manager, formal education in economics, and past achievements in managing budgets in a larger department, but that chief may be fired because he or she did not allocate appropriate resources to the department training program, a mistake that is discovered in the aftermath of a line-of-duty death.

Leadership and management challenges

Major areas of concern for leaders and managers of fire and emergency service organizations include service delivery, performance measurement, human resources, firefighter safety, labor-management relations, combination departments and volunteer recruitment and retention, collaboration, and ethics.

Service delivery

Four interdependent factors affect fire and emergency services delivery in both real and imagined ways. Evaluating and improving service delivery effectiveness requires an understanding of each factor:

- *Expectation:* Every service should be based on a clear description of the eventual customer's expectations, or on an answer to the question, "What does the customer want?" There is a tendency in fire and emergency services delivery to assume that the service provider knows what the customer wants and to "tell the customer what he or she wants." This practice can cause the relationship between the customer and the service provider to deteriorate over time, as the customer begins to feel that his or her opinions are being ignored.
- *Validation:* Both the customer and the provider need to determine how valid the customer's expectation is, given the environment surrounding the service. The challenge for fire and emergency services is that there are many expectations at every level of the delivery system, and without a validation process, both customers and providers can end up frustrated.
- *Communication:* There must be clear, consistent, and continuous communication between the customer and the service provider about the services that the customer expects to receive and the provider expects to provide.
- *Evaluation:* The customer answers the question, "Did I get what I expected?," and the provider answers the question, "Did I provide what was expected?"

Each of these factors has an impact on one or more of the other ones. Each needs to be considered in a balanced fashion. Overemphasis on one or more will create issues for the customer or the service delivery provider or both. These four factors are equally important to leaders and managers in their strategic, tactical, and task-level roles.

Performance measurement

Describing service delivery performance in a way that both the customer and the service provider understand may be the most important aspect of the performance measurement process. This understanding forms the basis for the evaluation of service delivery. Too often, fire service performance measures are created by internal customers and laden with jargon that external customers do not understand. For example, the traditional fire service has a difficult time getting the public to understand the implications of the "time temperature curve" or the value of particular levels of staffing in the suppression of fires. Fire and emergency service providers need to be able to describe performance in a way that is clear to customers, both internal and external. In the end, simpler descriptions are usually better.

What brings the performance management system together is the degree to which the data collected are related to customer expectations. Reports on performance need to demonstrate, where appropriate, that customer expectations were met. Where expectations were not met, this fact should not be hidden, but reasons can be explained. Unmet expectations can present opportunities for focusing the organization's attention, realigning resources, and identifying areas for improvement.

Performance reports should avoid excessive detail and instead emphasize a clear presentation of key measures. Information presented to jurisdiction executives should generally be in a format that not only helps them see that the organization is contributing to the completion of strategic jurisdictional goals but also validates the work of people inside the organization. In this way, the performance measurement process becomes a motivational tool that helps members feel connected to the work of the organization. The organization's performance management system must be coordinated with its performance evaluation system for individual members. Failure to connect the two can create an environment in which members question the organization's direction and effectiveness, and those who are motivated by achievement are discouraged. For more information on performance management, see Chapter 14.

Human resources

Within fire and emergency service organizations, contention over hiring, promotion, discipline, executive recruitment, and performance appraisal is common. Fire service executives must see that their organizations comply with legal requirements and develop defensible, job-related criteria for all personnel actions. Employee performance appraisals are difficult because supervisors are unwilling to critically assess their employees. The culture in many organizations encourages the company or small unit to protect its members, sometimes at the expense of organizational goals and objectives. Chapter 8 discusses human resource management challenges.

Although many parts of the country and many industries have seen progress in diversity and inclusion, the fire service continues to have trouble in these areas.[16] In fact, according to 2008 U.S. Bureau of Labor Statistics, the workforce composition of the fire service was the least diverse of any protective service occupation, both at the entry level and, to an even greater degree, at the supervisory level. A report by the U.S. Census Bureau in 2008 indicates that by 2042, the non-Hispanic white population of the United States will no longer be the majority.[17] Although it is impossible to predict the impact of this and other changes in the workforce, industries that have not made progress in reflecting the customer base they serve may well lose the support of that base, mainly because they will be perceived as not understanding the customer.

The following problems could also arise for organizations that are not able to improve their diversity and inclusiveness:

- Management relationships with labor (career or volunteer) may deteriorate.
- Relationships between career and volunteer members of a combination department may suffer.
- Ballot measures to fund fire services may fail to gain support.
- Negative stories about the organization may begin to appear in the media.
- Relationships between fire and other public safety organizations may suffer.

Firefighter safety

Firefighter safety is a major concern for fire and emergency service executives. Despite improvements in equipment, efforts in education and outreach, and changes in policy, the number of firefighter deaths nationwide has remained fairly consistent for years. As detailed in Chapter 11, heart attacks and vehicular crashes are major causes of line-of-duty deaths. Investigation of individual incidents often reveals that poor command practices, limited compliance with recognized safety practices, and poor personal physical conditioning or medical screening also play a role in a majority of line-of-duty deaths.

Despite recognition of the importance of quality command at emergency incidents, many departments continue to tolerate unsafe activities. Professional standards vary widely throughout the fire and emergency services. Consistent failure to ensure that policies and procedures are followed can be laid at the feet of management and leadership. The experience of many departments indicates that management controls need to be improved.

Labor-management relations

Rigid labor agreements and relations based on old assumptions about the demands placed on fire and emergency service organizations limit the ability of many organizations to adapt to their environments in the areas of human resource management and firefighter health and safety. Despite notable labor-management collaboration initiatives on health and safety issues, there is room for improvement. Fiscal scarcity and the changing nature of services demanded in many communities will encourage changes to traditional patterns of labor-management relations. Examples of new initiatives in some departments include building inspections, public health or preventive medicine outreach, and even expanded response activities or roles for events related to weapons of mass destruction.

Combination departments and volunteer recruitment and retention

Combination and volunteer fire departments pose unique leadership and management challenges. In combination departments, the human resource and cultural issues raised when career and volunteer personnel work side by side inevitably lead to conflict over roles, responsibilities, and perceived or real differences in treatment of personnel.

In volunteer departments, recruitment and retention of adequate numbers of personnel present challenges across the country. Community economic structure, social conditions, and increased training requirements for volunteers have been cited as reasons for the decline in the number of personnel joining fire and emergency service organizations. Length-of-service award programs, which offer deferred cash benefits in exchange for years of service, have grown in popularity. Likewise, "junior member" programs and other long-standing programs that engage youth continue to attract members. Limited research has shown that some of the basic "good management" practices that should be common to all organizations can play a role in helping to recruit and retain members. In particular, empowering members to be involved in decision making and providing opportunities for training and service delivery are thought to be important motivators for volunteers.[18] Some departments have invested in larger and more luxurious facilities as an enticement to attract and retain members.

The overall success of these strategies has not been systematically evaluated, and little research has been published to offer definitive guidance to fire and emergency service chief officers on which incentives or practices are best suited for their departments. Surveying the membership can be a good way to collect information on members' long-term plans, challenges to greater participation, and areas for improvement.

Collaboration

The traditional fire service often rewards and brings attention to those who perform self-sufficiently. However, the concept of interdependence should be deemed of equal importance as it focuses on the *team* aspect of the service. In fire and emergency services delivery, an individual's own performance is enhanced by his or her ability to work with others. As the ability to work in a team develops, leadership and management skills develop as well.

The need for interdependence stems from the limitations that all human beings have. Those who recognize this need are generally those who are self-assured enough to accept their personal limitations and intelligent enough to use the strengths of others for the achievement of common goals.

Promoting teamwork* One of the chief's most important leadership and management responsibilities is building and maintaining effective fire and emergency service teams within the department. Because every department consists of various broad categories of employees (e.g., firefighters, apparatus operators, administrative staff, emergency medical service personnel, and management personnel), the interactions between employees in different categories bear heavily on the department's ultimate effectiveness. External customers should see the fire department as a single agency speaking with a single voice. On a day-to-day basis, cross-functional cooperation is essential. The successful team must extend its valuing of diversity well beyond sex and cultural background to include sworn and nonsworn personnel and all members regardless of assignment.

---

*This section is based on pages 250–251 of Chapter 8, "Leading and Managing," by Bob Hart and Robin Paulsgrove, in the 2002 edition of this volume.

Developing effective decision-making teams

In today's world a chief officer cannot manage effectively without input and participation by others within and, in some cases, outside the organization. One way of ensuring buy-in of new management goals is through the creation of effective decision-making teams. An effective team can go a long way in curtailing any resistance by the rank and file to modern management of the programs and services that a department provides.

When appointing team members, it is important to be inclusive. Effective teams have a wide range of characteristics, such as influence, integrity, technical expertise, and effective communication skills. Every member does not have to possess all of the above traits; however, the team should include a diverse mix of members to ensure a broad representation of views and a wide array of skills. Ideally, all team members should share a mutual enthusiasm for tasks that the team has been assigned. Members who intentionally obstruct or disrupt the team's work can keep the team from being effective.

Equally important, a "can do" attitude is paramount to effective and meaningful outcomes of the team's work. Ideally, team members have an ability to creatively solve problems. Members should also have the ability to say how they truly feel about an issue even though it may make others feel uncomfortable. And it is equally important that there exist an air of respect and courtesy during the course of the team's work. Being nice and respectful to one another is a primary ingredient of effective teamwork.

Other considerations when developing effective teams are as follows:

- **Expectations:** Has senior management clearly communicated its expectations for the team's performance and outcomes? Management should be sure not to "overpromise" regarding the team's influence over a final decision or course of action.
- **Purpose:** Do team members understand the reason the team was created?
- **Support:** Can the department support the team with resources such as people, time, and money?
- **Innovation:** Does the department truly embrace creative thinking, unique solutions, and new ideas?
- **Attention:** Does the work of the team receive sufficient support in terms of time, discussion, attention, and interest from top-level managers?
- **Participation:** Do team members understand why they are participating on the team?
- **Worth:** Do team members understand how the strategy of using teams will help the department attain its stated goals?
- **Importance:** Can team members define the team's importance to the accomplishment of the department's goals?
- **Context:** Does the team understand where its work fits within the total context of the department's goals, principles, vision, and values?

Source: John Cochran, fire chief, Russellville, Arkansas.

Fire and emergency service organizations represent themselves as professional teams, all members of which are equally important to effective service delivery, but there remains a wide chasm in desirability between staff assignments and field assignments. Shift (field) positions are generally viewed as conferring a distinct personal advantage over the traditional forty-hour-per-week staff assignment. Work assignments have an obvious effect on morale and productivity, and those that are seen as less desirable may prompt high turnover in staff technical positions. High turnover in any position means high training costs and loss of valuable experience. In management positions it can also result in inconsistent leadership, ineffective long-range planning, and limited institutional memory.

Although firefighters may resist the conversion of many dispatch, training, and fire positions (i.e., staff positions) to nonsworn status, developing and maintaining staff assignment policies for sworn personnel is an ongoing problem in many fire and emergency service departments. Balancing a desire for consistency (associated with having a credible assignments policy) with the flexibility necessary to accommodate a dynamic organization is often a challenge. Efforts to increase the incentives associated with staff assignments are difficult to "sell" to the local government manager who questions the logic of proposing pay incentives to induce someone to work forty hours per week with weekends off instead of a fifty-six-hour shift. And because staff employees are fewer in number, they may often be underrepresented by employee bargaining groups when benefits are being negotiated.

Furthermore, training programs to develop and adequately prepare an employee to function effectively in a specialized staff assignment are very limited. Thus, in many departments new firefighters receive up to six months of training before going into a highly supervised field company, but when these firefighters are reassigned to staff positions that, by contrast, might be in an unsupervised work environment, the only orientation they receive may be a two-week overlap with a predecessor.

The fire and emergency service can fulfill its expanded mission only with the coordinated efforts of both staff and field divisions. The challenge is to lead all divisions to work together as equal partners. Introducing a continuing process to build effective teamwork among staff and field positions may include efforts to

- Model support for staff positions
- Expand cadet training programs to introduce new department members to a broadened department mission
- Communicate the importance of staff experience for career progression
- Develop recruiting brochures and procedures that introduce prospective applicants to all positions
- Improve the quality and consistency of staff training and orientation
- Conduct a thorough job analysis, and evaluate options to break down traditional staff descriptions and division barriers to create new jobs that balance job duties seen as desirable with those seen as less desirable
- Increase communication to educate personnel about the work that takes place in staff divisions
- Introduce short-term internships so that personnel can be exposed to staff divisions without undergoing more than limited personal disruption.

Working across boundaries A major issue for the fire and emergency services is the perception that they do not interact well with other services. Despite the fire service's "hero image" in the community, a number of barriers lie between the fire service and other organizations. Although working across these barriers should be a priority for both leaders and managers, the department chief will likely be in a better position to bridge them. At a personal level, any barrier between fire and emergency service leaders and their bosses, peers, or customers diminishes the organization's ability to function at peak efficiency and effectiveness.

Fire and emergency service leaders must be particularly aware of the perception that the organization creates in the larger community. Of all the services that local government provides, fire and emergency services have traditionally enjoyed the highest level of respect from customers. However, providers of other services do not always share this sentiment.

No fire chief should forget the importance of his or her role as a jurisdictional manager and its juxtaposition against his or her role as a department leader. A proposed action may appear to benefit the department, but it is important to consider how it will affect the jurisdiction as a whole. If the jurisdiction fails, the organizations within it fail as well. For example, while the fire and emergency services department may support extending sprinkler requirements to single-family dwellings, the jurisdiction may oppose such a policy on the grounds that it will affect housing affordability. If the jurisdiction makes a decision contrary to the department's position, the fire chief (after raising objections in an appropriate venue) must accept and support the jurisdiction's decision in his or her role as a manager of the jurisdiction. The jurisdiction's decision may be related to the economic competitiveness of the community or it may reflect the community's desire to reduce costs of construction.

Each division within the fire and emergency services organization depends on others to achieve its mission. The suppression or operations division depends on the maintenance division to ensure that apparatus is maintained and ready for service. The fire prevention division may depend on the operations division to perform some inspections and report violations observed while on incidents. Outside the department, the fire prevention and operations divisions depend on the buildings department to maintain basic building safety standards and to follow up on reports from fire services of code violations. Developing and maintaining close relations with key supporting agencies is an example of using collaboration to improve service delivery.

An example of a barrier to achieving better collaboration between fire and emergency services and other government organizations is the chief's uniform. The fire and emergency services chief who is more interested in being a firefighter than in being an executive is a stereotype that most chiefs want to avoid. Wearing a uniform all the time can feed into this stereotype. In their role as organizational leaders, fire and emergency service chiefs wear a uniform to connect to their internal audience of personnel in the field. To connect with peers in their role as jurisdictional managers, however, chiefs should wear business attire. Wearing business attire minimizes the natural "standing out" that occurs when a chief wears a uniform and demonstrates the chief's interest in being part of the jurisdictional team. This strategy can actually increase the benefit and effect when the chief does wear the uniform. The uniform, worn strategically, can support a strategic message that the chief is trying to convey.

Ethics*

Public confidence is the foundation for the community's engagement in and financial support of government programs. Lack of public confidence can mean that people refuse to participate or refuse to support funding needs. When a fire official acts other than in the public's best interest, public confidence in the organization is undermined. Community support can evaporate instantly with one serious lapse in ethical decision making, or even the appearance of one.

Ethical decision making covers such basic matters as how services are allocated, how resources are managed, and how people are treated. For example:

- Are services provided that favor a particular income level or part of town? Are services excluded that those with little political influence need?
- Are the funds spent on a legitimate public purpose? Did those funds really have to be spent? And what about the way the funds were spent: Was a fair bid process used? Were any personal benefits received from vendors?
- Are employees put in a situation in which they are expected to take an ethically questionable action? For employees as well as employers, effectiveness, motivation, and job satisfaction depend on how well they identify with the organization's values, whether those values are consistent with their own, and whether the values that the organization professes are consistent with what the organization actually does.

Types of ethical problems likely to arise Recognizing potential problems allows time to keep them from materializing. A few types of potential ethical (possibly even legal) problems are discussed here.

Criminal activity The most damaging ethics problem for the fire and emergency services is arson by fire personnel or theft from fire or medical victims. Criminal activity may also include theft from the department—for example, taking equipment, overcharging for travel expenses, seeking compensation for a non-duty-related injury that is presented as duty related, and requesting pay for time not worked. Crimes committed by fire employees off duty can have the same negative effect on the department's reputation in the community as those committed on duty.

Racial and sexual discrimination Actions ranging from blatant discrimination to a seemingly unjustified decision, and including insensitivity to those who are different, have prompted discrimination complaints and lawsuits pertaining to appointment, promotion, discipline, and discharge.

*This section is based on pages 89–96 of Chapter 3, "Leadership Strategies for the Political Process," by Steven C. Carter and Lyle J. Sumek, in the 2002 edition of this volume.

Sexual and other forms of harassment Treatment of employees, particularly female employees, by supervisors, peers, and the public is regulated by law and agency policy. A 1998 court decision, *Oncale v. Sundowner Offshore Oil Services,* 523 U.S. 75 (1998), also recognized "same-sex" sexual harassment as actionable.

Drug or alcohol abuse A small but significant portion of any workforce is likely to have a problem with drug or alcohol abuse. The problem is often reflected in high absenteeism, a high accident rate, or strained relationships with other employees.

Acceptance of gifts People like to give fire employees gifts. An inexpensive gift (e.g., a plate of cookies) as an expression of appreciation for helping a family member with a medical emergency may be harmless, but an expensive gift in return for favored treatment is entirely different. (Employees charged with enforcing the fire code may be more likely to attract expensive gifts.) Discounts on food and other merchandise for fire employees are not uncommon but are probably inappropriate. Was the gift meant to influence a decision? What value would be acceptable? Would a gift be perceived by others as improper influence? There should be a clear organizational standard as to what is acceptable.

Irregularities in purchasing Buying goods and services from employees and diverging from the regular process to buy from a "friendly" business are both improper. Also improper is accepting travel, entertainment, or other things of personal value from equipment manufacturers, yet in some areas this practice is still engaged in.

Incompatible employment With so many employees holding second jobs, potential conflicts between the two jobs need to be carefully monitored. Examples of possible incompatibility are when a fire inspector works for an establishment that he or she is responsible for inspecting, and when an employee provides a service that may be needed after an inspection (e.g., recharges fire extinguishers).

Endorsements of private products With an ever-increasing variety of public-private partnerships, endorsements may or may not be proper. Personal benefit from an endorsement is clearly unacceptable.

Political activity Some political activity by employees is permitted under state laws. But the law usually frowns on using one's official position in support of political candidates. And even though some political activity may be allowed by law, that does not make it wise. Political candidates seem to be attracted to fire equipment or personnel for campaign ads, but this pairing should not be allowed.

Disclosure of confidential information The confidentiality of personnel information, medical collective bargaining information, identity of complainants, and so forth varies by state. Federal law covers medical information. Care should be taken to identify what is confidential and to maintain that confidentiality. By the same token, it is important not to restrict disclosure of public information and to encourage the sharing of information that is helpful to other agencies; for example, the fire department would identify a home with unhealthy living conditions to the local agency responsible for child welfare.

Illegal meetings State statutes define requirements for public meetings (i.e., the conditions under which a gathering is required to be open to the public). If fire managers are not sensitive to those requirements, they may put elected officials in a difficult situation. A politically active union may also put elected officials in the position of violating an open-meeting law if the union is not careful when hosting incumbent elected officials.

Use of public equipment or facilities for private benefit The nature of this unethical act can vary, from taking an office pen or pad of paper for use at home to taking or "borrowing" expensive tools or other equipment.

Remedies for errors in judgment After making an error in judgment, many people rationalize their error and hope that the matter goes away quickly. The sidebar "Mind over Matter"

Mind over manner: Excuses for wrongdoing

Denying or trivializing its significance	"Show me a victim." "It's not illegal." "You can't legislate morality." "It's just a technicality."
Invoking the double standard	"Morality is a personal matter." "I don't mix business with my personal feelings."
Arguing necessity	"It's cutthroat out there." "If I don't do it, someone else will." "It's my job." "It will save some jobs."
Arguing relativity	"It's not illegal elsewhere." "In the United States, ideals are turned into laws." "No act is inherently illegal." "We are no worse or better than society at large."
Professing ignorance	"I wasn't told." "Ethics is a gray area." "The rules are inscrutable."

Source: Gary B. Brumback, "Institutionalizing Ethics in Government," *Public Personnel Management* 20, no. 3 (1991): Table 1. Reprinted with permission of *Public Personnel Management*, published by the International Personnel Management Association (IPMA), 1617 Duke Street, Alexandria, VA 22314; 703/549-7100, ipma-hr.org.

lists many of the common forms that such rationalization may take. Unfortunately, in the public's mind, this kind of excuse only compounds the error. Better responses to an error in judgment are as follows:

Tell the boss(es) everything Before the bosses learn of an error from someone else, the erring person should meet with them at the absolutely earliest time and ask for no interruptions; should explain what happened as fully as memory allows (making some notes in advance is a good way to make sure that nothing is forgotten); should be most explicit about the part that is most difficult to explain (otherwise, when that part comes out in the open later, the person will seem to have been trying to hide something); and should not only have a plan in mind for dealing with the problem but also ask for suggestions.

Make a complete public disclosure A "voluntary" statement at a public meeting or news conference allows one to take the initiative in addressing the problem and ensures that the media get all the relevant facts. If the issue is strictly internal to the organization, a meeting with staff can be substituted for the public meeting—but one should not be surprised if someone in attendance makes the "internal" issue public.

Apologize to all interested parties There is no substitute for a timely, sincere, personal apology.

Take corrective action The erring person should do whatever he or she can to minimize the effect of the immediate problem and should then act to prevent its recurrence. The preventive action, too, should be explained publicly.

Steps toward greater consistency in ethical behavior Fire service leaders and managers can take some simple steps to make decision making in the department more ethical and increase the public's confidence in the department and the department's effectiveness in the public arena.

Clearly define organizational values and expectations An ethical framework for an organization can be provided by (1) a set of legal requirements, (2) a statement of values, (3) an ethics policy or ordinance, or (4) performance standards or expectations.

Hire employees who are sensitive to ethical issues In its recruitment material the organization should cover values, and in interviews it should include questions involving ethical situations.

Providing ethical leadership

Ethical behavior is essential for all of us involved with public administration. If we as chief fire officers violate the ethical expectations of our communities and departments, our personnel will most probably refuse to follow us, and the public will likely attempt to have us removed from our positions.

It is essential that we provide ethical leadership for our organization. We need to attempt to avoid any situation that could be interpreted as a conflict of interest, we need to refrain from making decisions based on our personal preferences, and we must diligently ensure that we do not abuse the power of our position.

If we are in doubt about a proposed action, we should ask what we would like to see reported on the front page of the local newspaper. If we wish to keep our actions from public view, it is a strong indicator that we may not think our actions are ethical.

The following is the current adopted Code of Ethics of the International Association of Fire Chiefs (IAFC), which represents the leadership of America's fire and emergency departments and those of forty other nations.

> Every member of the IAFC shall with due deliberation live according to ethical principles consistent with professional conduct and shall
>
> > Recognize that we serve in a position of public trust that imposes responsibility to use publicly owned resources effectively and judiciously.
> >
> > Keep in mind our obligation not to seek advantages or favors for ourselves, friends, or family.
> >
> > Use information gained by virtue of our positions only for the benefit of those we are entrusted to serve.
> >
> > Conduct our personal affairs in such a manner that we cannot be improperly influenced in the performance of our duties.
> >
> > Recognize and avoid situations wherein our decisions or recommendations may have an impact on our personal financial interests.
> >
> > Seek no favor and accept no form of personal reward for influence or official action.
> >
> > Engage in no outside employment or professional activities that may impair or appear to be in conflict with our primary responsibilities as fire officials.
> >
> > Handle all personnel matters on the basis of merit.
> >
> > Carry out policies established by elected officials and policy makers to the best of our ability, even when they are contrary to our recommendations.
> >
> > Refrain from financial investments or business that conflict with, or are enhanced by, our official position.

Source: Adapted with permission from the IAFC, "Fire Chief's Code of Ethics," IAFC Board of Directors, 2002.

However, the best way to determine whether prospective employees are sensitive to ethical issues is with reference checks.

Offer regular ethics training and education for employees Regular formal training is important for all employees, especially managers and supervisors. And it is particularly important that this training be interactive. Most effective, however, may be discussions between supervisors and employees as issues come up: evaluating the issues from different perspectives, weighing alternative courses of action, and clarifying the organization's position or decision.

Provide consultation on ethical issues for employees Employees need to be able to get advice they can rely on to keep them out of trouble with their employers.

Maintain reasonable means for monitoring and control Monitoring key processes and decisions to make sure that there are no problems in the department is very important. The way to do this is to check periodically. For example, it is management's responsibility to check payroll, long-distance telephone service logs, or Internet usage records; review travel reimbursements; verify purchases or any handling of cash; or ask employees in protected classes if they are being treated in a manner that is consistent with relevant laws, policies, or organizational values.

Respond to ethical problems by correcting systems and holding employees accountable When an ethical problem occurs, one of the first questions to ask is, "How could this have happened?" In some cases the cause may simply be an employee error. In other cases the cause may be a faulty procedure or system, such as an ambiguous purchasing policy, requiring a change in the procedure or more training for employees.

Set a good personal example When a leader models the kind of behavior expected of employees, the employees will display that behavior more consistently themselves.

Leading and managing change within fire and emergency service organizations

Clearly there are several areas of challenge for fire and emergency service organizations where effective leadership and management are needed. In one or more of these areas, the chief may need to change the culture of the organization.

Changing the culture of an organization is one of the most challenging objectives that a leader or manager will undertake. Cultural change in and of itself is not a strategic goal; it is a tactic that should support a strategic goal. "Change for the sake of change" has an extremely negative connotation, especially in cultures where the status quo is celebrated to the extent that it is in the traditional fire service. Cultural change is only implemented on the tactical level after leaders and managers have established clear strategic goals that require change. As mentioned earlier, diversity is one area in particular where cultural change may be necessary if the fire and emergency services are to remain relevant in a changing world over the next few years. Fire safety is another if performance results are to change (see Chapter 11).

The role of organizational culture

Sociologists recognize that organizations are complex and that each has its own culture, which affects how the organization relates to its environment. An organization's culture must be assessed in conjunction with the environment, and there is no such thing as a "good" or "bad" culture in itself.

According to Edgar Schein, culture has several levels.[19] The first level includes statements and actions, known as artifacts, that are readily seen by outsiders—for example, the organization's mission statement. At the next level are the attitudes of the organization's members. Most people in an organization have personal attitudes and beliefs that are not necessarily part of the official organization's life. If enough people within the organization share similar attitudes and beliefs, these attitudes and beliefs will dominate the organization. At the most intimate level are "tacit assumptions"—unspoken aspects of an organization's culture that can be revealed only through extended and detailed inquiry. Together these statements and actions, attitudes, and tacit assumptions are known as culture, and they can be used to understand and predict the behavior of the organization.

Fire and emergency service organizations have very strong cultures, all reinforced by strong team identity, paramilitary heritage, dangerous work, and selective entry requirements. These cultures persist for long periods of time; they can (and usually do) outlast individual chiefs and elected officials. The cultural norms in the fire and emergency services can be very effective in building loyalty and cohesiveness among members.

However, fire and emergency service organizational culture is not monolithic. For example, each company, shift, or station may have its own subculture. Perhaps more powerful are subcultures associated with job assignments—for example, fire inspection, dispatch, or ladder companies. Other subcultures may be associated with ethnic or fraternal organizations: many departments have ethnic societies that are very active. Multiple subcultures are common, but if these subcultures are too numerous or too strong, they may overpower the organization's primary culture, greatly complicating attempts to implement change within the organization.

Growth of cultural "literacy"

In dealing with different cultures within an organization, it is helpful to consider various ways in which people interact with a culture that is different from their own and how such interactions evolve over time. Just as people grow in intellectual skills, from concrete to abstract thinking, so too can attitudes and approaches to other cultures grow. The growth of cultural thinking can take the following course:

Our way is their way.

Their way is different—it's wrong.

Our way is "X," their way is "Y."

Both our way and their way have strengths and weaknesses.

We can learn from them, and they can learn from us. (Cultural synergy)

We can bridge differences during our interactions by adjusting our behaviors. (Cultural flexibility)

With this partner, we can bridge in this way; with that partner, we can bridge in another way. (Cultural literacy)

We can prevent conflict and, where it is already present, can defuse it, keep it from escalating, and resolve it. (Cultural mediation)

Adapted from Wendy Hall, *Making Strategic Relationships Work* (New York: John Wiley & Sons, 1995), 22, 31. From handouts prepared by the Innes Strategy Group in Auckland, New Zealand. Reproduced with permission.

In extreme cases, organizational culture may be so badly splintered or divided as to create a perception that there is more than one fire department.

Culture is important not only within the organization but also with respect to the community it serves and the political oversight structures in place. Community change can require adjustment of a fire and emergency service organization's culture.[20] If the population or economic structure changes or becomes more diverse, the department may need to increase outreach and incorporate language or other training to enable responders, including 911 operators, to be effective at their jobs and to ensure that there is always someone on duty who can speak the most popular second language in a community. Training or proficiency in certain languages may also become important for the hiring and compensation process. Failure to reflect community change can cause a department to lose the support of the community.

Important contributors to the public's perception of fire and emergency services culture are the media and popular entertainment. Television and film portrayals of fire and emergency service organizations are a double-edged sword. While they cultivate images of high-quality service delivery and showcase positive aspects of culture, they may also play into negative stereotypes of the fire and emergency services and create false expectations for risk taking and behavior that may be modeled by new employees.

Preparing for cultural change

Change in a fire and emergency services department is driven primarily by the jurisdiction. Without a clear vision from the leadership of the jurisdiction, the department will not get the right leaders or managers. The leaders of both the jurisdiction and the department will be the most important catalysts for strategic change initiatives, developing and communicating the vision for the future and milestones to measure progress. The managers of both the jurisdiction and the department will keep changes on track, focused, and strong. As this section makes clear, several actions will give the effort the greatest chance for success (see sidebar on facing page).

Assess the current situation to ensure the need for change The first step in implementing cultural change is to carefully evaluate what is currently working and what is not working. There is an unfortunate tendency for change agents to "throw the baby out with the bath water." This is particularly likely when the change agent predetermines what the new situation will be or applies "cookie-cutter solutions." Just because a program works in one department or setting does not mean that it can be copied and applied to another organization effectively. For the long-term health of the organization, it is as critical to evaluate the existing culture for elements that are working and bring value as it is to determine elements that are not adding value.

Essential steps for successful change

Ensure the need: Leaders must make sure change is needed and communicate the need to others.

Prepare a plan: A plan for change should include a vision of the future, strategy and action steps, and milestones for measuring progress.

Build internal and external support: Successful change needs the support of top management, agency members, and external stakeholders.

Provide resources: Necessary resources include political support, skills, time, and finances.

Memorialize change: The "rules" must be rewritten to make sure new patterns of behavior replace old ones.

Integrate changes throughout the agency: Changes should be reflected in all the operations of the agency.

This list incorporates determinants of successful change in public sector organizations compiled by Hal G. Rainey in *Understanding and Managing Public Organizations*, 4th ed. (San Francisco: Jossey-Bass, 2009), 409.

The evaluation should begin by comparing the stated vision, mission, and values of the organization with what is actually occurring on a daily basis. The real situation may take some time to understand. Outside help may be needed to get an objective view of the organization's culture, particularly if the top managers have spent their entire careers within the department.

Assess resources for change Any change initiative requires resources. A person who initiates change or directs that it occur without providing resources to implement it is either uninformed about what is necessary or uncommitted to the change process. Effective change of culture requires

- *Time:* Typically, culture change in a fire and emergency services organization will take between three and five years. If the organization is to change, the jurisdiction will have to make a commitment of time to see the change to fruition.
- *Political capital:* Any leader or manager is given a certain amount of political capital or "clout" by the person who made the appointment, the group or groups that initially confirmed that appointment, and some percentage of his or her colleagues and followers. The amount of political capital that leader or manager carries forward is generally based on a mix of perceptions of competence combined with the strength of the relationships that develop between that leader or manager and the leaders and managers of the jurisdiction, members of the organization, and everyone else involved in the service delivery system. In working toward change, a leader must constantly monitor this "political capital account."
- *Competence:* Professional knowledge, skills, and abilities in the fire and emergency services, and the personal ability to "cause things to happen," are needed to lead a successful change effort. The fire service is generally evaluated by customers according to its ability to solve problems, especially in emergencies. To the degree that people believe a fire official is competent, they are more likely to trust his or her decision, even when they may not agree with the decision itself. When a leader or manager is perceived as lacking competence, the focus shifts from how the change will affect the ability of the jurisdiction or the organization to achieve its strategic goals to the personal characteristics of the change agent.
- *Financial and other resources:* No change in the public or private sector will be effective in the long term without the investment of fiscal or other resources. It is simply impossible to continue spending the department budget on maintaining the status quo and get change at the same time. Fiscal investment is often a barrier in the public sector because of the focus of managers on the costs of change. This is where leaders must be able to shift the discussion to the value of the change. Managers focus on cost, leaders focus on value, and followers focus on results and getting their needs met. A case should be made that the desired changes are worth the cost and will produce positive results for the department and community.

Assess risk and resistance to change Plans for cultural change in a fire and emergency services department need to balance risks to the strategic goals of the department against predictable resistance from those who will be affected by the change. The focus must be on the strategic purpose for the change, but a leader or manager who acts as a change agent must also think about the tactical implications of both risk and resistance in order to prioritize the tactical and task-level implementation of change initiatives.

When a change effort is implemented in a fire and emergency services department, there are risks not only for the organization if its strategic goals are not met but also for leaders and for members who work at the task level. As the initiators of change in most cases, leaders are likely to receive most of the credit for success—or blame for failure. At the task level, where change usually has its most significant impact, members will feel positive about successes and not so positive about perceived failures. Unfortunately, those who take a very visible role in leading change efforts can find themselves the targets of those who do not support the change, especially when results in the early stages are disappointing. An important key to success from a leader's perspective is being able to survive the change long enough to see it to completion.

If cultural change is initiated by the jurisdiction at the behest of the customer, the change effort has the best possibility of success. The department chief can function in a managerial role with respect to the change and stay out of the spotlight. However, the chief does need to maintain control over how the change is implemented and provide leadership throughout the implementation process. If members of the department see that the jurisdiction executive is managing the change process, the chief's authority is undermined and the chief gets no credit for the success of the effort.

Just as the leader faces personal risks if the change is not successful, department members are also exposed to negative consequences. Members invest in the change effort and exercise influence on their peers to adapt. If the change effort fails, they bear consequences that can be both personal and collective if the department's image or reputation is damaged. There is a direct correlation between members' perception of vulnerability in their current state and their willingness to accept change. The more vulnerable people feel, the more likely they are to consider alternatives to their current approach. For example, a department may have little interest in the diversity outcomes of hiring processes. However, a federal lawsuit and attendant publicity may make department members more open to change. The challenge for fire and emergency services leaders and managers is to help members see the vulnerability without attempting or being perceived as attempting to drive change through fear. The more sophisticated the members, the less likely they are to be motivated by fear.

No one who attempts to bring change to a fire and emergency services organization should underestimate the resistance that will arise when the word *change* is discussed, let alone when the reality of change appears. Resistance can come from any quarter—a boss, a colleague, or customers inside or outside the jurisdiction or organization. And not all resistance is irrational: the bottom line is that when people see that their needs are not being met or fear that their interests will not be served, they will resist. The traditional fire service has had a number of successes upon which current practices are built. Many people focus more on past successes than on the current goals of the agency or jurisdiction. Effective changes occur when leaders find a method of reducing resistance by appealing to the unique interests of those who will be most affected by the change.

Implementing change and making it last

Once the prerequisites for change are in place, leaders should consider how quickly the change needs to occur, how it will be made permanent, and how to make sure that it is integrated into daily routines throughout the organization.

Pacing the change As discussed, the pace at which change is implemented should balance risk against resistance. In decreasing order of urgency, organizational change can be described as revolutionary, moderate, or evolutionary. A revolutionary change is paced for completion

Leading change: Developing a multiagency approach to safe housing

The city of White Plains, New York (2009 pop. 57,442), is protected by a career fire and emergency service. Along with police, contracted emergency medical services, and emergency management, fire service personnel report to a public safety department headed by an appointed, full-time commissioner.

The combination of an expensive housing market, proximity to a major city, and a stock of older, larger homes all helped to create pressures for illegal subdivision of homes and illegal subletting of apartments, which led to overoccupancy and unsafe housing conditions. Some tenants sublet space in their apartments or houses, often creating multiple bedrooms in basements, living rooms, and other spaces. Some unscrupulous landlords created boarding houses with kitchenettes in former bedrooms and numerous locked units within what appeared to be single-family homes. Landlords often worked through resident managers who collected rents in cash, providing the property owner with a convenient excuse for being unaware of conditions at any particular property.

These properties tended to suffer from inadequate maintenance, produced excess refuse, placed stress on neighborhood parking spaces, and generated complaints from neighbors about excessive activity and traffic. The fire and building agencies had limited success in gaining access to these buildings, and landlords would often delay inspections by missing appointments or simply refusing to respond to requests for access.

Realizing that multiple agencies had an interest in this problem, the public safety department formed a safe housing task force with the buildings department and the city attorney's office. The task force emphasized tenant protection and occupant safety. When unsafe conditions were discovered, the property owner would be called to the property to correct conditions on the spot. When this was not possible, fire bureau personnel would install smoke detectors in sleeping areas, bill the property owner, and initiate a code enforcement proceeding. Residents were displaced only as a last resort. This approach allayed concerns that the program might be targeting certain ethnic groups instead of being truly focused on safety and tenant protection.

Police officers were trained at roll call on signs of unsafe housing and on steps to take when they encountered it in the course of their regular duties. Noise complaints, disputes, and other calls for investigation quickly generated numerous cases of possible overcrowded or illegal housing. When these conditions were observed, a trained on-duty fire company officer was called to the scene, and photographs and other documentation were created for a court proceeding. If building violations were observed, a building inspector could also be called to the scene. Police stood by throughout this process.

The support of the public safety structure has enabled this partnership to endure and maintain high-level attention. The participation of diverse agencies allows a systematic approach to the problem of unsafe housing and gives each partner agency added leverage in achieving its goals. The police have an additional tool for dealing with locations that may generate complaints and criminal activity; the building department enjoys greater support from the public; and the inspection programs of both building and fire inspectors benefit from having turned every police patrol officer and firefighter into "eyes and ears" for code enforcement and overoccupancy. Finally, the city attorney sees streamlined case preparation and has a greater awareness of patterns and repeat offenses by problem landlords.

The program has sent a clear message to the community, and several "bad actors" who owned multiple properties with patterns of code violations and other problems have sold their properties or improved their management.

within a relatively short period; this is because the risks to the jurisdiction's or organization's goals are too severe to allow the current situation to continue. Revolutionary change is often monitored by jurisdictional leaders and the media. Moderate change takes place over a time frame of a year or more, and may be monitored and reported on by the department's performance measurement system. Evolutionary change is change that is allowed to take its own course: "it will happen when it happens." This is when the risk and resistance are in virtual balance. Resistance to this change may be strong enough that it threatens the achievement of the organization's strategic goals.

Memorializing the change Cultures in organizations tend to develop over time, without a specific plan. When a jurisdiction initiates a specific plan to change culture, the changes themselves are only a part of the process. Unless there is a specific plan to memorialize the changed culture, the old culture is likely to reemerge over time. Memorializing change is, in effect, the process of "rewriting the rules of the game," and it starts with the same clear vision—articulated in a vision statement—that guided the change process. In addition to the vision statement, an organization should have a mission statement, a statement of values, and standard operating procedures (SOPs) to help ensure that it does not revert to its old ways of thinking and acting.

The vision statement for a fire and emergency services department should stretch, but not break, the department. It should create a compass for the organization and describe the major indicator of success. However, a vision should be a "road map" for the journey toward a changed culture, not a destination. The function of the vision is to keep the organization focused on the future, on the benefit the customer will receive if the organization is successful, and on the organization's contribution to the jurisdiction's success. A vision that describes only the fire suppression aspect of the emergency services delivery system will not do these three things well enough. Moreover, it will not resonate with those in the customer base who are not concerned about catastrophic fire.

Jurisdiction and organization leaders should develop the vision of the organization. In this case, leaders include not only people in formal positions of leadership but also various representatives of the customers served by the jurisdiction and the organization.

While a vision statement describes the journey, a mission statement provides the "road signs" that will keep the organization on the right road (see Figure 7-3). The mission statement describes the organization's activities (its reason for existing) and defines the organization's journey in terms of tactical implementation of strategic goals.

A values statement describes the guiding principles in the journey toward the vision (Figure 7-4). Values help organization leaders and managers at strategic, tactical, and task levels evaluate right and wrong with respect to how they should interact with the service delivery system.

As the skeleton for the new culture, a statement of values must be strong enough to hold the weight of the mission and nimble enough to provide direction for operating procedures, rules, and regulations. It also provides guidance for human interactions within the organization and generally includes statements about safety, inclusiveness, competence, and the importance of service to the customer.

Integrating change throughout the agency If it is to be effective and lasting, change must become part of daily operations at all levels and in all parts of the agency.

At the task level, cultural change is reinforced through the development and implementation of standard operating procedures (Figure 7-5). "Standard" means that they are consistent across the organization and are applied all the time; "operating" means that they apply to functions necessary to accomplish organization goals at the strategic, tactical, and task levels; and "procedures" means that they describe how these functions are to be carried out. SOPs that are outdated, inaccurate, or not applied in a standard manner must be revised, corrected, or abolished. An SOP not enforced is just as bad as an SOP not in place. Procedures of concern span task-level work in human resources, information technology, and emergency operations—in short, work throughout the organization.

Figure 7-3 To successfully implement change, an organization needs a shared vision statement to describe the journey and a mission statement to provide the road map.

VISION

Dedicated to being the best community-focused fire and rescue department ensuring a safe and secure environment for all.

MISSION

Provide the highest quality services to protect the lives, property, and environment of our community.

Source: Fairfax County (Virginia) Fire and Rescue Department, at fairfaxcounty.gov/fr/.

Fairfax County
Fire and Rescue Department

CORE VALUES

Professional Excellence
We believe the pursuit of excellence and demonstrating high professional standards are critical to our work. To ensure the best possible service for our community, the Fire and Rescue Department supports continuous training and encourages professional development.

Health and Safety
We believe our health and safety are essential to fulfilling the Fire and Rescue Department's mission. We are committed to providing the best health and safety programs for our members' well-being and operational readiness.

Diversity
We know Fairfax County is a diverse community, and we commit to meeting its ever-changing needs. We are dedicated to reflecting and respecting that diversity throughout our organization. We will respect the diversity of our community by providing compassionate and quality service to all.

Teamwork and Shared Leadership
We know well-functioning teams of people are more effective than individuals working separately; our lives depend on it. We believe individuals have the capacity to lead, and our organization values leadership at all levels. Teamwork and shared leadership are integral to our organization, and we will seek out and value the opinions of our members.

Effective Communication
We believe communication is essential to the cohesiveness and performance of our organization. We are committed to providing effective and responsive means of communication throughout the organization and the community.

Integrity
We understand the trust placed in us by the public and our colleagues is integral to the performance of our duties. We are committed to honest and ethical behavior, and we will hold ourselves accountable to these values.

Community Service and Involvement
We believe we have a duty to be involved in the communities where we work. Our responsibility is to protect life, property, and the environment. We are committed to fulfilling our responsibility and to deepening our involvement in the community we serve. No request or inquiry will go unanswered.

Innovation
We recognize and understand that the constancy of change in our community and industry impacts our business daily. We are committed to seeking out and implementing innovative and progressive thinking to address change effectively to benefit those we serve.

Figure 7-4 The statement of values describes the guiding principles in the organization's journey toward its vision.

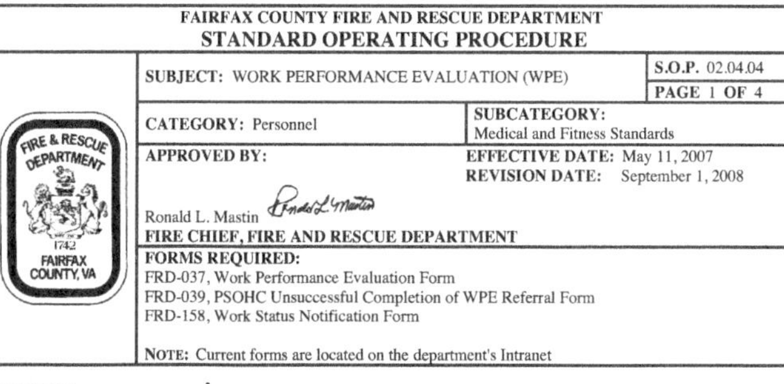

FAIRFAX COUNTY FIRE AND RESCUE DEPARTMENT
STANDARD OPERATING PROCEDURE

SUBJECT: WORK PERFORMANCE EVALUATION (WPE)		S.O.P. 02.04.04 PAGE 1 OF 4
CATEGORY: Personnel	SUBCATEGORY: Medical and Fitness Standards	
APPROVED BY: Ronald L. Mastin FIRE CHIEF, FIRE AND RESCUE DEPARTMENT	EFFECTIVE DATE: May 11, 2007 REVISION DATE: September 1, 2008	
FORMS REQUIRED: FRD-037, Work Performance Evaluation Form FRD-039, PSOHC Unsuccessful Completion of WPE Referral Form FRD-158, Work Status Notification Form NOTE: Current forms are located on the department's Intranet		

PURPOSE:

To ensure uniformed Fire and Rescue Department (FRD) members can meet the physical demands of firefighting, rescue, and emergency medical duties in a safe and effective manner. To identify Work Performance Evaluation (WPE) procedures and guidelines for proper administration.

I. PREFACE

The WPE was developed by the Health and Safety Division as a task-orientated physical performance evaluation. It was statistically validated by a private contractor, Human Performance Systems.

The WPE is supported by a strong departmental infrastructure including the Public Safety Occupational Health Center (PSOHC), the Health and Safety Division, mandatory physical fitness training, company operations training, and peer fitness trainers.

Process of Assessments and Events Included in the WPE

Preparation:	Pre-Assessment Screening/Warm-up
Event 1:	Protective Gear Donning
Event 2:	Ladder
Event 3:	Forcible Entry
Event 4:	High-Rise Pack
Event 5:	Handline Advance
Event 6:	Handline Withdrawal
Event 7:	Pike Pole
Event 8:	Equipment Carry
Event 9:	Ventilation/Sled
Event 10:	Victim Rescue
Conclusion:	Post-Assessment and Rehabilitation

Figure 7-5 This excerpt is from the Fairfax County (Virginia) Fire and Rescue Department's Standard Operating Procedure.

Conclusion

Leadership and management in the fire and emergency services go beyond the technical aspects of a leader's or manager's performance to activities that have much in common with leadership and management in other public organizations. Leadership and management practices and approaches that work in other environments also work in a fire and emergency services organization. These practices and approaches include "battlefield leadership" on the fire ground as well as other types of leadership for other organizational challenges.

Although the skills of leadership and management are distinct, ideally both are found in the fire and emergency services chief officer. Knowing when to lead, when to manage, and how to balance the two types of skills is important. The chief must learn to move fluidly between managing and leading as he or she sets a direction for the organization and supervises operations.

Leaders and managers can practice their craft strategically, tactically, or at the task level, depending on the goals, objectives, and activities at hand. The most effective chiefs realize that they are always balancing their roles as leader in the department and manager for the jurisdiction. When they lead strategically in the department, they are managing tactically for the jurisdiction. In the end, the effectiveness of leaders and managers is most evident in their ability to apply their craft to a variety of situations in the organization, including perhaps the most challenging—that of leading organizational change and managing the new culture that change creates.

The challenges facing the fire and emergency services are growing and increasingly involve strategic issues of organizational focus, funding sustainability, identification of a meaningful mission, and competition for resources and recognition as a part of a larger system of government agencies. At the same time, the cultural dimension of the fire and emergency services has limited the ability of many organizations to make measurable progress in key areas. The future of the fire and emergency services demands effective leadership and management to meet the challenges.

Notes

1. Frederick Winslow Taylor, *The Principles of Scientific Management* (New York and London: Harper & Brothers, 1911).
2. Warren Bennis, *Why Leaders Can't Lead: The Unconscious Conspiracy Continues* (San Francisco: Jossey-Bass, 1989), 18.
3. John P. Kotter, *Leading Change* (Boston: Harvard Business School Press, 1996), 25.
4. See, for example, Richard L. Daft, *The Leadership Experience*, 3rd ed. (Mason, Ohio: Thomson South-Western, 2005), which builds on Fayol's ideas. For more on the relevance of Fayol's 14 Principles to modern management, see *Henri Fayol: Critical Evaluations in Business and Management*, ed. John C. Wood and Michael C. Wood (London: Routledge, 2002).
5. *Merriam-Webster's Collegiate Dictionary*, 11th ed., s.v. "manage."
6. Alan Brunacini, *Essentials of Fire Department Customer Service* (Stillwater, Okla.: International Fire Service Training Association, 1996).
7. David Ammons, *Leading Performance Management* (Washington, D.C.: ICMA Press, 2008).
8. Ronald A. Heifetz and Marty Linsky, *Leadership on the Line: Staying Alive through the Dangers of Leading* (Boston: Harvard Business School Press, 2002), 2.
9. Kotter, *Leading Change*, 25.
10. Stephen Covey, *The Seven Habits of Highly Effective People* (New York: Simon & Schuster, 2004), 95.
11. Karen Huffman and Gary Piggrem, *Psychology in Action* (New York: John Wiley & Sons, 2003).
12. Kurt Lewin, Ronald Lippitt, and Ralph K. White, "Patterns of Aggressive Behavior in Experimentally Created 'Social Climates,'" *Journal of Social Psychology* 10 (1939): 271–301.
13. Paul Hersey and Kenneth Blanchard, "Life Cycle Theory of Leadership," *Training and Development Journal* 23, no. 5 (1969): 26–34.
14. Paul Hersey, Kenneth H. Blanchard, and Dewey E. Johnson, *Management of Organizational Behavior: Leading Human Resources*, 8th ed. (Upper Saddle River, N.J.: Prentice-Hall, 2001).
15. U.S. Fish and Wildlife Service, *USFWS Leadership Competency Development Model: A Tool for Developing the Service's Leaders* (March 2008), 136–137, training.fws.gov/LED/competencymodel/USFWS_Leadership_Competency_Development_Model.pdf.
16. I. David Daniels, "Diversity and Inclusion in the Fire Service," in *International Association of Fire Chiefs: Chief Fire Officer's Desk Reference*, ed. John M. Buckman III, 149–166 (London: Jones and Bartlett, 2006).
17. Bureau of Labor Statistics, *Current Population Survey*, "Table 11, Employed Persons by Detailed Occupation, Sex, Race, and Hispanic or Latino Ethnicity" (Washington, D.C.: U.S. Department of Labor, 2010), 15–20, bls.gov/cps/cpsaat11.pdf.
18. Alexander M. Thompson III and Barbara A. Bono, "Work without Wages: The Motivation for Volunteer Firefighters," *American Journal of Economics and Sociology* 52, no. 3 (July 1993): 323–344.
19. Edgar Schein, *Organizational Culture and Leadership* (San Francisco: Jossey-Bass, 2004).
20. Carl W. Stenberg, "Meeting the Challenge of Change," in *Managing Local Government Services: A Practical Guide*, ed. Carl W. Stenberg and Susan Lipman Austin, 1–27 (Washington, D.C.: ICMA Press, 2007), 11.

CHAPTER 8

Human Resource Management

Donna P. Brehm

This chapter provides an understanding of

- Federal laws that have directly affected the fire and emergency services and how they have altered human resource practices within it
- Common components of promotion processes in both career and volunteer fire service organizations
- The organizational advantages of recruiting and maintaining a diverse workforce
- Common recruitment challenges facing volunteer fire and emergency service organizations
- Common components of a fire and emergency service organization's hiring process
- The role of a union in the development of collective bargaining agreements
- The importance of conducting a job task analysis and linking knowledge, skills, and abilities to both hiring and promotional processes
- The certification, credentialing, and educational opportunities that are available to fire and emergency service members for professional development.

Fire and emergency service providers are among the most respected individuals in communities of every size. A citizen's perception of the quality of services is often inexorably linked to an individual provider or a small crew of providers. These providers touch lives when personal situations are at their very worst. They have the opportunity to slow or stop devastation from fire, medical challenges, and natural or man-made disasters. Even when there is no viable solution, the individual fire or emergency service provider plays a vital role in establishing a sense of calm, control, compassion, and hope. As a result, there is general public support for fire and emergency services.

However, there is also an expectation from taxpayers for service quality commensurate with the fiscal investment made in municipal fire and emergency services. The same emotions that lead citizens to support the fire services also raise the bar for the behavior of individual department members; the performance of crews at incident scenes; and the professional business management, behavior, and ethics of fire service leaders. Mindful of the daily importance of individual fire and emergency service providers in maintaining the quality of life for citizens, and recognizing citizen expectations for accountability, fire and emergency service career and volunteer departments across the world should and do put extraordinary energy and resources into the selection of personnel.

Three types of fire and emergency service departments are considered in this chapter: (1) fully volunteer; (2) combination volunteer and career (with two subtypes: the mostly volunteer departments, in which more than half the personnel are volunteer; and the mostly career departments, in which more than half the personnel are career); and (3) fully career (i.e., full time and fully paid). Because new departments are constantly being formed and smaller ones are regularly being consolidated into larger ones, the number of fire and emergency service departments in the United States varies from year to year.

The National Fire Protection Association (NFPA) estimates that as of 2009, there were 30,165 fire departments in the United States, made up of 1,148,100 firefighters, 71 percent of whom were volunteer and 29 percent were career members.[1] Included within these two classifications is a wide range of members who were compensated in myriad ways, including pay per call or per hour, deferred benefits, tuition reimbursement, room and board, and reduced residential or vehicle taxes/fees. Nearly 60 percent of fire departments in the United States provide some level of emergency medical service (EMS).

Although most fire and emergency service departments are volunteer, most of the U.S. population is centered in urban/suburban, high-density communities and protected by fully career departments. The 14 percent of all departments that are either fully or mostly career protect 64 percent of the population, whereas the 86 percent of all departments that are fully or mostly volunteer protect 36 percent of the population.[2]

Fire and emergency service departments are labor-intensive. In career departments in medium and large cities, salaries and benefits normally constitute over 90 percent of the total fire budget. In these departments, and in communities served by volunteer departments, the investment in the selection of members is directly related to the department's capability to provide quality emergency services.

Human resource (HR) management involves all processes, policies, practices, and decisions that directly affect or influence the people who work for a fire and emergency services organization. The commitment of the organization's leadership to human resources is directly related to the overall productivity, morale, and public perception of the organization.

This chapter takes a life cycle, or "cradle-to-grave," approach to explaining HR management. The very nature of the fire and emergency services draws members into a lifetime commitment. The lack of a nationalized fire and emergency services organization discourages lateral transfer from one department to another, so many employees spend their entire careers within a single organization. Many of the concepts discussed here apply to both career and volunteer departments. It is a mistake to automatically assume that one concept or another belongs solely to volunteer or career departments. There is much to be learned and shared among the various fire and emergency service agencies.

Human resource functions

In both career and volunteer fire and emergency service organizations, the function of managing human resources can fall to a single individual performing multiple roles or to an entire cadre of employees, each with a singular focus or area of responsibility. No matter the complexity of the system, the fire chief (or department director) is ultimately responsible for the hiring and firing of personnel within the organization. As the organization grows in size and complexity, the chief delegates many HR responsibilities and gives others the authority to act on his or her behalf.

There are as many ways to organize human resources as there are fire and emergency service departments. Additionally, some HR functions are highly specialized, legally mandated, and best accomplished by nonoperational members who have been thoroughly trained and formally educated in an HR management or organization management degree program. The complexity of the organization, its current and past practices, its strategic goals, and significant changes in its labor-management relations may all be factors in the number and type of personnel needed to administer the organization's HR functions. In very large cities, a completely separate HR department may manage or administer certain HR functions on behalf of the fire and emergency services department.

Recruitment: Finding the best potential applicants

The term *recruitment* is most often associated with the military. For the fire service it takes on a somewhat different connotation, which can best be described as "replenishment." Often the daunting task of a recruitment officer is to backfill a position held for decades by one firefighter or officer. The recruitment officer should not hope to match in a prospective recruit the retiring member's knowledge and skills gained through years of experience and training. Rather, the officer must match the future needs of the organization to the potential seen in each applicant. To evaluate this potential, fire and emergency service departments use a variety of assessment tools specifically chosen for each position, the organization, and the community. Recruitment should never be taken lightly. Finding the right applicant yields tremendous benefits in terms of quality of service delivery, member health and safety, personnel management, and maintenance of a pool of qualified and well-prepared candidates from which to select future organization leaders.

The recruitment officer: The "face" of the department

The recruitment officer is often the first contact a potential applicant has with the organization. Using the term loosely, the "recruitment officer" may be a fairly new member of the

Human resource functions

Common human resource activities and functions in career and volunteer fire and emergency service departments include

- Recruitment of new members
- Entry-level testing/evaluation for minimum qualifications
- Orientation of new members
- Management of salary and benefit packages
- Maintenance of member records
- Payroll system management
- Scheduling system management
- Management of promotional processes
- Oversight and/or processing of discipline, grievance, commendations, and performance evaluation systems
- Labor-management relations
- Maintenance and security of member medical records
- Retirement system management.

Civil service

The term *civil service* refers to a set of rules and procedures for hiring, promoting, disciplining, and terminating government employees. Merit is the underlying rationale for a civil service system, the principle being that the most qualified individuals shall be hired or promoted and that employees shall be removed from public service only when there is a clear showing of just cause.

Civil service examinations embody the civil service system. They are given to candidates to determine who meets the minimum qualifications of knowledge, skills, and abilities. Such tests must necessarily be free of cultural, racial, or ethnic bias. They must be administered fairly and impartially so that all candidates have an equal opportunity to demonstrate their qualifications and abilities to gain the desired position.

Many governmental organizations have established an independent body to oversee the administration of hiring, promotion, disciplinary, and termination policies and procedures. That body is usually referred to as a civil service commission. Civil service commissions are a visible means of assuring citizens that a public agency operates on the basis of merit, not patronage, spoils, or nepotism. Between 1975 and 2000 there were several important procedural reforms of the civil service, but the merit principle remained. In *Ricci v. DeStefano*, 557 U.S.___ (June 2009), the U.S. Supreme Court ruled that the New Haven (Connecticut) Fire Department should not have thrown out a promotional exam just because minority firefighters did not score highly on it. This case underscores the continuing difficulty in establishing fairness for all in public employment.

organization. It is often the excitement and job satisfaction expressed to potential applicants that creates the initial interest in the emergency services field. Members of an organization who feel valued and supported will speak well of the department and encourage others to consider joining the ranks. The recruitment officer may also simply be a designated member of the organization who becomes the initial point of contact. No matter how that officer fits into the organization, he or she is an integral part of a broader HR team that handles many important aspects of applicant and member relationships with the organization.

Large career organizations are often under greater constraints and pressures to ensure that the organization membership reflects the diversity of their communities and that the hiring process has no adverse impact on either sex or on any one ethnic group. The department may even be under an externally imposed mandate to increase the diversity of the membership in certain positions or ranks. To meet this goal, large departments often hire a person who has the background and training to effectively lead the recruitment process (see Figure 8–1).

The recruitment officer is trusted to promote and protect the organization. It is his or her task to learn about the department, the variety of technical services provided to the community, and the entry-level knowledge, skills, and abilities (KSAs) that candidates need in order to become successful members of the organization. The recruitment officer must know the organization's long-term mission and strategic initiatives. Does the organization expect to expand into new service delivery areas that will become part of every member's basic duty? For many years, EMS delivery was provided by personnel specifically trained in that field. Over time, many traditional fire departments have incorporated EMS delivery as a basic function, requiring all operational members to train and function in that role. In many departments the same could be said for hazardous materials or technical rescue service delivery. The recruitment officer must know where the organization is headed in order to advise potential applicants appropriately and attract those who share and understand the organization's long-term strategic vision.

The recruitment officer also needs to evaluate the job for which he or she is recruiting applicants. Public safety has historically been a career field that many members choose for life. The recruitment officer must fully understand the physical, social, educational, and psychological aspects of fire and emergency service careers and the KSAs tied to each position in order to help potential applicants make appropriate career choices.

Beyond the needs of the department and job, it is the recruitment officer's responsibility to learn about the community: its diversity, culture, service demand statistics, and perception

Photo by Donna Brehm

Figure 8-1 Many departments choose recruiters who are of the same culture and sex as the audience they are trying to attract.

of local government and public safety services. Understanding how a community feels about its public safety agencies will guide a recruitment officer in finding the most effective ways to reach out to diverse segments of the community. Many departments use organization members who are part of a unique ethnic community to assist in recruitment. These members can share their successful stories and help alleviate socially and culturally based anxieties about fire and emergency service careers.

The general employment situation within the local community can significantly affect the makeup of the applicant pool. As unemployment rises, the proportion of potential applicants looking for "work" versus a "career" will usually increase, temporarily expanding the applicant pool. This is not always a bad thing. Many recruitment officers have found applicants who had not taken the time to explore their long-term personal goals, but who discovered that they were a good match for fire and emergency services and turned out to be outstanding long-term organization members. The types of general employment opportunities within a community can also affect the potential pool of applicants. A community that has historically had steady opportunities for entry-level workers will attract more young adults just entering the workforce and, in turn, will support a broader and more diverse applicant pool for the fire service.

Accordingly, the recruitment officer needs to understand the workforce culture of the current pool of potential candidates. Recruiting and retaining a qualified and diverse workforce can be a challenge for both career and volunteer departments, especially with the changing demographics of U.S. communities and the broader national dialogue about the value of public service (Table 8-1). Many entry-level applicants are part of Generation Y, or the "Millennial Generation." They tend to be more willing than their parents to move from job to job instead of staying with one employer for many years or for their entire careers. They are very technology-savvy and are just as comfortable learning through online courses and simulation programs/devices as through traditional hands-on training methods or in classroom settings. The recruitment officer needs to find ways to demonstrate to young applicants that a fire and emergency services career can meet their employment goals, continue to challenge them, and provide a workplace that embraces new technology.

Table 8-1 Challenges to retention and recruitment

Sources of problems	Contributing factors
Time demands	• The two-income family and need to work at multiple jobs • Increased training time demands • Higher emergency call volume • Additional demands within department (fundraising, administrative)
Training requirements	• Higher training standards and new federal requirements • More time demands • Greater public expectation of fire department's response capabilities (broader range of services such as emergency medical service (EMS), hazardous materials [HAZMAT], technical rescue, etc.) • Additional training demands to provide broader range of services • Recertification demands
Increasing call volume	• Fire department assuming wider response roles (EMS, HAZMAT, technical rescue) • Increasing EMS call volume • Increase in number of automatic fire alarms
Changes in the "nature of the business"	• Abuse of emergency services by the public • Less of an emphasis on social aspects of volunteering
Changes in sociological conditions (in urban and suburban areas)	• Transience • Loss of community feeling • Less community pride • Less of an interest in or time for volunteering • Two-income family and time demands • "Me" generation
Changes in sociological conditions (in rural areas)	• Employers less willing to let employees off to respond to calls • Time demand • "Me" generation
Leadership problems	• Poor leadership and lack of coordination • Authoritative management style • Failure to manage change
Federal legislation and regulations	• Fair Labor Standards Act interpretation • "Two in/two out" ruling requiring four firefighters on scene before entering hazardous environment • Environmental Protection Agency live-fire burn limitations
Increasing use of combination departments	• Disagreements among chiefs or other department leaders • Friction between volunteer and career members
Higher cost of housing (in affluent communities)	• Volunteers cannot afford to live in the community they serve
Aging communities	• Greater number of older people today • Lack of economic growth and jobs in some towns
Internal conflict	• Disagreements among departmental leaders • Friction between volunteer and career members

Source: Adapted from *Retention and Recruitment for the Volunteer Emergency Services: Challenges and Solutions*, FA-310 (Greenbelt, Md., and Washington, D.C.: National Volunteer Fire Council and the U.S. Fire Administration, May 2007), 7, usfa.dhs.gov/downloads/pdf/publications/fa-310.pdf.

A fire service recruitment officer must take the time to become familiar with federal, state, and local laws, codes, and ordinances that govern the hiring processes of the organization. He or she must be constantly vigilant regarding major court cases or legislative activity that may alter hiring or internal HR processes, and must help the organization respond proactively to anticipated mandates. Resources abound to provide the uniformed or civilian recruitment officer with the tools and knowledge he or she needs to be proficient in the HR field and to stay abreast of current industry practices and laws (see "Further Readings and Resources" at the back of this book).

The recruitment process

Under the Civil Rights Act of 1964 (Title VII), fire departments must ensure that every person, regardless of race, color, religion, sex, or national origin, is given fair, just, and equitable treatment in both employment and promotion processes. Quite a few departments, both large and small, have been legally mandated to revise hiring practices and show concrete evidence that they are increasing the number of women and minorities in the ranks. Not merely a mandate for diversity, the act's purpose is to ensure fairness, openness, and equity in hiring processes where all people have the same opportunity for success in a process that is free of intentional or unintentional bias. For many departments, the achievement of diversity has been challenging as well as rewarding.

Each aspect of the selection process can affect the demographic makeup of the applicant pool. Thus, the HR staff must constantly monitor the results for various segments of that pool at each step of the process.

It is the recruitment officer's task to evaluate the pool of applicants and develop strategies for finding promising applicants from each demographic group. If, for example, a particular demographic segment of the population has difficulty with the physical requirements of the recruited position, a savvy recruitment officer will focus recruitment efforts on people within that segment who value physical conditioning and fitness, such as members of sports teams, health and fitness instructors, sports medicine college majors, etc. If the officer is filling a position that requires special skills—for example, fire safety educator—the most likely candidates will be found among people who have a background in education or public speaking and who enjoy working with people on a regular basis.

Organizational diversity that matches the community's diversity should be a goal of every department. The organizational understanding of different cultures and of how those cultures are integrated into the local community is vastly improved when diversity exists *within* the organization. Diversity helps the first responder understand citizens' culturally based reactions to emergencies, death, domestic issues, and requests to allow providers into their homes, as well as the level of trust that people from another culture are willing to give local government representatives, including first responders.

Preselection processes: Linking applicants to job requirements

Prior to the mid-1960s, many preselection processes were rife with bias and discriminatory intent. The traditions and culture of the fire service and the familial-type living arrangements at most fire stations did not provide a fertile environment for recruitment and acceptance of

Fairfax County's Magnet Housing Rental Program

The Fairfax County (Virginia) Redevelopment and Housing Authority has partnered with the Fairfax County Fire and EMS, as well as other departments, to provide affordable housing for qualified applicants in an effort to support a professional workforce. Communities experiencing a rapid rise in the cost of living often do not have affordable housing for public employees who are just starting out in their careers. Consequently, the applicant pool is constricted, and applicants who must relocate to accept an employment opportunity are particularly affected. Not only does applicant diversity suffer, but the size of the applicant pool can be severely diminished over time.

The Fairfax County Magnet Rental Program provides new employees with rental housing at a reasonable rate to allow them time to establish themselves and their families in the community and prepare financially to make a more permanent residential choice. Program housing units are located across the county so as to be convenient to a variety of worksites. Minimum and maximum incomes are specified for different family sizes to meet basic program qualifications. Program participants must remain employed with the county while living in these units, and public safety employees can take advantage of the program for up to two years.

The Fairfax County Department of Housing and Community Development manages this innovative program and plans to add more housing units as they become available to meet demands.

Source: Fairfax County, Virginia, "Fairfax County Rental Program," at fairfaxcounty.gov/rha/rentalhousing programs/fcrp.htm.

Resource for diversity

As documented in the 2006 International Association of Fire Fighters Diversity Initiative, *Achieving and Retaining a Diverse Fire Service Workforce*, "Diversity in the workforce will not occur simply because your department is located in a diverse metropolitan area or because your department follows the law regarding non-discrimination. In order to achieve diversity, you must have a strong commitment that includes an active recruiting strategy and you must take effective actions."[1] The report is a comprehensive look at recruitment practices across the country and among divers departments. It shares "best practices" used by departments that have documented success in recruiting and retaining underrepresented groups in the fire service. The value of recruitment methodologies such as "word-of-mouth" and websites is explored, and creative alternatives are offered to reach each segment of the population and maximize success.

1 Kathryn A. Fox, Chris W. Hornick, and Erin Hardin, *Achieving and Retaining a Diverse Fire Service Workforce* (Washington, D.C., and Lone Tree, Colo.: International Association of Fire Fighters and CWH Research, Inc., January 2006), 4, cityofmadison.com/fire/documents/Achieving%20and%20Retaining%20a%20Diverse%20Fire%20Service%20Workforce.pdf.

diverse members. Subtle and not-so-subtle practices discouraged and eliminated applicants from nontraditional backgrounds and cultures. As the fire and emergency services matured and developed more businesslike practices, discriminatory practices were eliminated voluntarily or through the legal system. National organizations such as the International Association of Fire Chiefs (IAFC), the International Association of Fire Fighters (IAFF), the International Association of Black Professional Fire Fighters, the National Association of Hispanic Firefighters, and the International Association of Women in the Fire and Emergency Services supported unbiased applicant assessment processes based on sound business practices. Best practices in hiring for diversity is a popular subject at professional seminars and conferences.

Minimum requirements for knowledge, skills, and ability Preselection begins with the establishment of minimum requirements to enter the workforce. Some of these requirements are legally mandated, such as the minimum age to work in a hazardous environment, but most are established by the locality or the individual department. In volunteer departments, once the applicant meets external requirements mandated by local, state, or federal codes or laws, such as those of state and federal Occupational Safety and Health Administrations, an interview with the chief or a group of organization leaders may be the extent of the hiring process. Career and volunteer departments often use minimum education levels to ensure that recruits come into the organization with the necessary cognitive skills to grasp the basic concepts and theory of fire and medical science.

The minimum requirements must tie directly to identifiable KSAs required to perform the essential functions of the job. They should not inadvertently create barriers to employment for the local workforce or impede an organization's efforts to improve diversity (see the sidebar on the next page). Most departments developing or revising their KSAs for a position take one of three approaches:

- Adopt the KSAs of another fire services organization that provides a similar range of services and has similar rank structures and associated duties
- Develop their own KSAs based on organizational roles and responsibilities and using current industry methodologies/best practices
- Hire a consultant with documentation to verify expertise in the HR field and experience with job task analysis within the fire service.

NFPA 1001, Standard for Fire Fighter Professional Qualifications (2008 ed.), is an excellent source for core firefighter KSAs. This document uses the term *job performance requirement* to identify a specific task, and it goes on to describe the "requisite knowledge" and "requisite skills" that are necessary to successfully complete the task. The choice to use NFPA 1001, an internationally recognized consensus standard, as the basis for KSAs provides a department with a defensible position if challenged in the future.

Job analysis and the Americans with Disabilities Act of 1990

The Americans with Disabilities Act of 1990 (ADA) makes it clear that job applicants must be told and must understand what the essential functions of a job are before they can respond to the question, "Can you perform the essential functions of the job for which you are applying?"

Essential job functions are functions that require relatively more time and in which error or nonperformance has serious consequences. A function may be essential because it is the reason that the position exists at all (e.g., a firefighter must necessarily be able to carry or drag a 200-pound person or mannequin).

Essential job functions can be systematically identified by the use of job analysis. If the physical, environmental, or mental demands of a job expand or change, the job analysis must be updated. Job analysis results are normally summarized in a written job description. For the fire and emergency services, this summary might be better presented through a video that provides an applicant with visual evidence of the job's physical and environmental demands (e.g., belligerent or combative EMS patients). Candidates whose physical or mental disabilities render them unable to perform a job may then self-select out, making it less likely that the department's hiring decisions will be challenged in court.

To ensure that the required KSAs and other characteristics on which candidates are assessed are job related, the department must be able to link this knowledge (etc.) to essential job functions. Under the ADA, "essential" job requirements must be distinguished from "nonessential" job requirements *before* a job opening is announced. "If a candidate with a disability can perform the essential functions of the job and is hired, the employer must be willing to make 'reasonable accommodations' to enable the person to work." Examples of such accommodations are

- Restructuring a job so that someone else does the nonessential tasks that a person with a disability cannot do
- Modifying work hours or work schedules so that a person with a disability can commute during off-peak periods
- Reassigning a worker who becomes disabled to a vacant position that he or she can handle
- Acquiring or modifying equipment or devices (e.g., a telecommunications device for the hearing impaired).

Source: Adapted with permission of The McGraw-Hill Companies from Wayne F. Cascio, *Managing Human Resources*, 5th ed. (Boston: Irwin McGraw-Hill, 1998), 138.

To one degree or another, most departments that conduct formal applicant selection processes include cognitive, physical ability, behavioral, and medical assessments. The importance of each is often debated, and each has its own pitfalls in terms of bias. A department must take the time to analyze the KSAs that apply to each position and tailor the assessment tools to those findings. The result will be a process that can help identify the candidates who are most likely to possess those qualities needed to successfully master the duties and responsibilities of the job and enjoy lifelong success in the fire and emergency services. When choosing applicant testing tools, departments may also consider consulting with an attorney knowledgeable in labor relations law to help protect both the department and the jurisdiction from legal challenges.

There are myriad resources for organizations developing or revising selection processes. A few are listed in the "Further Readings and Resources" section of this book, and many of the listed websites link to additional valuable resources. The choice and use of selection tools is another common session topic at state and national conventions and association meetings.

Cognitive tests Cognitive tests evaluate a candidate's skills in such areas as reading comprehension, mathematics, and spatial relationships, as well as in other KSAs that can be evaluated in a written format. There are a wide variety of testing tools. It is important to work with a testing firm that has had experience in the public safety field and whose testing tools either have not been challenged for adverse impact on a segment of the applicant pool or have withstood legal challenge. It should be noted that the contractor's historical record rests on the experience of those jurisdictions that have used those tools and may not apply to other jurisdictions. Organizations should consider performing a "transportability" study to determine the applicability of an existing testing tool to their jurisdictions and organizations. The testing firm will work with departments on evaluating both the testing tool and its scoring process for any potential unanticipated impacts on any particular social or ethnic group. Some test processes even provide a pretest study guide for each applicant to ensure that all applicants are equally familiar with terminology used in the testing device.

Physical fitness assessments Physical fitness assessments include any tests to evaluate a candidate's physical fitness for a particular position. Often the focus of sex discrimination complaints, this assessment tool is essential to ensuring that candidates for both fire and emergency medical services have the physical capability to perform the basic job tasks without injuring themselves, a team member, or a civilian. Again, it is important to ensure that the test is based on the skills and abilities required to perform the tasks assigned to the particular position being filled. And as is the case for cognitive testing, a fire department should consider conducting a transportability study. Just because a test is used by a nearby department does not mean that it will be appropriate for use elsewhere. The KSAs aligned with the position being hired may be different enough from the KSAs for the same lateral position in another department for the validity of the test to be questioned and the department's selection process to be challenged.

In 1999 The IAFF and the IAFC completed a two-year collaborative project and published a comprehensive program called the Fire Service Joint Labor Management Wellness-Fitness Initiative. The initiative addresses the physical fitness issues of fire and emergency service departments and includes the Candidate Physical Ability Test (CPAT):

> After considerable effort the Task Force agreed that, prior to establishing incumbent performance evaluations, fire departments must hire physically capable candidates, have comprehensive training programs and implement all components of the Wellness/Fitness Initiative. Fire Departments seeking to improve the quality and fitness of their workforce must begin by hiring candidates who can physically perform the job. It is expected that as qualified candidates are hired and trained, fire departments will train and maintain the wellness and fitness of all uniformed personnel, and incumbent performance will naturally improve.[3]

CPAT was based upon careful analysis of firefighter duties and tasks in ten departments across the country. A thorough job task analysis was conducted to validate the test. However, as with any selection or promotional tool, before a department implements CPAT it must conduct a transportability study to make sure that the duties and responsibilities on which the testing process is based match the corresponding duties and responsibilities of the particular job in that particular department. The transportability study will carry tremendous weight in protecting a department from legal challenges over implementing CPAT or any other testing device.

The extensive CPAT manual contains a wealth of information, instructions, templates, and implementation strategies for departments that are considering adoption of the program. Because it requires significant time and expense to implement, many departments are collaborating to develop regional CPAT programs to share expenses, reduce the manpower commitment to conduct CPAT training and testing, and share the subsequent pool of applicants who successfully complete the CPAT. More information on the CPAT can be found on the IAFF and IAFC websites (iaff.org and iafc.org, respectively).

Polygraph testing and psychological evaluations Two techniques that are often used in the selection process are psychological evaluations and polygraph testing. Both, however, should be used with great care.

Conceptually, it makes sense to develop an assessment tool for evaluating an individual's ability to deal with stressful and psychologically challenging situations affecting the health and safety of civilians, teammates, and themselves. Additionally, unique close-knit working environments require members who are flexible and of even temperament. Behavioral, or psychological, assessments are the most challenging to administer and evaluate objectively and to defend legally. The difficulty rests in a number of areas: the personality and cultural upbringing of the applicant, the personality and cultural upbringing of the assessor(s), the tool itself and its ability to isolate all acceptable responses for a given scenario, and the scoring system and definition of what constitutes "passing."

Many departments have either abandoned behavioral assessment tools or use them in an advisory manner, supplemented with feedback garnered in other phases of the selection process. The traditional postemployment probationary period is in many ways a far more effective time to evaluate a member's response to emergency scene situations and his or her communication and interpersonal skills when dealing with teammates or the general public.

Although polygraph testing is still popular in some organizations, its validity and usefulness as an objective evaluation tool remain questionable. Any information that it is illegal for an employer to request on a job application is also illegal to seek in a polygraph test. An employer may not ask questions about, for example, an employee's color, race, creed, religion, sex, national origin, and disability. Nor may an employer under any circumstances require a new hire (or, for that matter, any employee) to submit to a polygraph test, a voice stress test, or any other test that purports to measure "truth" as opposed to "employment suitability." An alternative use for the polygraph is to validate the accuracy or truthfulness of entries and statements made by the candidate on the job application that cannot be verified by required documentation, criminal and motor vehicle record checks, or interviews with past employers or personal references. Indications of untruthfulness can be immediately explored by the test administrator, giving the applicant the opportunity to correct the misinformation. A complete record of the events and interview is returned to the department for any appropriate action that might be warranted.

Interviews Many fire and emergency service departments conclude their preselection process with an interview. In larger departments, interview boards may consist of organization members representing various ranks or positions. The value of this strategy is that the representative of each rank brings a unique perspective to the interview process and to the interpretation of candidates' responses to the questions.

Interview questions must elicit answers of sufficient depth and diversity to discriminate one candidate from another. To accomplish this, the questions should be open-ended, allowing a candidate to express his or her feelings about the potential job, career goals and ambitions, and the community. Questions are often developed in-house. They may be a variation on themes used in the past, or they may be entirely new, based on current events or changes in the organization. Other departments as well as professional and industrial organizations and association literature are all excellent sources for question ideas.

Questions should be carefully developed to avoid bias of any sort; larger career departments often work with legal counsel to ensure that interview questions are strictly objective and job related. To avoid the perception of bias, real or not, it is essential that every candidate be asked the same set of questions by the same interview panel. Using the same set of interviewers helps to create an atmosphere of objectivity and fairness. The scoring system associated with the interview questions is also evaluated to ensure that the criteria for evaluation are appropriate for each question and are interpreted in a similar fashion by all members of the interview panel.

After the interview, members of the panel should compare their scores and discuss the reasoning behind any outliers—extreme highs or lows—to determine whether the scores in question are valid. The opportunity to talk out unusual scoring helps to reduce conscious or unconscious personal bias of panel members by encouraging them to reassess their scoring based on the feedback of organization peers. Some scoring systems automatically eliminate the extreme outliers to keep an isolated errant score that is not supported by the other panel members from tipping the scales too much in one direction.

Medical evaluation At the conclusion of all preselection processes and under the guidelines of the Americans with Disabilities Act (ADA), an applicant should be given a "conditional offer of employment" pending the successful outcome of a full medical examination. NFPA 1582, Standard on Comprehensive Occupational Medical Program for Fire Departments (2007 ed.), establishes comprehensive medical criteria for evaluating a candidate's fitness for the job of a

Relevant human resource legislation

National Labor Relations Act of 1935 (NLRA) The NLRA prohibits employers from interfering with the rights of employees to form unions or engage in union activity. The right to form unions and engage in modified collective bargaining began to be extended to public employees in 1962.

Fair Labor Standards Act of 1938 (FLSA) The FLSA has applied to public sector workers, including firefighters and medics, since 1985. For personnel whose main job is EMS or firefighting, the FLSA requires that overtime be paid for hours in excess of an *average* of 53 hours per week. There have been numerous legal challenges to the FLSA on the local and state level. Fire/EMS organizations should obtain legal counsel to determine how this law affects their departments.

Equal Pay Act of 1963 The equal pay provisions of the FLSA, as amended in 1963, 1968, and 1972, prohibit wage differentials based on sex. (The Equal Pay Act was an amendment to the FLSA of 1938.)

1964 Civil Rights Act, Title VII This federal law is the keystone of federal Equal Employment Opportunity legislation. Two of its important provisions, Sections 703(a) and 704(b), are as follows:

- **Section 703(a)** It shall be an unlawful employment practice for an employer (1) to fail or refuse to hire or to discharge any individual, or otherwise to discriminate against any individual with respect to his compensation, terms, conditions, or privileges of employment, because of such individual's race, color, religion, sex, or national origin, or (2) to limit, segregate, or classify employees in any way which would deprive or tend to deprive any individual of employment opportunities or otherwise adversely affect employee status, because of such individual's race, color, religion, sex, or national origin.
- **Section 704(b)** It shall be an unlawful employment practice for an employer, labor organization, or employment agency to print or publish or cause to be printed or published any notice or advertisement relating to employment by such an employment agency indicating any preference, limitations, specification, or discrimination based on race, color, religion, sex, or national origin.

Age Discrimination in Employment Act (ADEA) The ADEA of 1967, as amended in 1978 and 1986, makes it illegal for an employer to discriminate in compensation, terms, conditions, or privileges because of an individual's age.

Older Workers Benefit Protection Act of 1974 (OWBPA) The OWBPA restricts an employer's ability to obtain waivers of age discrimination claims when terminating or laying off older employees.

Veterans' Readjustment Assistance Act of 1974 This act provides that employees who leave their jobs to serve in the armed forces are entitled to reinstatement when their tours of duty are completed. To be covered by the statute, the veteran must have completed a tour of duty and must apply for a job within ninety days of release from active duty or within one year of

fire/EMS first responder. Although not a legal mandate unless formally adopted by a state or local jurisdiction, this NFPA standard provides an excellent resource not only for department physicians but especially for private physicians who must make medical judgments relating to an occupation he or she may be familiar with only through an occasional movie, television show, or general community association. For organizations that require potential members to provide their own medical statements of fitness for the job, requiring examining physicians to use the NFPA standard ensures consistency among physicians by providing consistent, medically based criteria, thus reducing the potential for bias. (See Chapter 10 for more on NFPA 1582.)

Probationary period Once selected to join the organization, a new member goes through a probationary period that includes training as well as time in the field. The length of the probationary period, as well as any limitations on pay, benefits, and access to employee procedural processes, is specifically defined in most organizations.

Probationary periods in public safety are often longer than in other occupations for a number of reasons. Training schools cover extensive curricula and last for months. The rules

service-related hospitalization. If the veteran meets these requirements, he or she must be either returned to his or her former position or placed in an equal position unless circumstances have changed so drastically that this would be impossible. After reemployment, the veteran may not be discharged except for just cause.

Pregnancy Discrimination Act of 1978 (PDA) The PDA, passed as an amendment to the Civil Rights Act of 1964, requires that women employees "affected by pregnancy, child birth, or related medical conditions will be treated the same" as any other employees or candidates for employment.

Immigration Reform and Control Act of 1986 The Immigration Reform and Control Act prohibits employers from knowingly employing illegal aliens.

Americans with Disabilities Act (ADA) The ADA was passed in 1990, and its requirements for employers were phased in from 1992 to 1994. The law defines a "qualified disabled person" as a person who, with reasonable accommodation, can perform the essential functions of the position. "Reasonable accommodation" is defined as steps an employer can take to help a disabled person perform the job—for example, providing a reader for a blind employee. If the accommodations would cause the employer "undue hardship," however, the employer is not obligated to accommodate a disabled employee. The ADA also forbids preemployment physicals unless the physical examination tests for job-related functions, is a business necessity, and is required only after the employer has made an offer of employment to the applicant.

Family Medical Leave Act (FMLA) The FMLA of 1993 protects a worker's job while the worker takes time off to care for a family member or to deal with a personal medical condition. The length of absence within a year is limited, and medical certification is required documenting that the employee is essential to the care and/or recovery of the family member. Department members should be counseled on the specific application of FMLA within the organization, procedural requirements, and responsibilities. Departments must also take FMLA into account when addressing staffing levels as the potential exists for significant costs to cover members using FMLA. Amendments added in 2008 and 2009 expanded FMLA rights for military veterans and their families.

Uniformed Services Employment and Reemployment Rights Act of 1994 (USERRA) This act expands protection of veterans' jobs and addresses other occupational issues. The U.S. Department of Labor website, dol.gov, offers expansive information regarding this act and its application to a variety of occupational settings.

Veterans Benefit Improvement Act of 2004 This act expands protection of veterans' jobs and addresses other occupational issues. The website at dol.gov offers expansive information regarding this act and its application to a variety of occupational settings.

The *Uniform Guidelines on Employee Selection Procedures,* published by the U.S. Department of Labor in 1978 and revised in April of 2008 (CFR Title 41, Chapter 60-3), provides an excellent starting point for human resource managers addressing the legal issues of selection processes.

for performance measurement in these training schools can be far different than the rules "out in the field." True performance expectations for the job classification are tied to the work a recruit will perform once he or she graduates from school and is assigned to a unit or station. The probationary period must be long enough to include not only recruit school but also a reasonable amount of time in a station where the recruit experiences and responds to station life and daily expectations, emergency response incidents and stressful situations, and unusual work schedules. Only after some time in the real work environment can a new member be properly evaluated for suitability for the job and potential success as a lifelong career professional.

Member support systems and retention issues

Once personnel are recruited, evaluated, selected, and on the job, the work of the HR manager is far from over. In career departments, the most visible and contentious issues are often related to compensation, leave, and promotional processes. However, to maintain a healthy, engaged, and motivated workforce, whether volunteer or career, the HR manager must also

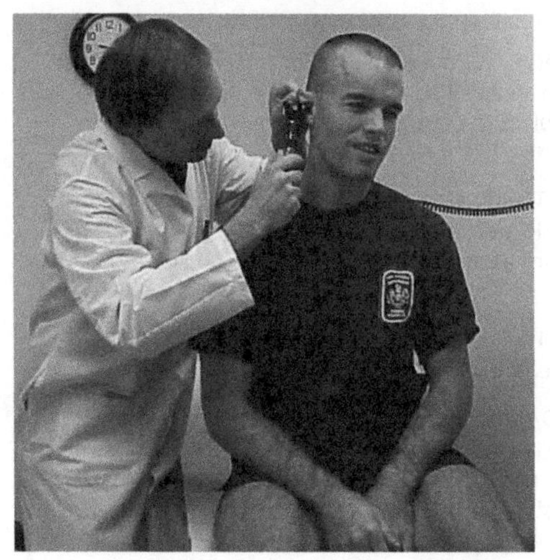

Figure 8-2 Fire and emergency service departments need to protect the health of their members and encourage positive steps toward improving general health.

Photo by Adam K. Thiel

give attention to support, development, and protection of each member's mental, emotional, and physical well-being over the course of his or her career.

Health and wellness

More than just a resource, department personnel are valuable assets and worthy of the organization's and community's investment in their general well-being. From the moment a new member joins the department, it should be the goal of the organization to ensure that he or she enjoys a positive lifelong relationship with the organization and leaves employment in good health. This outcome cannot be left to chance and often cannot be left up to the individual. Fire and emergency departments need to take assertive steps to protect the health of their members and create an organizational culture that encourages, supports, and rewards members' positive steps toward improving their general health (see Figure 8–2). Buy-in from membership and labor groups is essential to the success of any health/wellness program. Management must constantly monitor the health status and changing needs of the organization.

The IAFF/IAFC Fire Service Joint Labor Management Wellness-Fitness Initiative mentioned previously in this chapter and described in greater detail in Chapter 11 provides extensive guidance on maintaining member health and wellness. Recommendations are given for routine health screenings, in-house exercise programs for strength and cardiovascular health maintenance, immunization, and other health-related topics. NFPA 1583, Standard on Health-Related Fitness Programs for Fire Department Members (2008 ed.), also provides guidance for department health and fitness initiatives.

How a department manages personnel with job-related and non-job-related injuries or illness can affect the morale of not only the individual affected but also the entire organization. Members watch how the organization treats those who cannot perform their duties, whether because of short- or long-term incapacitation, as an indication of how the department values its general membership. Therefore, management must take the time to educate the membership about the laws and codes that affect how the organization treats members who become injured or ill. All members must understand what is within the control of the organization and what is mandated from outside. Within those parameters, the organization can then develop policies that align with its culture and value system. The balance between the needs of the individual and the needs of the organization is delicate, and parameters must be established to ensure that people are treated fairly and legally while the organizational missions are met.

Fire service organization leadership and HR staff must stay abreast of court rulings and decisions at the local, state, and federal levels and evaluate the impact of those rulings on the organization. For example, the ADA has sweeping impacts on the public safety sector, from hiring practices to the design of new facilities. Organizations must take the time to evaluate their policies on such vital issues as minimum hiring age, pregnancy, levels of disability that may determine retention versus retirement, limited duty, and fitness for duty assessments. (See Chapter 11 for a full discussion of health and wellness programs.)

Career development

Many fire departments have developed written career path guidelines for their members. Such guidelines set out the specific training, experience, and formal education qualifications that a member needs to move from one rank to another. They should be tied to the department's mission and strategic plan. Career path guidelines take an incremental approach that balances realistic assessments of job duties and responsibilities against the objective of encouraging members to improve their performance, their professional and general intellectual knowledge base, and their understanding of the world around them. (Chapter 9 addresses at length the topic of professional development.)

Many localities offer assistance with tuition, and scholarship programs exist to aid public safety members who desire to augment their career development with academic and advanced professional education. For example, the IAFC Volunteer and Combination Officers Section (VCOS) Symposium Scholarship Program awards funding to offset expenses to attend its annual education symposium. This section of the IAFC also provides scholarships to attend the annual Fire-Rescue International meeting. (For further information on these and other VCOS scholarship programs, visit vcos.org.) Colleges and universities have their own scholarship/ financial assistance programs to support emergency service members who are pursuing their educational goals.

Member participation: Committees and teams

Career development does not have to include promotion, and management should not focus solely on members who want to be promoted. Many members find one rank or another particularly appealing to their unique skills, personality, and career expectations, and while they do not seek promotion, they often welcome job enhancements and new challenges. They also welcome the opportunity to have more control over their daily activities. Management benefits in multiple ways when members participate in organization decisions and plans.

The use of a team or committee made up of participants who will be directly affected by the outcome of a decision to be made ensures that the department considers their valuable perspective, and it solidifies members' buy-in to solutions or decisions reached with their input (Figure 8–3).

Teams need clear direction on the parameters of their assignments. They need to know

- The number and rank of members eligible for the team
- Who will be the liaison with management
- Compensation for members (if compensation is appropriate or mandated)
- Funding available for research, testing, or equipment purchases
- Availability of department support staff and procedures for enlisting their assistance
- Time lines
- Reporting requirements
- How the team's decision will be used—as final or binding, or as a recommendation to be considered by management in a final decision.

Teams and committees should never be created simply to give the appearance of participatory management. Today's employee will quickly see through the façade, and the result will be mistrust of management and damage to leaders' credibility. If management feels that it is appropriate for a decision to be made at a high level, it should keep the decision-making process at that level. One important aspect of effective leadership is discriminating when, where, and how to make different decisions in

Photo by Adam K. Thiel

Figure 8-3 Team participation is a win-win for management and individual employees motivated by the opportunity to influence department decisions.

Teamwork for strategic planning and implementation

The Alexandria (Virginia) Fire Department depends heavily on teams of employees and volunteers to help guide its strategic direction and make important decisions about implementing organizational changes. The department's strategic planning team includes almost fifty members representing all ranks, labor groups, sections, and divisions. This core team is further divided according to five focus areas:

- Community engagement
- Prevention, health, and safety
- Readiness/infrastructure
- Professionalism
- Accountability.

With the common goal of achieving operational excellence, each focus area charters workgroups and task forces that include other department members with expertise, or particular interest, in a certain area where changes are contemplated. After being provided with broad direction and basic parameters (i.e., budget and safety considerations), the teams address specific projects and provide recommendations to the department's executive team.

In most cases, the teams' proposals are readily accepted with little or no modification; in other cases, minor changes are requested or additional study is required. Examples of successful projects for which employee teamwork resulted in policy changes or new procedures include

- Large-diameter hose specification, procurement, and training
- Uniform design, testing, and procurement
- Ambulance (medic unit) design, specification, and procurement
- Fire apparatus design and specification
- Identification of position-specific core competencies for all ranks
- EMS equipment design, specification, and procurement
- Tabletop incident command, exercise, design, and simulation.

The basic principle is that people closest to the front line, working together with appropriate policy guidance and administrative support, will make the best decisions for the organization.

Source: Adam K. Thiel.

accordance with the specific organizational culture and the nature of the decision to be made. (For more on decision making and member participation, see Chapter 7.)

Employee evaluation and performance management

In any organization, one of management's major responsibilities is evaluating how employees accomplish their tasks so as to guide and encourage safe, appropriate, and professional performance. Employee evaluation also serves to monitor the alignment of the employee's performance and behaviors with the goals and objectives of the organization.

A wide variety of evaluation and performance management tools are used throughout the fire and emergency services, ranging from the extremely informal, such as an undocumented conversation, to those tools that provide employees with extensive written feedback. Employees are more likely to accept and understand feedback that has direct links to job performance via a job task analysis. Without objective performance criteria, any evaluation system, and especially one tied to bonuses or "merit" raises, has little impact on performance. The result is that some supervisors become jaded and decide that it is not worth putting time or energy into the process, even for employees who are performing below organizational standards and need detailed feedback. A termination decision made in this negative environment will return to haunt the organization when it is challenged in court and periodic evaluations do not support the organization's assertions of unsatisfactory performance.

The organization should use the evaluation process to encourage career development and improve the performance of its members. Regular evaluation should refocus, reenergize, and reconnect members to the organization and its mission. It should remind them of their career

Comprehensive performance evaluation

Facing a period of significant organizational growth with a relatively new workforce, the Goodyear (Arizona) Fire Department embarked on a process to develop and implement a comprehensive performance evaluation program for all its employees, in every job, and at every rank.

With assistance from human resource specialists and significant input from department members, the department identified core competencies and created customized evaluation forms for every position. More importantly, department leaders began talking with employees and supervisors about the need to establish a continuous dialogue around individual performance and its effects on work units and the larger organization. According to then Fire Chief Mark Gaillard (as of this writing, Goodyear's interim deputy city manager), "The goal of the program is to develop confidence and competence, throughout the organization, by holding supervisors and their teams accountable for performing to clearly established standards and expectations."

Another key component of the program, in addition to the core competencies and supporting forms, is an emphasis on regular coaching and counseling. "Effective coaching by a caring supervisor is the best way to help employees be successful in their daily tasks," noted Chief Gaillard. "Performance evaluation doesn't work if it only happens after an employee makes a mistake, or just once a year when the form is due." The Goodyear program requires regular, and documented, interaction between supervisors and subordinates throughout the year, with intermediate formal evaluations at least quarterly.

During the implementation phase, training on the new evaluation system was delivered to all employees so that everyone had a clear understanding about the process, expectations, and desired outcomes. While the new system required a higher level of supervisory effort, which "took some getting used to," according to Chief Gaillard, "most employees appreciated the department's investment in supporting their personal success, growth, and development."

Source: Adam K. Thiel.

goals and define steps to achieve those goals. Organizations must not only create a credible performance feedback system but also train supervisors to implement that system to the best of their ability and with the explicit purpose of developing the careers of their subordinates.

A system that makes self-evaluation an integral part of the process solicits the members' involvement. Members disclose what they perceive to be their own strengths and areas needing improvement within expected performance parameters. They are asked to verbalize or write down their career goals, evaluate their efforts to achieve those goals, and revise plans for future activities where appropriate. The self-evaluation is an opportune time for members of the organization to reengage with the department's mission, purpose, and values.

Photo by Adam K. Thiel

Figure 8-4 A promotion ceremony can be used to highlight the importance of career development for all members.

Promotion

Many firefighters enter the fire service with the goal of working up through the ranks to achieve higher responsibility and greater participation in the organization. A career path process helps guide this ambition to meet the long-term goal of the member while ensuring that his or her efforts will be consistent with the needs of the organization—a "win-win" situation for both parties (Figure 8-4).

Promotions in the fire service are fraught with angst on the part of both employees and management. Management

Ricci v. DeStefano

When the results of two promotional exams given in the New Haven, Connecticut, fire department would have promoted a disproportionate number of white candidates, the New Haven Civil Service Board refused to certify the exams. White and Hispanic candidates who had taken the exams in order to be promoted sued the board. They argued that their rights under the Civil Rights Act of 1984 had been violated. The U.S. Supreme Court agreed. In *Ricci v. DeStefano*, 557 U.S. ___ (2009), it held that by discarding the exams, the City of New Haven violated Title VII of the Civil Rights Act. Title VII says that before an employer can engage in intentional discrimination for the purpose of avoiding a "disparate impact" on a protected trait (race, color, religion, national origin), the employer must have a "strong basis in evidence" that it will be subject to "disparate impact liability" if it fails to take the discriminatory action. The Court reasoned that New Haven failed to prove that it had a "strong basis in evidence" that not discarding the results of the exam would have subjected it to liability—because the exams were job-related, consistent with business necessity, and there was no evidence that an equally valid, less discriminatory alternative to the promotional exams was available.

Source: Based on the Oyez Project, *Ricci v. DeStefano*, 557 U.S. ___ (2009), available at oyez.org/cases/2000-2009/2008/2008_07_1428.

realizes the importance of promoting the right individuals to move the department forward, create positive working environments for subordinates, and provide effective service to the community. Meanwhile, the workforce formally and informally evaluates every promotional process for objectivity, internal bias, adverse impact, and relevance to the job. Promotional processes are no less subject to legal challenge than hiring processes. The 2009 New Haven, Connecticut, case of *Ricci v. DeStefano* is well-known (see sidebar), but many cases never reach the Supreme Court. Departments should research cases and decisions, taking each as a learning opportunity to evaluate their own promotional systems for strengths and weaknesses.

Promotion in volunteer departments

Volunteer departments may use one of several methods for promoting members to higher rank. Many volunteer departments have business or civil officers (president, vice president, secretary, treasurer, etc.) as well as operational officers (chief, assistant chiefs, captains, lieutenants, engineers, etc.). In most volunteer departments, the civil officers are elected by the membership of the organization, although positions such as secretary may be appointive. Line or operational officers may also be elected by fellow members, but in some volunteer departments the volunteer chief has the power to appoint subordinate officers.

The governing documents of a high percentage of volunteer organizations that promote via election contain provisions that stipulate prerequisites for leadership positions, such as years of prior service, levels and types of training, certification in types and levels of specialties, depth of involvement in department functions, and so forth. Some communities encourage volunteer departments to institutionalize meritorious promotions rather than what are often perceived as popularity contests. With federal agencies and some states imposing clear requirements for training in safety procedures, hazardous materials response, incident command, and other areas, the days of popularity-based elections for volunteer officers are fast disappearing. Volunteer departments are no less subject to challenge over their HR practices than career departments. The volunteer leader has been described as a "part-time officer with full-time responsibility."[4] This fact, along with the leader's generally high standing within the local community, challenges volunteer organizations to select officers who represent the highest standards of the profession and personal ethics, and who demonstrate their commitment to operating in a manner that places the safety and well-being of the members at the forefront.

Promotion in career departments

The promotion practices used in many career departments are outlined in the following passage from NFPA's *Fire Protection Handbook:*

> In the vast majority of fire departments, various officer ranks are filled by personnel moving up from the next lower rank or ranks, although more fire departments are recognizing the potential benefits of allowing lateral entry, transfers, and promotions of well-qualified personnel from other areas and departments. Promotion procedures take into account technical qualifications for the particular rank and fire department experience. It is essential that examination procedures in the civil service be fully competitive and nondiscriminatory.[5]

In general, promotion processes in career departments are administered by one of the following agencies, or by two or more of them working together: an external HR department, an internal HR division, or a state or local civil service authority. It is the responsibility of the person managing the process to stay abreast of legislation, court cases, and decisions, whether the process is developed and/or delivered by a vendor or in-house. Members of the department who have experience with and knowledge about the particular job classification may serve as subject matter experts, providing guidance as to the relative weight that should be given to experience, written examinations covering the technical qualifications of the position, the development of job-related interview questions, and the development of oral-visual tools such as tactical exercises.

In some organizations, experience and written examinations are supplemented by performance ratings, but these tend to introduce bias, even if such bias is unintentional. Some supervisors, for example, tend to be much more demanding than others when rating performance, and their subordinates often have lower-scoring performance evaluations than other employees who may actually be less qualified for promotion. Unless the organization has a strong, job analysis–based performance appraisal system, subjective performance ratings should be used sparingly in the promotion process.

A more recent addition to promotional processes for midmanager and supervisory levels is the requirement for formal education. A certain educational level may be among the prerequisites to enter the promotional process, or candidates may be assigned points based on the level of education achieved and the types of degrees or certifications they hold. Certificates or degrees in areas directly related to the job are usually given greater weight than non-job-related education. An organization that uses education as part of its promotional process needs to clearly spell out expectations in its career path guidelines and should not indiscriminately change the criteria from one promotional process to the next.

Clearly a sign of the heightening professionalism of the fire service, the addition of college-degree requirements requires a long-term commitment from members and should be carefully integrated into an organization. Timing for implementation should allow members aspiring to a position a reasonable chance of meeting the requirement once it goes into effect. The department must research and define what degrees or certifications will receive what point values and define what constitutes an acceptable educational institution or program. Not all higher education institutions are accredited by national or regional associations. Departments should require that college-level education be obtained through an accredited institution and specify the accrediting agency.

Promotion in combination departments

In combination departments, the ratio of career personnel to volunteers can vary considerably, and the several officer ranks, including that of chief, may be either career or volunteer. Thus, the procedures for promotion in combination departments vary widely.

Generally, in departments with officer ranks in both career and volunteer categories, promotions in each category follow the procedures as outlined in the two preceding sections. However, in combination departments that pay only skeleton crews, such as a driver and/or a driver and firefighter, there usually are no career officers. In combination departments that are predominantly career, there may be only one or two volunteers in the officer ranks, and they may be either elected by fellow volunteers or appointed by the paid chief. The level of responsibility and authority granted these officers can vary widely among organizations.

Certification standards

Certification standards for firefighters and emergency services personnel provide a backbone of professional expectations that a department can use to develop career path and promotion process parameters. Certifications can be granted by a local organization (often called the "authority having jurisdiction"), by a regional entity formed by a group of fire and/or EMS agencies, or by a state or national organization. Many states offer fire service certification programs in a wide variety of subjects and levels, beginning with basic firefighter certification and extending through several officer levels. Certifications in emergency medical services, from basic first aid to very challenging paramedic services, are also available and are administered under the auspices of local, regional, and state agencies.

Departments must carefully assess the relevance of all aspects of standards before incorporating them into their own processes. A validation study that includes a job task analysis will identify and link outside certification processes with internal job descriptions and actual duties and responsibilities. Creating a promotion process that is valid and does not have an adverse impact on any group is paramount. Using tools such as established certification standards is an excellent starting point for many departments.

Many U.S. states and Canadian provinces, as well as many local governments and regional entities, use the NFPA professional qualification standards as the basis for certification of individuals (see Chapter 9 for a partial list of these standards). The standards are used to develop written and skill tests that, when used in a credible testing process, are highly effective in ensuring that individuals meet the job performance requirements for a given position and level. Many agencies affiliate with a national certification group, such as the International Fire Service Accreditation Congress and the National Board on Fire Service Professional Qualifications.

Programs such as the National Fire Academy Executive Fire Officer Program and chief fire officer designation from the Commission on Professional Credentialing should be considered for management-level positions. When using such tools for internal promotion processes, care must be taken if not all candidates have had equal access to these programs or if department support to attend or participate in the programs has not been consistent. Many promotion processes recognize these certifications as equivalents to formal education and allow candidates to choose from among a variety of educational programs as well as to exercise more control over access and speed of completion.

NFPA 1021, Standard for Fire Officer Professional Qualifications, was first published in the mid-1970s and describes, in the terminology of job performance requirements, four different levels of fire officer qualification: first-line supervisor, midlevel supervisor, manager, and executive officer (Levels I through IV). These qualifications, or performance requirements, are common to most career and volunteer organizations. The standard acknowledges that not all departments require personnel certified at each level, but many of the performance items it discusses are required for an effective organization. The standard addresses both emergency response and routine performance requirements.

NFPA also offers a variety of documents related to professional qualifications for specialty positions, which can entail a qualifying or "promotional" process depending upon how the positions are integrated into the organization's position classification system. The development of so many fire service and EMS specialties is testimony that substantive career development can occur laterally as well as vertically in many organizations, offering members additional alternatives for professional growth. These new specialties also create new recruitment opportunities to interest prospective applicants who may have skills that are better suited to specialty positions versus traditional fire service roles.

Helpful tools for the promotion process

Table 8–2 provides a partial list of the advantages and disadvantages of several common promotional tools. Four of these tools—assessment centers, written tests, interviews, and oral-visual exercises—are discussed in this section.

Assessment centers Some fire and emergency service departments rely on assessment centers to evaluate candidates for promotion. Assessment centers, which can be expensive

Table 8-2 Promotional tools compared

Tool	Advantage	Disadvantage
Seniority	Easy to calculate	Disregards merit
Performance success	Based on work	Dependent on supervisor
Extra merit	Encourages brave acts	Unrelated to the needs of the job
Credit for military service	Compensates	Discriminates
Written tests	Job-related questions	Unrealistic, discriminates
Oral-visual exercises	Evaluates composure under pressure	Difficult to ensure consistency
Interviews	Flexible approach	Can be discriminatory and unreliable
Evaluation process	Job related	May be biased
Assessment centers	Job related	Complex and costly
Recommendations	Past performance evaluated	Negative statements perhaps withheld because of fear

depending on the degree of complexity, have been used for quite some time by general industry. They employ problem-solving, role-playing, and other exercises that require candidates to demonstrate certain abilities using a variety of communication modes common to the particular job description. Components should include a job knowledge test, a written skills test, an oral-visual exercise, and an oral interview. The oral-visual component is most often a tactical problem designed to elicit a set of verbalized actions appropriate to the situation as per standard practice and department policy. Written exercises can range from filling out common reports to writing multipage responses to a set of thought-provoking questions. Oral interviews can include a panel of interviewers with a set of questions and/or a role-play exercise. Each candidate's performance is observed and scored by a trained assessment team.

A well-designed assessment center is one of the most realistic ways to determine a candidate's suitability for a particular position. Assessment centers are most reliable when a combination of internal and external assessors evaluates candidates objectively against well-defined evaluation criteria that match the position KSAs.

Written tests Written tests for promotion contain job-related questions that, ideally, can be validated by an internal or external test review board for applicability to the department and for position description, roles, and responsibilities. All promotional testing tools should be evaluated carefully for adverse impact. (See sidebar on page 236 on *Ricci v. DeStefano* and the section "Discrimination" in Chapter 10 for more on this subject.) The testing process is administered by personnel specialists from within the department or the local government or by an external contractor. The administrator makes sure that all candidates are treated equally, oversees the test's timing and environment, oversees the security of the test documents, scores the completed tests, and places the scores in rank order. All candidates are notified of their test scores and rankings. A written test can be the promotion process in itself or the first phase of a larger process. The fire chief (or appointing authority) reviews the candidates who rank highest on the list. Local policy may allow the holders of a certain number of top-ranking positions (e.g., the top three or top ten test scorers) to be reviewed for appointment. This process is called the "rule of the list."

When the test is the initial phase of a process, the number of candidates who move to the next phase should be set by policy; many departments move a certain number of candidates forward according to the number of positions to be filled. In all cases, a promotional list has a defined life span (e.g., one year); however, the operating authority may have the option (depending on written personnel policy) of extending the life of the list by six to twelve months.

Interviews Many promotional processes include an interview. The interview may be brief and simple, with the applicant meeting only one interviewer—often the chief, or it may be longer and more formal, with an interview panel made up of peers or members of higher ranks.

The interview provides an opportunity for the organization to judge candidates' ability to verbalize their views on a variety of job-related topics. An interview process involving a large number of candidates should be conducted under the close scrutiny of a personnel specialist or facilitator so that any questions about promotional procedures can be answered. There should be more than one interviewer, and each should ask the same question or questions of each candidate to help ensure fairness and uniformity.

Personal questions or inquiries about race, religious beliefs, or other topics irrelevant to the position should be avoided, but a few personal questions may be necessary to fully evaluate a candidate's response. For example, an interviewer might ask for clarification as to why a candidate left a particular position or assignment before he or she became eligible to request reassignment as defined by organizational policy. The response may be related to a personal situation that warranted an exception to the policy as opposed to an arbitrary or capricious reason such as displeasure with the work schedule. The facilitator should discuss acceptable questions that might be asked of a candidate and should inform the interviewers of questions or types of questions that cannot be asked.

Oral-visual exercises Many departments use some form of oral-visual exercise to evaluate each candidate's knowledge of department policies and procedures. More commonly called tactical exercises, oral-visual exercises can be very valuable in assessing candidates' understanding of department field operations as well as common firefighting or EMS knowledge in a setting that requires them to verbalize appropriate action sequences and make decisions under time constraints. The complexity of the tactical problem presented should be appropriate to the decisions, situational awareness, and activities normally expected of the promotional position.

The exercise may be internally designed or designed by an outside agency. If an outside agency designs the exercise, it should use members of the department as subject matter experts. If actual structures are used in the visuals, they should be structures from another locality so that no candidate has prior experience or prefire planning/fire inspection knowledge of that structure, its access points, its construction type, or other special features.

The tactical exercise is one of the best ways to evaluate a candidate's composure under pressure. It is especially relevant to company and station officer positions that routinely make tactical decisions that can have significant operational and personnel/civilian life safety consequences. Some departments also use an oral-visual exercise to evaluate a candidate's ability to deal with stressful administrative issues, such as an irate citizen who comes into a station with a complaint, or an employee with a complaint against a shift mate or an allegation of sexual or race-related harassment. Role players should be carefully controlled and coached to keep the scenario within certain specified constraints in order for this kind of exercise to provide reasonable consistency among candidates.

Labor relations

HR management is often defined in terms of formal organizational processes, and the organization's employee policy manual often provides guidelines and standards for desired employee behavior. But management's desires must be constantly balanced with the rights of employees.

When career firefighters are unionized, their rights (which include wages, fringe benefits, living conditions, and a grievance procedure) can be formalized through collective bargaining between management and local union leaders and are usually spelled out in a written contract. Unions can also exist in departments without collective bargaining; they work with management in what is termed a "meet and confer" relationship.

All the significant labor relations legislation that was enacted, modified, and updated from 1935 to 1959 had to do with the private sector. Public employees were excluded from consideration because they were thought to work in an environment insulated from the entrepreneurial attitudes and competition that had produced labor inequalities and unionism.

The official beginnings of the public sector labor movement have been traced to Executive Order 10988, issued in January 1962. With that order, "President John Kennedy extended the rights of union organization and a truncated system of collective bargaining to federal employees. This action exerted pressure at the state level and laws giving public employees the right of union organization and collective bargaining soon were enacted in major states."[6]

This section discusses labor relations in fire and emergency service departments generally, collective bargaining, and mutual gains bargaining.

Labor relations in fire and emergency service departments

The fire and emergency services department is a special type of public service agency, and whether or not its employees are union members, good labor relations are possible for the fire administrator who is willing to research labor relations issues adequately and exercise professional understanding in dealing with employees.

In both unionized and nonunionized departments there is a contractual relationship between employer and employee. Although nonunion employees do not have a "contract" per se, there are usually policies, procedures, and codes that define how employees and employer relate to one another on a number of different levels. The result of professionally conducted labor relations is a cooperative atmosphere and a working relationship that is productive for both management and employees.

Collective bargaining

The set of rules, procedures, and laws under which today's leaders must perform is subject to judicial scrutiny. Thus, management is necessarily becoming more legally astute in labor relations and collective bargaining. Managers who understand the collective bargaining process and who exercise good judgment as leaders are successful in developing effective labor agreements and a productive workforce.

Although the term *collective bargaining* has become a household word, it also has a precise legal definition. Section 7(d) of the 1947 Taft-Hartley Act describes collective bargaining as follows:

> For the purposes of this section, to bargain collectively is the performance of the mutual obligation of the employer and the representative of the employees to meet at reasonable times and confer in good faith with respect to wages, hours, and other terms and conditions of employment, or the negotiation of an agreement, or any question arising thereunder, and the execution of a written contract incorporating any agreement reached if requested by either party, but such obligation does not compel either party to agree to a proposal or require the making of a concession.

A community that has established a working collective bargaining procedure with its firefighters can expect (and will need) numerous and sometimes lengthy negotiating sessions. Only the insignificant, inexpensive items can be handled in single sessions. Sufficient time must be allowed not only for the negotiating sessions themselves but also for each side to consider proposals and counterproposals and to conduct necessary research. And the union team may require time to confer with its general membership while the management team will need to conduct its own consultations, including some with the elected and appointed officials who are involved in the labor negotiations. If, in addition, the negotiating teams are

The role of the International Association of Fire Fighters

Since its inception in 1918 with twenty-four locals attending the first convention, the International Association of Fire Fighters (IAFF) has represented firefighters. As public employee unionism became more widespread, the IAFF grew. As of 2011, it represents nearly 298,000 full-time professional firefighters and paramedics in the United States (see iaff.org). Active in nearly every aspect of fire service working conditions, it is in the arena of health and safety that the IAFF has taken a leadership role and forged important relationships to advance programs such as the Wellness-Fitness Initiative undertaken in partnership with the International Association of Fire Chiefs.

dealing with potential major changes that are already in the hands of long-standing committees, time for liaison will usually be necessary.

In the end, a written labor contract provides a blueprint for personnel operations—a blueprint that is as helpful to management as it is to labor.

When labor-management negotiations result in an impasse, four standard options have been used to overcome the impasse: mediation, arbitration, fact finding, and strike.

Mediation When the two parties to a labor negotiation are diametrically opposed on one or more issues or are unsuccessful in reaching agreement, a neutral third party can often play a vital role. This third party is the mediator, who is usually a member of the Federal Mediation and Conciliation Service or a similar state agency. The role of the mediator is to help the opposing parties find common ground and reach agreement on various issues. At this stage, however, nothing is binding on either party.

Arbitration When management and union leaders remain unsuccessful in reaching agreement on some contract issue, grievance case, or disciplinary action, even after mediation attempts, they are said to be at an impasse. At this point the climate is ripe for arbitration, a process in which a neutral third party reaches a decision that is *final and binding;* the arbitrator actually dictates what the agreement will be. Arbitrators can be obtained through the American Arbitration Association.

Since arbitration is binding, compulsory arbitration is often considered an alternative to a strike. Strikes in fire and emergency service departments have particularly undesirable consequences, so arbitration is common and is often mandated by state law.

Fact finding Fact finding has proved extremely helpful for resolving an impasse in the public sector. Fact finding uses arbitrators, but their decision is not binding as it is in arbitration. It points the parties in a common direction and returns them to the bargaining table for further negotiations.

Strike Strikes are by no means an inevitable conclusion to a collective bargaining process, particularly if both sides adopt the professional approach advocated earlier in this section. Yet strikes do occur, and it is well-known that when they do, both management and the union suffer. When a fire and emergency services department goes on strike, the public also suffers. Nobody can win. In most states, strikes by firefighters are prohibited by law, and fire departments are legally required to submit to binding arbitration.

Collective bargaining, along with labor-management relations and contract administration (administration of the contract between the union and the local government), has historically had a major effect on the HR function in fire and emergency service organizations. In dealing with firefighter unions—in particular, the IAFF—management has been forced to be methodical, fair, and progressive in handling personnel issues. This effect will grow as departments become larger and as more departments unionize.

The collective bargaining process, however, is changing as new attitudes emerge and new management approaches to organized labor are devised. One example, mutual gains bargaining, is described below. Encouraging member participation on committees and teams, as discussed previously, can also help improve labor-management relations. (See Chapter 10 for more information on laws governing labor-management relations.)

Mutual gains bargaining

Although collective bargaining is often seen as a "zero-sum" process—that is, a process in which a gain for one side causes a loss for the other—a more recent approach aims at making it possible for both sides to achieve desired results. This "win-win" approach in collective bargaining is referred to as mutual gains bargaining. When both parties emerge from the collective bargaining negotiations with something gained, the community is the ultimate winner. The welfare of the community takes prominence in its own right as a focal point of the negotiations instead of being a proxy for each side's interests in an "us versus them" struggle.

Managing retirement and termination

Although many aspects of retirement and other forms of separation from an organization are controlled by law (federal, state, and local), collective bargaining, and local jurisdictional and organizational policy, it is often the job of the HR manager to facilitate the departure of members. Even voluntary separations can be extremely emotional events for members after a lifetime of public safety service. Disability-related separations are also fraught with emotional and psychological issues when the member does not want to separate from the organization and responds with frustration and hostility to those who are managing the separation process. The HR manager/designee can play a major role in creating a positive and supportive environment for members going through separation.

An employee checklist should be developed to ensure that all relevant issues are addressed for the employee and family, such as continuity of benefits coverage, timing of income payments, retirement funds management, and relationship of pay and benefits with federal programs such as Social Security and Medicare. In larger municipalities, the HR manager may be only one of many people with whom a separating member must deal to set his or her affairs in order. However, the department HR manager is the most important link and the representative of the department who can, and should, create a caring and supportive environment.

In most departments many of the decisions that affect separation are tightly controlled, frustrating employees and creating an atmosphere of distrust. In the absence of active labor union roles in this area, organizations might consider creating employee teams that are charged with monitoring changes in legislation, policies, and procedures. Team members might also mentor separating employees by educating and supporting them through the necessary steps. Organizations might consider using retired members as advocates and mentors for future retirees to help guide them through the process and ensure that current and comprehensive information is provided to facilitate important personal and family decisions.

Managing involuntary terminations for cause is among the most difficult tasks a manager faces. Clear performance and behavioral expectations should be communicated to all members in writing as well as regularly reinforced by supervisors to ensure that all members understand expectations, why those expectations are important and valued, and the consequences of violating or failing to perform to each expectation.

The termination process varies greatly from organization to organization and may be strictly controlled by labor agreements or adopted policy. Strict procedural controls can facilitate a smoother process, but at the same time they reduce a manager's ability to tailor the process to the individual employee and infraction. A lack of flexibility in discipline and termination processes that restricts options for addressing the issue is often as frustrating for the manager as it is for the member.

Permanent employees have extensive protection from arbitrary discipline and/or termination. Many states have adopted what is known as the Firefighter's Procedural Bill of Rights (FFPBOR). The FFPBOR requires organizations to adhere to a specific set of procedures in the process of questioning a firefighter in relation to a disciplinary matter. Managers should become familiar with these procedural rights and incorporate them into policy to ensure that they are integrated into disciplinary procedures.

Probationary employees usually have far less job protection and may have limited or no access to grievance procedures or other recourse. In many departments, probationary members are held to rules that are not enforced for permanent members. These rules should always be clearly communicated and understood at the beginning of the probationary period so that when discipline is administered incrementally, the probationary member understands the consequences if his or her behavior does not change.

If terminated, a probationary member is due a process that is professional and as positive as possible under the circumstances. Clear explanations of infractions, the consequences, and expected behaviors should be provided for self-development. As many probationary members are young and just beginning their lives as full-time career-oriented employees, a conscientious manager hopes to relate the termination event as one not of failure but of self-discovery.

Termination of a permanent employee is a stressful process and should be handled with the utmost care, confidentiality, and respect. Members should be aware of the process and

Florida Firefighters Bill of Rights

Whenever a firefighter is subjected to an interrogation, such interrogation shall be conducted pursuant to the terms of this section.

1. The interrogation shall take place at the facility where the investigating officer is assigned, or at the facility which has jurisdiction over the place where the incident under investigation allegedly occurred, as designated by the investigating officer.
2. No firefighter shall be subjected to interrogation without first receiving written notice of sufficient detail of the investigation in order to reasonably apprise the firefighter of the nature of the investigation. The firefighter shall be informed beforehand of the names of all complainants.
3. All interrogations shall be conducted at a reasonable time of day, preferably when the firefighter is on duty, unless the importance of the interrogation or investigation is of such a nature that immediate action is required.
4. The firefighter under investigation shall be informed of the name, rank, and unit or command of the officer in charge of the investigation, the interrogators, and all persons present during any interrogation.
5. Interrogation sessions shall be of reasonable duration and the firefighter shall be permitted reasonable periods for rest and personal necessities.
6. The firefighter being interrogated shall not be subjected to offensive language or offered any incentive as an inducement to answer any questions.
7. A complete record of any interrogation shall be made, and if a transcript of such interrogation is made, the firefighter under investigation shall be entitled to a copy without charge. Such record may be electronically recorded.
8. An employee or officer of an employing agency may represent the agency, and an employee organization may represent any member of a bargaining unit desiring such representation in any proceeding to which this part applies. If a collective bargaining agreement provides for the presence of a representative of the collective bargaining unit during investigations or interrogations, such representative shall be allowed to be present.
9. No firefighter shall be discharged, disciplined, demoted, denied promotion or seniority, transferred, reassigned, or otherwise disciplined or discriminated against in regard to his or her employment, or be threatened with any such treatment as retaliation for or by reason solely of his or her exercise of any of the rights granted or protected by this part.

Source: Florida Statute 112.82 Rights of firefighters, adopted August 10, 2007.

what will be expected of them in such matters as returning organizational property, access to organizational facilities, and communications access—such as e-mail accounts. The organization needs to take the time to clearly communicate what will happen to the member's pay and benefits, including leave on the books, retirement accounts, and health insurance. In more complex organizations, the HR officer often takes charge of such activities and ensures that the appropriate paperwork and documentation are completed, that other departments are notified of the termination when appropriate, and that the transitioning member is advised of actions he or she must take to address items such as continuity of health care coverage and access to retirement or deferred compensation funds.

As fire and emergency service departments become more focused on creating a positive working environment and an organizational culture that support a lifetime commitment from members, it is vitally important for the leadership to take as much interest in how members leave the organization as they do in how new members are brought into it.

Future challenges and conclusion

As the twenty-first century progresses, the fire service will be facing a number of challenges affecting its workforce, whether career or volunteer. These challenges will require innovation and adjustment in the human relations approaches of many fire and emergency service departments.

For example, the growing diversity of the workforce will require policies that recognize and respect the diversity of employees' culture and needs. The demographics of the fire service will mirror the demographics of society, and the changed demographics will be accompanied by changes in priorities and attitudes, mobility, and other elements that affect the relationship between the workforce and the organization.

In addition, the variety and complexity of tasks assigned to the fire and emergency services will continue to evolve. The "all-hazards" approach to public safety and expectations of service from the public will continue to challenge fire and emergency service departments, altering many internal processes such as training, transfers, career development, health and safety, prevention efforts, policy development, strategic planning, and public education. HR management is especially vulnerable to these changes in public expectations, changes in the cultural makeup of the community, and changes in the complexity of KSAs required for each job within the fire and emergency services. Fire service personnel will have to maintain attitudes and levels of productivity commensurate with the changing expectations of their customers.

Regardless of whether a fire and emergency services department is career, combination, or volunteer, it relies nearly exclusively on people and their ability to deliver a range of vital services. This reliance will remain constant for many years to come.

The volunteer fire service in particular will continue to be under incredible pressure to recruit and retain personnel who are intelligent, healthy, energetic, available, compassionate, and committed. Changing social values, increased demands for productivity in regular employment, the time and energy needed to comply with mandated requirements for training and certification, dual-income households, and the increased mobility of the general workforce are just a few of the issues that will continue to challenge established volunteer systems. It will be critical for leaders of such systems to expand their knowledge of best practices, novel approaches, and opportunities to build regulatory support to encourage investment in volunteer organizations that are proactive and professional in their approach to community service delivery.

The management of human resources can be complex. Local elected officials and fire and emergency service leaders must manage personnel within limits defined by law, national labor initiatives, the civil service system, and a complicated web of cultural and individual motivations and expectations. Nevertheless, the concepts and guidelines presented in this chapter will help fire and emergency service leaders harness the boundless energy of their complex and valuable "human resources" and in return provide members with a lifetime experience in a profession nurtured by rich tradition and energized by daily events that challenge all members to find the very best within themselves in the service of others.

Notes

1. Michael J. Karter Jr. and Gary P. Stein, *U.S. Fire Department Profile through 2009* (Quincy, Mass.: National Fire Protection Association [NFPA], October 2010), firecompany4.com/wp-content/uploads/2010/07/National-Volunteer-Firefighters-Profile-2009.pdf, ii.
2. Ibid., 18.
3. *The Fire Service Joint Labor Management Wellness-Fitness Initiative: Candidate Physical Ability Test* (Washington, D.C., and Fairfax, Va.: International Association of Fire Fighters and International Association of Fire Chiefs, 1999), 2.
4. This paragraph is based on William Beetschen, "Part-time Officer, Full-time Responsibility," *Fire Engineering* 152 (May 1999): 10–12.
5. William Peterson, "Fire Department Administration and Management," in *Fire Protection Handbook: NFPA Codes, Standards and Recommended Practices*, 17th ed., ed. Arthur E. Cote and J. L. Linville (Quincy, Mass.: NFPA, 1991), 9–44.
6. Ralph J. Flynn, *Public Work, Public Workers* (Washington, D.C.: New Republic Book Company, 1975), xi, as cited by William M. Kramer and William V. Donaldson, "Labor Relations: No Arena for Amateurs," in *Managing Fire Services*, ed. John L. Bryan and Raymond C. Picard (New York: International City Management Association, 1979), 336.

CHAPTER 9

Professional Development

Adam K. Thiel

This chapter provides an understanding of

- The national assessment models and their respective approaches to certification
- Essential elements of an effective training program
- Essential elements of education for the fire and emergency services
- The functions of certification, qualification requirements, national standards, and credentialing in the fire and emergency services
- Challenges to succession planning and strategies for overcoming them
- Ways to increase and reward professional development efforts
- The core skills essential for administrative success.

As contemporary fire and emergency service organizations assume additional mission responsibilities and strive to keep pace with a constantly changing world of hazards, the need for professional development—also known as career or employee development—becomes increasingly obvious. The days of recruiting firefighters for their strength and courage alone are long past. Today's firefighters, both volunteer and career, must be able to work in "all-hazards" fire and emergency service departments, with skills in firefighting, prehospital emergency medical care, incident command, hazardous materials (HAZMAT) response, technical rescue, terrorism and weapons of mass destruction response, fire prevention and life safety education, arson investigation, and many other disciplines.

Beyond maintaining a broad range of technical skills, as firefighters assume progressively responsible leadership positions within their departments, they must be able to function as knowledgeable public administrators in a complex public policy environment. Ability in many areas—strategic planning, budgeting, policy analysis, conflict resolution, organizational behavior, executive leadership, community engagement, and other facets of public administration—becomes critical for success in the supervisory, management, administrative, and executive ranks.

The term *professional development* denotes the combination of training, education, experience, and self-development required to achieve proficiency in the many aspects of managing a contemporary fire and emergency services organization.

Training is the process of delivering essentially vocational skills and knowledge; it is distinguished from education by a focus on practical application and hands-on skills development (Figure 9–1). Training is delivered through either traditional or nontraditional modalities by a broad spectrum of institutions, and it generally results in the achievement of a certain training objective, which may or may not lead to a professional certification.

Education is the process of delivering essentially academic knowledge. It is typically defined by an emphasis on developing critical-thinking skills, a broad worldview, and the ability to appreciate multiple perspectives on various topics. Adult education is generally delivered in traditional and nontraditional settings by institutions of higher learning as part of a program of study leading to a degree or certification conferred by an accredited degree-granting institution.

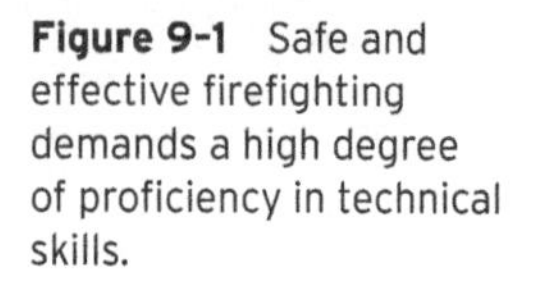

Figure 9-1 Safe and effective firefighting demands a high degree of proficiency in technical skills.

Photo by Adam K. Thiel

Portions of this chapter have been adapted from Chapter 9, "Training for Fire and Emergency Response Services," by Douglas P. Forsman, in the 2002 edition of this volume.

Although on paper the distinction between training and education seems clear-cut, in reality it is not, and organizations regularly ignore the boundaries between the two. In the fire and emergency services, continual innovation means that the lines of demarcation between training and education will remain blurred, for both are necessary to meet changing mission requirements.

The value of experience, or more precisely *experiences,* is also encompassed in a comprehensive professional development program. While experience is often considered synonymous with seniority, the two are not always directly related. As fire and emergency services personnel mature in their roles and responsibilities through increased technical competence and varied experiences, they must also devote continued attention to self-development, which includes many areas of personal development not covered by training and education requirements.

National professional development initiatives

Several national-level initiatives have been created to advance professional development throughout the U.S. fire and emergency services. These efforts all support the integration of training, education, experience, and self-development—validated by certification/qualification, credentialing, and professional designations—for building individual professional competence and creating strong, sustainable fire and emergency service organizations.

Fire and Emergency Services Higher Education (FESHE)

In 1998, the National Fire Academy (NFA), part of the U.S. Fire Administration (USFA), began a project to support the development of fire and emergency services–related higher education programs throughout the United States. With this move, the Fire and Emergency Services Higher Education, or FESHE, initiative was born. Since its inception, FESHE has broadened its mission to include not just college-based higher education programs but also state fire training/certification agencies, local fire and emergency services personnel interested in higher education, and delegates from professional associations such as the International Association of Fire Chiefs (IAFC) through its Professional Development Committee. FESHE's goals have also expanded to fully encompass professional development, to which end FESHE has created a competency-based model for helping firefighters achieve the rank of fire chief, and professional development models for fire prevention and emergency medical services.

FESHE's strategic direction

The mission of the Fire and Emergency Services Higher Education (FESHE) program is to establish an organization of postsecondary institutions to promote higher education and to enhance the recognition of the fire and emergency services as a profession to reduce loss of life and property from fire and other hazards.

Strategic challenge

In an effort to acquire an associate's or bachelor's degree or their next desired level of certification, fire service personnel typically accumulate college transcripts with unnecessary courses and dozens of training certificates. During this typical process of professional development, duplications of effort are common and desired certifications or degrees delayed. The national challenge is for state and local providers of training, education, and certification to integrate their activities to eliminate these duplications while enhancing the overall professional development of the fire and emergency services.

Strategic goal

Working collaboratively, the professional development community will produce a

- National model for an integrated, competency-based system of fire and emergency services professional development
- National model for an integrated system of higher education from associate's to doctoral degrees
- Well-trained and academically educated fire and emergency services preparing the nation for all hazards.

Source: U.S. Fire Administration/National Fire Academy, FESHE Strategic Direction, usfa.dhs.gov/nfa/higher_ed/feshe/feshe_strategic.shtm.

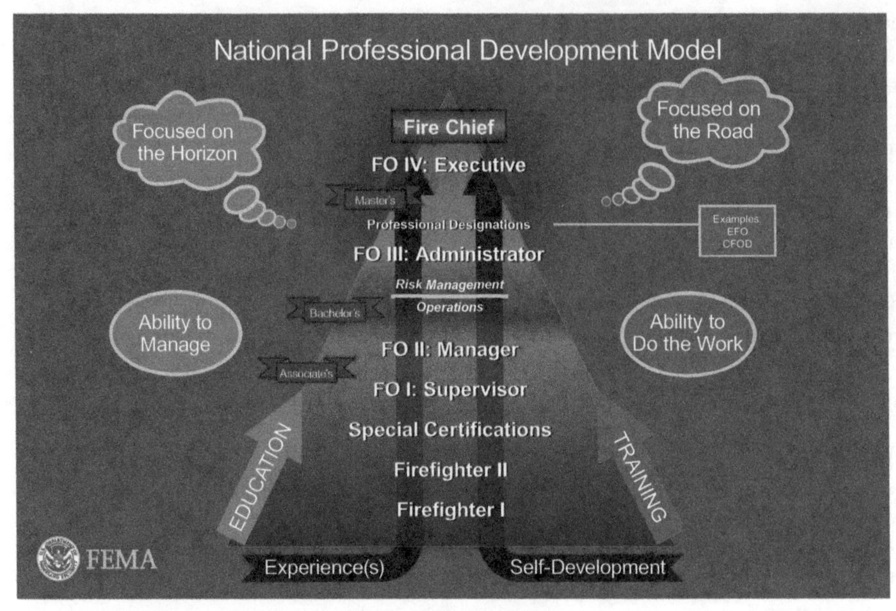

Figure 9-2 The National Professional Development Model was created by the National Fire Academy.

Source: Federal Emergency Management Agency (FEMA), at usfa.dhs.gov/nfa/higher_ed/feshe/feshe_strategic.shtm.

The National Professional Development Model

The cornerstone of the FESHE program is the National Professional Development Model (NPDM), which incorporates training, education, experience(s), self-development, and professional designation into a unified framework (Figure 9-2). One model provides the steps for structuring the journey from firefighter to fire chief; a second, from fire prevention officer to fire marshal; and a third, from emergency medical service (EMS) provider to EMS chief.

As a federal agency, the USFA/NFA does not adopt these FESHE-developed models, nor does it dictate or mandate them. Rather, its role is to promote and support them by encouraging their adoption by public and private institutions of higher education.[1]

To assist states, regions, and local fire and emergency service departments with implementing the NPDM, NFA produced a computer-based template, the National Professional Development Matrix (see Figure 9-3). The matrix cross-walks Fire Officer I–IV competencies

Figure 9-3 The National Professional Development Matrix can be customized by any state or local organization to help guide firefighters' training and educational endeavors.

National Professional Development Matrix
Supervisory Fire Officer (FO I)
Fire Prevention Officer

		Competency/Standards		Training
		Fire Officer/Prevention Competencies	Correlating NFPA Standards	State & Local Courses
CESS (R107)	English Composition (A)	**SFO-01** Ability to write detailed prose.	1031, 1035, 1037	
CESS (R107)	Public Speaking or Oral Communications (A)	**SFO-02** Understanding and using basic interpersonal, group and public communication skills.	1021, 1033, 1035, 1037, 1041	
CESS (R107)	Business or Written Communications (A)	**SFO-03** Ability to write accurate and clear letters, memos, technical reports and business communications.	1021, 1031, 1033, 1037, 1041	
	Biology or Physical Science (A)	**SFO-04** Understanding about ecosystem construction and destruction, energy production and use and waste generation and disposal.		
ALSRHMI (R247), CER (R233)	Chemistry (A)	**SFO-05** Understanding basic principles of general chemistry including the metric system theory and structure.	1033, 1037	
	General Psychology I (A)	**SFO-06** Understanding basic principles of areas of psychology: physiology, cognition, motivation, learning, intelligence, personality, and mental health.	1035, 1037	
	Introduction to Sociology (A), Community Risk Reduction for the Fire and Emergency Services (FBC)	**SFO-07** Understanding basic principles of social groups, forces, structures, processes, institutions, and events.	1031, 1037	
	Beginning and Intermediate Algebra (A)	**SFO-08** Understanding and using the basics of mathematical models; elementary concepts of probability and simulation; emphasis on business applications.	1035, 1037	
	Basic Computer Applications (A)	**SFO-09** Understanding basic principles of information technology and business computer systems for effective daily use.	1031	

*College Courses: A-Associate's, B-Bachelor's, G-Graduate, FAC-FESHE Associate's Course, FBC-FESHE Baccalaureate Course

Source: Federal Emergency Management Agency/U.S. Fire Administration/National Fire Academy.

from NFPA 1021, Standard for Fire Officer Professional Qualifications (2009 ed.), with "national" level courses that include NFA training courses, FESHE model associate's and bachelor's degree courses, and general education courses recommended by the IAFC in its *Officer Development Handbook* (see below).

The matrix brings competencies, education, and training together in one document. Three separate versions address fire, emergency medical services, and fire prevention. Departments of any size, kind, or type can use the matrix as a starting point for developing their own professional development roadmaps. Designed to accommodate the many differences among state fire and emergency services training, certification, and education systems across the United States, the matrix can be customized to meet the needs of various organizations at the state and local levels. Individuals can also use it to help structure their own professional development journeys.

IAFC Officer Development Handbook

SUPERVISING FIRE OFFICER: *EXPERIENCE*

Element	Application
Agency Operations	Qualified Responder: 3–5 years
Coaching	Peer coaching; e.g., recruits and other organizational workgroups Small group leadership; sports teams, youth clubs, etc.
Directing Resources	Acting officer: 200 hours Include emergency response and non-emergency activities
Incident Management	Function as the supervisor of a single resource unit
Planning	Participate in a planning process
Instruction	Develop and deliver training classes
Human Resource Management	Develop teamwork skills
Financial Resource Management	Participate in or contribute to a station, project or small program budget
Project Management	Participate in an organizational work project
Interagency	N/A
Emergency Management	Participate in mass casualty training, exercises and incidents
Community Involvement	Interact with homeowners associations, service clubs, etc.
Professional Associations	Network with others in the service; involvement in local, state and/or regional professional association(s); e.g., instructors, EMS, inspectors, investigators, safety officers

Source: International Association of Fire Chiefs (IAFC), *Officer Development Handbook*, 2nd ed. (Fairfax, Va.: IAFC, 2011), 16.

Figure 9-4 This sample page from the IAFC *Officer Development Handbook* details the experience required for the position of supervising fire officer.

IAFC *Officer Development Handbook*

The Professional Development Committee of the IAFC created the *Officer Development Handbook* (Figure 9-4), which informed the construction of the NPDM/National Professional Development Matrix and serves as an essential companion document.[2] The handbook lays out professional competencies for fire and emergency service officers at all levels—supervisory, managing, administrative, and executive—and describes the importance of training, education, experience, and self-development for producing successful officers. The current edition of the handbook should be required reading for all fire and emergency service officers and aspirants.

Professional development and organizational strength

The need for continued attention to systematic and formalized professional development in the fire and emergency services is described in the proceedings from Wingspread V (2006), a conference of fire and emergency service leaders held every ten years since 1966 to identify issues of national importance for the fire service and those it serves:

> Significant strides have been made in fire service professional development, but improvement is still needed. The fire service needs to continue to evolve as a profession as have other governmental entities that operate in the environments where we work as well as other governmental organizations and the private sector. These skills are as important in the volunteer and combination fire services as they are in the career fire service.[3]

The career ladder

As fire and emergency services personnel advance through their careers, a notable shift of emphasis occurs in their professional development (Figure 9-5). At the beginning of their service, the focus is on training in essential technical knowledge and practical skills for fighting fires, providing emergency medical services, responding to HAZMAT emergencies, accomplishing technical rescues, etc. Firefighters and EMS providers in their early careers are truly the "front line" for protecting their communities. As they collect relevant experiences and hone their skills, emergency workers become highly skilled at performing tasks; these skills and their associated knowledge base are perishable, however, and must be maintained through continuous formal and informal training. The progression of a firefighter from recruit/trainee to a highly proficient fire and emergency services technician has an analog in the progression of other technical trades from apprentice, through journeyman, to the master level.

Figure 9-5 As firefighters advance up the career ladder, the focus of professional development changes.

Photo by Adam K. Thiel

As careers move past the master level, the focus of professional development shifts to supervisory and leadership skills. This marks a significant transition as firefighters prepare for involvement in the daily management of the organization, often as first-line supervisors. Beyond completing additional training and educational requirements, new supervisors start gathering new types of experiences and developing new competencies. First-line supervisors still spend most of their time addressing technical challenges, but an increasing percentage of the day is spent managing people in a specific work unit.

Moving beyond the first-line supervisor, fire and emergency service employees must develop the skills of any other middle manager. They must oversee the daily administration and management of several work units, and develop proficiency in managing fire and emergency incidents involving multiple response units. Generally speaking, at the middle management level, most of an employee's daily workload shifts to managing people instead of performing technical tasks. This level usually marks another transition—from specialist to generalist—as the scope of an individual's duties broadens past the point where specialized knowledge, skills, and abilities can be reasonably maintained.

As fire and emergency service employees approach the executive level, typically as chief officers, education and a different type of experience become the principal foci of professional development. Strategy, planning, budgeting, finance, policy analysis, conflict resolution, organizational behavior, leadership, community engagement, and other dimensions of public administration become critical as subordinate personnel handle the daily management and emergency response workload. Even a small volunteer fire department, just like any other small business or nonprofit organization, requires effective management and leadership to remain strong.

A professional development institute for the fire and emergency services

The goal of the Arizona State University Fire Service Institute is to build the capacity of civilian and sworn fire and emergency service professionals. The institute is specifically designed for command officers, company officers, and civilian managers with a dedicated interest in professional development. In five days of highly interactive sessions, participants explore the dynamic nature of government and the communities they serve, focusing on strategic and operational issues that affect the current and future mission of the American fire service. The topics covered in those sessions are as follows:

- Critical Issues in the Fire Service
- The Politics of the Fire Service: National Trend and Local Impacts
- Building Effective Collaborations
- Leadership Approaches That Make the Difference
- Critical, Creative, and Transformational Thinking
- The Economics of the Fire Service
- Recruiting and Developing the Next Generations of Fire Service Professionals: Creating Realistic Expectations and Opportunities
- Positive Influence, Ethics, and Integrity
- Leaving a Legacy: It Begins on Day One.

Source: Adapted from the website of Arizona State University School of Public Affairs, Fire Service Institute, ramseyexecutive .asu.edu/programs/fire-service-institute/fsi.

Executive leadership is a competency of its own and one that demands extensive preparation that is not available without embracing all aspects of the professional development continuum. Ideally, a fire chief at the executive level should be equally competent administering the activities of any other operating department within a city or county government, just as chief executive officers in private industry manage activities even though they are not intimately familiar with the nuts and bolts of their firms' daily work. This does not diminish the value of rising through the ranks, but perhaps more important is staying attuned to the varied perspectives of employees at different levels and in different mission areas of the organization.

Succession planning

Providing opportunities for firefighters to accrue experiences is critical for succession planning. Beyond operational experiences, future fire department leaders must be exposed to situations that give them experience in the broader realm of public administration and local government management. Ultimately, succession depends on professional development to ensure that the next generation of fire and emergency service managers has the right combination of training, education, experiences, and self-development to lead the organization into the future.

Fire and emergency response managers continually point to the lack of high-quality staff development programs—opportunities for employees and volunteers to grow—as a significant problem in their organizations. That the lack still remains well after it has been recognized attests to the difficulty of designing and implementing a good staff development program. But such programs must be created. Training resources are well spent if expended in this area—and a good program requires much investment in time and money. The ever-increasing demands on fire and emergency service managers will continue to put a premium not only on good leadership and basic management skills but also on sound problem-solving skills and the ability to manage multiple functions.

Good staff development programs do not rely principally on internal resources. Instead, they make use of higher-education offerings, state and national fire academy programs, and training opportunities made available by the private sector. In this training, diversity is important to quality. Providing a broad scope of input will expose future leaders and managers to various approaches and philosophies in both public and private sector settings.

A city/county manager's perspective

Firefighting and emergency medical services are core services for any local government. Our communities rely on dedicated professionals to keep them safe and save lives. Consequently, staying at the top of your professional game is critically important.

One does not get to that point, nor maintain it, by taking a casual course or training once in a while. It requires a devotion to professional development. It means that each person must continually assess his or her strengths and weaknesses and develop a plan for addressing the same. Being introspective and taking a good look at oneself and one's abilities is sometimes difficult but always useful. It's all about striving for excellence.

I spent eight years in the U.S. Coast Guard (USCG), whose organizational ethic begins and ends with preparation and training. We were expected to be *semper paratus* (always ready). The USCG emphasizes training and development at all levels and at all times so that everyone can make the critical decisions necessary to do their jobs and save lives. The standards are high and commitment is required and valued.

Likewise, in the fire and emergency medical services, professional development is the foundation for advancement in rank or responsibility. The labor market is competitive, whether internal or external, and decisions are often made on the basis of one's effort and dedication to developing the knowledge and skills necessary for these important jobs. Professional development increases competency and builds significant value.

Serving in municipal governments for nearly three decades, I have observed that although commitment to professional development requires a sacrifice of time, it produces the great reward of satisfaction in personal accomplishment and one's value to the organization and the community.

Source: James K. Hartmann, county manager, Seminole County, Florida, and formerly city manager of Alexandria, Virginia.

Certainly, college degrees in management, public or business administration, fire service administration, or other related areas will go a long way toward developing the skills necessary for fire and emergency service officers. Some fire departments even require a degree for certain levels of promotion. But there are always local issues and policies that make a supplementary professional development program necessary. Planning and organizing such a program using the National Professional Development Matrix described earlier will help to create a strong and sustainable department.

Training

Fire and emergency service organizations depend on training to safely, effectively, and efficiently respond to emergencies arising from all hazards. Firefighting in the twenty-first century is a complicated endeavor that demands extensive and continual training in a long list of technical subjects ranging from basic knot-tying to the chemistry and physics of combustion. All-hazards fire and emergency responders also require formal training in numerous other disciplines, from HAZMAT and technical rescue operations to public fire education and many subjects in between.

It is not acceptable for contemporary fire and emergency service departments to use on-the-job training as a substitute for properly designed training delivered by certified instructors who are qualified to teach a given subject. Failure to adequately train fire and emergency service personnel for their roles and responsibilities is a prescription for tragedy and opens sponsoring organizations to substantial legal liability. (See Chapter 10 for more on legal obligations to train.)

Fire and emergency services training is initially focused on trainees' ability to meet specified job performance requirements (JPRs) through practical and written testing. JPRs are developed in accordance with specified performance standards, such as those maintained by the National Fire Protection Association (NFPA). Meeting JPRs is a prerequisite for certification in most fire and emergency service training programs.

As employees advance through their careers, developing and demonstrating additional required competencies becomes the focus of professional development training. Training for competency goes beyond the basic "teaching, telling, training" approach. Competency arises not just from passing an examination but also from continual practice, repetition, and experiences applying what is learned in training to realistic scenarios under actual or simulated conditions (Figure 9–6).

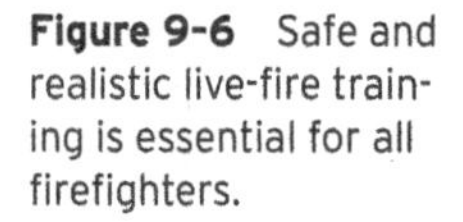
Figure 9-6 Safe and realistic live-fire training is essential for all firefighters.

Photo by Adam K. Thiel

Planning training

Developing an overall training plan is a crucial first step for any department seeking to advance professional development. To be effective, planning should involve management, labor, training personnel, and any appropriate external experts such as vocational training specialists, regional or state fire training personnel, community college fire science program coordinators, and others who can contribute special skills or knowledge to the planning process.

Planning for a fire service training program should start with the departmental mission and goals (see Chapter 7). The next step is to develop specific training objectives. The plan should also identify the resources necessary to achieve the objectives, contain benchmarks, and undergo regular evaluation and revision. Overall, the plan (and the document formalizing it) should reflect the realistic capabilities of the organization, and it should be available for everyone within the organization to review at his or her convenience as often as necessary.

Identifying training needs

Training needs for specific fire and emergency service roles are mandated or recommended by a variety of sources. The impact of federal Occupational Safety and Health Administration (OSHA) standards/regulations on fire and emergency services professional development can depend on several factors. Generally speaking, however, all U.S. firefighters and emergency responders are required to obtain HAZMAT training and certification under Title 29 *Code of Federal Regulations* (CFR) 1910.120, the Hazardous Waste Operations and Emergency Response standard (Figure 9-7). Those in "non-OSHA" states (see Chapter 10) must receive the same training as promulgated by the federal Environmental Protection Agency under Title 40 CFR parts 264–265. HAZMAT training/certification is typically overseen by state emergency management and fire training or certification agencies.

The potential applicability of the OSHA general duty clause is discussed in Chapter 10; depending on a firefighter's employment status and state statutes, OSHA may require additional training/certification according to NFPA or other (state) standards. NFPA maintains a set of voluntary, consensus-based standards for professional qualification (often referred to as the "ProQual" standards) that are the basis for most officially sanctioned state and local

Photo by Adam K. Thiel

Figure 9-7 Firefighters don chemical protective clothing during a hazardous materials technician course.

NFPA professional qualification standards

Numerous National Fire Protection Association (NFPA) standards detail minimum job performance for various fire service positions. NFPA's performance standards may not be mandated, but many jurisdictions adopt them as requirements, and even where not specifically adopted, they effectively serve as industry guidelines. Among the applicable standards are

- NFPA 1001, Standard for Fire Fighter Professional Qualifications (2008 ed.)
- NFPA 1002, Standard for Fire Apparatus Driver/Operator Professional Qualifications (2009 ed.)
- NFPA 1003, Standard for Airport Fire Fighter Professional Qualifications (2010 ed.)
- NFPA 1005, Standard for Professional Qualifications for Marine Fire Fighting for Land-Based Fire Fighters (2007 ed.)
- NFPA 1006, Standard for Technical Rescuer Professional Qualifications (2008 ed.)
- NFPA 1021, Standard for Fire Officer Professional Qualifications (2009 ed.)
- NFPA 1026, Standard for Incident Management Personnel Professional Qualifications (2009 ed.)
- NFPA 1031, Standard for Professional Qualifications for Fire Inspector and Plan Examiner (2009 ed.)
- NFPA 1033, Standard for Professional Qualifications for Fire Investigator (2009 ed.)
- NFPA 1035, Standard for Professional Qualifications for Public Fire and Life Safety Educator (2010 ed.)
- NFPA 1037, Standard for Professional Qualifications for Fire Marshal (2007 ed.)
- NFPA 1041, Standard for Fire Service Instructor Professional Qualifications (2007 ed.)
- NFPA 1051, Standard for Wildland Fire Fighter Professional Qualifications (2007 ed.)
- NFPA 1061, Standard for Professional Qualifications for Public Safety Telecommunicator (2007 ed.)
- NFPA 1071, Standard for Emergency Vehicle Technician Professional Qualifications (2006 ed.)
- NFPA 1521, Standard for Fire Department Safety Officer (2008 ed.)

fire and emergency service training programs. These standards include competency-based guidelines for structural, aircraft, and wildland firefighters; fire officers; fire inspectors; and public fire educators. NFPA standards are not certification requirements unless adopted by the authority having jurisdiction at the state or local level. Some states and provinces use variations of these standards or use standards that they have generated themselves.

State fire training and certification systems vary widely in their specific organizations, missions, processes, standards, jurisdictions, and mandates. The North American Fire Training Directors and National Association of State Fire Marshals are the major players in this arena. Some states unify training and certification in a single agency while others maintain separate training and certification entities. It is important to understand how fire and emergency services training/certification works in one's particular state or province.

Other training needs arise from fire and emergency service departments' various missions. In areas where wildland or wildland-urban interface fires are a major threat, departments may participate in the National Wildfire Coordinating Group (NWCG) training and certification process, colloquially known as the "Red Card" program. The NWCG maintains an extensive list of training courses delivered by federal wildland agencies, state forestry agencies, state fire training/certification systems, local fire departments, and other organizations.

EMS training and certification are typically mandated and regulated through state and provincial health departments and/or EMS offices (Figure 9–8).

Fire and emergency service departments should not rely solely on external mandates and requirements to develop their training programs. Training needs frequently change and often depend on other organizational considerations. For example, a department undergoing rapid growth may emphasize preparing company officers to fill new positions; those facing substantial attrition may be heavily engaged in recruit training to fill line firefighter vacancies.

In addition to the mandates and standards just discussed, an analysis of training needs should look at changes in departmental goals and objectives; critical skills and knowledge that are used infrequently; high-consequence skills and procedures; and input from incident experience.

Photo by Adam K. Thiel

Figure 9-8 EMS training is regulated at the state/provincial level.

Recruit training

Recruit training is essential for providing the basic job knowledge, skills, and abilities required for employees and volunteers to contribute to achieving the department's mission (Figure 9–9). Recruit training can take many forms—from formal programs lasting months to those accomplished over a series of evenings and weekends, especially for volunteers. Regardless of the specific format, recruit training also serves as the members' indoctrination to the department's organizational culture and values.

Training programs must be designed to provide a standard level of competence for those employees or volunteers who are about to fill a given position (in most cases, that of firefighter). In many jurisdictions, incoming personnel will be required to meet the skill level of either Firefighter I or Firefighter I and II, as described in NFPA 1001, Standard for Fire Fighter Professional Qualifications (2008 ed.). Specialized training in policies and procedures for the given jurisdiction are also part of the initial training. And if the department offers emergency medical services, the basic training often covers first responder or emergency medical technician (EMT) training.

Some communities require incoming personnel to have certain credentials before they are employed. Requirements for a Firefighter I certificate, an EMT certificate, or both are not unusual, especially in areas where preemployment training for these certificates may be easily accessible to large numbers of people.

When preemployment certificates are required, it is a good idea for the employer to be in close touch with the preemployment training community. Moreover, it is critical for the employer to be certain that the community colleges, states, or other agencies doing the training are covering the desired topics and testing the students in a high-quality and comprehensive manner. The amount of training that the hiring entity must do is inversely proportional to the amount of training required before hiring. However, the responsibility to field a properly trained team remains the employer's.

Some agencies require a certain number of hours of classroom and field training for each recruit, whereas others offer much of the cognitive training as take-home work or

Figure 9-9 Recruit training is the first step in members' professional development.

Photo by Adam K. Thiel

work to be done at the computer. However, the critical factor in determining the level of competence is a thorough knowledge- and skills-based testing effort. Because such tests are difficult and expensive to develop and administer, most departments use a standard, validated process developed by a fully accredited testing agency. Very often, testing services will be offered by an agency of a state or provincial government or by a local community college.

One critical and continuing debate about the training of recruit firefighters involves the question of when the recruits are ready to respond to incidents. In many volunteer, small-community fire departments, new personnel may be added in very small numbers; thus, the concept of a "recruit class" for training is not applicable. Some of these departments simply spread the initial training over months of training sessions and thus have uncertified personnel responding to calls for many months after initial hiring or membership. NFPA 1001 certainly implies (although it does not state) that firefighters should complete the requirements for Firefighter I before responding to calls.

In-service training

In some fire and emergency service departments, the conclusion of recruit training marks the end of intensive formal training opportunities. This is extremely unfortunate since continued proficiency and professionalism demand ongoing training in multiple topics. While a few states require continuing education for firefighters, analogous to requirements for maintaining EMS certification/licensure, it is not the norm, and many firefighters can maintain their certifications without doing any additional training. Successful fire and emergency service organizations, however, provide multiple in-service training opportunities for their members and generally require a minimum level of attendance and participation; they use in-service training to address skills degradation, advances in technology, expansion of services, changes in policy, and many other topics (Figure 9–10).

Providing in-service training to busy response units, whether career or volunteer, can be challenging. Not only may units have a class interrupted if they remain in service, but very busy fire companies may also have literally no good training time available in the normal work

Photo by Adam K. Thiel

Figure 9-10 Continual in-service training is critical for maintaining knowledge, skills, and ability.

setting. In these cases, units may have to be removed from service even to cover the simplest of subjects. Although declaring units out of service for training is undesirable, it is every bit as important as taking them out of service for response to incidents or for maintenance. Declaring units out of service for training implies that the vacated response district will be covered to the best of the organization's ability.

Distributed or distance learning modalities can be of great value for delivering training across time and space, potentially reducing interference with operational readiness. Computer-, web-, and video-based training programs are available from private firms, community colleges, the Federal Emergency Management Agency (FEMA), NFA, state training agencies, and others. While these products are useful adjuncts to more traditional instruction, they must be integrated into a broader in-service training plan that includes face-to-face instruction and hands-on application of practical skills and knowledge.

Customer service training

Albany, Oregon, enjoys unusually high customer satisfaction ratings, thanks in part to in-depth customer service training that is required for all firefighters and emergency medical service personnel. Recruits are taught that excellent customer service is required of all employees and that it is important "not to disqualify the customer with our qualifications." In other words, recruits learn to speak and interact with customers in a manner that makes customers feel comfortable.

The department also provides several hours of refresher training each year, covering such topics as

- How to comfort trauma victims
- How to manage bystanders
- What customers are saying on their customer service surveys
- The concept that "stations and equipment belong to the community"
- The concept that "every citizen is a customer and shareholder regardless of their economic status."

Source: ICMA Center for Performance Measurement, *What Works* (Washington, D.C.: ICMA Press, 2008), 51–53.

National Fire Fighter Near-Miss Reporting System

The National Fire Fighter Near-Miss Reporting System is a voluntary, confidential, nonpunitive, and secure reporting system designed to improve firefighter safety. Departments can submit reports of near-miss incidents for review by fire service professionals and for posting on an open website (firefighternearmiss.com/) so that other departments can use their experience as a learning tool. Examples of the type of near misses reported (without identifying the department involved) include a firefighter pinned while backing apparatus, an accident prevented by a well-set wheel chock, and a firefighter's entanglement in the wiring of a heating, ventilating, and air conditioning system.

Learning from incidents

An important component of in-service training is the formal process of learning from experience. Nearly every fire department conducts some type of critique (formal or informal) after major incidents. Only a small percentage of departments have in place a policy describing the process and the "afterlife" of critiques, but critiquing exercises are of little value unless the lessons learned are documented, integrated into training and practice, and evaluated again.

Postincident evaluations (PIEs) and after-action reviews (AARs) should be governed by a written policy. Done properly, a PIE/AAR can be a very high quality training tool that will enhance customer service and personnel safety. Done improperly, it can be threatening, hurtful, and of little technical merit. When a PIE/AAR policy is being developed, the following points (among others) should be considered:

- Participation should be broad and the input process inclusive.
- Adequate materials (audiovisual, written, etc.) should be prepared.
- The environment and process should be nonthreatening.
- The time frame for each element should be defined.
- A record should be made of the session and its conclusions.
- A follow-up process for applying the lessons learned should be established.

It is essential to make sure that lessons from incidents are integrated back into the training program, and it is even more critical to ensure that these lessons become part of properly implemented standard operating procedures (see sidebar above). The incident scene provides the most realistic training that any organization can experience. Failure to carefully scrutinize operations at the scene is a training opportunity missed.

Training resources

Professional development is a critical function for every fire and emergency services organization; it should be funded as a high-priority item through the department's annual operating budget. While there is no rule of thumb or best practice for identifying per capita annual spending on fire and emergency services training and education, it is important to recognize throughout the budget process the recurring cost of implementing the planned training program.

As with many endeavors, partnerships can provide access to vast training resources. Many jurisdictions run their own "fire academies" for recruits, but others partner successfully with community colleges or other agencies to provide basic training. Some fire and emergency service departments have found great success partnering with private industry to develop specialized training props and equipment. Some organizations, including state and federal agencies, provide grants to local fire and emergency service departments for conducting certain types of training or for obtaining facilities, equipment, and instructors.

Training curricula Training curricula to support fire and emergency services professional development are available from a broad range of sources. NFA develops curricula and delivers training on the National Emergency Training Center campus, as well as through state fire

Training Resources and Data Exchange (TRADE)

The Training Resources and Data Exchange (TRADE) program is a regionally based network designed to foster the exchange of fire-related training information and resources among federal, state, and local levels of government.

TRADE was initiated in 1984 to address the difficulties that state and local fire training systems were experiencing in disseminating quality training programs effectively. The essential components of the TRADE system are the ten regional networks that correspond to the existing federal regional boundaries. These networks provide a mechanism for the exchange of resources and materials within and among regions. Regional TRADE co-chairs, one selected from the state fire training systems and the other from the metropolitan fire services in each region, serve as the points of contact for both intraregional and interregional networking activities.

The objectives of TRADE are to

- Identify fire, rescue, and emergency medical service training needs at the regional level
- Identify and exchange training programs and resources within regions and, whenever possible, replicate those resources
- Provide to the National Fire Academy an annual assessment of fire training resource needs within the region, together with recommendations as to how TRADE can better support federal, state, and local fire training systems
- Identify national trends with an impact on fire-related training and education.

Source: U.S. Fire Administration, National Fire Academy, TRADE, usfa.dhs.gov/nfa/trade/index.shtm.

training agencies and academic institutions. Most state fire training and certification agencies maintain standardized course curricula for their programs. Some colleges and universities also deliver training programs and maintain curricula for that purpose. Nonprofit organizations such as the International Fire Service Training Association develop training curricula and supporting materials based on NFPA standards and best practices. Professional associations, including the IAFC, International Association of Fire Fighters, Fire Department Safety Officers Association (FDSOA), and International Society of Fire Service Instructors (ISFSI), also develop and deliver training for their members and others. Private firms and publishing houses offer a wide range of training curricula and course packages for almost any conceivable fire and emergency services training topic.

Training facilities and equipment Some fire and emergency service departments are able to build training/classroom space into fire stations or, for larger departments, a dedicated training facility or academy (see sidebar on page 262). For those that are not, classroom spaces can be found using partnerships with neighboring departments, local government agencies, community colleges, National Guard armories, and even private firms.

Safely and effectively conducting some fire and emergency services training also demands specialized facilities and equipment, such as a specialized burn prop (burn building) for conducting live-fire training evolutions (see Figure 9–11 on page 263). However, not every fire and emergency services department can afford such facilities, and many departments maintain robust training programs with limited access to specialized structures, props, and equipment. In many cases, specialized structures have been constructed through regional partnerships or are shared by organizations with different missions.

Several state fire training agencies deploy mobile live-fire training props to deliver a safe and effective training environment across a wide geographical area. Some local fire and emergency service departments have also embraced this concept, bringing training to their firefighters instead of bringing firefighters to the training site.

Training safely

Successful training programs have to recognize two important aspects of safety. First, the overall mission requires that all participants be trained and kept up-to-date in safe methods of accomplishing their tasks. But if learned safety behaviors are not continually reinforced,

National Fire Academy

The mission of the National Fire Academy (NFA) is to promote the professional development of the fire and emergency response community and its allied professionals. NFA supports state and local training organizations and develops, delivers, and manages educational and training programs that have a national focus and are outside the state and local training mission or exceed state and local capabilities because of cost or audience. NFA programs are designed to support the goals of the Department of Homeland Security (DHS) and the Federal Emergency Management Agency (FEMA) to help state and local response agencies prevent, mitigate, prepare for, and respond to local, regional, and national emergencies.

NFA develops curricula for management, executive development, emergency medical services, incident management, planning and information management, hazardous materials, emergency response to terrorism, arson prevention/detection, community risk reduction/fire prevention and protection, public education, and the National Response Framework (NRF)/National Incident Management System (NIMS). It provides training and education in classrooms at its Emmitsburg, Maryland, campus and elsewhere, as well as online.

Through the Fire and Emergency Services Higher Education program, NFA offers curricula for associate's, bachelor's, and graduate degree programs. It also encourages the inclusion of fire prevention and fire protection/detection technology and practices in the education and professional practices of architects, builders, city planners, and others engaged in the design and construction of buildings and structures, as well as of those in the emergency services community.

NFA coordinates with DHS/FEMA program offices to ensure that fire prevention and control activities are included in the agency's risk-based evaluation and risk-reduction programs. It also develops doctrine and training to support the implementation of the NRF/NIMS and the Incident Command System in emergency response, and it helps develop training and assistance in response to evolving fire and emergency issues and strategies and lessons learned.

NFA works with other DHS organizations, with public and private standards-making bodies, and with professional organizations to advance community risk reduction strategies. It also administers the Preparedness Leadership Institute, a program to train elected and politically appointed officials in their responsibilities for community risk reduction and response.

Photo by Adam K. Thiel

Source: Adapted from the website of the U.S. Fire Administration, National Fire Academy, usfa.dhs.gov/about/orgchart/nfa.shtm.

people will invariably compromise them. Accordingly, initial and subsequent training must contain the safety elements for the given subject every time it is taught.

Second, fire and emergency services training can be dangerous. Participants are often subjected to conditions similar to those found in real-world incidents. Training evolutions should be conducted with every effort made to ensure a safe learning environment, including proper student/instructor ratios, where students can make mistakes without suffering injury or death;

Figure 9-11 Specialized structures and props support safe and effective fire and emergency services training.

Photo by Adam K. Thiel

it is imperative that proper oversight and safety measures be in place during all training activities, even those involving experienced participants.

NFPA 1500, Standard on Fire Department Occupational Health and Safety Program (2007 ed.), outlines a comprehensive safety program for fire departments and in some states or provinces is the law. Several other NFPA standards are also very important for helping to ensure a safe training program:

- NFPA 1401, Recommended Practice for Fire Service Training Reports and Records (2006 ed.)
- NFPA 1402, Guide to Building Fire Service Training Centers (2007 ed.)
- NFPA 1403, Standard on Live Fire Training Evolutions (2007 ed.)
- NFPA 1451, Standard for a Fire Service Vehicle Operations Training Program (2007 ed.).

Additional resources are available from the ISFSI and the FDSOA. These organizations and many of their state affiliates concentrate on helping their members achieve training that is high in quality and safety.

Training records

The importance of maintaining thorough records of employee (career or volunteer) training cannot be overemphasized. A variety of commercially available software packages can be used to record training, or a simple paper-based system can be developed. Because records should reflect training given and received, one important factor cannot be overlooked when computer-based record systems are used: there must be some process, either within the software or in a parallel paper-based system, to register the acknowledgment (signature) of both the trainer and the trainee. Many court decisions have underscored the importance of this dual acknowledgment.

Training records for a given trainee should reflect more than just the titles of courses or sessions taken. Many courts have confirmed the need to record the course/session content. For instance, if an evening training session covers HAZMAT awareness, the department would be wise to list the table of contents from the course material or at least reference the title of the commercial curriculum being used.

Accurate and complete training records not only provide legal reference in disputes but also form the basis of a training history for every employee. Using good records, the training officer can easily schedule timely recertifications, required continuing education, and annual skill evaluations. Further, by examining records for groups of employees, he or she can readily discern gaps in the teaching of certain skills and knowledge.

Record keeping should also include program evaluations documenting participants' reactions to specific classes. Without candid (usually anonymous) evaluations of instructional quality, effectiveness cannot be ensured and continuous improvement is not possible.

Finally, records that substantiate the level and quality of training are required by insurance rating services and fire service accrediting authorities. The records may also form the basis for individual applications for certification and/or for reviews by promotional boards.

Training instructors

Instructors are the critical link for ensuring that all aspects of the training program are safely and effectively planned, delivered, recorded, and evaluated. Even the most well-conceived and comprehensive professional development program can fall apart if delivered by incompetent or uncaring instructors. It is also important to reiterate that training is a principal venue for maintaining, or changing, an organization's dominant culture. Instructors are, by definition, placed in positions of leadership, where they can heavily influence how department policies are perceived and carried out.

Training is too important for an organization's strength and sustainability to trust it to uncertified or unqualified instructors. State fire training and certification agencies maintain extensive programs to develop and maintain instructional quality through classes in educational methods, training program administration, safety, and topic-specific "train-the-trainer" courses that help instructors stay current with ever-changing standards and best practices. Allowing uncertified instructors to plan or conduct training evolutions opens the department to substantial risk and potential legal liability.

Beyond instructor training and certification programs administered by state entities and local departments, the ISFSI offers a professional credential for fire and emergency service instructors. On the basis of a portfolio describing relevant life experience, education, and training, the ISFSI board of directors will confer such designations as master fire instructor (MFI), professional fire instructor (PFI), and expert fire instructor (EFI). More information on this program is available through the ISFSI website, isfsi.org.

Education

There is perhaps nothing more critical to the future of the fire and emergency services than embracing the value of higher education for developing the next generation of fire service professionals, both career and volunteer. One way of distinguishing education from training is that education teaches students not just *what* to learn but also *how* to learn. The ultimate aim of higher education is to develop critical thinking and reasoning skills that underpin the ability to appreciate different perspectives.

The basic formula for higher education has developed over many years and is reflected in the general educational curriculum of most colleges and universities. Basic reading, writing, math, and research skills are an essential foundation for higher-order learning in any academic discipline. An appreciation of the physical and social sciences, philosophy, and the arts is also considered critical for undergraduate students. This basic foundation is common and important to all professions, the fire and emergency services included.

In most colleges and universities, a student cannot advance to a specific degree program/track until he or she has completed general education prerequisites, with other general courses required before graduation, regardless of academic specialty. In the twenty-first century, higher education is also concerned with civic engagement and service learning, professional and academic ethics, readiness for graduate educational endeavors, and participation in our global society. The foundation provided by any regionally accredited academic institution should be sufficient preparation for pursuing fire and emergency services professional development.

Higher education institutions are turning toward the elaboration of specific core competencies for their students. This approach often goes beyond traditional coursework to include other experiences, such as service-based learning, internships or cooperative educa-

Mesa Community College/Mesa Fire Department CONNECTOR Program

The CONNECTOR Program was developed in 1998 as a partnership between Mesa Community College and the Mesa (Arizona) Fire Department. The goal was to design and implement a program that could serve as a resource for the fire department as well as a service learning site for the community college students.

The Mesa Fire Department responds to many 911 calls that are not of an emergency nature but that bring to light needs for social services that are beyond the scope of the department's expertise and time. Volunteers are trained to recognize these special needs and access agency resources to assist the citizens.

CONNECTOR volunteers can earn credit through the Service Learning program at Mesa Community College, whose mission is to integrate academic study with active service.

Source: Mesa Community College, CONNECTOR PROGRAM, mc.maricopa.edu/dept/d12/fsc/connector/index.html.

tion placements, and participation in extracurricular activities/organizations. Emphasizing competency is particularly important in the fire and emergency services since the goal of professional development is the application of knowledge on the job (versus theory building or pure research).

Educational partnerships are a major opportunity for fire and emergency service organizations. Partnering with a local community college to provide undergraduate-level courses using "firefighter-friendly" locations and schedules can go a long way toward facilitating firefighters' participation in professional development. These partnerships can also provide benefits in terms of recruiting volunteers and employees.

Undergraduate general education curricula are typically prescribed by colleges and universities. Beyond the basic general education curriculum that is common to all undergraduate students, most degree programs require a "core" set of courses that place all students on an equal footing for the remainder of their education. The FESHE model curricula for associate's and bachelor's degree programs in fire sciences follow this same approach. After completing a common core, students can specialize in a certain aspect of their degree program by choosing relevant electives.[4]

Graduate education in the fire and emergency services can take several forms. Some colleges and universities offer graduate degrees, certificates, or concentrations in fire and emergency service leadership, management, or administration (Figure 9–12). A number of other graduate programs can also be relevant to various aspects of managing fire and emergency service

Photo by Adam K. Thiel

Figure 9–12 Graduate students participate in a master's-level fire service administration course.

departments. Given the competencies required of chief fire officers at the executive level, perhaps the best preparation is a master's degree in public administration (MPA) or public policy (MPP). The MPA provides academic preparation tailored to managing public and nonprofit organizations and is the de facto standard for city and county managers; MPPs are similar in scope. A master's degree in business administration (MBA) contains a similar blend of courses, although the public environment is different from the world of private firms.

Closely tied to higher education for professional development is the need for research capacity in the fire and emergency services field. Developing theories and testing their application through rigorous empirical research is the foundation of any profession. But high-quality academic research is sorely limited in the fire and emergency services, and this lack of research hampers the creation of best practices and effective doctrine. As professional development increases its reach through the fire and emergency services, it is expected that more research will follow.

Experience

The value of experience in the overall professional development of fire and emergency services personnel at all levels cannot be overstated. Historically, however, the word *experience* is often conflated with tenure or "time on the job." While seniority generally offers more opportunities for exposure to different challenges, perhaps a better focus is on the experiences accumulated by a firefighter during his or her tenure in the department. For example, if two new firefighters are given different assignments—one to a busy fire company and one to a slow fire company—after one year they will probably have had very different experiences. Similarly, a firefighter who takes advantage of opportunities to work in staff assignments, participate on committees and task forces, become involved in labor groups and professional associations, or complete administrative tasks is collecting relevant experiences for a move to the supervisory level.

In the wildland fire community, the value of experience is addressed through the use of taskbooks documenting preparation for specific roles and responsibilities. To achieve the next level of qualification, an individual must not only pass the appropriate certified training course(s) but also demonstrate competence under real-world conditions (during actual incidents or exercises/simulations). How long it will take each person to demonstrate proficiency in all required tasks depends on each person's exposure to various experiences, not just the time spent at a certain level.

The true value of experience is in converting theory to practice. Experiences provide firefighters with opportunities to apply what they have learned, through training and education, in real-world applications. This application of theory to practice is essential for knowledge development and enriches the overall continuous learning experience.

The value of experience is obvious when thinking about the practical skills that firefighters and other emergency service workers use in their daily jobs. Attacking a fire under "controlled" conditions in a specially constructed burn building is a close simulation but cannot substitute for experience under actual fire conditions. Similarly, firefighters gain proficiency across the whole range of firefighting skills—from aerial ladder operations to forcible entry, search and rescue, water supply, etc.—as they gain experience under both simulated and actual conditions. It is important to note again that a fire is a fire, and firefighters can be injured or killed during training evolutions unless proper safety and accountability procedures are followed to the letter.

Less obvious as firefighters advance through their careers is the importance of experience beyond the fire and emergency scene as a basis for developing leadership and management skills. For a model system to aid leadership development through a diversity of experiences, one can look at the U.S. military and its practice—in all branches—of rotating officers through successive one- to two-year staff assignments, interspersed with their operational assignments. The military has long recognized the importance of exposing officers to different types of experiences as they rise through the ranks. This practice helps develop the complete set of experiences these officers will need as they ascend the ranks from lieutenant to general officer. Just as the most proficient soldier may not be the best choice for a general, so might the best firefighter, without exposure to appropriate experiences, not be the best choice for a fire chief.

These experiences can take many forms, from participating in committees and workgroups to engaging in community service activities, becoming involved in a local union or labor group, doing ride-alongs or taking detail assignments with other agencies (e.g., law enforcement, public works, human resources, management and budget, or emergency management), and gaining specialty training/certification in various aspects of the department's mission (e.g., hazardous materials, technical rescue, training, wildland firefighting, communications).

Self-development

Self-development is sometimes considered part of experience, but there is a subtle distinction that is very important to aspiring fire and emergency service managers. The process of self-development centers around personal awareness, attributes, attitudes, and abilities. While training, education, and experiences can help foster self-development, success in this aspect of professional development demands an ongoing commitment to introspection, self-awareness, and physical/mental preparation. The dimensions of self-development articulated in the IAFC's *Officer Development Handbook* include health/fitness, physical ability, career mapping, communication, interpersonal dynamics/skills, diversity, ethics, legal issues, technology, and local and/or contemporary hazards/issues.

Although measuring success in self-development can be somewhat subjective, demonstrable progress in this area is no less important than the relatively easily measured achievements in training, education, and experience. A firefighter can pursue self-development throughout his or her career by participating in seminars, self-evaluation processes, professional associations, peer groups, performance appraisals, and mentoring. Trusted peers, supervisors, and subordinates are perhaps the best sources of feedback on self-development, provided the firefighter is willing to ask and can learn from candid responses.

Mentoring, formal or informal, is an essential component of the self-development process. Mentoring often occurs informally, with mentors and mentees developing their relationship while serving together in a particular assignment, on committees, or doing work for professional/trade associations. Some organizations have processes for identifying promising candidates for succession who are then "groomed" to accept increasingly responsible assignments and positions.

For an organization seeking sustained high performance, it is probably not enough for mentoring to occur by accident. Formal mentoring programs can be developed to assist firefighters, from the time they first enter the department, by assigning properly trained mentors who demonstrate the positive qualities sought by the organization for its employees. (It is important to realize that mentoring will occur in the absence of a formalized program, but informally selected mentors may not possess the attributes valued by the organization.)

Professional development recognition

Recognition of a firefighter's professional development efforts can take several forms. Many departments issue certificates of completion or rely on their regional/state training entity to do so. Some departments require professional development for promotion to supervisory ranks or to be given certain special assignments. Whether professional development is completed for a specific purpose or simply to maintain competence, awards and recognition for those availing themselves of training and educational opportunities send a positive message about the importance of professional development to the organization.

Certification and qualification

In the fire and emergency services, it is often said that "every day is a training day." While all training is valuable, not all training opportunities are created alike. Formal training conducted to meet job performance requirements (JPRs) and based on established standards, such as those maintained by NFPA or promulgated by state/federal agencies and academic institutions, represents the highest level of fire and emergency services training and typically leads to certification, qualification, and/or credentialing.

Usually a student is certified after completing a prescribed course of instruction and successfully passing an objective examination(s) demonstrating the ability to meet applicable

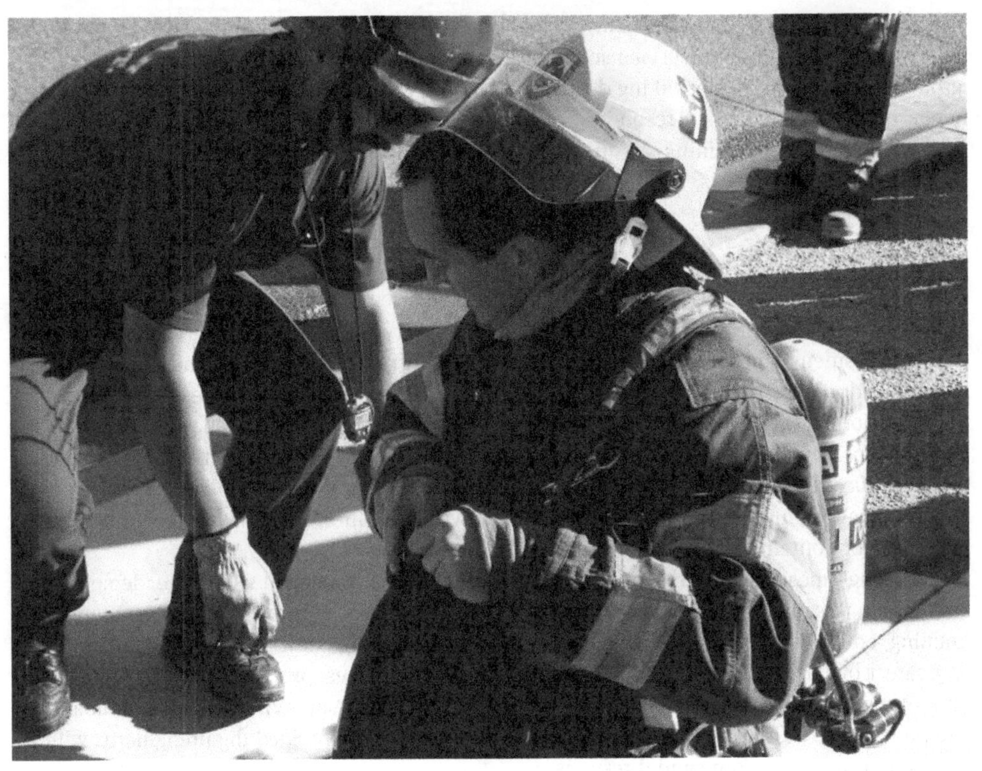

Figure 9-13 Firefighters must pass written and practical tests to obtain certification.

Photo by Adam K. Thiel

JPRs (Figure 9–13). Once a certification is earned, it may be good forever, or it may require periodic retraining and recertification.

A number of commercial entities provide instruments to test both the skills and the knowledge specified by the standards. And many states and provinces provide the testing process and tools through an agency that has been legally authorized to provide them. For example, most states provide Firefighter I/II training and certification.

Some training organizations differentiate between certification and qualification. Certification generally occurs as described above, while qualification must be achieved and maintained through certain professional experiences and/or ongoing training in specific topical areas.

Accreditation

As noted, when standards are used to specify job performance requirements, a system of evaluation and certification testing is also used. This process, in turn, may be accredited by the International Fire Service Accreditation Congress and/or the National Board on Fire Service Professional Qualifications (the ProBoard). Accreditation reasonably ensures that the certification process is conducted in a manner that is fair, open, relevant, and in accordance with the applicable standards. It is important to note that accreditation applies to the training or education program and not to the individual receiving a certification or degree from an accredited provider.

Credentialing

Professional credentialing of fire and emergency services personnel is evolving at all levels of government in the United States. Perhaps the best model of national credentialing that currently exists in the United States is the National Wildfire Coordinating Group's "Red Card" program mentioned earlier in this chapter. Responders from throughout the United States and other countries who are credentialed under the Red Card model can be assembled as part of an effective incident organization even when they have never worked together in the past!

Since it was established in 2002, the U.S. Department of Homeland Security has pursued several initiatives aimed at credentialing first responders across the country.

National Capital Region First Responder Authentication Cards

The Office of National Capital Region Coordination (NCRC) is coordinating a major initiative to develop a "smart" identity card system for emergency responders. These smart cards would enable first responders from across the region to quickly and easily access government buildings and reservations in the event of a terrorist attack or other disaster. The initiative is designed to remedy access problems such as those encountered by state and local emergency officials responding to the 9/11 attack on the Pentagon.

In February 2006, NCRC coordinated a multiagency demonstration ("Winter Fox") to test the interoperability and usability of this credentialing trust model through simulated emergency incidents at federal, state, and local facilities, including the Pentagon, a Virginia state facility, a port controlled by the state of Maryland, and a checkpoint in a Maryland county. For the demonstration, it issued approximately 500 First Responder Authentication Cards (FRACs) to senior federal, state, and county public safety officials. Standardized electronic identity verification was required for passing various levels of perimeter security at all demonstration sites regardless of one's agency affiliation. As a result, incident commanders requiring a certain emergency support function or sector qualification could readily determine if anyone at the scene met the requirement.

In addition, use of the FRACs assisted incident commanders in preparing after-action reports and assessments by enabling them to electronically reconstruct the time and attendance of each individual within the incident area upon entry and departure. These reports were electronically transmitted real-time via satellite communications to national, state, and local emergency operations centers, including Northern Command Headquarters (NORTHCOM) in Colorado, Pentagon Emergency Operations Center, NORTHCOM NCR (National Capital Region) Joint Operations Center, and Maryland Emergency Management Agency.

Source: Adapted from U.S. Department of Homeland Security, First Responder Authentication Credentials, dhs.gov/xfrstresp/standards/editorial_0849.shtm.

While the bulk of fire and emergency services credentialing remains at the state and local levels, fire and emergency services personnel across the United States are covered by the training and certification requirements of NIMS (see sidebar below). NIMS contains a number of training requirements for employees at all levels of government, in any organization that might be called upon to participate in an event of national significance.

National Incident Management System/Incident Command System (NIMS/ICS) training

Q: Who has to take NIMS and ICS training?

Stakeholders will define the emergency management/response personnel within the jurisdiction, agency, or organization who require ongoing training. This includes all emergency service–related disciplines, such as emergency medical services, hospitals, public health, fire service, law enforcement, public works/utilities, skilled support personnel, and other emergency management response, support and volunteer personnel, as follows:

Entry level:

- FEMA IS-700: NIMS, An Introduction
- ICS-100: Introduction to ICS or equivalent

First line, single resource, field supervisors:

- IS-700.A, ICS-100, and ICS-200: Basic ICS or its equivalent

Middle management: Strike team leaders, division supervisors, emergency operations center (EOC) staff, etc.:

- IS-700.A, IS-800.B NRF, ICS-100, ICS-200, and ICS-300

Command and general staff; area, emergency, and EOC managers:

- IS-700.A, IS-800.B NRF, ICS-100, ICS-200, ICS-300, and ICS-400

Source: Adapted from Federal Emergency Management Agency, fema.gov/emergency/nims/FAQ.shtm#item9.
Note: IS = independent study; NRF = National Response Framework.

Professional designation

The Center for Public Safety Excellence (CPSE), formerly known as the Commission on Fire Accreditation International, developed the chief fire officer (CFO) designation to help advance professionalism through its Commission on Professional Credentialing. The CFO credential is obtained through an extensive application process in which candidates demonstrate competency in various areas by detailing their training, education, experience, technical competencies, professional contributions, association memberships, and community involvement in a portfolio or application. The credential must be renewed every three years by demonstrating continual learning and self-development. CPSE also manages chief medical officer (CMO) and fire officer (FO) designation programs.[5]

The Institution of Fire Engineers (IFE) was founded in 1918 as an international organization to uphold professional standards within the fire service. Based in the United Kingdom and with branches in thirty-nine countries, including the United States (ife-usa.org) and Canada (ife.ca), the IFE confers professional recognition according to examination, portfolio, and reciprocity with other organizations, including CPSE. The U.S. branch currently nominates members to the grades of student, graduate (GIFireE), associate (AIFireE), member (MIFireE), and fellow (FIFireE).

NFA's Executive Fire Officer Program (EFOP) also results in a professional credential for graduates who complete all requirements of its four-year, four-course sequence, including four applied research projects. The program is designed to provide fire officers and key leaders with executive-level knowledge and skills to lead contemporary fire and emergency service organizations. EFOP graduates earn the EFO designation that is often used as a preferred qualification for chief officer recruiting nationwide. Other EFOP goals are to give participants an understanding of

- The need to transform fire and emergency service organizations from being reactive to being proactive, with an emphasis on leadership development, prevention, and risk reduction
- The need for fire and emergency service organizations to reflect the diversity of America's communities
- The value of research and its application to the profession
- The value of lifelong learning.[6]

Summary

Not all fire and emergency services personnel can, should, or want to advance through the entire career progression from recruit to fire chief. While promotion to the top job is sometimes considered the ultimate goal of professional development, it is equally important to provide all employees with opportunities for continual training, education, experience, and self-development, especially those who remain in their roles for a long time. These members are the backbone of any successful organization since they provide continuity and highly skilled technical expertise where it matters most: on the front line.

A successful fire and emergency services department benefits from the diversity of its members' training, education, and experiences as well as from those members' different roles and responsibilities within the overall organization. There are few fire chiefs who remain as proficient in all the basic firefighting skills as they were when their daily work included pulling hose lines and throwing ladders. Similarly, few firefighters would find themselves comfortable in, or prepared for, the fire chief's daily work environment. The balance between specialists and generalists is an important one for any organization; the fire and emergency services are no exception.

The knowledge-based economy of the twenty-first century places a premium on training, education, experience, and self-development. Many fire and emergency service departments reflect this trend by offering pay incentives, tuition assistance programs, and other means for helping employees achieve their career goals. Investing in the success of individual employees through creating and maintaining a robust professional development program is essential for the overall strength of every contemporary fire and emergency services organization.

Notes

1. See the U.S. Fire Administration (USFA), Federal Emergency Management Agency, "Interoperability for Professional Development: The National Professional Development Model and Matrix," usfa.dhs.gov/nfa/higher_ed/feshe/feshe_interoperability.shtm.
2. International Association of Fire Chiefs (IAFC), *Officer Development Handbook,* 2nd ed. (Fairfax, Va.: IAFC, 2011).
3. International Association of Fire Chiefs Foundation, *Wingspread V: Statements of National Significance to the Fire Service and to Those Served* (conference report, Atlanta, Ga., April 2006), 8, nationalfireheritagecenter.com/2006Wingspread.pdf.
4. See the Fire and Emergency Services Higher Education (FESHE) website (usfa.dhs.gov/nfa/higher_ed/feshe/feshe_model.shtm) for a list of courses in the FESHE model curricula for associate's and bachelor's degrees, including the National Fire Academy's Degrees at a Distance Program courses available online, and in other formats, through several regionally accredited colleges and universities.
5. Further information on professional credentialing by the Center for Public Safety Excellence can be found at publicsafetyexcellence.org.
6. USFA, Executive Fire Office Program, usfa.dhs.gov/nfa/efop/index.shtm.

CHAPTER 10

Regulations, Standards, and Issues of Liability

J. Curt Varone, Esq.

This chapter provides an understanding of

- The ambiguities and interrelationships among the terms *standard, code,* and *regulation*
- The history and function of fire protection codes
- The impact of Occupational Safety and Health Administration regulations on the fire and emergency service
- The role of the National Fire Protection Association in creating standards
- The most important legal issues confronting fire and emergency service managers
- Strategies for reducing legal liabilities associated with delivery of fire and emergency services.

Since the late 1960s and early 1970s, regulations and standards have become integral to the day-to-day operations of the fire and emergency services. They are routinely used to specify apparatus, protective clothing, and equipment; address occupational health and safety; guide public education programs; and enhance professionalism. In addition, they serve as a mechanism to capture best practices, institutionalize knowledge, and effect positive and lasting change.

The terms *regulations, standards,* and *codes* are frequently used synonymously—and often improperly. The problem is that each term has multiple meanings, which creates the potential for ambiguity. In addition, common usage has blurred the distinctions. Let us start by defining each term.

The term *regulation* has two relevant meanings to fire and emergency service officers. First, some administrative agencies are authorized to create laws, called "regulations," through a process known as rulemaking. Once issued, these regulations are legally binding and enforceable. For example, a federal agency such as the Occupational Safety and Health Administration (OSHA) is authorized to create regulations governing workplace health and safety.

The second meaning of the term *regulation* refers to internal personnel rules and policies commonly found within an organization such as a police or fire department. While fire and emergency service department regulations may be enforceable against the members of the department, they do not carry the force of law among the general public and are not to be confused with the regulations that are created by an administrative agency.

The term *standard* is often confused with *regulation.* In its truest sense, a standard is a voluntary guideline or recommendation that does not carry the force of law. Standards may be created by governmental agencies, by private organizations such as the National Fire Protection Association (NFPA), or by partnerships between government and private organizations.

The term *standard* is confusing for several reasons. First, some standards are adopted into law and thus have the full effect and weight of law. For example, many states have adopted NFPA 1, Fire Code, into law as the state fire code; in these states, NFPA 1 carries the weight of law. In other words, in some states NFPA 1 is both a standard *and* a law. Second, OSHA refers to many of its safety requirements as standards. Hence, we have standards that are also laws and laws that are referred to as standards.

To further complicate matters, standards and compilations of standards may also be referred to as "codes." For example, the National Electrical Code is a standard produced by NFPA. However, the term *code* is also used to identify a compilation of laws, such as the *Code of Federal Regulations* (CFR) or the *United States Code,* a compilation of statutes enacted by Congress.

Despite the potential for confusion, fire and emergency service leaders need to know what standards and codes have been adopted by state or local authorities so that they know what they are required to comply with. This chapter surveys the implications and impact of the regulations and standards that are of greatest general relevance to the fire and emergency services, and explains the liability of a fire and emergency services organization for negligence in carrying out its duties.

Fire protection codes

Fire protection and building codes go back at least as far as Hammurabi, the law-making Babylonian ruler who reigned from approximately 1792 to 1750 BC. The *Code of Hammurabi* stated: "In the case of collapse of a defective building, the architect is to be put to death if the owner is killed by accident; and the architect's son, if the owner's son loses his life."

Obviously, society no longer endorses Hammurabi's ancient law of retaliation but nevertheless seeks to prevent accidents and the loss of life and property. From this objective have

This chapter is a revised and updated version of Chapter 13, "Regulations, Standards, and Issues of Liability." by Stephen N. Foley and Maureen Brodoff in the 2002 edition of this volume. Portions of this new chapter are derived from two publications that Chief Varone has written: *Legal Considerations for Fire and Emergency Services* (Delmar Cengage Learning, 2006) and *Fire Officer's Legal Handbook* (Delmar Cengage Learning, 2007). ICMA owns the copyright to the material as it is expressed in this chapter.

The origin of modern fire safety codes and standards

Modern fire safety codes and standards trace their origin to the development of automatic sprinklers in the nineteenth century. From the beginning, sprinklers performed well as extinguishing devices but were installed in so many different ways by different installers that their reliability was uncertain.

In 1895, a small group of concerned citizens representing sprinkler and fire insurance interests gathered in Boston, Massachusetts, to discuss these inconsistencies. They knew that nine radically different standards for piping size and sprinkler spacing could be found within one hundred miles of the city. This plumber's nightmare had to be resolved.

The group, which called itself the National Fire Protection Association (NFPA), eventually created a standard for the uniform installation of sprinklers. This standard, which would become NFPA 13, Standard for the Installation of Sprinkler Systems, was NFPA's first fire safety document. Today NFPA maintains some three hundred fire safety codes and standards, and they are in widespread use around the world.

Source: Adapted with permission from "Codes and Standards for a Safer World," copyright © 2009, National Fire Protection Association, Quincy, Mass. All rights reserved. At nfpa.org/assets/files/PDF/CodesStandards/CodesStandardsBrochure2009.pdf.

evolved not only contemporary life safety and building codes, but also standards for fire prevention, fire protection, fire suppression, and firefighter occupational health and safety. Over the past twenty years, health and safety, along with fire service organization and deployment, have become a driving force for the development of and revisions to fire and emergency service standards and regulations.

Complying with codes, standards, and regulations has become an integral part of managing the fire and emergency services. Accordingly, fire service managers and their governing authorities need to stay abreast of these requirements and know how to participate in the process of developing and reviewing them.

In the United States, codes, standards, and regulations related to fire and emergency services developed through the combined efforts of federal government agencies and organizations such as NFPA, the American National Standards Institute (ANSI), and the American Conference of Governmental Industrial Hygienists.

One of the primary agencies with which the fire service interacts is OSHA within the Department of Labor (DOL) (see the sidebar on the next page on federal and state OSHAs). Other agencies whose rules and regulations bear on the fire and emergency services are the National Institute for Occupational Safety and Health (NIOSH); the Environmental Protection Agency (EPA); the Centers for Disease Control and Prevention (CDC); the Department of Homeland Security (DHS) (which includes the Federal Emergency Management Agency and the U.S. Fire Administration [USFA]); and the Departments of Transportation, Justice, and Defense.

The next two sections of this chapter describe, respectively, the regulations of OSHA and NIOSH that are most relevant to the management of fire and emergency services; they also discuss EPA and CDC regulations. Thereafter, the chapter reviews the most prominent NFPA standards that apply to fire and emergency service organizations. It concludes with an overview of the legal issues associated with regulations, standards, and codes and the liability of fire and emergency service organizations for negligence.

Occupational Safety and Health Administration regulations

Congress created OSHA when it passed the Occupational Safety and Health Act (OSH Act) of 1970 (29 U.S.C. 651 *et seq.*). The act made OSHA responsible for promulgating and enforcing regulations to protect the health and safety of U.S. workers. OSHA regulations address a broad range of health and safety issues related to the fire and emergency services, such as hearing conservation, respiratory protection, infection control, confined space operations, and hazardous materials.

OSHA develops and revises its regulations through a comprehensive public review and hearing process in which the public is encouraged to participate. Proposed revisions and information about hearings are published in the *Federal Register.*

Federal and state Occupational Safety and Health Administrations

The jurisdiction of the federal Occupational Safety and Health Administration (OSHA) is limited to private sector employers and certain federal agencies. Federal OSHA has no jurisdiction to investigate or cite state or local agencies, including municipal fire departments. It can enforce OSHA regulations only with regard to private sector employers and nonexempt federal agencies.

Many states adopt federal OSHA standards and assign a state agency, such as the state department of labor, to enforce them over state and municipal employers. Enforcement varies greatly state to state. Some states take a hard-line approach with public sector employers, conducting formal investigations into alleged violations, issuing citations when violations are found, and levying fines against cities, towns, and state agencies. Other states choose instead to rely on political and bureaucratic mechanisms to ensure compliance.

OSHA encourages states to take over OSHA enforcement and offers a financial incentive for them to do so. Should a state choose to assume full responsibility for enforcing OSHA regulations, it must agree to enforce them over public and private sector employers to the same extent that federal OSHA does over private sector employers. In exchange, the federal government will reimburse the state up to 50 percent of the salary costs for state inspectors, and the state can keep whatever money in fines that it collects. To qualify for such a federal subsidy, a state must submit a plan to OSHA explaining how it will enforce federal OSHA regulations. Twenty-one states and Puerto Rico have accepted the federal government's offer; these states are referred to as Approved-Plan OSHA States or "State Plan States."[1]

Federal OSHA has also offered states a financial incentive to adopt a public sector-only enforcement model; under this arrangement, the federal government subsidizes some of the costs associated with enforcement, and the Public-Sector Approved-Plan states must agree to enforce federal OSHA regulations over state and local employers in a manner that is at least as effective as federal enforcement of OSHA requirements over private sector employers.

States that are neither Approved-Plan OSHA States nor Public-Sector Approved-Plan States, but that nevertheless enforce federal OSHA regulations over public sector employers, are referred to as Non-Approved Plan OSHA States.

Fire and emergency service leaders need to be aware of the status of their states as Approved-Plan, Public-Sector Approved-Plan, or Non-Approved Plan States. In addition, where a department sends apparatus and personnel on mutual aid into an adjoining state, the OSHA ramifications of that state should be researched and understood.

1 The states and territories that had state OSHA plans as of 2009 are Alaska, Arizona, California, Connecticut, Hawaii, Indiana, Iowa, Kentucky, Maryland, Michigan, Minnesota, Nevada, New Mexico, New York, North Carolina, Oregon, Puerto Rico, South Carolina, Tennessee, Utah, Vermont, Virgin Islands, Virginia, Washington, and Wyoming. In California, Connecticut, and New York, the plans apply only to state and local government employees.

As explained in the sidebar above, federal OSHA has no direct enforcement authority over state and local governments. Private industry, including private sector fire and emergency service organizations, are subject to OSHA requirements either directly or through state-plan programs. However, in Approved-Plan States, public sector employers, including municipal fire departments, must comply with all OSHA regulations, and the OSH Act requires that these states establish and maintain an effective and comprehensive occupational safety and health program for all public employees that is as effective as the state's program covering private employees. All fire and emergency services department employees (whether state, county, or local) in any of the states or territories where such an agreement is in effect therefore have the protection of the minimally acceptable safety and health standards promulgated by federal OSHA. Individual states may provide more stringent standards if they wish.

General duty clause

While much has been written about the OSH Act, at its core are two important duties placed upon employers. First, employers must comply with all duly promulgated OSHA regulations. Second, employers must maintain a workplace that is free from recognized hazards. While the duty to comply with OSHA regulations is clear, well-known, and seemingly burdensome, it is the second duty—usually referred to as the general duty—that places a more significant burden on employers.

The general duty requirement obligates employers to ensure that a workplace is safe even where there are no specific OSHA regulations. An obvious example of a general duty violation occurs when an employer fails to investigate the cause of a worker's injury and to take remedial steps to prevent a recurrence. Another example would be the failure to ensure that personnel comply with a manufacturer's safety instruction for the use of dangerous equipment.

Probably the most important consideration that fire and emergency service leaders need to understand regarding the general duty requirement is that the failure to comply with a nationally recognized safety standard applicable to a certain industry could be considered a violation. An industry-wide safety standard is evidence that industry experts have identified a hazard and determined that precautions are necessary. For the fire and emergency services, the failure to comply with an NFPA standard, such as NFPA 1500 (see page 282), could give rise to a general duty clause violation.

Hazardous waste and materials (29 CFR 1910.120 and companion EPA regulation 40 CFR 311)

There are two sets of regulations applicable to fire and emergency services personnel who respond to hazardous materials (HAZMAT) incidents: 29 CFR 1910.120, issued by OSHA, and 40 CFR 311, issued by EPA. These two regulations specify minimal initial training levels (see the sidebar below), with annual documented training thereafter. Personnel who are assigned to supervisory positions at incidents should be trained in the specific positions of responsibility, such as incident commander, sector/division/group officer, HAZMAT safety officer, and other functional positions within an incident management system. Proper training in and use of personal protective clothing and equipment, and annual medical evaluations for responders, are also required.

In the twenty-five OSHA-plan states, the state OSHAs are responsible for enforcing the two regulations; in the other states, EPA is responsible for enforcement.

The two regulations are complemented by two NFPA standards. NFPA 472, Standard for Competence of Responders to Hazardous Materials/Weapons of Mass Destruction Incidents (2008 ed.), outlines the professional competencies in specific terms for both private and public sector employees who respond to HAZMAT incidents. NFPA 473, Standard for Competencies

Definitions of responder levels at hazardous materials incidents

There are four levels of responder at hazardous materials (HAZMAT) incidents: awareness, operational, technician, and command.

Awareness level First responders who, in the course of their normal duties, can be first on the scene of an emergency involving hazardous materials are expected to recognize the presence of hazardous materials, protect themselves, call for trained personnel, and secure the area.

Operational level First responders who, as part of the initial response to an incident, respond to actual or potential releases of hazardous materials for the purpose of protecting nearby persons, the environment, or property from the effects of the release should be trained to respond defensively to control the release from a safe distance and keep it from spreading. NFPA 1001, Standard for Fire Fighter Professional Qualifications (2008 ed.), requires all firefighters to be trained to the operational level.

Technician level (HAZMAT technicians) Those who respond to actual or potential releases of hazardous materials for the purpose of controlling the release are expected to use specialized chemical protective clothing and specialized control equipment.

Command level The incident commander is responsible for all decisions relating to management of the incident and is in charge of the incident site.

It is important to note that it is the employer's inherent responsibility to train and certify all personnel. The employer cannot avoid this responsibility by using outside entities to certify personnel because, in addition to any outside certifications that an employee possesses, the employee must be certified by the employer as being capable of safely performing the duties required by that employer.

for EMS Personnel Responding to Hazardous Materials/Weapons of Mass Destruction Incidents (2008 ed.), applies these same criteria to public and private sector emergency medical service (EMS) personnel. If a jurisdiction uses a third-party EMS provider or has a third-service rescue crew/squad (a contractual ambulance service) that responds to these incidents, the personnel must be trained and able to operate within the jurisdiction's incident command system. If a fire service is providing emergency medical capabilities at incident scenes, it has probably addressed the issues dealt with by NFPA 473, Standard for Competencies for EMS Personnel Responding to Hazardous Materials/Weapons of Mass Destruction Incidents (2008 ed.).

Respiratory protection (29 CFR 1910.134)

OSHA initially promulgated the respiratory protection regulation in the early 1970s to regulate the training, staffing, use, and medical evaluations of personnel assigned to use respiratory protection. Over the years, with equipment and procedural improvements, revisions and clarifications became necessary, and the regulation was reissued on January 8, 1998. It applies to employers whose employees use respiratory protection because of occupational exposures or unknown atmospheres. Other applicable standards that are referenced in the OSHA regulation are ANSI Z87.1, Practice for Occupational and Educational Eye and Face Protection; ANSI Z88.5, Practices for Respiratory Protection for the Fire Service; and ANSI/CGA (Compressed Gas Association) G7.1, Commodity Specification for Air.

Also referenced in the respiratory protection regulation are several NFPA standards listed here in accordance with their most current editions as of July 2011: NFPA 1500, Standard on Fire Department Occupational Safety and Health Program (2007 ed.) (discussed on page 282); NFPA 1981, Standard on Open-Circuit Self-Contained Breathing Apparatus (SCBA) for Emergency Services (2007 ed.); NFPA 1404, Standard for Fire Service Respiratory Protection Training (2006 ed.); and NFPA 600, Standard on Industrial Fire Brigades (2010 ed.).

Three important safety issues associated with this regulation have come to the forefront of firefighter health and safety. These issues are (1) the "two-in/two-out" requirement, (2) the requirement for maintaining communication and accountability between interior and exterior personnel, and (3) annual medical examinations and their compatibility with NFPA 1582, Standard on Comprehensive Occupational Medical Program for Fire Departments (2007 ed.) (discussed on page 285.)

The two-in/two-out requirement has had a major impact on many departments' practices regarding deployment and organization at an incident scene (see Figure 10–1). OSHA is very

Figure 10-1 The two-in/two-out requirement demands that fire departments assemble sufficient resources on scene to provide for the safety and effectiveness of emergency operations in a hazardous atmosphere.

Photo by Adam K. Thiel

clear about the need to assemble a minimum of four personnel before any personnel can enter an atmosphere that is actually or potentially *immediately dangerous to life and health* (IDLH). First surfacing as a fire service issue in the 1992 edition of NFPA 1500, the regulation was revised and clarified in the 1997 edition. Since then, OSHA has again revised its requirement to clearly align with the intent of NFPA 1500: that personnel at an incident scene should be deployed safely and efficiently.

The second issue concerns the ability of persons outside the IDLH atmosphere to keep track of personnel inside. In the fire service, this issue has come to be known as accountability. An important aspect of accountability is communications. Personnel on the interior of an IDLH atmosphere must have a means of communicating with personnel on the exterior in the event that help is needed. One option is for the interior and exterior personnel to remain within visual or voice contact. Although the OSHA regulation does not specifically allow for radios to be used as tools for direct communication between personnel, NFPA 1500 does, and OSHA generally defers to that standard for firefighting operations.

The last issue involves the OSHA requirement that personnel who must wear respiratory protection pass medical examinations. OSHA's medical regulations, which provide a checklist to be completed by an occupational physician, are considerably less comprehensive than those contained in NFPA 1582, the specific requirements of which are discussed later in this chapter.

Fire brigades (29 CFR 1910.156)

The term *fire brigade* means different things to different people. Federal OSHA uses the term to refer to an employer-sponsored response team capable of responding to fires and emergencies within the employer's facility. In the United Kingdom, the term is used to describe a municipal fire department. NFPA, however, differentiates between fire departments, industrial fire departments, and fire brigades. An industrial fire department is a private fire department that provides rescue, fire suppression, and related services to an industrial location, whereas an industrial fire brigade is defined as "an organized group of employees within an industrial occupancy who are knowledgeable, trained, and skilled in at least basic fire fighting operations, and whose full-time occupation might or might not be the provision of fire suppression and related activities for their employer."[1] NFPA 600, Standard on Industrial Fire Brigades, covers health and safety issues for industrial fire brigades, whereas NFPA 1500 covers the same issues for fire departments, including industrial fire departments.

In many respects, the needs of industrial fire brigades and industrial fire departments are not far different from the needs of local fire departments. The primary difference between the two is that an industrial fire organization deals only with conditions and hazards that exist within a given facility, generally one that is privately owned and operated. Although these site-specific hazards can and do represent the same degree of hazard to both industrial fire brigade members and local government firefighters, industrial fire brigade members are not usually concerned or expected to deal with hazards and emergencies beyond the boundaries of the facility.

Bloodborne pathogens (29 CFR 1910.1030)

In 1991 OSHA issued a regulation on workplace protections from bloodborne pathogens, outlining how firefighters, emergency medical technicians, and other health care workers are to be equipped and trained to protect themselves from these pathogens. OSHA recognizes that bloodborne pathogens, including the hepatitis B virus (HBV) and the human immunodeficiency virus (HIV), have been responsible for morbidity and mortality in the workplace. It estimates that "for every 1000 workers with occupational exposure to blood or other potentially infectious material, between 83 and 113 will become infected with HBV over the course of their working lifetime because of occupational exposure to the virus."[2]

The bloodborne pathogens regulation relies on several mechanisms to protect workers: engineering controls, a risk management plan, personal protective clothing and equipment, training, an exposure-reporting process, and the offer of hepatitis vaccinations to all at-risk employees at no cost to them.

Figure 10-2 These states have laws that allow for the testing of victims

Arkansas	Illinois	Mississippi	Pennsylvania[a,c]
Colorado	Iowa	Montana[a,c]	Rhode Island[a]
Connecticut[a,b]	Louisiana[a]	Nebraska	Texas
Delaware	Maine[b]	New Mexico	Utah[c]
Florida	Maryland[c]	North Dakota[c,d]	Virginia
Hawaii	Michigan	Ohio[b]	Washington
Idaho[c]	Minnesota[c,d]	Oregon[c,d]	Wisconsin

Note: "Victim" designates any person to whose blood a firefighter or emergency medical service technician has been exposed.
a Testing may be performed on any blood or bodily fluid previously drawn.
b A court order to require testing of the victim may be obtained.
c Informed consent from the victim is required.
d Consent is not required on deceased persons.

With over 70 percent of the fire departments in the United States providing emergency medical services at some level and with EMS response calls constituting 60–70 percent of those departments' total response calls, EMS providers (firefighters or third service) are facing increased risk. NFPA 1581, Standard on Fire Department Infection Control Program (2010 ed.) (discussed on page 284), reinforces the requirements of the OSHA regulation. Protection of workers against bloodborne pathogens is a key component of a fire department's occupational safety and health program.

Workers' rights sometimes come into conflict with patients' rights. All states have laws governing patient confidentiality. In 1996, Congress enacted the Health Insurance Portability and Accountability Act of 1996 (HIPAA, P.L. 104-191), which further emphasized an already widely understood concept: those who come into contact with confidential medical information in the course of treating a patient must maintain that confidence unless authorized by law to disclose it. HIPAA is actually more limited in scope than most state medical confidentiality laws, applying to health care providers who transmit health information in electronic form, to health insurance plans, and to health care clearinghouses. This patchwork of laws is concerned primarily with protecting patients' privacy.

What happens when a firefighter is exposed to a patient's blood through a needlestick exposure? These very same medical confidentiality laws pose a potential barrier to the exposed firefighter trying to find out whether the source patient was infected. Fortunately, HIPAA and all but six states—Alaska, Nevada, New Mexico, New York, South Dakota, and Vermont—have found a solution through worker notification laws that authorize the release of otherwise confidential medical information to workers who have been exposed. Figure 10–2 lists the states that have laws allowing the testing of people to whose blood a firefighter or EMS worker has been exposed. It should be pointed out that the details and scope of each state's laws vary significantly.

Hazard communication (employee right to know) (29 CFR 1910.1200)

OSHA's regulation on hazard communication requires that employees who work in areas in which hazardous substances are stored be trained in the chemical and physical hazards of stored materials and have access to information about the health hazards associated with the stored materials. Because fire and emergency services personnel have hazardous materials (gasoline, diesel fuel, and cleaning products) in their workplaces and respond to HAZMAT incidents, they fall under this regulation.

Material safety data sheets prepared in accordance with this regulation describe the composition of a material, its hazardous properties, mitigation of the hazard, and information about disposal of the material. Employers are required to provide the employee (in this case, each firefighter) with access to the information contained in material safety data sheets for the types of materials or substances that may be used or stored in the workplace.

HAZMAT terminology defined

The term *hazardous materials* is defined and described in many ways, depending on the nature of the problem being addressed and the purpose of the defining agency. The federal agencies involved, as well as state and local governments, have different purposes in regulating hazardous materials that, under certain circumstances, pose a risk to the public or the environment, and no single list or definition covers everything. This list touches on the major categories of hazardous substances.

Hazardous materials The Department of Transportation (DOT) uses the term *hazardous materials* to cover eleven classes of hazards, some of which have subcategories, called "divisions." DOT regulations put hazardous substances and hazardous wastes into Class 9 (Miscellaneous Hazardous Materials). Both hazardous substances and hazardous wastes are regulated by the Environmental Protection Agency (EPA) if their inherent properties would not otherwise be covered (i.e., by other regulatory agencies, such as the Nuclear Regulatory Commission or the Department of Energy).

Hazardous substances EPA uses the term *hazardous substances* for chemicals that, if released into the environment above a certain amount, must be reported; and depending on the threat to the environment, federal involvement in handling the incident can be authorized. A list of EPA-designated hazardous substances is published in 40 CFR 302, Table 302.4. OSHA uses the term *hazardous substance* to mean every chemical that is regulated by both DOT and EPA (see 29 CFR 1910.120, a regulation that resulted from Title I of the Superfund Amendments and Reauthorization Act [SARA] of 1986 and covers emergency response).

Extremely hazardous substances EPA uses the term *extremely hazardous substances* for chemicals that must be reported to the appropriate authorities if released above the threshold reporting quantity. The list of extremely hazardous substances is published in Title III of SARA (40 CFR 355).

Hazardous chemicals OSHA uses the term *hazardous chemicals* to denote any chemical that would be a risk to employees if they were exposed to it in the workplace. Hazardous chemicals cover a broader group of chemicals than the other chemical lists.

Highly hazardous chemicals OSHA uses the term *highly hazardous chemicals* for chemicals that fall under the requirements of 29 CFR 1910.119, Process Safety Management of Highly Hazardous Chemicals. Highly hazardous chemicals are chemicals that possess toxic, reactive, flammable, or explosive properties. A list of covered substances is published in Appendix A of the OSHA rule (i.e., 29 CFR 1910.119).

Hazardous wastes EPA uses the term *hazardous wastes* for chemicals that are regulated under the Resource Conservation and Recovery Act (40 CFR 261.33). Hazardous wastes in transportation are regulated by DOT (49 CFR 170–179).

Dangerous goods In Canadian transportation, hazardous materials are called "dangerous goods."

Many fire departments meet the training requirements of this regulation by incorporating them into the training requirements of 29 CFR 1910.120 (see "Hazardous Waste and Materials" above) for HAZMAT response.

Noise exposure and hearing protection (29 CFR 1910.95)

OSHA specifies a maximum permissible noise exposure level (permissible exposure limit, or PEL) of 90 dBA (A-weighted decibels) for an eight-hour duration, with higher levels allowed for shorter durations. This level is known as a time-weighted average (TWA) sound level. When firefighters are exposed to different levels for different periods, the TWA must be calculated. To protect the worker when sound levels exceed the PEL, OSHA requires sufficient engineering controls, a hearing conservation program, or a combination of both.

The OSHA requirements have been incorporated into NFPA 1500 as part of a hearing conservation program. Other NFPA standards, such as NFPA 1901, Standard for Automotive Fire Apparatus (2009 ed.), and NFPA 1582, Standard on Comprehensive Occupational Medical Program for Fire Departments (2007 ed.), also require noise-level engineering controls and audiometric testing as part of a hearing conservation program.

National Institute for Occupational Safety and Health rules and regulations

NIOSH, an agency within the Department of Health and Human Services and with offices across the country, has been actively involved in issues of fire service occupational health. Many fire and emergency services personnel may be familiar with NIOSH's certification of respiratory protection equipment—specifically, self-contained breathing apparatus (SCBA) (42 CFR 84). This certification process, formerly carried out in conjunction with the Bureau of Mine Safety (which is now part of NIOSH), certifies that every SCBA unit meets the standards. When an SCBA unit is approved under the NIOSH certification process, it is approved as a total unit with all the components, including facepieces and air cylinders. Use of components that have not been tested together (e.g., an SCBA from manufacturer A with an air cylinder from manufacturer B) would not meet NIOSH requirements.

In 1997, Congress appropriated $2.5 million for NIOSH to establish a dedicated firefighter fatality investigation team. The NIOSH website (cdc.gov/niosh/fire/) now contains hundreds of reports of firefighter fatality investigations that are a valuable resource for lessons learned. All firefighters should be familiar with the website and regularly review the various reports to understand what caused the fatalities and what steps need to be taken to prevent a recurrence.

In addition, NIOSH relies on existing databases (including those maintained by NFPA, the International Association of Fire Fighters [IAFF], and the USFA)[3] to help track short- and long-term trends in injuries, fatalities, and health-related exposures of firefighters, both career and volunteer. This effort has been supported by all fire and emergency service organizations.

National Fire Protection Association standards

NFPA is a nonprofit international consensus standards-making organization accredited by ANSI. Its standards address issues affecting fire and life safety, fire protection, fire prevention, public life safety education, and fire suppression. The fire service has always been actively involved in the development, adoption, use, and enforcement of NFPA codes and standards.

Each document is assigned to a technical committee of subject matter experts, balanced by interest so that no particular group can control a majority of committee seats. NFPA staff provide support to technical committees, develop handbooks, write articles, present papers at conferences and events, deliver professional development training, and provide answers in their respective areas of expertise to NFPA members and fire officials through the technical advisory service. Most staff within the Public Fire Protection Division have an extensive fire service background and come from many different types of fire departments as well as from various geographic areas.

In addition to the more well-known fire protection standards that focus generally on the health and safety of personnel, there are other NFPA standards that deal specifically with professional qualifications, training, personal protective equipment, apparatus, and hazardous materials (see "Other NFPA Standards Affecting Employee Safety" further on in this section).

NFPA Standards on Occupational Safety and Health

Fire and emergency service organizations use many NFPA standards directly affecting occupational safety and health.

NFPA 1500, Standard on Fire Department Occupational Safety and Health Program

Development of NFPA 1500 began in the early 1980s, when a contingent of fire service leaders and experts in the field of occupational safety and health began developing documents whose effect would be to reduce the number of firefighter fatalities and injuries. The result was the first edition (in 1987) of NFPA 1500, Standard on a Fire Department Occupational Safety and Health Program. Under the NFPA 1500 umbrella, several additional documents have been developed. The Technical Committee on Fire Service Occupational Safety and Health is now responsible for developing NFPA 1500, 1521, 1561, 1581, 1582, 1583, and 1584. The latest edition of NFPA 1500 (2007), continues the work begun more than two decades earlier.

About the National Fire Protection Association

The National Fire Protection Association (NFPA), headquartered in Quincy, Massachusetts, was established in 1896. Its mission is to reduce the worldwide burden of fire and other hazards on quality of life by providing and advocating consensus codes and standards, research, training, and education. With a membership that includes more than 70,000 individuals from nearly 100 nations, NFPA is the world's leading advocate of fire prevention and an authoritative source on public safety.

Codes and standards

As of 2011, NFPA is responsible for over three hundred codes and standards that have been designed to minimize the risk and effects of fire by establishing criteria for building, processing, design, service, and installation in the United States as well as in many other countries. Some of the most widely used codes are NFPA 1, Fire Code™; NFPA 54, National Fuel Gas Code; NFPA 70, National Electric Code®; and NFPA 101, Life Safety Code®. NFPA's more than 200 technical code- and standard-development committees comprise over 6,000 volunteers, who vote on proposals and revisions in a process accredited by the American National Standards Institute.

Public education

Sponsoring a variety of life-saving campaigns and training programs, NFPA devotes much of its efforts to protecting lives and property through education. The organization provides many resources for fire, electrical, and life safety instructions.

NFPA's outreach programs include the annual Fire Prevention Week in October, a national campaign for which the association has been the official sponsor since 1922; Remembering When®, developed to address the leading causes of injuries and death among older adults; Risk Watch® and Learn Not to Burn®, developed to address the leading causes of injuries and death among children; a variety of programs that focus on high-risk outreach; and the resources and activities associated with Sparky the Fire Dog®, the official mascot of NFPA.

Advocacy

NFPA oversees the operations of several advocacy campaigns dedicated to increasing fire safety and awareness. These operations include the Fire Sprinkler Initiative: Bringing Safety Home; the Coalition for Fire-Safe Cigarettes™; Firewise Communities; and the Alliance to Stop Consumer Fireworks.

Participating in the development of NFPA codes and standards

NFPA's standards-making process is open to everyone, from those with great technical expertise to the newest member of the fire service. In particular, parties who are affected by codes, standards, and regulations need to understand the process and should participate to the greatest extent they are able. People can participate as individuals or through representative associations, such as the International City/County Management Association, the International Association of Fire Fighters, the National League of Cities, the National Association of Counties, the International Association of Fire Chiefs, and the National Volunteer Fire Council. Membership in NFPA is not required for someone to serve on a technical committee or to submit proposals or comments.

NFPA documents are typically revised every three to five years. Proposals to change or revise a standard may be submitted to NFPA electronically or in writing. They may be submitted any time, but a proposal closing date will be announced as a standard enters its revision cycle. The submitter of a proposal will receive confirmation from NFPA that the proposal has been received.

After the closing date, a technical committee meets to review and respond to the proposals that have been submitted. The committee has a series of options for responding to proposals, including accept, accept in principle, or reject. Each submitted proposal must be addressed. For a proposal to be adopted, a two-thirds affirmative vote is required. If the committee chooses not to accept a proposal, it must explain the reason for its action. The original submitter is then informed of the committee's action and of the explanation for it.

The proposed revisions along with the committee actions are published for review on NFPA's website, and copies (on paper or in CD format) are available to the public free of charge. This publication of the actions of the committee is called a Report on Proposals, or ROP. Current information about the NFPA standards-making process can be found at nfpa.org.

NFPA resources

NFPA codes and standards are constantly reviewed by their respective technical committees to ensure that they are kept current with new fire protection knowledge and technologies. To keep the documents up-to-date, technical committees gather information via several resources:

On-site investigations To provide new information about the effectiveness and actual application of NFPA codes and standards, the NFPA Fire Investigations Department conducts on-site investigations of fires and related disasters that have occurred all around the world. After completing a thorough investigation of an incident, the department publishes a comprehensive report that thoroughly analyzes the fire or explosion, focusing on how NFPA codes and standards were used, how effective these guidelines were during the event, and—when the codes and standards were not followed—how they might have provided additional protection.

Statistical data archive The NFPA One-Stop Data Shop (OSDS), NFPA's statistical data archive, publishes reports measuring the size and characteristics of particular fire problems. The data are from the U.S. Fire Administration's National Fire Incident Reporting System (NFIRS), the Fire Protection Research Foundation (FPRF), the NFPA Fire Investigations Department, and various other fire data resources around the world. Data from the OSDS allow customized information to be compiled on specific hazards or safety issues, as requested by technical committees.

Independent research The FPRF conducts independent research on fire risk, new technologies, and fire strategies, and publishes research reports that serve the technical committees as primary resources. From time to time, technical committees ask for specific research on subjects relevant to them. The FPRF determines whether the specific study has been done before and, if it has not, helps the committees to obtain the needed information from research, testing, consulting, or other institutions.

Library NFPA's Charles S. Morgan Technical Library contains the largest fire protection collection in the United States and one of the largest in the world. It has a comprehensive collection of more than 3,000 books, 6,500 technical reports, 200 periodicals, films, videocassettes, and NFPA-published archives dating from the association's founding in 1896.

Website NFPA's website (nfpa.org) provides direct support for the codes and standards process, including the online submission of proposals and comments.

Source: Adapted with permission from "Codes and Standards for a Safer World," copyright © 2009, National Fire Protection Association, Quincy, Mass. All rights reserved. At nfpa.org/assets/files/PDF/CodesStandards/CodesStandardsBrochure2009.pdf.

NFPA 1521, Standard for Fire Department Safety Officer Originally developed in 1977 as Standard 1501, NFPA 1521 remains preeminent in defining the function and qualifications of a fire department safety officer.

NFPA 1561, Standard on Emergency Services Incident Management System A lesson that is learned and relearned, and that figures prominently in many of the NIOSH firefighter fatality investigations, is that breakdowns in command and control jeopardize firefighter safety. Although operational coordination and effectiveness are often considered to be the primary objectives of an incident management system (IMS), this standard establishes performance criteria for an IMS that contribute directly to the safety and health of firefighters.

When NFPA 1500 was being developed, several different incident management systems and many local variations were in use, including the Incident Command System (ICS). The technical committee's intent was to allow for a variety of systems while ensuring that firefighter safety remained a primary consideration. Since then, DHS has instituted the National Incident Management System (NIMS) and adopted the primary components of the ICS for all emergency responders. Nevertheless, NFPA 1561, which includes specific performance criteria needed to ensure that safety and health objectives are addressed, remains an essential document for the fire service.

NFPA 1581, Standard on Fire Department Infection Control Program NFPA 1581 was developed to address infection control practices. These practices are necessary for persons providing emergency medical care, persons who come in contact with potentially infectious victims, and other persons in both emergency and nonemergency settings. The standard was developed to be compatible with guidelines and regulations from OSHA, the CDC, and NIOSH that apply to public safety and emergency response personnel. (See the section above on OSHA bloodborne pathogens.)

NFPA 1582, Standard on Comprehensive Occupational Medical Program for Fire Departments Published in 1990, NFPA 1582 created two categories of medical conditions, Categories A and B. Conditions in Category A, if they exist in the candidate or current firefighter, will not allow this person to perform firefighting operations. Conditions in Category B, in contrast, must be evaluated on a case-by-case basis so that the fire department physician can determine whether the medical condition in a particular candidate or current firefighter will prevent that person from performing firefighting operations.

Over the years, NFPA 1582 has been revised and updated, and further explanation has been added regarding medical conditions and requirements under the Americans with Disabilities Act (ADA). Some of the original Category A medical conditions were moved into Category B while others were elaborated upon. The sidebar below provides additional information on this important standard.

Legal considerations in applying NFPA 1582, Standard on Comprehensive Occupational Medical Program for Fire Departments

When a decision is made to offer an applicant a job as a firefighter (or, in the case of an incumbent firefighter, to continue that person's employment), the medical or physical performance evaluations may have significant legal implications. Before making an adverse employment decision based on NFPA 1582, the authority having jurisdiction should consult legal counsel and understand the legal issues relating to (1) individuals with handicaps or disabilities, (2) antidiscrimination laws, (3) protected classes, and (4) pregnancy and reproduction.

Individuals with handicaps or disabilities The Rehabilitation Act of 1973, as amended, 29 U.S.C. 791 *et seq.*, and its implementing regulations prohibit discrimination against individuals with handicaps or disabilities under any program receiving financial assistance from the federal government. The Americans with Disabilities Act of 1990, 42 U.S.C. § 12101 *et seq.* (ADA), also prohibits employment discrimination by certain private employers against individuals with disabilities, and many states have enacted legislation to that same effect. These laws prevent the exclusion, denial of benefits, refusal to hire or promote, or other discriminatory conduct against an individual based on a handicap or disability when that individual can, with or without reasonable accommodation, perform the essential functions of the job without creating undue hardship for the employer or program involved. ADA requirements must be kept in mind when NFPA 1582 is applied, and they should take precedence over the guidance recommended in NFPA 1582.

The medical requirements of NFPA 1582 were developed by a committee of medical doctors, physiological specialists, and fire service professionals, who processed the requirements through NFPA's consensus standards-making system. The standard requires that, to the extent feasible, decisions concerning those with medical ailments, handicaps, or disabilities be made after case-by-case medical evaluations. For this reason, most medical conditions have been assigned to Category B (see the discussion in the text of Categories A and B).

The medical requirements contained in NFPA 1582 have been revised in light of the essential job tasks described in the standard. It is recognized that some firefighting functions and tasks can vary from location to location because of differences in department size, functional and organizational differences, geography, level of urbanization, equipment used, and other factors. Therefore, it is the responsibility of each individual fire department to document, through a job task analysis, that the critical core firefighting functions performed in the local jurisdiction are substantially similar to those mentioned in NFPA 1582.

A wide variety of job-analysis techniques are available to document the essential functions of the job of firefighter. At a minimum, any technique used should be current, be in writing, and meet the provisions of the ADA (29 CFR 1630.2(n)(3)). Job descriptions should focus on critical and important work behaviors and specific tasks and functions. The frequency and/or duration of task performance and the consequences of failure to perform the task should be specified. The working conditions and environmental hazards in which the work is performed should be described.

The essential job tasks and descriptions should be made available to the fire service physician for use during medical examinations whenever a determination of the medical suitability of an individual as firefighter will be made.

Antidiscrimination laws Users of NFPA 1582 need to be aware that, although courts are likely to give considerable weight to the existence of a nationally recognized standard such as NFPA 1582 (e.g., *Miller v. Sioux Gateway Fire Department*, 497 N.W.2d 838 (1993)), reliance on the standard alone may not be sufficient to withstand a challenge under federal and state antidiscrimination laws. Even in the case of Category A medical conditions, courts can still require additional expert evidence concerning an individual candidate's or firefighter's inability to perform the essential functions of the job. Until the courts provide further guidance in this developing area of law, some uncertainty as to the degree and nature of the evidence required to establish compliance with the antidiscrimination laws will remain.

Protected classes (race, sex, color, religion, or national origin) Title VII of the Civil Rights Act of 1964, as amended, 42 U.S.C. 2000e, and implementing regulations of the Equal Employment Opportunity Commission (EEOC) prohibit discrimination in employment on the basis of race, sex, color, religion, or national origin (i.e., protected classes).[1] Many states, cities, and localities have adopted similar legislation. Generally, employment requirements that result in an "adverse impact" on members of a protected class (e.g., physical requirements that prevent many women from qualifying for firefighting) must be validated through a study that accords with EEOC guidelines. Under these guidelines, a study validating employment standards in one jurisdiction can be transportable to a second jurisdiction (and therefore used instead of the second jurisdiction conducting a separate study). However, specific preconditions must be met in this regard, and the authority having jurisdiction should seek the advice of counsel before relying on a "transported" validation study.

Pregnancy and reproduction Federal regulations as well as the decisions of many courts (including the U.S. Supreme Court in *International Union et al. v. Johnson Controls, Inc.*, 499 U.S. 187, 111 S.Ct. 1196 (1991)) have interpreted the requirements of Title VII of the Civil Rights Act of 1964 to apply with respect to pregnancy and reproduction. Discriminating against a woman because she is or may become pregnant is actionable under Title VII. The authority having jurisdiction should seek the advice of counsel in resolving specific questions concerning Title VII requirements as well as other requirements that state or local laws may impose.

1 Under Title VII, employer is defined generally to mean a person with "15 or more employees for each working day in each of 20 or more calendar weeks in the current or preceding calendar year" (see 42 U.S.C. 2000e). Several federal jurisdictions have held that unpaid volunteers are not considered to be "employees" under Title VII.

Other NFPA Standards Affecting Employee Safety

NFPA standards in a number of other areas also address issues that affect the safety and health of firefighters and emergency service personnel. Discussed below are standards on professional qualifications, training, protective clothing and equipment, apparatus, firefighting tools and equipment, hazardous materials, and wildland and wildland-urban interface firefighting.

Professional qualifications NFPA has a large number of standards that address the professional qualifications of fire and emergency responders (see sidebar on page 256 in Chapter 9). Many departments use NFPA standards as the basis for defining competency in training, promotions, and credentialing. Many state and regional training agencies base their training curricula on NFPA's professional qualification standards, thereby assuring other agencies that personnel who have been trained and certified have achieved a known and trusted level of skill and knowledge.

Many jurisdictions require not only that their personnel be state or locally certified to meet certain NFPA standards, but also that the certification be issued by an accredited entity (see Chapter 9 for more on certification and accreditation).

Training NFPA training standards cover training for a number of activities, including use of SCBA, response to fires aboard marine vessels, initial operations at an emergency scene, and operation of fire service vehicles.[4]

A common theme in these standards is that fire departments need to properly plan for training, drills, and exercises, and ensure that the training environment is safe (Figure 10–3). All members should receive training before they are assigned to specific functions or job assignments. Members should not be placed in positions for which they are not trained

Photo by Adam K. Thiel

Figure 10-3 The safe conduct of live-fire training evolutions is covered by NFPA standards.

(i.e., no on-the-job training). An emergency incident scene is no place to train firefighters. Safety must be instilled into personnel while they are in the training environment and carried over to operations at actual incident scenes.

Protective clothing and equipment NFPA standards address a variety of fire service personal protective equipment (PPE), including PPE for technical rescue, proximity firefighting, HAZMAT response, structural firefighting, wildland firefighting, and emergency medical operations. These standards provide the minimum requirements for fire service PPE as well as a basis for purchasing specifications to ensure that what is purchased will perform to the level expected. They also require that the manufacturer provide third-party certification that the clothing and/or equipment meets the minimum requirements so that the user has a measure of security that goes beyond just the manufacturer's assurances.

NFPA standards also address the selection, care, and maintenance of PPE in separate documents.

Apparatus The safety of personnel riding and responding on apparatus has been highlighted in past NFPA annual firefighter fatality studies and continues to be a major safety problem. NFPA has several standards that address fire apparatus and related equipment. NFPA 1901, Standard for Automotive Fire Apparatus (2009 ed.), addresses the minimum requirements for automotive fire apparatus, with chapters specifically on engines, aerial ladders, mobile water supply vehicles, foam apparatus, command vehicles, and special service vehicles (see Figure 10–4). Prepared by the Technical Committee on Fire Department Apparatus, NFPA 1901 incorporates the lessons learned from accident investigations and studies into new vehicle requirements. These safety enhancements include passenger restraint systems, stability control systems, high-visibility markings, vehicle data recorders, maximum speed limiters, brake requirements, and hearing conservation.

The Fire Department Apparatus committee is also responsible for a standard for wildland firefighting apparatus and another that addresses inspection; maintenance and performance tests for pumps, aerial devices, and foam systems; criteria for placing apparatus out of service; and guidance related to the retirement of apparatus. Other standards address the decision of whether to rehabilitate current apparatus or buy a new one; and the design, maintenance, and testing of firefighting vessels.

Firefighting tools and equipment NFPA standards specify the minimum requirements for a variety of firefighting tools and equipment, such as hose, nozzles, ground ladders, and appliances. In addition there are accompanying standards that address the use, maintenance, and service testing of these devices.

Figure 10-4 Industry standards for fire apparatus design and construction are contained in NFPA 1901.

Photo by Adam K. Thiel

Hazardous materials NFPA has a number of documents that apply to fire department response to HAZMAT incidents, and an even larger number of documents that apply to safe practices and operations at facilities that manufacture, use, or store hazardous materials.

Wildland and wildland-urban interface There are NFPA standards that address wildland and wildland-urban interface (WUI) fire in several areas previously mentioned, including professional qualifications and minimum requirements for apparatus. Additional standards address fire prevention and preplanning for wildland and WUI fires.

Legal issues in the fire and emergency services

In 1955, a large quantity of gasoline was spilled onto a city street in Lawrence, Kansas, during the removal of gasoline storage tanks from a gas station. The local fire department was notified and quickly arrived at the scene. To determine the extent of the problem, the fire chief who was supervising the scene instructed a firefighter to touch a cigarette lighter to the ground. Not surprisingly a conflagration ensued, destroying several automobiles. In the lawsuit that followed, the court refused to hold the town liable for the action of its fire chief.[5]

The Lawrence case and many others from that period reflect the traditional view that local governments were not liable for their failure to provide effective fire protection. Indeed, even extreme carelessness in fighting fires would not give rise to liability. Now in the twenty-first century, however, in firefighting as in most other fields, the historical limitations on legal liability are eroding and theories of liability are expanding. Legal liability is now a major concern for the fire and emergency services.

Areas of concern

Fire and emergency service leaders today are confronted with a wide variety of legal issues that pose true tests of leadership for them and their organizations. Lawsuits and legal challenges can undercut a leader and wreak havoc in an organization. Many times, legal challenges are a tactic used by those intent on resisting change.

The types of legal issues that commonly arise today are complex, multifaceted problems that require a combination of leadership, vision, and legal advice to resolve. Consider the following scenario:

> A woman firefighter complains that her company officer was reading a *Playboy* magazine while on duty. When confronted, the officer admits to reading the magazine while on duty

> but denies that he displayed or read it in the presence of anyone else. With the support of the firefighter's union, the officer claims that he has a constitutional right to possess the magazine and pulls out a copy of a federal court case to prove it. The officer then alleges that the woman is incompetent and demands that she be transferred.

This scenario is typical of the real-life legal problems facing fire and emergency service leaders. The solution is not simply a legal strategy, but rather a strategy that incorporates legal considerations among a host of other factors, including leadership, human relations, training, administrative procedures, and collective bargaining.

The areas of legal concern addressed in this section include negligence, immunity, protections, discrimination, sexual harassment, wage and hour issues, collective bargaining, and public accountability laws. These are by no means the exclusive list of legal concerns for modern fire and emergency service leaders, but they do represent some of the major areas.

Negligence

In any endeavor, and particularly in one as fraught with danger and uncertainty as fire and emergency services, things can go wrong. Deaths and injuries will occur despite the best efforts of the fire service. Property may be damaged, not only by the fire or disaster but also by the activity of firefighting itself. A tactical decision made in the midst of impending disaster may, in hindsight, turn out to have been terribly wrong. Bad outcomes alone do not make the fire service liable. They do, however, set the stage for a potential lawsuit.

The principal theory of liability used in lawsuits for personal injury and property damage is known in the law as *negligence*. The law of negligence holds a person liable for any damage that results from an act of carelessness in circumstances in which the actor had some duty to act with reasonable care. This principle can be understood by way of an illustration from an actual case involving allegations of negligent firefighting.

In 1978 in the city of Lowell, Massachusetts, five brick buildings were destroyed by a fire that started on the sixth floor of one of the buildings.[6] The building where the fire started had a working sprinkler system, and indeed, in the initial stages of the fire, the system worked properly. But the firefighters who responded to the fire chose to use the available water source to operate hoses, reducing water pressure in the sprinkler system—in effect, turning it off. There was evidence that good firefighting practice would have been to rely on the building's sprinkler system to fight the fire rather than to divert the water from the system to fight the fire with hoses. There was also evidence that the sprinkler system, if allowed to operate, would have put out the fire or contained it until it could have been put out by manual means. Instead, because firefighters chose in effect to shut off the sprinkler system, the fire eventually engulfed and destroyed five buildings.

This case presents the four essential elements of a firefighting negligence case. First, under the law, all persons generally have a duty, once they undertake to act, to do so with reasonable care. Although (as discussed below) there is some controversy about whether firefighters owe such a duty of care, in this case it was conceded that once the firefighters undertook to fight the fire, they had a duty to do so with reasonable care.

Second, the firefighters breached their duty to act with reasonable care. In lay terms, this simply means that they acted carelessly in fulfilling their duty to fight the fire. Reasonable care in the context of firefighting means the level of care that the reasonably prudent firefighter would use in similar circumstances. Since the evidence in the case showed that proper firefighting practice would have been to leave the sprinklers on, turning them off is viewed in the eyes of the law as negligent.

Third, the firefighters' breach of their duty to reasonably fight the fire caused the destruction of the buildings. The evidence shows that, if the sprinklers had been allowed to function, the fire would have been contained. In other words, the firefighters were the legal cause of the destruction of the buildings because, first, that destruction would not have occurred had the sprinkler system been left on and, second, the consequences of shutting it off were reasonably foreseeable.

Fourth and last, the firefighters' negligence resulted in damages. In this case, the damages roughly equaled the value of the destroyed buildings and their contents.

This case of the turned-off sprinkler is a good example of what any case of negligence has to prove in order to be successful—that is, the existence of a duty of care, the breach of that duty, causation, and damages.

Actual cases that have been brought illustrate the wide variety of claims that can arise. In an Indiana case, for example, it was alleged that a fire service organization was negligent in failing to maintain a sufficient number of firefighters for the equipment that the organization intended to use.[7] In the same case it was also alleged that there was negligence in the organization's failure to supervise and train its firefighters in controlling and extinguishing fires under the conditions encountered in a particular fire. In an Alabama case, negligence was claimed in a fire department's failure to respond to a house fire because the driver of the truck had gone home sick.[8] In a Maryland case, negligence was alleged in the failure to properly control and extinguish a brushfire that eventually reignited and caused a second fire in which a warehouse was destroyed.[9] And in a Massachusetts case, it was alleged that firefighters were negligent inasmuch as they fought a fire burning at the rear of a house by spraying water on the front of the house, where there was no fire.[10]

In a particularly dramatic Alaska case, liability was alleged and found for negligent failure to rescue a person stranded on an upper floor of a burning building.[11] The rescue failed because the ladder used in the attempt was too short to reach the victim's window. Although the court said that this fact alone did not constitute negligence, the firefighters had failed to use other commonsense methods of rescue that were available as alternatives. In particular, the court was deeply disturbed that spectators who had obtained an extension ladder long enough to reach the victim—and had raised the ladder and started to extend it—were ordered by a fire official to get away from the building and were driven off by fire hoses when they refused to obey.

These illustrations would seem to indicate that liability potentially exists around every corner. Although allegations of negligence are easily made, however, not all negligence claims result in a finding that the fire service was liable.

Sovereign immunity

At one time, the doctrine of sovereign immunity fully protected governments from lawsuits. Under this doctrine, the government as "sovereign" could "do no wrong" and could not be sued. In the case of firefighting activities, this meant that no matter how negligent a fire department might be or how much damage to life or property its negligence might cause, the local government whose firefighting had caused the damage could not be sued.[12]

The doctrine of sovereign immunity left individuals who had suffered injuries—not just in the firefighting context but also as a result of other government activities—no remedy. As might be expected, over the years the injustice that sovereign immunity often seemed to impose led to much criticism of the doctrine and calls for its reform.

Beginning in the 1970s, the federal government and the states began—either through court decisions or, more often, through the passage of legislation—to severely limit the absolute immunity that governmental entities had enjoyed. The most common type of legislation, now in existence in some form in all states as well as in the federal government, is generally known as a *tort claims act.* Each state's tort claims act is different, but for the most part, the acts provide that public entities are liable for injury caused by their negligence in the same manner and to the same extent as a private individual.[13] There are important qualifications, however, that provide the fire and emergency services with significant protections against liability.

Legal protections for the fire and emergency services

While tort claims acts serve to create potential liability for governmental entities, they also quite commonly provide the fire and emergency services with certain protections. These protections consist of (1) limits on the amount of damages that a governmental entity can be required to pay, (2) exemptions aimed specifically at the fire service, and (3) the discretionary function exception. In addition to these protections, there is a fourth type of protection, the public-duty doctrine, which offers further protection from negligence liability.

Limits on the amount of damages Although in many cases government entities can be held liable for their negligence just as a private individual can, tort claims acts place rather stringent limits on the amount of damages that the government can be required to pay. For example, some states cap that amount at $100,000 per claimant.

Exceptions aimed specifically at firefighting and related activities Several state tort claims acts have exceptions that specifically retain sovereign immunity for firefighting and related activities. North Dakota, for example, retains sovereign immunity for failure to provide adequate fire prevention personnel or equipment unless gross negligence can be proven. Illinois retains sovereign immunity for any injury caused by the failure to suppress or contain a fire or while fighting a fire. Kansas and Texas retain immunity for the failure to provide, or for the inadequate provision of, fire protection.[14]

There are also other types of exceptions that relate to the fire service. Alaska specifically retains sovereign immunity for the performance of duties "in connection with an enhanced 911 emergency system" and for the performance of duties upon the request of or by agreement with the state "to meet emergency public safety requirements."[15] Some states retain immunity for claims relating to the provision of or failure to provide emergency services.[16] Many states specifically retain immunity for the failure to make an inspection or for the making of an inadequate or negligent inspection.[17]

The discretionary function exception In addition to the exceptions in some states expressly relating to firefighting and related activities, most state tort claims acts recognize another type of exception that provides significant protection for the fire service. This is known as the *discretionary function exception*.

Although the lawmakers of the various states, in passing tort claims acts, wished to make it possible for citizens to obtain compensation for injuries caused by governmental entities, they were reluctant to abolish immunity for all governmental activities. They were concerned that lawsuits might be used to second-guess every governmental policy decision and that the constant fear of lawsuits could severely hamper the ability of local government officials to govern and to freely exercise the discretion of their office. To address these concerns, lawmakers created an exception in the tort claims acts that preserved governmental immunity for "discretionary functions."

The main problem has been determining the breadth of the discretionary function exception. Taken literally, the exception could be quite broad indeed. In its essence, the word *discretion* implies the exercise of judgment, and therefore a literal interpretation of the discretionary function exception might lead to the conclusion that all conduct involving the exercise of judgment is immune from negligence liability. In addition, because virtually all firefighting activities involve the exercise of judgment even if only in relation to minor details, one might conclude that all firefighting activities are immune from suit. This, however, is not the case.

In the context of firefighting, what does discretionary function mean? The decisions are far from clear and vary widely in how they treat particular fire service activities. Nevertheless, certain themes emerge.

First, there are aspects of fire service decision making that have an obvious basis in planning or policy making and will therefore be considered discretionary. These are administrative policy decisions involving the overall structure and makeup of the fire department, the training and equipping of firefighters, and the allocation of limited firefighting resources within the community. They include decisions about the number and location of fire stations, the amount and type of equipment to purchase, the size of the firefighting staff, the type and extent of firefighter training, the number and location of hydrants, and the adequacy of the water supply.

When lawsuits blame these types of administrative policy decisions for bringing about injury or death, they are frequently dismissed on the basis of the discretionary function exception. For example, a claim that firefighters were unable to suppress a fire because the nearest fire station was too far away to make timely firefighting possible would generally fail because decisions about where to locate a fire station, even if patently unreasonable, are protected from liability under the discretionary function exception.

Some courts are more stringent in applying the exception than others. Many courts, for example, will view any broad administrative-level policy decision as categorically immune from liability without any inquiry into the thought processes of the decision makers. Other courts, however, will require that the fire service organization, in order to claim immunity, present evidence showing that the decision makers actually went through a weighing of policy choices. In a case alleging that firefighters had not been supplied with a particular type of rescue equipment that would have prevented an injury, such a court would, for example, require that the fire service organization show that its failure to provide such equipment was the result of a conscious policy-making decision involving the balancing of competing interests, rather than the result of a simple failure to consider whether the equipment was needed.

While court decisions in this area vary widely from jurisdiction to jurisdiction, it can be said that the discretionary function exception provides immunity to the fire service from liability for most broad administrative-level decision making and for many operational-level decisions as well. Although the discretionary function exception is far from comprehensive and is less than certain in any individual case, it still provides the fire and emergency services with substantial protection from liability.

The public-duty doctrine Another type of liability protection recognized in many jurisdictions is known as the *public-duty doctrine*. Under the public-duty doctrine, firefighting and other public protective services are viewed as an obligation that governments owe to the public as a whole but not to any particular individual. The public-duty doctrine holds (somewhat paradoxically) that because firefighting is for the benefit of all, no legal duty is created to anyone in particular. Under the rule, therefore, no individual can seek damages for injuries caused by the negligence of firefighters because, in essence, the fire service owes no duty to act reasonably to any particular individual.

While not immunity per se, the public-duty doctrine effectively shields fire and emergency service organizations from lawsuits alleging negligence. However, it has an important limitation known as the *special-duty exception*. This exception holds that, even though firefighting and other emergency services are considered to be a duty owed to the public at large, a fire or other emergency services organization can, by words or actions in a particular case, create a special duty to particular private parties.

How does a fire service organization create for itself this special duty to private parties for which it may incur liability? In practice, courts have been very reluctant to apply this exception to hold the fire service liable. It seems clear that a fire department does not create a special duty to an individual property owner merely by responding to the owner's call for assistance and fighting the fire on the property.[18] To expose a fire department to liability under this exception, firefighters would have to do one of two things: (1) offer a special service or protection to an individual that was different from that offered to the general public, or (2) induce an individual, through specific assurances of assistance or safety, to reasonably rely upon that assurance and thereby put him- or herself (or a loved one) in danger.

Discrimination

The 14th Amendment to the U.S. Constitution contains a provision that prohibits states from denying equal protection of the laws to all persons. This provision, the equal protection clause, is the basis for the prohibition against illegal discrimination. The term *discrimination* is commonly associated with an offensive act that treats another person differently because of the person's race, religion, sex, or other prohibited classification. However, the term *discriminate* is actually much broader. It refers to the fact that we all make distinctions and therefore discriminate. We choose what we will eat for our next meal or what type of car we will buy. However, legal issues associated with discrimination emerge when a person's race, religion, national origin, sex, disability, or age are involved; when those factors are brought to bear on employment, housing, or any other activity to which discrimination laws apply, the discrimination is illegal.

To ensure equal protection, Congress has enacted many laws, including Title VII of the Civil Rights Act of 1964, the ADA, and the Age Discrimination in Employment Act. Collectively, these laws prohibit employment discrimination that is based on race, national origin, sex, religion, disability, and age in

- The testing, hiring, firing, and discipline of employees
- The compensation, assignment, or classification of employees
- Transfer, promotion, layoff, or recall
- Recruiting and advertising
- Training and apprenticeship programs
- Fringe benefits, retirement plans, and disability leave
- Other terms and conditions of employment.

Proving unlawful discrimination can be difficult. There are two categories of discrimination: disparate treatment and disparate impact. Between the two, the more commonly understood type is *disparate treatment,* which refers to discrimination in which a particular victim (or group of victims) is treated differently because of a prohibited classification. Disparate treatment discrimination is intentional discrimination that results from a decision, act, or practice based on a person's race, sex, religion, or other prohibited classification.

Disparate impact discrimination is a bit more complicated. Certain types of decisions appear to be nondiscriminatory but have the effect of discriminating. This type of discrimination is evident only by looking at a statistical analysis. In many cases of disparate impact, it may prove impossible to clearly identify the reasons for the statistical difference and just as impossible to prove that the discrimination was intentional.

A typical fire service example of disparate impact discrimination involves the use of an entrance examination or prerequisites that have a tendency to eliminate minority or protected-class candidates more frequently than they do white men. Irrespective of the employer's actual motivations for using such an examination or prerequisites, when the statistics show that a protected class has been unlawfully affected, the disparate impact theory will apply. While recent case law has limited the ability of a department to disregard the results of an otherwise validated examination process merely because the department does not agree with the racial makeup of those passing (*Ricci v. DeStefano,* 557 U.S.__ [2009], discussed in the sidebar on page 236), the underlying principles of disparate impact largely remain. Fire and emergency service managers need to understand the importance of evaluating examinations and criteria to ensure that they do not burden protected classes of candidates and incumbent firefighters.

In addition, it is important to understand that many states and local jurisdictions have adopted antidiscrimination laws that may go beyond federal requirements. Fire officers need access to legal counsel and human resource personnel to effectively manage this dynamic aspect of their organizations.

Sexual harassment

As the fire and emergency services have become more diversified, complaints about sexual harassment have increased. Sexual harassment is a type of sex-based discrimination, prohibited by Title VII of the Civil Rights Act of 1964 as well as by many state and local antidiscrimination laws. It covers unwelcome sexual advances, requests for sexual favors, and verbal or physical conduct of a sexual nature when submission to or rejection of this conduct affects an individual's employment, unreasonably interferes with an individual's work performance, or creates an intimidating, hostile, or offensive work environment.

There are two main types of sexual harassment: quid pro quo and hostile work environment.

Quid pro quo sexual harassment The term *quid pro quo* is Latin for "this for that." Quid pro quo sexual harassment occurs when an employee's work opportunities or benefits are affected because of the person's submission or refusal to submit to sexual advances or requests for sexual favors. A single act of quid pro quo harassment can trigger liability if linked to an adverse employment decision. For example, a female firefighter who refuses her supervisor's requests for sexual favors and is then transferred to a less favorable assignment would have an action for quid pro quo harassment. With quid pro quo harassment, the harasser is usually in a supervisory position relative to the victim, and generally, when this is the case, the employer is strictly liable.

Hostile work environment sexual harassment Hostile work environment sexual harassment occurs when unwelcome sexual conduct unreasonably interferes with an individual's work performance or has the effect of creating an intimidating or offensive work environment. Unlike quid pro quo, the harassment need not result in tangible or economic consequences, or in physical or psychological harm.

The hostile work environment can be created by the conduct of supervisors, co-workers, and even customers, patients, or clients. However, the liability of a fire and emergency services department for hostile work environment sexual harassment may be triggered only when the employer (1) knew or should have known about the harassment and (2) failed to take immediate and appropriate corrective action.

Also to be kept in mind is that sexual harassment is not limited to male harassers and female victims. Women have been found to have harassed men as well as other women, and men have been found to have harassed other men. In some cases, heterosexual men have been found to have sexually harassed other heterosexual men.

Addressing sexual harassment in the workplace All fire and emergency service organizations should have sexual harassment policies and provide ongoing training programs to educate personnel. Besides helping to ensure a safe and healthy work environment for all employees, such policies and programs have the added benefit of helping to minimize liability. The U.S. Supreme Court has held that if accused of sexual harassment, an employer can maintain an affirmative defense that it acted reasonably so long as the victim has not been adversely affected. For this defense to apply, the employer must have exercised reasonable care to prevent and promptly correct any sexually harassing conduct. Fire and emergency service departments that have sexual harassment policies and training programs are in a better position to argue that they have exercised reasonable care to prevent sexually harassing behavior.

It is also important for the employer to have a credible complaint procedure in place and to maintain ongoing efforts to keep personnel informed of it. The complaint procedure should ensure that subordinates have a way to bypass superiors who may be involved in the harassment. Fire and emergency service leaders need to remember that courts will consider the organization's response to the victim's complaint, including how promptly the department investigated, whether the department followed its own procedures, and whether the punishment imposed on the wrongdoer was prompt and adequate.

Fair labor standards

In 1938 Congress enacted the federal Fair Labor Standards Act (FLSA) to address a number of concerns relating to wages and hours, including minimum wage, maximum hours, overtime, and child labor. The DOL enforces the FSLA, which until 1974 applied only to private sector employers; in 1974, Congress extended the minimum wage and maximum hour protections of the FLSA to state and local employers.

Cases involving firefighters and EMS personnel have played a pivotal role in shaping the FLSA. The major impact that they have had on the act is a function of the long hours that firefighters have historically worked; their unconventional work shifts of 10, 14, or 24 hours; the fact that fire and emergency service departments typically allow firefighters to sleep, cook, and eat while on duty; and the fact that fire service supervisors commonly meet the criteria to be treated as hourly employees.

The following explanation is, by necessity, a brief introduction to a very complex area, and a word of caution is warranted: FLSA cases can be financially devastating to an organization. If you have questions related to the application of FLSA to your organization, seek competent legal counsel.

Maximum hours A principal tenet of the FLSA is that hourly employees are entitled to overtime compensation for all hours worked in excess of 40 hours per week. Overtime compensation is paid at a rate of one and one-half times normal hourly compensation. Because typical fire service work schedules involve rotating shifts that vary in hours from week to week and commonly exceed the statutory maximum of 40 hours, the FLSA provides an exemption for personnel engaged in fire protection activities for a public employer. Under this exemption, public sector firefighters are entitled to overtime only when their hours exceed 212 hours in a 28-day period, or a proportionately lower number of hours within a shorter work period. Each organization is required to formally adopt a work period ranging from 7 to 28 days. For departments that adopt a 7-day work period, the maximum number of hours per week before overtime compensation is required is 53 hours.

Employee The FLSA definition of *employee* is rather simple: it includes anyone who is employed, whether full time, part time, temporary, or permanent. It does not include volunteers, even those who receive a nominal fee. Generally, a nominal fee is considered to be anything less than 20 percent of what a full-time employee would receive for the same work.

Volunteer While a volunteer is not considered to be an employee for FLSA purposes, an employee is not allowed to "volunteer" to work for his or her employer without compensation if the volunteer activity involves the same type of work for which the person is employed. For the fire and emergency services, this means that a paid firefighter cannot volunteer to work as a firefighter for the same department while off-duty without compensation. This often-misunderstood rule is intended to prevent exploitative employers from coercing employees into volunteering on their time off. The employer–fire department is responsible for enforcing this requirement. A fire department that allows paid firefighters to volunteer for the same department is required to compensate those firefighters for all hours worked. This requirement does not extend to personnel who volunteer with other fire departments, nor does it apply to personnel who volunteer to engage in activities outside the scope of their employment. For example, a career firefighter for a town may volunteer to coach a town-sponsored youth baseball team.

Supervisors Executive, administrative, and professional personnel who are paid on a salaried basis are exempt from the FLSA overtime requirements. In many occupations, these exemptions apply to supervisory personnel regardless of how many hours are worked. However, one of the important considerations of whether an employee is a salaried executive or an hourly employee with supervisory responsibilities is whether the employee has a set number of hours that must be worked each day or earns a salary that is independent of actual hours worked. The typical shift work associated with fire and emergency service departments tends to result in fire service supervisors (ranging from captains and lieutenants up to battalion and deputy chiefs who work on shifts) meeting the test for hourly wage earners. The hundreds if not thousands of cases interpreting the executive exemption are all over the board; in some cases, lieutenants have been found to be executives and exempt from overtime, while in other cases deputy chiefs have been found to be hourly wage earners and entitled to overtime. In a particular situation, the case will turn on the specific facts surrounding the department involved.

Substitutions Many fire departments with paid personnel allow firefighters to voluntarily substitute for one another. From an FLSA standpoint, tracking substitution hours can become an administrative nightmare. Fortunately, the FLSA allows a fire department to ignore substitutions when tracking the hours of the firefighters involved. Firefighters who substitute for one another may be treated as having worked the hours they were scheduled to work on their regular work shift, not the hours they actually work.

Collective bargaining

Collective bargaining is the process in which an employer and the duly appointed representatives of the employees negotiate an agreement pertaining "to wages, hours, and other terms and conditions of employment."[19] An important premise implicit in collective bargaining is that both parties come to the bargaining table with open minds in a genuine effort to reach a mutually satisfactory agreement. The concept of *bargaining in good faith* is at the center of labor relations.

While collective bargaining for private sector employees is governed by the National Labor Relations Act in all fifty states, the collective bargaining rights for most firefighters are governed by state law. As a result, there is a great deal of difference from state to state in terms of the rights of firefighters, the scope of what can be negotiated, and the mechanisms by which labor disputes may be resolved.

Collective bargaining laws Most jurisdictions that permit collective bargaining for firefighters have done so through the enactment of state statutes. A smaller number of jurisdictions authorize collective bargaining through constitutional provisions, local ordinances, or executive orders. States may have a single labor relations act that governs all public employees, or they may have separate acts that apply to state workers and municipal workers. Other states have collective bargaining laws that are specific to certain categories of public employees, such as teachers, firefighters, and police officers. A relatively small number of states prohibit public sector collective bargaining completely.

Generally, collective bargaining laws expressly authorize the parties to negotiate and reach agreement on matters related to *wages, hours, and other terms and conditions of employment.* Furthermore, the laws describe conduct that constitutes an unfair labor practice, and they assign responsibility for administration and enforcement to a governmental agency such as a state labor relations board. They also set forth the available remedies in the event that the parties reach an impasse.

Scope of bargaining There are three basic subject categories for collective bargaining: mandatory, prohibited, and permissive. *Mandatory* subjects are those about which the parties are required to bargain. While most labor relations laws describe the scope of bargaining as "wages, hours, and other terms and conditions of employment," this description is subject to varying interpretations. For example, some jurisdictions hold that residency is a "term or condition of employment" and thus a mandatory subject whereas others do not. Clearly, wages, promotions, health benefits, pensions, and related matters are within the definition of mandatory subjects. A party cannot refuse to bargain over a mandatory subject.

Prohibited subjects are subjects that the parties are prohibited from bargaining over. Subjects are usually considered to be prohibited because they contravene an existing law or would violate public policy. Even if the parties were to reach an agreement over a prohibited subject, it would not be enforceable. An example of a prohibited subject would be a provision whereby the firefighters union could veto city council ordinances related to the fire department.

Between the extremes of mandatory subjects and prohibited subjects is a broad range of subjects that the parties may agree to bargain over; these are called *permissive* subjects. Permissive subjects may be discussed, negotiated, and incorporated into a collective bargaining agreement if both parties agree. However, neither party is under an obligation to bargain over a permissive subject, nor may one party force the other into bargaining over a permissive subject.

Dispute resolution mechanisms Despite the fact that the parties have bargained in good faith, an impasse is a common result of the collective bargaining process. There are three different types of impasse disputes, each with its own type of remedies.

Representational impasse disputes arise when the parties cannot agree on (1) whether the employees desire union representation, (2) who should be the employees' bargaining representative, or (3) which positions should be included in the bargaining unit. Representational impasse disputes are usually resolved by the agency designated in the labor relations act through either election or formal hearings.

Interest impasse disputes are disputes that arise when the parties are unable to reach a negotiated collective bargaining agreement. In the private sector, once an interest impasse is reached, management is free to unilaterally implement its final offer and the union is free to strike. Strikes by public employees are nearly universally prohibited, and concern about the consequences to public safety of a strike by fire and emergency service workers has led a number of states to adopt formal dispute resolution mechanisms, such as mediation, fact finding, voluntary arbitration, and compulsory arbitration.

Grievance impasse disputes, often referred to simply as "grievances," are disputes that arise over the interpretation and administration of an existing collective bargaining agreement. Generally, for a grievance to exist, there must be a binding collective bargaining agreement. Usually, the agreement will specify how disagreements involving the collective bargaining agreement will be resolved. The nearly universal mechanism for resolving grievances involves submitting the matter to arbitration. The most common and economical method in grievance arbitrations is to submit the issue to a single arbitrator. Some collective bargaining agreements require the use of arbitration panels or the appointment of a permanent arbitrator to hear all cases between the parties during the course of the agreement. Unless the agreement or state law dictates otherwise, the arbitrator's ruling is binding upon the parties.

A question that commonly arises in regard to grievances relates to which party—the member affected or the union—has the right to pursue a grievance. As a general rule, a grievance can be brought forward only by the union, not by the individual member or members affected. In addition, it is the union that has the right to withdraw or settle the grievance irrespective of the wishes or demands of the individual(s) involved.

Public accountability laws

Public accountability laws are a broad range of laws that have been enacted to promote openness and public confidence in government. A relatively new phenomenon spurred in part by the Watergate scandal in the 1970s, these laws seem to be reemphasized regularly in the public's eye by a steady stream of scandals involving public officials.

Public accountability laws include

- Open meeting and open records laws
- Laws governing the disclosure and regulation of political campaign contributions
- Mandatory financial disclosure by public officials, public employees, political candidates, and nominees for governmental positions
- Regulation and control of lobbyists and disclosure requirements for lobbying activities
- Standards of ethical conduct for public officials and employees
- Laws governing conduct of campaigns and elections
- Public financing of political campaigns
- Conflicts-of-interest laws for public officials and employees.

Public accountability laws have been enacted at federal, state, and local levels, and they affect virtually every fire and emergency services department to some degree. Most important, they pose a potential minefield for the unsuspecting. Consider the following scenario:

> A municipal fire chief also serves on the board of directors of the local little league, a private nonprofit corporation. The chief donates to the league surplus, worn-out, nonserviceable fire hose that belonged to the fire department, which the league can place over the top of the chain-link outfield fence to protect players from injury.

Believe it or not, the chief in this case could be charged with a criminal offense in some states for giving away public property, and with an ethics violation in most states for a conflict of interest because he served on the little league board of directors when he made the decision to donate the hose. It does not matter that the chief received no financial benefit or that he acted with the best of intentions. Factor in that fire chiefs are often the target of disgruntled firefighters, taxpayers, community groups, and others, and the importance of understanding public accountability laws comes sharply into focus.

Conflicts of interest The term *conflict of interest* refers to the existence of a conflict between the responsibilities imposed by virtue of a governmental position and some other duty or interest, whether it be financial, business, family, or otherwise. Conflicts of interest are not inherently illegal, nor are they inherently improper, but they arise in nearly every jurisdiction on a daily basis. The challenge with conflicts of interest is to properly manage them in such a way that the integrity of government is not compromised.

The first step in dealing with a conflict of interest is to recognize when one arises. Conflicts of interest arise out of decisions. If a public position requires a person to make, or participate in making, a decision that may result in a benefit to that person, a family member, a business associate, or an employer, that person has a conflict of interest and must not participate in the decision. In addition, certain categories of public officials are required by law to file conflict-of-interest disclosure forms with an appropriate governmental agency whenever such a conflict arises. Many jurisdictions have created ethics boards or commissions to oversee, investigate, and enforce conflict-of-interest laws. There is a great difference from state to state relative to conflicts of interest, so it is important to know the law that is applicable in your state.

Two terms should always be interpreted broadly with regard to conflicts of interest. First, the term *business associate* should be interpreted to include organizations for which a public official serves on the board of directors or as an officer. Secondly, the term *participation* should be interpreted broadly to include influencing others involved in the decision. Abstaining from a decision may not be adequate. Discussing a matter with and/or recommending an option to the decision makers would constitute participating even though the official abstained from the final decision.

Ethics laws Ethics laws and, in particular, ethics codes have been enacted at all levels of government to address the concerns that are at the heart of public accountability. Ethics codes are comprehensive guidelines for the conduct of public officials and employees, often incorporating conflicts of interest as well. Ethics codes have been adopted by statute, ordinance, local charter, and regulation. They commonly prohibit such activities as dual-office holding, soliciting or accepting gifts, using confidential information learned through official duties for financial gain, and participating in decisions despite conflicts of interest.

In addition, there are various other ethics-related laws that are not formally part of an ethics code but that apply to public officials to create an overlapping matrix of ethics laws. For example, a local jurisdiction may have a strict code of ethics for all employees that is supplemented by various state laws pertaining to matters such as nepotism and postemployment lobbying. It is vitally important that public officials and public employees know and understand the laws that are applicable to them.

Open records laws All fifty states have adopted laws that allow the public to have access to the records normally created and maintained by the government. Often called freedom of information laws after the federal Freedom of Information Act, these laws generally grant any person the right to inspect and/or obtain copies of all documents, forms, papers, letters, maps, books, recordings, photographs, electronic records, computer data, and even e-mail messages that are created or received by a governmental agency.

Open records laws define those governmental entities that must comply, usually including all executive, legislative, judicial, and administrative bodies. State and municipal fire and emergency service departments are universally included in such laws. In addition, some states extend open records requirements to various private entities that serve a public role, including volunteer fire companies.

The laws will usually set forth a statutory time period that a governmental agency has in which to comply with the request for information, the maximum costs that the agency can charge for research time and copying, and a list of exceptions to the open records requirements. Exceptions usually are based upon the need for confidentiality, as is the case with medical records, home addresses of employees, financial information such as credit card or bank account information, trade secrets, correspondence with attorneys, and criminal investigation reports.

Open records laws are usually enforceable by the state's attorney general or by a party who has been refused access to a public record.

Photo by Adam K. Thiel

Figure 10-5 Internal fire department meetings are generally exempt from the requirements of open meeting laws.

Open meeting laws In addition to open records laws, open meeting laws have been enacted in all states to ensure that governmental bodies conduct their meetings and deliberations in public. The governmental bodies subject to open meeting laws are considerably fewer than are subject to open records laws. Open meeting laws identify the public bodies subject to the law, define what constitutes a meeting, require that all meetings be held in public unless one of the listed exceptions is applicable, list the exceptions, establish penalties for violations, and assign responsibility for enforcing the law.

The key concern of open meeting laws is to ensure that deliberations among public decision makers be conducted in an open forum. Accordingly, there is a clear presumption that all meetings of a governmental body will be open to the public unless otherwise exempted. Notice of the meeting must be provided in the manner prescribed by law, and minutes must be kept of all proceedings. Provisions are allowed for the body to meet in closed session, but the grounds for such a meeting are quite specific and narrow. In addition, while in closed session, discussion of matters outside the scope of issues warranting the closed session is prohibited.

The distinction between bodies that are subject to the law and those that are not must be addressed in accordance with the language of the applicable open meeting law. Generally, meetings of a legislative body (state legislature, city council, county commissioners) or administrative body (zoning board, purchasing board, personnel review board) are subject to the open meeting requirements, as are subcommittees of such bodies in most instances. However, a meeting of employees (e.g., a fire chief's staff meeting) would not be subject to the law because the fire chief's staff is not a public body (see Figure 10-5).

Summary

The primary mission of the fire service has always been to protect lives and property. Although the scope of the mission will probably not change, the manner in which the fire service deploys and operates to fulfill its multifaceted mission is constantly evolving. In addition to fire suppression, the fire service now provides EMS, technical rescue services, community-based risk management, life safety education, and a host of other services that further the core mission. Progressive fire service leaders have seized the opportunities presented and made the most of them.

Rules, regulations, codes, and standards will continue to be developed and promulgated for a growing array of services provided by modern fire and emergency service departments. Fire service leaders need to understand these documents, participate in developing them, and use the standards-making process as a tool to effect positive change in the fire service (see again the sidebar on page 283).

As the roles of fire and emergency service organizations transition and evolve, the proactive leader will use the codes, standards, rules, and regulations as the basis for ensuring that fire protection, health, and safety are properly addressed. At the same time, the leader must be prepared to operate strategically in a complex legal environment that seems ever poised to stop progress. Only through a good understanding of the legal landscape can the modern fire and emergency services leader navigate his or her organization successfully.

Notes

1. NFPA 600, Standard on Industrial Fire Brigades (2005 ed.).
2. Leslie D. Putnam and Neal Langerman, *OSHA Bloodborne Pathogens Exposure Control Plan* (Boca Raton, Fla.: Lewis Publishers, 1992), 179.
3. NFPA has tracked firefighter fatalities since 1980, issuing statistical reports and case studies each July.
4. See List of NFPA Codes and Standards, nfpa.org/aboutthecodes/list_of_codes_and_standards.asp, standards 1401 through 1452.
5. *Perkins v. City of Lawrence,* 281 P.2d 1077 (Kan. 1955).
6. The fact pattern used for this illustration is drawn from the Massachusetts case of *Harry Stoller & Co. v. Lowell,* 412 Mass. 139 (1992).
7. See *City of Hammond v. Cataldi,* 449 N.2d 1184 (Ind. App. 3d Dist. 1983).
8. See *Williams v. City of Tuscumbia,* 426 So.2d 824 (Ala. 1983).
9. See *Utica Mut. v. Gaithersburg-Washington Grove,* 455 A.2d 987 (Md. App. 1983).
10. See *Cryan v. Ware,* 413 Mass. 452, 469 (1992).
11. See *City of Fairbanks v. Schaible,* 375 P.2d 201, 206 (Alaska 1962).
12. Although in most cases a fire department is clearly part of the government and is entitled to sovereign immunity, some cases are not so clear-cut because fire departments can be organized in a variety of ways—for example, as a department of a local government, as an independent corporation receiving varying degrees of funding from a local government, as a fire district, and so forth. In determining whether—and, if so, to what degree—a fire service organization may enjoy immunity from liability for negligence, one needs to know what type of organization it is and how that organizational form is viewed by applicable case law and statutes. Thus, for example, in one case a court found that a volunteer fire department that was formed as an independent corporation; owned its own property, buildings, and equipment; paid its own nonvolunteer staff; and enacted its own rules and regulations was not sufficiently controlled by the municipal government it served to be considered a governmental entity entitled to any sovereign immunity (see *Utica Mut. v. Gaithersburg-Washington Grove* in note 9). Because sovereign immunity is not completely abolished by tort claims acts (i.e., legislation limiting absolute sovereign immunity—see discussion in text) and its protections still exist except to the degree that a tort claims act decrees, it remains important for fire and emergency service organizations to know whether they are covered by sovereign immunity.
13. It is important to note that state tort claims acts vary significantly. In a few states, for example, tort claims acts abolish the sovereign immunity only of the state and not of local governments (see *Vermont Statutes Annotated,* title 12 §§ 5601–5605; *Hawaii Revised Statutes* § 662-2, *et seq.*). In other states, the degree to which sovereign immunity is abolished depends, at least to some degree, on whether the governmental unit has liability insurance that covers the alleged claims (see, e.g., *Colorado Revised Statutes* § 24-10-104; *General Statutes of North Carolina* § 160A-485; *Vermont Statutes Annual,* title 12 § 560(f) and title 29 § 1403; and *Wyoming Statutes* § 1-39-118(b)). In addition, not all states have adopted the general approach taken by the tort claims acts described here. Some states, for example, rather than enacting a general abolition of immunity together with various exceptions and qualifications, have instead abolished immunity for specific types of governmental activities (see, e.g., *Delaware Code Annotated,* title 10 § 4012 [abolishing immunity only for certain designated activities, including the operation of a motor vehicle and the maintenance of public buildings]). The importance of consulting individual state laws to determine the scope of immunity, therefore, cannot be overemphasized.
14. See *North Dakota Century Code* § 32-12.1-03(3); *Illinois Revised Statutes,* chap. 85 § 5-102, 5-103; *Kansas Statutes Annotated* § 75-6104(n); and *Texas Civil Practice and Remedies Code Annotated* § 101.055(3).
15. See *Alaska Statutes* §§ 09.65.070(d)(6) and (d)(5).
16. See, e.g., *Iowa Code* § 613A.4; *Texas Civil Practice and Remedies Code Annotated* § 101.055(2).
17. See, e,g., *Kansas Statutes Annotated* § 75-6104(k).
18. See, e.g., *Commerce & Indus. Ins. Co. v. City of Toledo,* 543 N.E.2d 1188 (Ohio 1989), but also see *Ziegler v. City of Millbrook,* 514 So.2d 1275 (Alabama 1987).
19. National Labor Relations Act, 29 U.S.C. § 158 (8)(d), nlrb.gov/about_us/overview/national_labor_relations_act.aspx.

CHAPTER 11

Health, Safety, and Survival

J. Gordon Routley

This chapter provides an understanding of

- The benefits and challenges of health, safety, and survival programs in a fire and emergency services department
- The employer's legal responsibility to provide a healthy and safe work environment for employees, and the role of laws and standards in establishing health and safety expectations
- The trend in annual line-of-duty deaths and the particular causes that are responsible for the greatest numbers of deaths each year
- Risk management as applied to structural firefighting operations
- Safety culture in relation to the fire and emergency services and the sixteen Firefighter Life Safety Initiatives
- The relationship between adequate staffing and firefighter safety
- The roles of fire department physician, health and safety officer, and incident safety officer
- The major health risks to firefighters
- The major components of a comprehensive health-wellness-fitness program for a fire and emergency services department.

Efforts to reduce line-of-duty injuries and fatalities and to improve the overall health and physical fitness of firefighters have become an organizational preoccupation within the modern fire and emergency services. From a management perspective, there are compelling reasons to direct attention toward keeping firefighters alive and healthy.

The importance of a proactive approach to operational safety is evident in a service that specializes in responding to fires and emergency incidents. Firefighters routinely confront myriad hazards and frequently deal with situations that involve risks of traumatic injury or sudden death. Such occupational hazards can have both short-term and long-term negative consequences for the health of many firefighters, contributing to a high rate of disability retirements and shortened life expectancy after retirement. A wide range of occupationally related illnesses and disabling medical conditions have been identified among firefighters, including cardiovascular and respiratory diseases, stress disorders, and several forms of cancer. Reducing the rates of these illnesses is a primary objective of health and wellness programs.

The public expects firefighters to be prepared to deliver essential services effectively and reliably. To perform many of the duties that are expected of them, firefighters must be physically fit. Those who are unfit or unhealthy place themselves and their co-workers at additional risk and compromise the ability of the fire department to provide important emergency services to the public.

Although the work of firefighters is inherently dangerous, it has become unacceptable, from a legal perspective, to expose firefighters or any other employees to avoidable and preventable risks to their health and safety. The hazards and risks confronting firefighters are well known, and their employers have a clear responsibility to ensure that firefighters are well trained, closely supervised, properly equipped (see Figure 11–1), and physically fit to meet the predictable demands of situations they are likely to encounter.

In addition to an employer's legal and moral responsibility to provide a healthy and safe work environment for employees, there are often economic justifications for investing in this area. Fire and emergency service departments usually pay high premiums for workers' compensation coverage, and in many cases the overtime that is expended to replace injured and disabled firefighters is a significant component of the overall budget; reductions in injuries and occupational illnesses should produce savings in both of these areas. The employer's cost to develop and implement a health and safety program should also be weighed against the economic impact of a single service-related fatality or a disability retirement.

Figure 11-1 Contemporary firefighters benefit from personal protective equipment their predecessors could never imagine.

Photo by Adam K. Thiel

Courtesy of the Library of Congress, Prints and Photographs Online Catalog (LC-DIG-ppmsca-01571)

Portions of this chapter have been revised and updated from Chapter 11, "Health, Wellness, and Injury Prevention," by James L. Schamadan, M.D., in the 2002 edition of this volume.

Evolution of health and safety programs in the fire service

The health and safety movement within the fire service paralleled the evolution of similar programs for other high-risk occupations. Most of the current framework of laws and regulations relating to occupational health and safety was developed during the 1970s and 1980s, during a period of increasing general awareness of workplace hazards. Initially these laws and regulations were applicable to general industry and to a number of particularly dangerous occupations, while the fire service and other governmental functions were often excluded from enforcement. At that time, firefighter deaths and injuries were generally viewed as inevitable given the hazardous and unpredictable nature of the work, and very little attention was directed toward their prevention. Firefighter health, safety, wellness, and physical fitness programs were almost nonexistent.

The Occupational Safety and Health Administration (OSHA) Fire Brigade Standard, 29 CFR 1910.156, which came into effect in 1980, was the first national effort to establish basic safety regulations for firefighters in the United States. While most local government agencies are exempt from federal health and safety regulations, this standard became applicable to many fire departments through the delegation of enforcement authority to state agencies. Subsequent federal regulations addressing hazardous materials, respiratory protection, contagious diseases, and blood-borne pathogens have all had a direct impact on fire departments, although most authorities having jurisdiction in the United States still view the fire service as a special case for enforcement of occupational health and safety regulations. Chapter 10 discusses the application of OSHA regulations to fire and emergency service departments.

The National Fire Protection Association (NFPA), a consensus standards-making organization, also addresses matters related to firefighter safety and protection. Regulatory enforcement of NFPA's occupational health and safety standards is generally limited to specific documents or sections of documents that have been incorporated by reference into laws or regulations, although most occupational health and safety laws include a general duty clause that requires an employer to provide a reasonable level of protection for employees from all known hazards. The NFPA documents are often cited under the general duty clause as the accepted standard of care for North American fire and emergency service departments. All NFPA documents are revised periodically, usually on a five-year cycle.

The release of NFPA 1500, Standard on Fire Department Occupational Safety and Health Program, in 1987 provided a comprehensive model framework for the fire service to develop such programs. This document, along with several supporting guides and standards that have been developed since, was produced through a voluntary consensus process. Considered avant-garde at the time of its initial adoption, the standard was initially received with skepticism: it established expectations that could be more accurately described as goals for most fire departments at the time. The document included guidelines for developing a program approach to bringing a fire department into compliance with the standard over a period of time, with periodic assessments of progress and compliance levels. Efforts to develop and implement programs to meet NFPA 1500, or specific parts of it, have gained widespread acceptance since the standard was adopted. Each new edition of NFPA 1500 has moved the goals to a higher level, so the effort to achieve compliance is an ongoing process for most fire departments.

The level of enforcement of occupational health and safety regulations for fire and emergency service departments varies considerably among states and provinces, as well as among the particular standards that are applied. Although regulatory enforcement is inconsistent, the investigation of a firefighter fatality or serious injury will almost invariably focus attention on the department's level of compliance with the applicable NFPA standards. Civil litigation cases involving fire and emergency service departments almost invariably cite NFPA standards.

Most of the leading fire service organizations, including NFPA, the International Association of Fire Fighters (IAFF), the International Association of Fire Chiefs (IAFC), and the National Fallen Firefighters Foundation (NFFF), have undertaken major efforts to focus attention on health and safety. The U.S. Fire Administration, National Institute of Occupational Safety and Health, and National Institute of Standards and Technology have also dedicated significant resources and efforts to support health and safety programs. Projects to enhance firefighter health and safety are eligible for Assistance to Firefighters Grant funds through the federal government and several state programs.

National Fire Protection Association (NFPA) standards

The following NFPA standards relate directly to occupational health and safety for fire departments:

- NFPA 1500, Standard on Fire Department Occupational Safety and Health Program (2007 ed.)
- NFPA 1521, Standard for Fire Department Safety Officer (2008 ed.)
- NFPA 1561, Standard on Emergency Services Incident Management System (2008 ed.)
- NFPA 1581, Standard on Fire Department Infection Control Program (2010 ed.)
- NFPA 1582, Standard on Comprehensive Occupational Medical Program for Fire Departments (2007 ed.)
- NFPA 1583, Standard on Health-Related Fitness Programs for Fire Department Members (2008 ed.)
- NFPA 1584, Standard on the Rehabilitation Process for Members during Emergency Operations and Training Exercises (2008 ed.)

NFPA standards also set the requirements for almost all of the vehicles, tools, and equipment used by firefighters, including protective clothing and self-contained breathing apparatus (SCBA). Each subsequent edition of a standard introduces new and more advanced requirements; however, items that were in compliance with the edition that was in effect at the time of manufacture or acquisition are generally recognized as acceptable for a normal life cycle. Many fire departments prefer to periodically upgrade certain types of equipment through a total replacement program rather than have a variety of models of different vintages in service, with each version meeting a different set of requirements. The total replacement option is particularly recommended for SCBA and similar technologically complex equipment.

Staffing for health and safety

Occupational health and safety should have the status of a major program within a fire and emergency services department. Many larger departments have established administrative units with several staff positions working specifically on health and safety program management.

Several individuals could be involved in providing specific expertise in different areas. These individuals might include fire department members and experts from particular disciplines, such as physicians, engineers, technicians, industrial hygienists, toxicologists, cardiologists, exercise physiologists, physical/occupational therapists, and clinical psychologists.

Health and safety officer

NFPA 1500 refers to the program manager as a fire department health and safety officer (HSO). The HSO should be familiar with all the different subject areas that fit within the broad scope of health and safety programs; it is unrealistic, however, to expect one individual to develop expertise in every aspect of health, wellness, physical fitness, and operational safety.

The program management responsibilities could be assigned to one individual in a smaller fire department, while a larger department might subdivide them between a safety officer, who would be primarily concerned with operational safety programs, and a health, wellness, and fitness coordinator, who might be located within the human resource division.

Incident safety officer

An incident safety officer (ISO) is specifically assigned to identify and evaluate safety issues and to ensure that appropriate measures are in place to prevent accidents and injuries at an incident scene. This officer should be looking at each situation and making recommendations from the perspective of a safety specialist, reporting directly to the incident commander. The ISO is also responsible for investigating and monitoring incidents that cause firefighter injuries as well as "near-miss" incidents that could have caused injury.

The role and qualifications of an ISO are defined in the NFPA standards. An ISO must be very familiar with all aspects of incident command and emergency operations and be specifically trained to perform the specialized duties of a safety officer. At least one qualified ISO should be assigned to respond to every serious incident. Some fire departments designate one ISO to respond to significant incidents, while others train several individuals and make the assignment at the scene.

Line-of-duty deaths

The figure of 100 line-of-duty deaths (LODDs) per year has become a benchmark in the effort to promote health and safety within the U.S. fire service. The officially reported LODD toll in the United States has hovered in the 100–120 range for more than thirty years despite numerous efforts to reduce firefighter fatalities, including major improvements in protective clothing and equipment. During the same period, the rates of fire occurrence, civilian fire deaths, and civilian fire injuries have all declined.

In most years, fewer than twenty-five firefighters die as a direct result of exposure to flames or from being trapped by the structural collapse of a burning building. More than half of the reported firefighter LODDs are attributed to heart attacks, incident-related stress, and overexertion, while vehicular collisions represent the second leading cause of fatalities. The officially reported figures do not include a large number of firefighter deaths suspected of being directly related to occupational exposure to carcinogens at fire scenes, at other types of emergency incidents, or in the fire station environment. In Canada, where several types of cancer are presumed to be occupationally related, cancer has become the leading cause of recognized LODDs. Contagious diseases have also become an increasing concern since most fire departments now respond to more medical emergencies than to any other types of incidents.

The generally accepted definition of an LODD excludes off-duty deaths caused by heart attacks, strokes, or other cardiovascular and respiratory conditions unless they occur within twenty-four hours of response to an emergency incident. There is growing recognition that such health conditions are shortening the lives of both active and retired firefighters to an alarming extent.

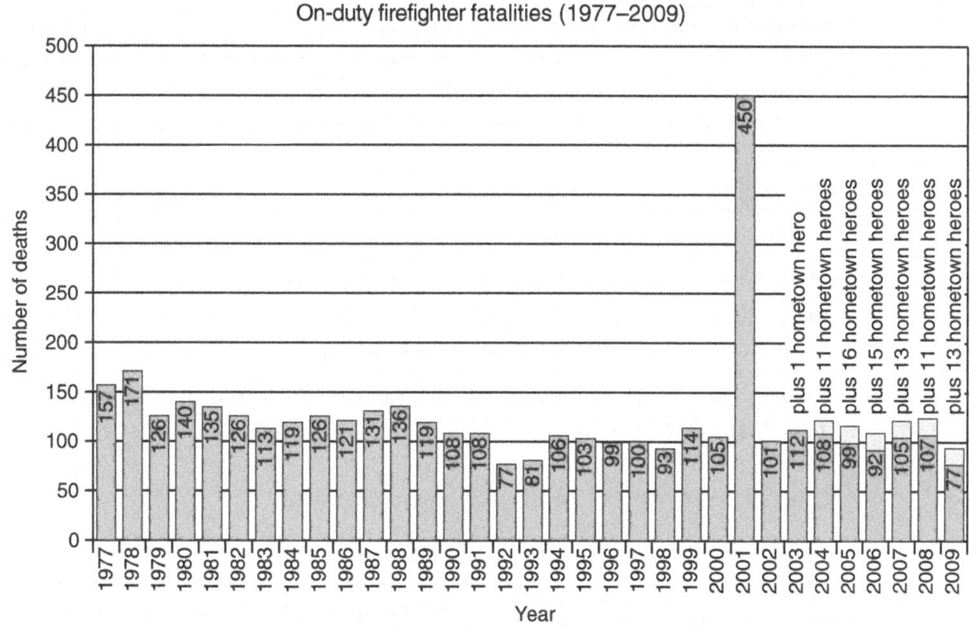

Source: U.S. Fire Administration, *Firefighter Fatalities in the United States in 2009* (Washington, D.C., July 2010), 5, usfa.dhs.gov/downloads/pdf/publications/ff_fat09.pdf.

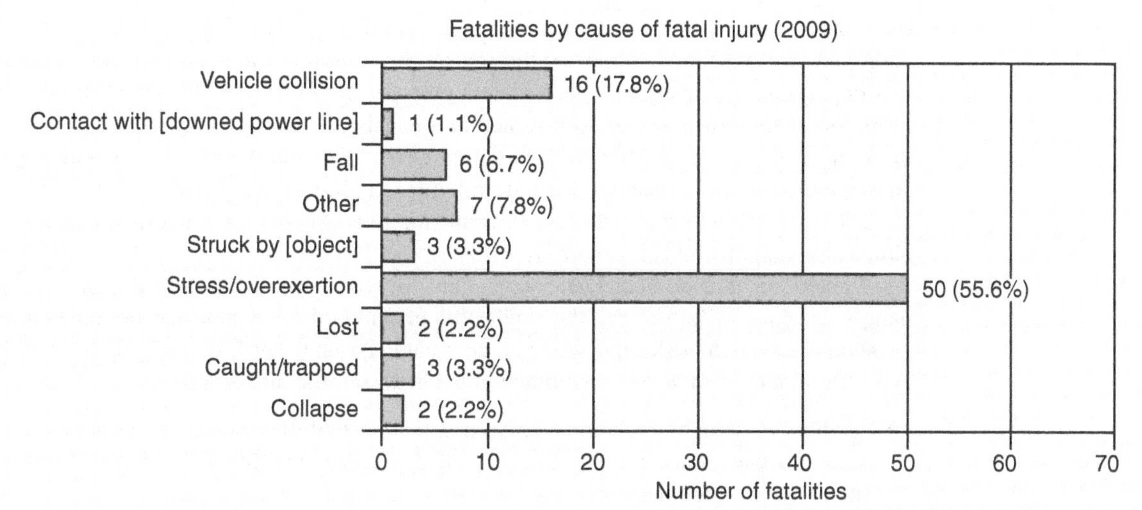

Source: U.S. Fire Administration, *Firefighter Fatalities in the United States in 2009* (Washington, D.C., July 2010), 13, usfa.dhs.gov/downloads/pdf/publications/ff_fat09.pdf.

The positions of HSO and ISO are related but involve different duties, responsibilities, and qualifications. The two roles may be performed by the same individual or by different individuals.

Fire department physician

NFPA 1500 refers to the appointment of a fire department physician to provide professional medical oversight for health and safety programs. If available, an occupational medicine specialist would be very appropriate for this role.

Very few fire and emergency service departments can afford to employ a full-time physician; most contract with a physician or group of physicians to provide medical services on a part-time basis. Some departments contract with external providers to conduct medical examinations. This may be the least costly option for obtaining required medical examinations; however, it may not provide access to a particular physician who could develop an ongoing relationship with the department and its firefighters.

The fire department physician should be familiar with the unique nature and special demands of a firefighter's work environment and the range of hazards that are likely to be encountered. One of the primary responsibilities of the physician is to make individual determinations of fitness for duty, particularly for firefighters who are recovering from injuries or illnesses. The physician should have access to a network of experts and specialists to consult on particular cases. Other services that the physician should provide might include

- Consulting with firefighters about their exposure to infectious diseases and guiding them through the prescribed protocol
- Coaching department members on lifestyle changes necessary to improve wellness
- Analyzing statistical data to forecast the future needs of the health and wellness program and to monitor the status of department members.

The physician should be equally valued as an adviser to management and a resource to the individual members of the organization.

Operational safety and risk management

The fire and emergency services routinely perform inherently dangerous functions in situations and circumstances that are out of control. While many risks may be limited or prevented through code enforcement, public education, and other mitigation strategies before an incident occurs, others are unavoidable, and fire and emergency service departments must be prepared to deal with a wide range of predictable—and often unpredictable—situations. These factors create a compelling responsibility to ensure that firefighters are trained, equipped, managed, and supported to perform their mission safely and effectively. While it is impossible to prevent or be adequately prepared for every possible situation that could occur, every incident must be approached in a consistent manner, using a structured and disciplined process to identify and evaluate the risk factors and apply the most appropriate strategies and tactics. Most operational firefighter fatalities are not attributed to miscalculated risk assessments but rather result from situations in which the imminent danger was either unanticipated or unrecognized.

While firefighting and emergency operations involve unavoidable risks, the nature of the dangers is generally known and the application of standard safety practices by skilled firefighters should reduce the risk exposure to an acceptable baseline level. Beyond that level, risk exposure should be managed according to the circumstances. In general,

- The lives of firefighters should be placed at risk beyond the baseline level only in situations where their actions create a realistic chance of saving a life and no less risky alternative is available.
- Actions to save property, when there are no lives to be saved, should not expose firefighters to risks beyond the acceptable baseline level.

- When there is no possibility of saving lives or property of value, there is no justification for risking the lives of firefighters; operations should be conducted in a manner that minimizes risk exposure.

The most critical decision point in relation to risk management is that between offensive and defensive strategies (Figure 11–2). In an offensive situation, firefighters will enter a burning building to attack a fire, attempting to rapidly gain control by extinguishing the flames. In a defensive situation, firefighters will operate from safe positions, usually outside a burning building, and direct their efforts toward confining the fire to a particular area. A defensive strategy is appropriate when the incident commander determines that the risks associated with interior fire attack are not justified. It is not unusual for operations to be initiated in an offensive mode and to switch to a defensive mode if the initial attack is unsuccessful. By the same token, a defensive attack will sometimes control a fire sufficiently to allow the switch to an offensive strategy.

The incident management process should regulate the actions that firefighters are permitted to take of their own volition as well as the strategies and tactics that are used to gain control of the situation. Propelled by their enthusiasm and perceptions of urgency, firefighters are often inclined to disregard standard safety practices and expose themselves to higher levels of risk than necessary.

The concepts of risk management and operational safety are relatively new to the fire and emergency services, and many individuals have found it difficult to adapt to this new paradigm. Earlier generations of firefighters were indoctrinated with organizational values that accepted, encouraged, and often rewarded high-risk behaviors. This predisposition toward risk acceptance was a very positive factor in relation to performing the mission of saving lives and property, but it tended to result in very negative consequences for the firefighters themselves. For many years the fire service took pride in being recognized as "the most dangerous profession," and it remains among the most dangerous in terms of deaths and injuries.

Efforts to change perceptions relating to acceptable and unacceptable risks often result in a tug-of-war between old and new values. While some fire departments have fully adopted the new value system, others cling to tradition and scoff at policies that appear to compromise the heroic and fearless image of firefighters. Within many fire departments the struggle involves competing factions, and it is strongly influenced by the orientation of the leadership and by the policies that are promoted and reinforced within the organization. The most effective leaders have managed to preserve many of the traditional values that produce positive results while convincing their followers that there is an important difference between bold and foolhardy actions.

Situations that are entirely within the control of the fire and emergency services department, such as training exercises and nonemergency activities conducted on premises, do not allow for any risk acceptance. The employer is fully responsible for ensuring that every

Figure 11-2 The choice of an offensive or defensive strategy is a critical decision affecting the overall safety and effectiveness of managing a fire or other emergency incident.

Photos by Adam K. Thiel

predictable risk factor is identified and every reasonable precaution is employed to prevent accidents and injuries.

Safety culture

The effort to promote health and safety within the fire service is often described in terms of a cultural change. A summit convened by the NFFF in 2004 produced a list of sixteen key initiatives designed to reduce the rate of firefighter fatalities by 50 percent within a decade. Changing the organizational culture, particularly the perceptions and behaviors of firefighters themselves, was identified as the greatest challenge to be addressed in order to achieve that objective. The summit participants noted that the fire service in general was placing too much value on daring and heroism and too little on training, physical fitness, and sound judgment.

The introduction of a safety culture does not mean that concerns for firefighter safety become the primary preoccupation of the fire and emergency services department, ahead of saving civilian lives, protecting property, and intervening in a wide range of emergency situations to prevent negative consequences. A healthy organizational approach to safety (and health) means that the risks and potential consequences of every action are considered in an appropriate context.

The "old" fire service culture placed the mission of saving lives and property "at all costs" ahead of concerns for firefighter safety; the "new" value system calls for a realistic risk assessment of dangerous situations before taking actions that could jeopardize the lives of firefighters. The objective of this philosophy is to prevent firefighters from being exposed to needless

Firefighter life safety initiatives

The National Fallen Firefighters Foundation adopted the motto "Everyone Goes Home" to symbolize the ongoing campaign to implement the sixteen initiatives that were produced at the first Firefighter Life Safety Summit, held in 2004:

1. Define and advocate the need for a cultural change within the fire service relating to safety; incorporat[e] leadership, management, supervision, accountability and personal responsibility.
2. Enhance the personal and organizational accountability for health and safety throughout the fire service.
3. Focus greater attention on the integration of risk management with incident management at all levels, including strategic, tactical, and planning responsibilities.
4. All firefighters must be empowered to stop unsafe practices.
5. Develop and implement national standards for training, qualifications, and certification (including regular recertification) that are equally applicable to all firefighters based on the duties they are expected to perform.
6. Develop and implement national medical and physical fitness standards that are equally applicable to all firefighters, based on the duties they are expected to perform.
7. Create a national research agenda and data collection system that relates to the initiatives.
8. Utilize available technology wherever it can produce higher levels of health and safety.
9. Thoroughly investigate all firefighter fatalities, injuries, and near misses.
10. Grant programs should support the implementation of safe practices and/or mandate safe practices as an eligibility requirement.
11. National standards for emergency response policies and procedures should be developed and championed.
12. National protocols for response to violent incidents should be developed and championed.
13. Firefighters and their families must have access to counseling and psychological support.
14. Public education must receive more resources and be championed as a critical fire and life safety program.
15. Advocacy must be strengthened for the enforcement of codes and the installation of home fire sprinklers.
16. Safety must be a primary consideration in the design of apparatus and equipment.

Source: "Everyone Goes Home: Firefighter Life Safety Initiatives," at everyonegoeshome.org/initiatives.html.

and unjustifiable risks, not to stop them from taking bold and aggressive actions where the risks are justified.

The effort to promote a culture of safety within a fire department often encounters resistance from members who feel that a tendency to avoid risk will detract from the heroic image (and self-image) of the firefighter. Fire and emergency service leaders have to enforce an appropriate balance between bold action—where it is appropriate to deal with dangerous situations—and a realistic emphasis on keeping firefighters alive.

The concept of a safety culture reinforces additional values within an organization. In order to operate safely and effectively, every firefighter must be ready to perform at the required level in terms of training, operational skills, physical strength, and endurance. All the related systems that are required to support safe and effective operations must also be in place, and their reliability must be ensured.

The development of a mature safety culture has to reach the level of individual firefighters and first-line supervisors to ensure that an appropriate concern for safety is incorporated into every aspect of the job. The policies that reinforce the new value system have to be established at the highest levels of the organization and enforced through the chain of command.

Modeling safety

Fire and emergency service departments are in the business of ensuring public safety, and the manner in which health and safety are addressed within the organization should set a positive example. The fire service has gradually abandoned the old-school perception that because firefighters were involved in a dangerous business, it was unrealistic to focus attention on their safety in the fire station, on fire department premises, and in fire department vehicles. The fire department should ensure that all applicable health and safety standards are met or exceeded inside the department first.

- Fire stations should comply with every applicable code requirement and should demonstrate an unquestionable commitment to safety: it is difficult to promote the installation of smoke alarms and sprinklers in private property when they are absent from the local fire station. Firehouse kitchens should be as clean as a restaurant that is anticipating an inspection by the health department.
- Fire department vehicles should be inspected regularly and thoroughly (Figure 11–3). The maintenance facility should be the cleanest and best-maintained repair shop in the city, and every potential hazard should be managed "by the book."
- Equipment inspection and testing schedules, particularly for protective equipment such as structural firefighter protective clothing and self-contained breathing apparatus (SCBA), should be rigorously followed.

Safety training

Safety is a learned behavior; people are not genetically either safe or unsafe. By the time recruits enter a fire service program or a fire training academy, they have already had twenty-plus years of learned behavior involving, among other things, traffic situations; sports; the military; recreational activities; use of vehicles; use of tools and firearms; and exposure to disease, alcohol, and drugs. From a practical standpoint, safety training, or safety learning, is a career-long effort that covers both on-the-job and off-the-job situations. Hence, all training programs must include safety as an integral component of the curriculum.

Safety training should

- Teach new patterns of safe behavior
- Allow trainees to practice techniques of safe behavior
- Supplement safety concepts with physical activities, drills, and exercises
- Reinforce and refine existing patterns to cause the safe behavior to become ingrained.

Figure 11-3 All fire department vehicles should be regularly inspected and exceptionally well maintained to ensure safety and operational reliability. Investigations of many incidents involving fire department vehicles have found that these expectations were not met.

Photo by Adam K. Thiel

- Members should be issued protective clothing that meets all applicable standards and is regularly inspected and professionally maintained. Regular cleaning is important to remove contaminants that accumulate through exposure to fire environments and other types of incidents.
- Routine vehicle inspection and safe driving should be taught and enforced.

Promoting safe driving

Mishaps that occur en route to or from emergency incidents are the second-leading cause of firefighter fatalities, as well as the cause of large numbers of serious injuries and very costly property damage. The mission of responding to emergency incidents justifies the use of red lights and sirens and allows firefighters to take advantage of specific exceptions to traffic laws; however, this legal privilege is governed by specific limitations, legal responsibilities, and moral duties. The public should have confidence that all drivers of fire and emergency service department vehicles will be well trained, closely supervised, and governed by strict guidelines to ensure that they operate those vehicles safely, skillfully, and with good judgment at all times.

The occupants of most other vehicles are at a significant disadvantage in terms of size and weight when they are involved in collisions with fire apparatus; crashes involving civilian and fire department vehicles are more likely to result in injuries or fatalities to the occupants of the smaller vehicles than to firefighters. It is impossible to rationalize any injury or fatality that results from an unsafe response that was intended to save lives or property.

The same factors that influence firefighters to engage in high-risk behaviors while fighting fires also tend to promote aggressive driving, excessive speed, and failure to stop at red lights and stop signs to ensure that approaching traffic has yielded the right of way before proceeding. Emergency vehicles are particularly susceptible to intersection accidents and crashes related to excessive speed. Some of the most serious intersection collisions involve two emergency vehicles responding to the same incident via converging routes. Water transport vehicles (tankers or water tenders) are prone to rollover accidents because of their weight and high center of gravity, particularly when they are operated by inexperienced drivers on poorly maintained roads. In the volunteer fire service, the rate of fatalities involving firefighters responding to alarms in their privately owned vehicles is a particular concern.

Falls from moving fire apparatus have been greatly reduced by requiring all firefighters to ride inside and be properly seated and secured when a vehicle is in motion. But despite apparatus design standards that require enclosed cabs, approved seats, and seat belts for all passengers, many fire departments have experienced serious injuries and fatalities as a result of firefighters not fastening their seat belts and being ejected from their vehicles in crashes. All fire and emergency service departments should adopt and strictly enforce mandatory seat belt use policies. The standards for new fire apparatus are changing to provide additional space and more user-friendly systems to secure firefighters inside crew compartments.

Significant efforts are being directed toward improvements in vehicle design, including emergency lighting and high-visibility marking, to reduce the risk of emergency vehicles being struck while stopped at emergency scenes (see Figure 11-4).

Relationship between staffing and safety

The relationship between fire department staffing and firefighter safety has been widely debated over the past two decades. There is clearly a relationship between the number of firefighters at the scene of a fire or any type of emergency incident and the ability of those firefighters to safely and effectively perform their mission. However, numerous additional factors, including response times, standard operating procedures, the training and competency of the firefighters, and the nature of the community, add complexity to the problem.

The increasing cost of salaries and benefits for career firefighters in relation to limited tax revenue creates pressure to reduce or severely limit staffing in many communities. At the same time, firefighter safety and public safety are cited as compelling justifications to maintain or increase staffing. Of course, the community's needs for fire and emergency services will be balanced against other needs at the level of local government managers and elected officials.

The connection between adequate staffing and operational effectiveness is seldom questioned. Staffing levels that provide the capability to quickly and effectively extinguish fires and

Figure 11-4 Firefighters and paramedics working along the roadway use high-visibility traffic vests and are aided by conspicuous markings on emergency vehicles.

Photo by Adam K. Thiel

control other types of emergency situations obviously enhance public safety and reduce risks to the public. However, the relationship between staffing and firefighter safety is often debated. The debate hinges on avoidable and unavoidable risks and the obligation of firefighters to take action when faced with a situation that endangers lives or property. On one side of the debate is the argument that understaffed crews and insufficient resources place firefighters at severe risk because they must take unnecessary risks and work without backup teams in dangerous situations. The opposing view is that firefighters should apply the principles of risk management and refrain from engaging in activities that involve excessive risk or dangerous exertion if they do not have the resources that are needed to operate safely.

The staffing discussion focuses on the number of firefighters assigned to each company as well as on the number of companies that are in service. Surveys indicate that most North American cities operate engines and ladders with either three or four crew members; larger cities tend to maintain four-person crews, while only a few of the largest urban fire departments routinely operate with five or six crew members per company. Many communities develop automatic mutual aid response agreements with neighboring fire departments in order to assemble an adequate total response capability for structure fires.

NFPA 1710, Standard for the Organization and Deployment of Fire Suppression Operations, Emergency Medical Operations, and Special Operations to the Public by Career Fire Departments (2010 ed.), calls for a minimum of four crew members on engine and ladder companies, and recommends five or six crew members for companies in high-risk areas. The recommended company staffing levels are based on ensuring that each company has the ability to perform standard fire suppression tasks efficiently and effectively as an independent operating unit. NFPA 1710 also calls for a minimum response of four firefighters within four minutes of travel time and of fourteen firefighters within eight minutes for a fire in a single-family dwelling, based on the number of firefighters needed to simultaneously perform a combination of tasks.

Occupational safety and health standards, both OSHA regulations in 29 CFR 1910.134 and NFPA 1500, require a minimum of four firefighters to be present before interior fire attack operations may be initiated: a two-person attack team and a two-person backup team. (This requirement is commonly referred to as the "two-in/two-out rule.") These standards do not require that the four individuals respond to the fire scene on the same vehicle. NFPA 1500 recommends but does not require a minimum of four crew members per company.

The applicability of studies, including quasi-experimental studies, of minimum company staffing levels to real-world situations has been debated. Several recent studies appear to demonstrate the efficacy of staffing levels that comport with NFPA 1710, but additional research and replication are needed to validate these results across the breadth of the United States and Canada.

NFPA 1710 is a voluntary compliance standard; local jurisdictions are not "required" to comply with the staffing provisions although they may choose to adopt them. NFPA 1710 also includes an "equivalency clause" that acknowledges that local governments can comply with the standard if their policies and practices are considered to produce an equivalent level of service. Some localities undertake an analysis of response coverage as part of their accreditation process, but no single method has been agreed on for demonstrating equivalency under 1710.

Regardless of whether a department follows the 1710 recommended staffing or its equivalence analysis, each fire department should conduct a risk-hazard analysis and deploy its resources after determining what outcomes are desired by the community weighed against what tasks must be performed to mitigate the emergency.

In addition to costs of recruitment, base salaries, pensions, and other benefits, maintaining staffing at desired levels will likely require substantial budgets for overtime to cover leave for regularly assigned personnel.

Communities faced with significant budget challenges may be compelled to reduce public safety expenditures, including fire protection, since these costs typically make up a substantial proportion of the local government's budget. When reducing fire protection expenditures, there are essentially two difficult alternatives: reduce the number of units in service or reduce unit staffing. It can be argued that reducing staffing and maintaining units maintains response times, or that reducing the numbers of units in service maintains the effectiveness of the remaining companies. There is little firm guidance that can be given in this situation, as there has been little research on the trade-off between these two alternatives. The alternative of reducing unit staffing is sometimes selected because there is a belief that the public may not be as concerned with unit staffing as with the prospect of a fire unit or fire station closing.

A community needs to carefully assess risks versus costs in the context of that specific community. Objective research can be used to inform the public, other stakeholders, and decision makers. Reductions in the number of units or in staffing can seldom be accurately portrayed as having "no effect" on service levels, and neither a fire chief nor a manager should make such a claim without carefully reviewing the details of any particular situation. Sometimes tough decisions have to be made, but it is always important to be honest about the impacts, remaining factual and objective.

Outside urban areas, the staffing and safety issue often involves very different factors. The vast majority of fire departments in the United States and Canada are staffed by volunteer firefighters or combinations of career and volunteer members. The fire departments that operate in rural areas and suburban communities, as well as in many smaller cities, are often severely limited in the resources they can deliver to a fire or emergency scene within the time that is available to intervene effectively. NFPA 1720, Standard for the Organization and Deployment of Fire Suppression Operations, Emergency Medical Operations and Special Operations to the Public by Volunteer Fire Departments (2010 ed.), which is a companion to NFPA 1710 and addresses staffing for volunteer and predominantly volunteer departments, emphasizes assessment of risk as part of the process of making staffing decisions.

Operating aggressively in dangerous situations to compensate for limited resources is very likely to expose firefighters to excessive risks. Firefighter training must focus on the application of appropriate strategy and tactics in order to manage risk exposure in relation to the resources that are available.

Incident investigation

An important part of any safety program is to investigate and keep track of situations that result in firefighter injuries, as well as near-miss situations that could have had more serious consequences. The National Fire Fighter Near-Miss Reporting System was developed by the IAFF and IAFC as an open forum to exchange valuable experience among fire departments. Chapter 9 discusses this program and its connection to training.

Major injuries and fatalities should be very thoroughly investigated and documented by a team that has been trained to apply a comprehensive investigation protocol. Recommended procedures for conducting investigations have been developed by the IAFC (iafc.org) and the IAFF (iaff.org).

Health, wellness, and physical fitness

While safety is generally focused on immediate risks to the individual, programs that are directed toward health, wellness, and physical fitness deal mainly with longer time periods and more general concerns. The concepts of health and wellness are difficult to define with precision since there are no units of measurement that can be applied to either term. There is no index that allows an individual to be classified as "83 percent healthy" or as "B+ on the wellness scale."

As used in this chapter, the terms *health* and *wellness* overlap a great deal. Both health and wellness are influenced by factors such as occupational and environmental exposures, sex, age, genetic makeup, and lifestyle.

Health describes the physical state of the body, generally in terms of things that can be measured (e.g., blood pressure, height, weight) or evaluated (e.g., x-ray studies, blood and urine analyses, vision testing). Mental health can also be assessed, although the results are more often qualitative or descriptive.

Wellness includes health but extends beyond it and is best thought of in terms of overall fitness for certain specific activities. "General wellness" can be thought of as fitness for living in general. The difference between health and wellness is illustrated by the hypothetical example of an Olympic skier with a broken leg: this person can be considered healthy but is not fit at the present time.

For people in physically taxing occupations such as firefighting, the measurable objectives of a wellness program include such things as the achievement or maintenance of a healthy heart rate and blood pressure, an improvement in the blood lipid profile to lower the coronary risk ratio, a change (usually a lowering) in body fat composition, an increase in strength and flexibility, and an improvement in cardiovascular conditioning. Any wellness program, however, must also address the mental aspects of wellness.

This chapter is also concerned with the concept of *injury prevention,* which is equally difficult to measure. Based on reports from a variety of occupational settings, there is presumed to be a close connection between wellness and prevention of injuries. The data strongly support the hypothesis that workers who are healthy, physically fit, alert, content, and well trained tend to have lower accident rates and suffer less severe injuries.

However, prevention program reporting can be deceiving, as there is no direct way to prove how many accidents a program has actually prevented. Thus, if a report quantifies the number of accidents prevented, managers should look long and hard at the mathematical assumptions underlying the data. Fire and emergency service departments should keep track of accidents and injuries over several years to determine whether safety practices are producing downward trends.

Benefits

Health, wellness, and physical fitness programs that are available, easily accessible, and specifically tailored to meet the needs of firefighters will substantially improve the chances that a firefighter will survive to enjoy a healthy and extended retirement. The essential components of this system include proper training, superior protective equipment, a competent administration and command structure, and a continual emphasis on healthy lifestyles.

The military services provide a good model for the fire and emergency services in placing emphasis on the health and physical fitness of their members. The armed forces depend on their people to perform essential and dangerous missions, and they invest in the health and fitness of their personnel to ensure that they are prepared to get the job done. The fire and emergency services should have the same expectations and make an equivalent commitment to the health and fitness of firefighters.

The importance of periodic medical examinations and realistic physical fitness standards for active firefighters has been proven and widely accepted, although many fire departments have been slow to adopt mandatory programs. The effort that is required to develop and implement sound programs is usually rewarded by very positive results. There are countless anecdotal reports of firefighters who have been diagnosed with potentially life-threatening conditions in time to be successfully treated and who then return to full duty.

The positive economic return produced by reductions in injuries and sick leave absences generally establishes the net benefit of well-planned and well-managed investments in health, wellness, and physical fitness programs. While cost is a valid obstacle in many cases, the cost of failure to develop and implement such programs is often overlooked. Most fire and emergency service departments that have invested wisely in health and wellness programs have found that the net savings and benefits far outweigh the costs. The Fire Service Joint Labor Management Wellness-Fitness Initiative program guide contains a review of the literature in this area and examples of successful programs in departments that have implemented programs using recognized guidelines.[1]

For example, the Orange County (California) Fire Authority reported significant net cost savings resulting from the implementation of a comprehensive health-wellness-physical fitness program in 2004 and 2005. The program cost was offset by much greater savings produced through reduced absences, medical claims, and disability costs. Further savings resulted from reductions in firefighter injuries and compensation claims, reductions that could be associated with improved physical fitness and fitness for duty.

The natural spinoffs from health and wellness programs can be repackaged to have a very positive effect on other components of the local government or the community. Many fire and emergency service departments sponsor health-oriented educational activities and projects for their communities, including childhood immunization programs, urban survival, pool safety, and classes in cardiopulmonary resuscitation. The Phoenix (Arizona) Fire Department's Urban

Health and fitness produce cost savings: Anne Arundel County, Maryland

The Anne Arundel County (Maryland) Risk Management Office estimates that a $1 million investment in employee health and wellness yielded a $3.5 million reduction in costs for injuries over a period of three years. The cost savings were attributed directly to reductions in compensation, lost time, and overtime replacement costs, exemplified by a 29 percent reduction in firefighter sprains and strains. The county paid about $2 million per year for firefighter injuries before the Health and Wellness Program was implemented. Since implementation, the cost has been less than $1 million annually.

An $800,000 grant through the federal Assistance to Firefighters Grant Program was matched by $200,000 in county funds in 2006 to purchase exercise and fitness equipment for all fire stations, establish fitness training programs, and hire an exercise kinesiologist as a full-time physical fitness program coordinator. The grant also covered the initial cost of a thorough medical exam for every member of the department, which became a mandatory requirement for the ongoing Health and Wellness Program. The exercise equipment, including cardiovascular machines and free weights, is available to firefighters twenty-four hours a day in thirty-two county fire stations.

The Anne Arundel County Fire Department is committed to maintaining the program and will absorb the ongoing annual costs. Even greater savings are anticipated in future years through reductions in traumatic injuries, heart attacks, and disabilities. Over the past century, the department sustained eighteen line-of-duty deaths, ten of which were attributed to heart attacks. The program is expected to lead to significant improvements in the overall health and fitness of firefighters, which will mean fewer heart attacks and occupationally related diseases. The longer-term impact should be evaluated periodically, beginning ten years after the program initiation.

Survival Program is directed toward personal safety within the community and touches on thirty-five different dangers to children.

Challenges

The challenges involved in introducing mandatory programs and requirements to an organization that has not had them in the past are very real. There is always a suspicion that a mandatory medical examination is a camouflaged effort to weed out undesirable employees. Members who know they are out of shape are likely to resist the imposition of a mandatory physical fitness program, especially if it leads to a fitness-for-duty evaluation. Job security is a strong motivating force, and firefighters who have not been involved in wellness programs are likely to react defensively, even if they know that poor health and fitness place them and their crews at significant personal risk.

It is much easier to phase in programs for new employees who understand that fitness for duty is a mandatory condition of their employment (or their active participation as volunteers) from the outset. However, an implementation strategy that allows existing members to abstain from participation may saddle the fire department with a legacy of individuals who are known liabilities to themselves and the organization.

In a career fire department, the development of a mandatory medical and physical fitness program requires active labor-management participation and a commitment to work with existing employees in a supportive and nonpunitive manner. The model programs that have been developed by the IAFF and the IAFC demonstrate a joint labor-management commitment at a national level, and their successful implementation in many fire and emergency service departments establishes that those objectives can be achieved. Similar models are available for volunteer organizations through the National Volunteer Fire Council. Programs for in-service members are discussed in more depth later in this chapter.

Health concerns for firefighters

Individuals who are hired as career firefighters or who meet the requirements to become volunteers are presumably in better health and more physically fit than the general population. However, programs that are designed to meet the needs of employees who work in an office environment on a 9-to-5 schedule are far from appropriate for most fire and emergency service departments.

The demands of the firefighter's job are physically challenging, highly stressful, and random in occurrence. Firefighters who are already mentally or physically exhausted from their response to one call may have to respond to subsequent requests for emergency services before their shifts end. Health, wellness, and physical fitness are directly related to the work environment, in terms of both the individual's ability to perform and meet the demands of the job and the impact of the job on the individual.

Firefighters are trained and equipped to work in hazardous and unfriendly environments. They perform their duties in spite of heat, noise, swift water, darkness, fatigue, and pain because they have been trained to deal with all these challenges. In addition to the problems that they can see or feel, firefighters are likely to be exposed to occupational perils that cannot be readily seen or felt. These perils include serious infectious diseases (human immunodeficiency virus [HIV], hepatitis B and C, tuberculosis, meningitis, measles, etc.) and the wide range of silent toxins associated with hazardous materials and products of combustion (carbon monoxide, hydrogen cyanide, oxygen deficiency, etc.).

The long-term health effects on the emergency responders who were involved in operations at the World Trade Center following the terrorist attacks on September 11, 2001, are being closely monitored. Very high rates of respiratory impairment have been directly linked to exposure to the thousands of tons of pulverized "products of destruction" that were released when the towers collapsed. Elevated rates of particular cancers are also believed to be related to exposure to this debris during the lengthy search and recovery operations. Long-term monitoring of these workers should provide valuable information relating to more general health risks and consequences for firefighters.

The most important known health concerns of firefighters are discussed next.

Heart disease and stroke

Cardiovascular wellness is absolutely essential to any general wellness program for firefighters. Heart attacks are by far the leading cause of line-of-duty deaths, accounting for 43 percent in 2008,[2] and firefighting ranks among the occupations with the highest frequency of cardiovascular deaths. Investments in cardiovascular wellness generally produce substantial financial savings over a period of years.

The cardiovascular system is the primary target of the contemporary wellness movement, the goal of which is to reduce the risk of a heart attack or stroke by modifying the so-called changeable risk factors (e.g., blood pressure, percentage of body fat, tolerance for exercise, blood lipid profile, and lifestyle) in the general public. All these factors are even more critical in relation to firefighters.

The wellness movement has also focused on decreasing or eliminating the use of tobacco, drugs, alcohol, and certain prescription medications—all of which are risk factors for heart disease and stroke—while encouraging education related to stress-reduction techniques and diet. The sources of specific information about cardiovascular wellness are almost limitless.

Cancer

When firefighters discuss the long-term occupational risks associated with their work, the question they most often ask is "Am I more at risk for developing cancer because of my job?" While many questions remain unanswered in establishing the definitive link between firefighting and cancer, there is increasing acceptance of a presumed causal relationship given the elevated rates of certain types of cancer among firefighters. This presumption has been incorporated into workers' compensation laws and regulations in several states and most Canadian provinces.

Behind this presumption is the fact that firefighting entails exposure to a wide variety of chemical compounds that are known or suspected to cause cancer (Figure 11–5). The presence of known carcinogens in fire environments has been extensively documented and is known to be continually increasing with the overwhelming presence of plastics and synthetic materials in every aspect of modern life. While the presence and concentration of particular contaminants at a typical fire is very difficult to predict, the potential for exposure exists at the great majority of fires.

Photo by Adam K. Thiel

Figure 11-5 All fires occurring today create toxic products of combustion that expose firefighters to a wide range of chemical hazards affecting their long-term health and safety.

Chemical carcinogens can enter the body in several ways: via the respiratory tract (breathing), by ingestion, by injection or penetration, or by direct contact with the skin or mucous membranes (see the sidebar on the following page). SCBA should provide reasonable protection of the inhalation and ingestion paths for as long as it is in use. That protection ends when the facepiece is removed, which is a strong incentive for policies that require SCBA use for all exposures to fire environments, even during the overhaul stage.

There is increasing concern over exposure to carcinogens through other routes, particularly through the skin. After a firefighting operation, the skin of firefighters is often covered by a film of black greasy residue that includes a mixture of sweat and contaminants from the fire environment. In addition, the firefighter's protective clothing and whatever was worn underneath are likely to be saturated with the same cocktail of chemical residue. Current recommendations include removal of all contaminated clothing, showering with soap and water, and dressing in clean uniforms after episodes of firefighting. The recommendations include washing contaminated items at the firehouse instead of bringing them home to mix with the family laundry. Industrial-grade washers and dryers have become standard equipment in fire stations to meet this objective.

Protective clothing and equipment that was worn or used in the fire environment is also likely to be contaminated and should be washed or professionally cleaned. Many fire and emergency service departments are issuing two full sets of protective clothing to their firefighters to allow for regular cleaning cycles and to provide a backup if one set is contaminated.

Many of the precautions that are recommended to reduce the risk of exposure to carcinogens are also applicable to other contaminants, particularly bodily fluids that firefighters are likely to come into contact with at medical and rescue incidents.

Many fire and emergency service departments (as well as many individual firefighters) document incidents of actual and potential exposure to chemical compounds, although in most cases it is not known precisely what chemicals were encountered. Cancer researchers generally try to correlate the risk factors with the length of an individual's exposure to a known concentration of a particular substance. In an industrial environment, the particular substance can usually be identified, the concentration can be quantified, and the exposure time is often measured in months or years. Firefighters are more likely to be exposed to unknown concentrations of unknown carcinogens in much higher concentrations for much shorter time periods; and there may be several suspected carcinogens in the atmosphere at the same time. The individual records of exposure to potential carcinogens usually do not provide sufficient information to establish causal relationships. However, what is known about the toxic atmosphere present in contemporary fires suggests a prima facie case for increased risk of certain cancers over the course of a firefighter's career.

Furthermore, firefighters, like everyone else, are exposed to the "invisible" factors, such as x-rays and microwave energy, that have also been linked to cancer. And like the general population, firefighters are more or less at risk of developing cancer as a result of lifestyle (diet, drugs, use of tobacco, etc.), genetic profile (sex, ethnicity, heredity), and the state of their immune systems (which is affected by everything from mental health to ingestion of antioxidants).

No discussion of cancer would be complete without reference to tobacco. Very little needs be said here about the use of smoking tobacco, which has been clearly shown to have carcinogenic effects and be responsible for a significant financial burden in relation to public health. Many fire departments have adopted policies prohibiting the use of tobacco by firefighters in any form, whether on duty or off duty.

When smoking is banned or discouraged on the job, some individuals are tempted to substitute smokeless (or spit) tobacco. The ingredients in spit tobacco are not listed on the containers, nor are the manufacturers required to affix warning labels (as they are for smoke tobacco), so the long-term effects of spit tobacco are not widely publicized. Nevertheless, there is a mounting body of evidence pointing toward mouth and tongue cancer as harmful effects of spit tobacco.

Presumptive heart-lung laws (according to which any firefighter's death or disability from heart or lung disease is presumed to be job related) have been adopted in many states and provinces, and there is a growing trend toward similar presumptions for cancer. Some of these laws stipulate that firefighters who smoke or use any tobacco products are excluded from these valued pension benefits.

Cancer prevention for firefighters

Chemical carcinogens can enter the body in four ways (breathing, ingestion, injection or penetration, or direct contact with the skin or mucous membranes).

The respiratory tract is the most vulnerable part of the body. Self-contained breathing apparatus should be mandatory for any exposure to products of combustion, even in small concentrations. Potential respiratory exposure must be recognized postfire, especially during overhaul. Filter masks may provide suitable postfire protection if the area has been thoroughly ventilated.

Diesel exhaust has been identified as a carcinogen. Fire stations should be equipped with exhaust capture systems, and apparatus areas should be physically separated from living and work spaces. Apparatus motors should not be operated in enclosed areas.

Firefighters are presumed to be at increased risk of cancer because of their occupation. Fire and emergency service departments should establish monitoring programs to detect signs of cancer at an early stage. Such programs should include prostate cancer screening for men, Pap tests for women, and colon exams and melanoma screening for members of both sexes. Ideally the monitoring and early detection efforts will be woven into a comprehensive health program designed for the monitoring and early detection of all diseases and medical conditions. (See the section on "A Comprehensive Health and Wellness Program for Front-Line Firefighters.")

Protective clothing and equipment provide the primary and essential barriers to carcinogens. Firefighting ensembles, when properly worn and maintained, offer good protection for most situations.

Smoking and diet are primary risk factors for cancer. Eating fruits and vegetables may exert a protective effect on the body. Some nutritional experts recommend supplemental intake of the antioxidants, vitamins A (beta carotene), C, and E.

Research into the environmental and behavioral risk factors for cancer is ongoing. Studies have shown that the immune systems of cheerful, happy people are generally stronger than those of dejected or depressed people.

Once disease is detected, treatment must be initiated without delay. Successful treatment depends on getting the best medical opinions, the best facilities, and the best physicians.

Musculoskeletal injuries

It is not surprising that firefighters withstand relatively high rates of sprains, strains, dislocations, and fractures, as well as contusions, cuts, and abrasions. While most of these injuries are relatively minor, they result in considerable amounts of lost time, and the cumulative effect is much higher disability rates than are found in less strenuous professions. An appropriate combination of physical fitness, training in proper work techniques, rehabilitation from injuries, safety awareness, and proper resources (i.e., staffing, equipment, and on-scene rehabilitation) can have a very significant impact on reducing these types of injuries.

Back injuries are responsible for more lost time and premature retirements than any other type of musculoskeletal injury. Such injuries are even more prevalent in fire and emergency service departments that operate ambulances, because personnel continually lift patients. Conditioning exercises and training in appropriate lifting techniques are particularly important in reducing back injuries. Equipment innovations, as well as ensuring that additional hands are available to assist with heavy patients, can also reduce the stresses involved in lifting patients.

Heat, cold, and environmental stress management

Heat stress is a very significant occupational disease among firefighters. The human body is designed to operate at a constant temperature and requires continuous cooling when subjected to a hot environment.

Natural cooling is accomplished almost entirely by the evaporation of sweat. For the cooling process to function efficiently, the body must have a supply of fluid (water) and certain electrolytes (principally sodium and potassium); it must also have some "free" surface area *from* which sweat can evaporate; and it must have air space (the drier the better) *into* which sweat can evaporate. Heat stress becomes more severe in hot and humid climates, where the evaporative cooling process is less efficient. The kidneys help manage this evaporative cooling process by sorting, saving, excreting, and filtering the fluids and electrolytes presented to them.

When the body is unable (for whatever reason) to achieve adequate cooling, a condition called *heat stress* develops rapidly. The body's core temperature starts to rise, other body systems are affected, and strength and reflexes deteriorate rapidly. The reduction in fluid volume due to the loss of water thickens the blood and places greater demands on the cardiovascular system as it tries to maintain circulation.

Heat-stress disease within the fire and emergency services has been well documented. Encasing the body in a heavy insulating envelope of protective clothing (see again Figure 11–1) effectively halts sweat evaporation, the principal process by which body temperature is regulated. The severe heat produced by a fire adds even more energy to the heat balance equation. The addition of physical activity accelerates the onset of symptoms (fatigue, syncope, cramps).

Heat stress itself is treatable, especially if detected early. However, if the stress continues, the body gives up: it loses its ability to cope with heat. This condition, usually characterized by loss of consciousness and lack of sweating, is termed *heat stroke.* Heat stroke is a bona fide medical emergency. The result can be acute exertional rhabdomyolysis (AER): small fragments resulting from the breakdown of muscle clog the kidneys' filtration system. AER can cause permanent kidney damage and kidney failure.

When firefighters are engaged in emergency activities, they run the risk of becoming dehydrated in hot and cold weather alike. Maintaining hydration is extremely important because it is now known that firefighters can become ill with symptoms associated with dehydration (including cramping and kidney failure) even after incidents are completed. Emergency scene rehabilitation (rehab) programs are designed to bring fluid and food to the scene to rehydrate department members and restore their energy. Small departments can accomplish basic rehab by bringing an ice chest to the scene along with fluid-replacement drinks and nutrition bars. Large departments normally have dedicated resources available to set up a rehab sector (Figure 11–6). As the scene develops into a large-scale emergency operation, the need for rehab services grows accordingly.

Figure 11-6 Firefighters from several Phoenix-area fire departments rehydrate and receive medical monitoring in a designated on-scene rehab center.

Photo by Adam K. Thiel

In hot climates, departments may use misting systems, fans, or both to provide a cool-down area for the rehab of members. To prevent cold-related injuries when the weather is cold, dry blankets should be provided to keep members warm after their protective clothing is removed; consideration should also be given to providing heaters and enclosed rehab areas because clothing will be wet from water and activity.

Monitoring is important. When each firefighter enters the rehab area (whether enclosed or not), his or her vital signs should be taken and documented; they should then be monitored throughout the rehab process. If, after a period of time, the vital signs do not stabilize, the firefighter should be transported to a hospital for evaluation by a physician. In the past, when there was no rehab area and proper hydration was not maintained, severely dehydrated firefighters had to be placed on dialysis until their kidneys began functioning again.

Mental health and the SAD (stress, alcohol, and drugs) diseases

Mental health is a major component of total wellness. It is said to be responsible for everything from depression and anxiety to eating disorders and drug and alcohol problems.

People absorb and tolerate stress in many different ways. In addition to the stress factors common to everyone, firefighters must cope with additional stressors related to what they see and do on the job, including incidents and situations that can leave severe emotional scars. Their stress levels are also affected by work schedules that often disrupt normal patterns of sleep and by the need to continually operate in a "cocked-and-ready" mode—ready to face severe challenges at any moment.

Depression Cumulative or repeated stress is believed to be one cause of depression. Depression, a feeling of intense sadness, may follow a loss or other sad event, but it tends to be out of proportion to the event and persists beyond an appropriate length of time. Depression can accompany other medical problems and is often mentioned as an underlying condition associated with suicide. In addition, there is mounting scientific evidence that depression can adversely affect the immune system. In most cases depression can be successfully treated if it is recognized and diagnosed.

Dealing with stress

Very few organizations outside of the military specifically train people to deal with the stress they can expect to encounter on the job. One of the best mental health support systems is built into the fire and emergency services, and that system is the close bond of collegiality and friendship that characterizes people who must work together as a team under stressful and potentially dangerous conditions. In certain circumstances, however, this support system is a disadvantage for the firefighter—for example, when it encloses him or her so effectively that the needed external treatment (such as professional counseling, medical treatment, or both) is either delayed or withheld. The aftermath of the terrorist attacks of September 11, 2001, is adding a great deal of new information about the mental health aspects of firefighting.

Drug and alcohol problems Drug and alcohol problems, too, may be exacerbated by stress. But although the magnitude of these two problems is staggering, treatment programs exist for them as well as for virtually every other addiction and addictive behavior (e.g., Alcoholics Anonymous for people addicted to alcohol, Narcotics Anonymous for drug addicts, and Gamblers Anonymous for gamblers).

Post-traumatic stress disorder Post-traumatic stress disorder (PTSD) is a severe manifestation of psychological trauma that can have a debilitating and long-lasting impact on individuals who are involved in life-threatening or highly disturbing incidents. Firefighters are often involved in situations that can produce PTSD, the symptoms and long-term consequences of which are extremely variable, depending on the nature of the occurrence and the psychological resiliency of different individuals.

During the 1990s, many public safety agencies began using a variety of support mechanisms to help members deal with the impact of incidents likely to cause severe psychological reactions. In some jurisdictions this type of assistance is also extended to the families of firefighters and to the victims of fire, violence, and other disasters. The specific measures that are employed combine various professional and peer support services.

There are significant differences in opinion among mental health professionals regarding the particular models and processes that are most effective in managing postincident stress. Critical incident stress debriefing (CISD) teams provide immediate and ongoing support to firefighters and other first responders in the wake of incidents that are likely to precipitate unusual stress or anxiety. The purpose of CISD is to provide emotional support by listening to, supporting, and counseling firefighters in times of great emotional stress. But while some mental health professionals strongly advocate mandatory postincident debriefing, others believe that it can produce undesirable consequences and so they recommend different intervention strategies. A consensus appears to be emerging that mandatory group peer counseling may not be appropriate for all personnel attending an incident.[3]

Effective intervention is most likely to occur when there is an established system in place to respond to highly stressful occurrences. Providing an intervention model that is different from CISD, the NFFF is developing a network of local and regional response teams to provide trained personnel to support the psychological needs of firefighters in the wake of traumatic incidents.

Gender-based medical issues

The increasing proportion of women within the ranks of firefighters has made it essential to expand the scope of fire department health and wellness programs. For example, cancer screening and early detection programs should include the Pap test for cervical/uterine cancer and mammography for breast cancer.

The most complicated workplace issue involving women's health has to do with the potential for pregnancy. Every female firefighter in her childbearing years who has an intact reproductive system can become pregnant. In the very early stage of a pregnancy, before it is detected, occupational exposure to toxic substances may create a risk for the developing fetus.

Once a pregnancy is ascertained, any accommodations, restrictions, or limitations with respect to duty assignments should be addressed carefully. Some women and many physicians will insist that a pregnant firefighter should immediately be placed on medical leave or reassigned to duties that avoid exposure to hazardous or strenuous situations; others may take the position that such mandatory policies constitute gender-based discrimination. Administrators and policy makers must walk a narrow line between reasonable accommodation and gender discrimination in determining the duty status of any pregnant firefighter. The fire department physician should address each situation on a case-by-case basis.

Issues for recruitment, selection, and basic training

One of the primary objectives of a fire department's recruitment and selection process is to identify individuals who are medically and mentally healthy and physically fit for entry-level positions. In this regard, the fire and emergency services are similar to the military, the airline industry, law enforcement, and other fields that have established medical and physical fitness standards as qualifications for selection and retention.

The recruitment and selection process must be conducted within the framework of applicable laws, rules, and administrative regulations (see Chapter 10). Most fire departments have incorporated rigorous physical standards within their fundamental requirements for recruits. The NFPA 1500 series standards have been developed through research and public comment and are an excellent starting point for discussion and action. In many places these standards are referenced by laws and ordinances.

Public safety administrators must balance two sets of responsibilities. On the one hand, they must abide by the legal definition of *qualified* as it applies to public safety employees, including applicants and trainees. They must also ensure the safety and protection of citizens who need to have confidence in the physical, technical, and emotional proficiency of the people responding to their emergencies.

On the other hand, because departmental rules and physical standards are frequently challenged, resulting in lengthy and costly litigation, managers and administrators should ensure that fire department requirements for recruitment, selection, and training are based on valid standards and recommended testing procedures. They should develop a clear picture of their departments' expectations *before* making decisions that can have costly legal consequences.

Once in training, firefighter recruits usually spend a great deal of time in physical conditioning. Most moderate injuries incurred during training (e.g., shin splints, sprains, strains, contusions, and bruises) occur during physical conditioning or when the recruits are becoming familiar with the equipment. The more severe medical problems—for recruits as well as for experienced firefighters—are related to heat stress, which is exacerbated by hard physical work. Some mental health problems may arise in connection with beginning a new career. Occasionally, previously masked problems of substance abuse may emerge.

A comprehensive health and wellness program for frontline firefighters

The basic goal of a comprehensive health and wellness program should be to support the overall goals of the organization by addressing the health (physical and mental) and fitness of the organization's human resources. Investments in the health and fitness of the workforce should produce a more operationally effective team and reduce injuries and disabilities. They should also be cost-effective in terms of net cost savings. The program should be designed to meet the needs of firefighters and other emergency responders, both career employees and volunteers, as well as support staff.

A comprehensive health and wellness program should incorporate physical health, physical fitness, mental health (stress reduction), attention to substance abuse, and nutrition. The Fire Service Wellness-Fitness Initiative is an excellent model. Successfully adopted by many

Testing for physical performance and trainability

In some jurisdictions the recruitment and selection process for firefighters is supplemented (or preceded) by pretest educational programs. Agencies may wish to consider whether pretesting and remedial programs should be considered for the physical performance part of the selection process as well. Local organizations such as community colleges, the YMCA or YWCA, private gyms, and sports teams might be resources for a physical conditioning effort.

Starting a health and wellness program

Typically, the person or group appointed to manage a wellness program in a fire and emergency services department is already interested in some areas of health and fitness and thus has the interest and knowledge to develop the basic elements necessary for starting a program. The fire chief's first step should be to identify this person (or group) to develop, implement, and manage the program.

A departmental labor-management team can be used to gather information about personal needs, produce operating procedures, identify the equipment and facilities needed, and propose a plan to start (and maintain) a meaningful wellness program. The team must have representation from throughout the department and must gain all necessary approvals as it proceeds.

The program manager must be responsible for surveying the department's members about their specific needs, evaluating the resources available, establishing time frames, and identifying the issues of department members as a group. Maintaining confidentiality, making the program mandatory, and dealing with those who do not wish to participate are the kinds of group issues that can make or break the program.

Depending on the size of the department, this preliminary work could take considerable time and become somewhat complicated, especially with respect to personal issues. The program manager, fire chief, and departmental labor-management group, however, must stay focused on what the program can do for the majority of members and the department; they must be careful not to focus on issues that affect only a few people, lest the program be undermined by a lack of support from the membership as a whole.

Care should be taken to make sure that the program is versatile enough to be attractive to as many department members as possible rather than being focused on the organizer's favorite activity. For instance, some people do not like to run or jog but can get the same fitness results from a brisk walk or other activity.

Source: Thomas Healy, former fire chief, Daisy Mountain Fire Department, Phoenix, Arizona.

fire and emergency service departments, it is a complete wellness program specifically designed to fit the needs of firefighters. The Wellness-Fitness Initiative is sponsored jointly by the IAFF and the IAFC and was developed by a committee on which both management and labor from several different fire departments were represented.[4]

A comprehensive program should extend beyond the basic measurable elements (e.g., strength in bench-press pounds, endurance in time on the treadmill, percentage of body fat, and blood pressure) to focus on an individual's overall wellness and fitness in relation to the duties that the person is expected to perform. Mental health is as important as physical strength and endurance. Thus, an effective health and wellness program must address ten fundamental and interconnected elements:

- Health baseline
- Periodic assessments
- Prevention programs
- Prompt and competent intervention
- Treatment
- Rehabilitation
- Fitness for duty: policies on return to work and alternative duty assignments
- Physical fitness
- Mental health (stress reduction)
- Tobacco and nutrition.

Health baseline A health baseline should be established for every member of the fire and emergency services department. This requires a physical examination, a medical and occupational history, and appropriate laboratory testing. In most departments this step will require a comprehensive initial examination for all existing employees, while the baseline for new employees should be established during the selection process.

Periodic assessments Periodic assessments of each individual's wellness and fitness are used to detect any variation in health status. Regularly repeated comprehensive evaluations by a physician are also essential if the health and wellness program is going to be successful in maintaining members' health. NFPA 1582, Standard on Comprehensive Occupational Medical Program for Fire Departments (2007 ed.), provides specific recommendations for annual physical examinations and evaluations.

Early detection is a primary objective of a truly effective health and wellness effort. Medically, early detection is achieved by means of screening exams or tests, which are commonly used to detect such things as cancers (of the prostate, testicle, breast, cervix, colon, skin); infectious diseases (HIV, hepatitis, tuberculosis); enlargement or abnormalities of the thyroid, lymph nodes, and internal organs; and hearing loss; as well as diabetes and heart disease. Mental health issues, including depression and problems related to drugs and/or alcohol, may also surface during the early detection health assessment.

Despite the importance of periodic assessments and examinations for tracking health status and providing early detection of treatable conditions, cost may limit the scope and frequency of such screenings for departments with limited budgets. The cost should be prioritized within the fiscal planning process, but the potential economic benefits can often be expected to offset program costs. Many fire departments have obtained grants or donations from civic groups or local labor organizations to conduct medical examinations.

Paramedics and other medically trained members of the department can assist in conducting parts of the process. Hospitals and clinics may be willing to offer examinations and laboratory tests at reduced rates, while medical doctors, physicians' assistants, and nurses sometimes volunteer to conduct examinations for local firefighters. Charitable organizations may be willing to provide financial support to ensure that firefighters receive appropriate periodic assessments.

It is very important to note that medical records must always be treated as confidential. Managers should ensure that the laws, customs, and conventions affecting access to medical records in the particular jurisdiction are being followed and that everyone involved is aware of the rules. See Chapter 10 for information on federal and state legal requirements regarding confidentiality.

Prevention programs Prevention programs should be directed first at known exposure risks. Prevention can take several forms: a medicine, the use of specific techniques or equipment, or education. In the case of hepatitis B, prevention takes all three forms. A vaccine is available to inoculate individuals; there are standard precautions to take with patients; and there are specific techniques for disposing of contaminated waste and equipment. Fire departments that provide emergency medical care should have ongoing training in disposal and decontamination procedures. NFPA 1581, Standard on Fire Department Infection Control Program (2010 ed.), provides further information on this topic.

The more mundane aspects of protection that are intrinsic to the fire and emergency services service should not be overlooked. These include seat belts and personal protective equipment, such as earplugs and other personal hearing protection devices, gloves, SCBA, safety glasses, and face shields (see Figure 11–7).

While they are vital, prevention programs for mental health receive much less emphasis, partly because they can be perceived to involve an invasion of privacy. Posters in the workplace can remind personnel that mental health is important and that counseling is available.

Prompt and competent intervention Prompt and competent intervention is critical for any health problem. The time and competency factors are equally important. The system must be geared to respond promptly and effectively when a firefighter is injured; has been exposed to a toxic, hazardous, or infectious substance; or is found to have a physical or mental problem.

Treatment A process or pathways must be in place to manage commonly encountered or expected medical situations. In addition to treatment for physical problems, treatment programs (not necessarily cures) are available for virtually every addictive behavior problem as well as for depression, stress, and burnout.

Photo by Adam K. Thiel

Figure 11-7 Fire department paramedics at the scene of a structural collapse incident are clad in appropriate personal protective equipment.

Rehabilitation The recovery process for most medical events continues after the initial treatment. Larger departments should consider providing some of the commonly needed rehabilitation (e.g., physical therapy and work hardening) internally or through a provider that specializes in working with firefighters. Mental health monitoring can usually be provided through an employee assistance program (EAP), although specialized providers may be needed for PTSD. Monitoring the rehabilitation process makes good sense both fiscally and clinically.

Fitness for duty Policies on returning to work and alternative duty assignments often involve difficult decisions for the health and wellness staff. In most jurisdictions the official process for determining duty assignments is an administrative decision, but the recommendations of a medical or nursing professional are usually followed.

It is absolutely essential to have in place a method or process for resolving medically based conflicts equitably. The arbitration model is often effective: each party selects a medical expert, and the two experts together select a third expert. The parties agree in advance to abide by the majority decision of the three experts.

The level of fitness that should be expected or required of the more senior members of a fire department is often debated. In larger departments, where chiefs and other senior officers are not required to perform heavy physical tasks on the fire ground, their required fitness levels may be geared to the demands of a strictly administrative job. In departments where the chiefs and senior officers may be required to perform strenuous emergency operations, their fitness for duty must be based on those requirements, and the determination should be based on realistic expectations as opposed to arbitrary mandates.

Physical fitness Physical fitness is an essential requirement for anyone who engages in firefighting and related strenuous activities. Individuals who are physically fit are able to perform their duties at a higher level, with greater endurance and resiliency. They are also less likely to be injured while performing their duties or to suffer from occupational illnesses. Higher levels of physical fitness, when combined with the other wellness components, enhance the body's ability to fight off a variety of conditions related to poor health.

Reducing heart attack risk

In 2007, the National Institute for Occupational Safety and Health Fire Fighter Fatality Investigation and Prevention Program released a study of on-duty heart attacks and the risk of sudden cardiac events among firefighters, and offered the recommendations provided below, among other. Many of these recommendations (e.g., the screening of firefighters for coronary artery disease [CAD] risk factors) are consistent with the general practice of preventive medicine,[1] so their implementation should reduce not only the number of on-duty fire-fighter heart attacks and sudden cardiac events but also those occurring off-duty as well.[2]

Recommendations for candidates

- Provide postoffer/preplacement medical evaluations to ensure that candidates are capable of performing job tasks with minimal risk of sudden incapacitation.
- Ensure that the physicians conducting the postoffer/preplacement medical examinations are knowledgeable about the physical demands of firefighting, the essential job tasks of firefighting, and the consensus guidelines developed by the fire service.[3]
- Ensure that medical clearance for full-duty fire suppression and SCBA (self-contained breathing apparatus) use is conducted by either (1) the fire department physician or (2) a primary care physician knowledgeable about the physical demands of firefighting and the consensus guidelines developed by the fire service.[4]
- Ensure that firefighter candidates have the physical ability and capacity to perform the essential job tasks of firefighting.[5]
- Designate personnel to administer the fire department postoffer/preplacement and annual medical evaluations.
- Refer candidates with cardiac conditions or CAD risk factors to their health care providers for further evaluation and treatment.

Recommendations for fire department members

- Ensure that firefighters understand the importance of wearing respiratory protection during all phases of firefighting—from initial attack through overhaul.
- Provide mandatory annual medical evaluations to ensure that members are capable of performing job tasks with minimal risk of sudden incapacitation.
- Ensure that physicians conducting the annual medical examinations are knowledgeable about the physical demands of firefighting, the essential job tasks of firefighting, and the consensus guidelines developed by the fire service.[6]
- Ensure that medical clearance for full-duty fire suppression and SCBA use is conducted by either (1) the fire department physician or (2) the primary care physician, as previously noted. The medical clearance letter should state what essential job tasks the firefighter can and cannot perform.[7]
- Develop a comprehensive wellness-fitness program for firefighters to reduce risk factors for cardiovascular disease and improve cardiovascular capacity. NFPA and IAFF/IAFC documents can provide guidance.
- Encourage firefighter participation in the fire department's wellness and fitness program.
- Ensure that a smoking cessation program is included in any wellness program.
- Ensure that all fire stations and other fire department facilities are nonsmoking facilities.
- Place and maintain (automated external defibrillators (AEDs) on all fire department apparatus that are not equipped and staffed for manual defibrillation.
- Train firefighters on the proper use of AEDs.
- Remind emergency department personnel and medical examiners to perform carboxyhemoglobin testing on all firefighters who experience a cardiac arrest.

Source: Adapted from National Institute for Occupational Safety and Health (NIOSH), *Preventing Fire Fighter Fatalities Due to Heart Attacks and Other Sudden Cardiovascular Events*, NIOSH Publication No. 2007-133 (Atlanta, Ga.: Centers for Disease Control and Prevention, June 2007), 16-17, at cdc.gov/niosh/docs/2007-133/#sum.

1 U.S. Preventive Services Task Force, *Guide to Clinical Preventive Services*, 2nd ed. (Baltimore, Md.: Lippincott Williams & Wilkins, 1996).

2 In considering these recommendations, fire and emergency service departments need to be aware of federal laws, such as the Americans with Disabilities Act of 1990 (ADA), as well as applicable state and local laws that may affect their implementation. For example, the ADA requires that medical examinations take place only after an offer of employment has been made.

3 National Fire Protection Association (NFPA), NFPA 1582: Standard on Comprehensive Occupational Medical Program for Fire Departments (Quincy, Mass.: NFPA, 2007).

4 Ibid.

5 International Association of Fire Fighters (IAFF) and International Association of Fire Chiefs (IAFC), *Candidate Physical Ability Test* (Washington, D.C.: IAFF/IAFC, 1999).

6 NFPA 1582.

7 Ibid.

Checklist for a comprehensive health and wellness program

Agreement between labor and management: Do labor and management agree on the process by which medical disputes are resolved? In health and wellness programs, this is a key point.

Medical control: Definitive administrative control of the medical aspects of a program should rest with a licensed medical professional. So, too, does the responsibility for ensuring the confidentiality of medical information.

Ancillary staff: In addition to having the services of a dedicated and licensed physician, a comprehensive program should have access to the services of a licensed or certified physiotherapist, exercise physiologist, registered nurse, physician's assistant, and dietician.

Cost-effectiveness: The harvest of such programs as prevention by early detection and screening will be proportional to the depth and breadth of the programs, which are proportional to the dollars spent.

Baselines: At a minimum, everyone should have an age-based medical exam to establish baselines and comparative trends.

Incorporation into training: Some aspect of health, wellness, and prevention of injuries should be incorporated into every company training session.

A physical fitness evaluation, similar to a baseline medical examination, should be conducted for all members who are involved in performing emergency operations. This evaluation will indicate specific areas on which firefighters need to focus to protect their bodies from injury or disease.

Structured physical fitness activities should be an officially recognized component of the work cycle for firefighters (see Figure 11–8). The program must offer assistance to firefighters in either maintaining or improving their physical fitness levels. NFPA 1583, Standard on Health-Related Fitness Programs for Fire Department Members (2008 ed.), provides guidance on developing a fitness program that is specifically oriented to the needs of firefighters.

In addition to encouraging or requiring fire department members to participate in physical fitness activities, members should have access to trainers and qualified individuals to support their efforts. Certified peer fitness trainers are incorporated into the IAFF/IAFC Wellness-Fitness Initiative model that is used in many larger departments. Smaller fire departments may have to seek this type of support from external sources.

Ideally, every fire station should provide equipment to allow members to exercise while on duty (Figure 11–9). Commercial-grade equipment is preferable because of the heavy use to which it will be subjected. The equipment can be elaborate or simple, but it must be durable and of high quality. When exercise equipment is not available at fire stations, it is often

Figure 11-8 Goodyear, Arizona, firefighters participate in their annual wildland firefighting fitness assessment, commonly known as the "pack test."

Photo by Adam K. Thiel

Figure 11-9 Firefighters engage in routine physical fitness training to enhance their safety and effectiveness while reducing the potential for debilitating injuries and illness.

Photo by Adam K. Thiel

possible to make arrangements with local fitness organizations, community colleges, or high schools to obtain access to their equipment and facilities. Many fire and emergency service departments use equipment donated by organizations that were upgrading their facilities.

The objective should be to maintain a level of fitness to protect the body, not to build super athletes. The equipment should provide a full-body workout to maintain overall muscle tone. Multistation machines that include exercises for chest, back, arms, and legs can easily fit into most rooms. Free weights consisting of barbells and dumbbells with benches are very popular but require more room. Aerobic equipment such as stationary bikes or treadmills should also be provided.

Mental health (stress reduction) The ability to remain psychologically and emotionally stable and healthy is as important as medical health and physical fitness. Some medical experts have suggested that even cancer and heart disease might be tied to mental stress and the lack of stress management.

A high level of mental stress is endemic to firefighting. People choose to become firefighters because of their desire to help others, and they are therefore exposed to many negative life situations: they are called on to assist in the aftermath of assaults, shootings, stabbings, cardiac arrests, automotive crashes, and fires. These incidents can have lasting emotional effects on the caregivers. These unavoidable mental stresses must be appropriately managed to allow firefighters to enjoy their family, friends, and life in general.

EAPs and full-family assistance programs are increasingly being provided by employers as a health benefit to their employees. Needless to say, the providers of such services must understand the special nature of the fire service work environment. Exercise, nutrition, stress management techniques, and even family counseling are all tools that an EAP can give firefighters to help them cope with work stress and prevent that stress from interfering with their home lives. The overall cost-effectiveness of these investments in mental wellness have been established in many different types of organizations.

Tobacco and nutrition Campaigns to stop the use of tobacco (in all forms) and improve nutrition can be initiated through a departmental information and advisory program. The American Lung Association and the National Cancer Society provide posters and information that can be set out in the workplace. Using this material is the simplest, most effective way to begin a program with minimal funding.

Professional nutrition counseling can have a very positive impact on firefighter diets and lead to improvements in overall health and wellness. If professional consultation cannot be funded, magazine articles can provide information to firefighters on how to reduce fat and

Checklist for a substance abuse and mental health program

Begin with a team and a plan. Start (or energize) your educational programs with respect to drugs, alcohol, and other addictions by focusing on those at the supervisory level. Teach them how to recognize addictive and self-destructive behaviors, and give them access to the network and tools to move people into treatment channels.

Get some expert help. A trained, dedicated medical clinician can provide advice and guidance. And do not overlook or minimize the potential contribution that, for some people, spiritual support may make in this effort. Besides providing access to a physician, therefore, a department may arrange to make a chaplain's time available as well.

Be alert to the use of drugs and alcohol. Recognize, understand, and accept that the use of drugs and alcohol in the workplace (except for a few prescription medications) is illegal and dangerous for everyone involved. If you have an employee assistance program, use it. If not, create one. Get Alcoholics Anonymous or another treatment program involved. If a problem of drug or alcohol abuse exists in your department, seek legal advice about the disciplinary and other options available to you.

Recognize inappropriate or destructive behavior. Pay attention to behavior that is destructive (to an individual or others) or that does not seem to fit the situation. Do not make light of such behavior or dismiss it, facilitate it, or escalate it. Above all, do not look the other way. Plan in advance how you are going to deal with inappropriate behavior. Remember that discipline alone does not resolve every case of inappropriate behavior.

Become more observant. Become more observant, especially of changes in attitude and/or participation in group events or discussions. Does the person's body language or conversation send a message of despair? Such a message may be a subtle plea for help.

Be ready to act. As of 2008, suicide was the fourth leading cause of death among people between the ages of 25 and 44 in the United States, accounting for 14 percent of deaths in that age group.[1] If someone attempts or threatens to commit suicide, make absolutely certain that he or she is not left alone until the management of that person is formally turned over to a mental health professional capable of dealing with the situation.

Accept the fact that a price will have to be paid. Accept the fact that a price almost always has to be paid for relief of depression and removal of the person's concomitant dependence on drugs and alcohol. For some, loss of social status and of close friendships may become the price for sobriety: giving up drugs or alcohol may mean giving up one's former "drinking buddies" or avoiding friends whose social activities revolve around drugs. Some "friends" who use alcohol or drugs themselves may not support a person who has given these substances up; thus, the former abuser may be cut off from his or her former social circle. The person's supervisor may then have to deal with an employee who now feels lost, alone, or rejected and may have to encourage the employee to develop compensations for the loss.

1 National Center for Health Statistics, "Deaths: Preliminary Data for 2008," *National Vital Statistics Reports* 59, no. 2 (December 9, 2010): 56, cdc.gov/nchs/data/nvsr/nvsr59/nvsr59_02.pdf.

make other improvements in their diet. The important thing is to get started at some level and build from there.

Health and wellness center

An increasing number of jurisdictions are establishing health and wellness centers for public safety employees or specifically for fire department members. This concept usually combines a medical office with a physical fitness center that is specifically designed to meet the needs of the workforce. This concept begins to make economic sense when the range and scope of activities and the number of employees create a workload that justifies the cost. A group of smaller jurisdictions might be able to join forces to establish a shared facility.

Providing a designated health and wellness center helps to establish the importance of the program within the fire and emergency services department. The center should be the location where firefighters receive their scheduled physical examinations and other occupational medical services. It should provide exercise equipment as well as access to qualified trainers, a physiotherapist, and other specialists such as a nutrition counselor. Behavioral health services should be located at a different facility in order to protect patient confidentiality.

The fire department physician should have designated office hours at the health and wellness center to conduct examinations and meet with individual members regarding their health concerns. A physician's assistant or nurse practitioner could be employed full time to conduct

Phoenix Regional Fire Fighter Health Services Network

The Phoenix Fire Department Health Center is nationally recognized for its comprehensive approach to managing the health, wellness, and physical fitness of the organization's employees. In addition to serving more than 2,000 fire department members, the center provides annual physical examinations and health surveillance for the members of seventeen outlying fire departments through intergovernmental agreements. The regional program provides access to a state-of-the-art system at an affordable cost for the smaller fire departments, while the revenue helps to offset the fixed operating costs of the health center for the city of Phoenix. Funding for the center is included in the fire department budget, and all the services are provided by full-time or part-time employees or through contractual agreements.

The primary goal of the program is to strengthen individuals so that they can withstand both the physical and the emotional aspects of the job. Operating for more than twenty years, the program is one of the original participants in the IAFF/IAFC Fire Service Joint Labor Management Wellness-Fitness Initiative and has proven to be cost-effective in reducing firefighter injuries, occupational illnesses, and disability retirements.

In addition to supporting programs to develop and maintain high levels of health and physical fitness, the health center manages the rehabilitation of firefighters recovering from injuries and illnesses to facilitate their return to regular duty. It also operates tracking systems that record exposures to hazardous materials and infectious diseases, and it provides members with direct access to a wide range of medical specialists and professional services.

A parallel behavioral health program is funded as an employee benefit and operated through the firefighters' union local. This program provides almost unlimited access to a wide range of services for fire department members and their dependents. It includes peer counseling and professional psychological support for members affected by traumatic incidents or displaying various manifestations of occupational stress.

Source: Phoenix Fire Department, Health Center Home Page, at phoenixfirehealth.com/.

the hands-on portion of annual medical examinations under the physician's supervision. A medical assistant or nurse receptionist would be valuable in organizing and administering the medical services that are provided at the center.

Health and wellness centers usually contract with a medical laboratory or a hospital network for blood evaluations, x-rays, and access to additional services that are impractical to provide at a dedicated facility. The hospital network could also be interested in contracting for the overall management of health services, which would include employee salaries and benefits, malpractice insurance, and administrative functions. The contract should allow the fire department to manage the work schedules of the individuals who provide the services to ensure that the hours of operation fit the department's shift schedule.

Conclusion

Fire and emergency service departments expect firefighters to expose themselves to a variety of hazards over the course of their careers. Managers provide firefighters with a protective envelope of clothing, SCBA, and the rest, but sometimes something gets neglected: the effects of the hazards on the person inside the envelope are not always addressed. The true asset to the department is the person inside, and that person is the focus of a health and wellness program. Beyond the obvious value of maintaining a safe and effective workforce, comprehensive health and wellness programs can provide economic benefits to fire departments and local governments by reducing the cost of employee injuries and illnesses.

Notes

1. International Association of Fire Fighters (IAFF) and International Association of Fire Chiefs (IAFC), *The Fire Service Joint Labor Management Wellness-Fitness Initiative,* 3rd ed. (Washington, D.C., and Fairfax, Va.: IAFF and IAFC, 2008), iafc.org/files/healthWell_WFI3rdEdition.pdf.
2. U.S. Fire Administration, *Firefighter Fatalities in the United States in 2009* (Washington, D.C., July 2010), Figures 10 and 12, usfa.dhs.gov/downloads/pdf/publications/ff_fat09.pdf.
3. Jonathan Bisson et al., "Early Psychosocial Intervention Following Traumatic Events," *American Journal of Psychiatry* 164 (July 2007): 1016–1019.
4. IAFF, "Fire Service Joint Labor Management Wellness-Fitness Initiative," at iaff.org/hs/well/wellness.html.

PART THREE

Managing Fiscal Resources

CHAPTER 12

Fiscal Management

Bruce J. Moeller

This chapter provides an understanding of

- The link between public policy and budgeting for fire and emergency services
- The distinction between policy and service delivery, and the definition and role of efficiency and effectiveness
- The importance of budgeting for the achievement of department goals
- Methodologies for preparing budgets
- Issues related to the cost of service and equitable distribution of that cost
- Methods of generating revenue for fire and emergency services, with their advantages and disadvantages
- Major components of fire and emergency service expenditures
- Basics of financial controls and auditing as they apply to public budgets
- How to manage financial risk.

Every citizen wants—and expects—a quick response from the fire department. Firefighters and chief fire officers are quick to point this out when they argue for better funding for their departments. But this raises a basic question: how much is enough? When fire and emergency services get too costly, citizens and politicians will demand better justification for the dollars they invest.

Leading a fire and emergency services organization requires many skills. Among them is the ability to develop, implement, and account for the organization's budget. This chapter describes the basic procedures and considerations for developing the fire and emergency service's budget.

Before we begin, however, it is appropriate to sketch the importance of the fire and emergency services as a portion of the average local government budget. These services are quite expensive. With approximately 70 percent of the nation's population protected by fully career or combination fire departments, the cost of operating these agencies is predominantly accounted for by personnel salaries and benefits—often exceeding 85 percent of the department's entire budget. Data from over 19,000 fire departments in 2006 show that the average cost for department operations was over $120 per capita. Volunteer departments have average costs approaching $30 per person protected, while combination departments average $65 per capita. For local governments, the cost of fire protection can often make up anywhere from 15 percent to 20 percent of the community's total general budget.[1]

It is because of the significant costs for fire protection that strong fiscal management of fire and emergency services is necessary. Citizens want the fire and emergency services in their communities to be effective. Should they need to dial 911, they want emergency responders to be able to handle the problem. But they also want to know that the cost for that emergency response is affordable and that the services will be delivered efficiently. Developing appropriate benchmarks that permit apples-to-apples comparisons between fire and emergency medical service (EMS) departments has proven difficult. Yet some basic structural elements can provide chief fire officers with a roadmap to strong financial management. These elements of financial management are strategic planning, budgeting, management of revenues and expenditures, financial controls, asset management, and financial risk management.

The budget as public policy

Many public agencies simply muddle through their decision making, arriving at important decisions on the basis of limited information and perhaps limited experience. The following discussion presents some of the basic issues involved in convincing policy makers to support fire and emergency service initiatives. Additional information on public policy and agenda setting can be found in the list of further readings at the back of this book.

Any meaningful endeavor in government, especially the protection of life and property, requires resources. In the fire and emergency services, the location and construction of fire stations, the purchase of apparatus and equipment, and the recruitment and training of fire personnel all require significant financial investment. Budgeting for these components is a clear expression of the public policy to safeguard citizens and their property from fire. The bottom line is that in government, we put our money where our mouth is.

In local government, elected officials set policy, government staff implement policy by planning and managing services, and local government employees deliver services to the public. However, citizens and other community stakeholders (including fire and emergency service employee groups) provide feedback on the policies to the elected officials. This feedback loop, illustrated in Figure 12–1, is a critical component of the policy-making process.

There is a common belief that citizens will always object to paying higher taxes. This is not true. Research has shown that residents only want to be assured that their tax dollars are being well spent—without abuse or inefficiency. Therefore, to the degree that the fire service can prove that precious tax dollars are being used wisely, citizens are likely to support appropriate levels of funding for essential public safety services. Demonstrating that fire and emergency

---

This chapter is a revised and updated version of Chapter 6, "Fiscal Management," by Gail Stephens, Robert P. Gannon, and William H. Clark, in the 2002 edition of this volume.

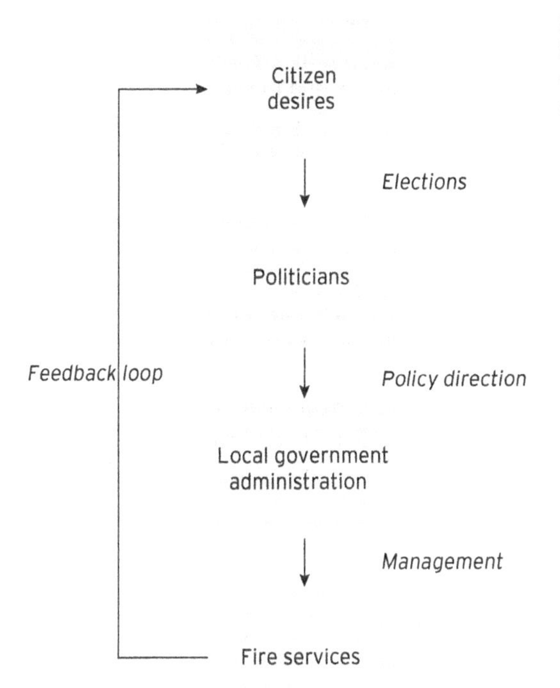

Figure 12-1 The feedback loop that operates in setting local policy includes citizens, elected officials, local government administrators, and service delivery professionals.

services are effective requires the chief fire officer to quantify the department's performance. Demonstrating that the services are being delivered efficiently requires the performance to be accomplished with the least amount of resources (dollars). Demonstrating both effectiveness and efficiency justifies the expenditure of tax dollars and helps chief fire officers get their projects and initiatives high ranking on the public policy agenda, thereby ensuring that these programs will be approved and funded.

Financial management for fire and emergency services within the larger framework of the local government's policy making includes

- Strengthening the organization's financial position
- Developing and delivering the financial information needed for decision making
- Making visible the costs of delivering individual programs and outcomes to enhance accountability
- Integrating financial considerations with operational decision making and organizational planning
- Managing financial risks and exposures.[2]

Financial management also means managing expenditures by analyzing the cost of delivering services, considering alternative strategies for delivering services, and evaluating new strategies for generating revenues.

Strategic planning

Policy makers must consider the needs of the community and determine how to allocate available resources to fund them. To do this, the local government organization defines a strategic vision, agrees on a strategic plan, and then develops a budget that applies fiscal resources to its strategic priorities. It has been argued that this policy-making process is nothing more than determining who gets what, when they get it, and how they get it. In essence, budgeting is public policy, and strategic planning is the foundation for budgeting.

The relationships among the three groups—citizens, elected officials, and local government administrators—produce public policy. Yet this policy-making process is ineffective if the three groups do not share a strategic vision that can guide decisions about basic programs and fiscal priorities. When the groups share a strong strategic vision and the interchange among them is working well, the local legislative body exhibits strong leadership, senior administration provides sound direction in the form of planning, and the services offered to the public are seen as providing good value. When a strategic vision and a strategic plan are lacking, the effectiveness and the financial health of the organization will suffer.

A basic role of any local government is to provide for the health and safety of its residents. This fundamental mission is accomplished through many players, including law enforcement, public health, emergency management, and social service agencies. Historically, the fire service has been the "go to" organization when significant incidents affect the community. Thus, the chief fire officer must participate in the development and implementation of the strategic plan as well as advocate for those programs that ensure that this basic purpose of government is met.

Once the local government has established its strategic plan, the fire and emergency services department must develop its own plan to support the government's overall plan. Strategic planning does not require a consultant, but consultants are often hired to educate the department on how to complete proper strategic planning.

Organizational purpose

Just as the local government needs a broad strategic vision for the community, the fire department needs to define its own vision, mission, and values in order to develop a strategic plan to guide its financial management. For the fire and emergency services, we often say the mission is to "fight fires and save lives." But is it really that simple? Does every community require the same services from its fire department?

Vision is defined as the desired or future state of the organization. Vision is long term. *Mission,* on the other hand, defines the basic purpose of the organization—basically, why it exists and what it does from day to day. Finally, *values* are the beliefs shared among the stakeholders of the organization. These beliefs define the organization's culture and priorities; they are also essential in defining the organization's vision (long-term objective) and mission (short-term objective).

One of the first issues that must be settled in determining the organization's mission and vision is its legal construction. Is the fire and emergency services department part of a local city or county government, as are 80 percent of such departments in the country, or is it an independent fire district, as are the other 20 percent? If it is part of a larger general-purpose government, then the department must align its strategic mission with that of the larger organization. If the entity is a special-purpose district, then it is important to understand how its mission interacts with those of the other governmental entities, such as the local law enforcement agencies and other local government components.

At least in concept, a strategic plan allows a fire and emergency services department to achieve increased operational and financial autonomy. Each department budget is a component of the department's strategic plan. In other words, the goals and tasks that are outlined in the strategic plan have identified in principle the cost and revenue that must be budgeted in order to achieve the department's strategic objectives. When the legislative body approves each department's budget, it also approves the premise of the department's strategic plan. The budgeting and strategic planning process is an attempt to educate the financial decision makers (local elected officials) about the relationship between departmental actions and costs, making it difficult for them to reduce funding while simultaneously demanding that levels of service remain unaffected.

The value of strategic plans lies in both the process and the product. The process of planning (1) engages policy makers, administrative managers, employees, and other key stakeholders in a healthy dialogue; (2) stimulates creative and critical thinking; (3) focuses participants on the strategies and actions critical to success; and (4) ensures a connection to political priorities and the goals of the overall organization and government structure. The strategic plan itself encourages communication between a public organization and its stakeholders; enhances accountability; and documents where the fire and emergency services organization is, where it is going, and how it will get there. And finally, a successful strategic plan ensures that programs and services will support the local government's strategies and goals. (Chapter 3 provides more detail on the strategic planning process and how the analysis of strengths, weaknesses, opportunities, and threats [SWOT] can help define the organization's mission.)

Risk assessment

In establishing the organization's purpose and thereafter the budget, one of the first steps is to conduct a risk assessment to determine the level of risk to life and property in the community. The levels of human resources, physical assets, and so forth that are needed to respond to the identified risks are also determined (see Chapter 3). Although many smaller departments cannot afford to do so, those that can afford the expense often hire a consultant to conduct the risk assessment; this is because when a department conducts its own risk assessment and subsequently advocates a higher level of funding for itself, it may be accused of empire building. Moreover, consulting experts can look at such factors as demographics, population and structural densities, and incident trends that have a huge effect on how service is actually delivered. Only large departments have the internal staffing to do this themselves.

In lieu of a consultant-based approach to determining the level of risk acceptable in the community, some agencies have embraced the accreditation model to justify specific service levels. One such model is managed through the Center for Public Safety Excellence (publicsafetyexcellence.org/).

Analysis of services

The services rendered by fire and emergency service organizations are generally very direct and visible, and they attract extensive public and media attention. Therefore, managers must be clear and explicit about the services they provide, the objectives underlying those services, and the standards or benchmarks by which performance will be measured. This analysis serves as the foundation for comprehensive performance measurement.

Typical emergency response services include fire suppression, emergency medical services, hazardous materials (HAZMAT) removal, and technical rescue. Other direct services include code enforcement, fire prevention/inspection, and public education activities (see Chapter 4). All these deliverables generally fall into the category of public safety. Emergency response providers must continually review the fundamental question of why they are providing each service. Can the service be provided better and more efficiently by a different supplier or through alternative processes (contracting out, partnering, charging user fees, establishing special operating agencies, etc.)?

A financial model organized around individual services may be a helpful tool for analyzing services that are under the local government umbrella, including fire and emergency services. (For some ideas about various models, see the section later in this chapter on potential sources of revenue.) The concept of alternative service delivery is key here: any service or mode of service delivery for which the value of outcomes to the community (benefit) is greater than the value of inputs to provide that service (cost) should be considered for continuation. Where the benefit does not exceed the cost, alternatives must be considered.

An emergency response organization that is focused on service outcomes as opposed to inputs is better prepared to be proactive and thus have an increasingly positive effect on the community it serves. The organization can have this effect by (1) establishing a strategic planning process that takes into account all of the organization's internal and external stakeholders (see the discussion in Chapter 3 on SWOT analyses); (2) integrating the financial imperatives into the political context; and (3) completing the process by establishing service-based budgets, which value the cost outcomes of a service, as opposed to line-item accounting, which considers only inputs. However, moving from inputs to outputs is not easy and requires the extensive education of, and commitment from, all employees.

To identify service deliverables properly, an organization must understand who its "customers" are. Services and customers must be linked in some meaningful fashion; the service delivered must match exactly what the customer wants or demands. Too often, public organizations offer services that in fact can be delivered more effectively through other means. Understanding the customer profile is essential when a department is analyzing its services.

Strategy formulation

Once the organizational purpose, risk assessment, and service analysis are complete, it is time to develop specific strategies. These are generally identified through the use of goals and objectives. *Goals* identify an ideal state and may be abstract. *Objectives* are more tangible and concrete. Each goal is generally supported by several specific objectives, and in many strategic plans, each objective is supported by several specific tasks for greater clarity. Many organizations assign tasks to specific groups or individuals who are then responsible for achieving the specific objectives and, eventually, the organization's goals. At the task level of detail, it is possible to define specific programs and resources required, as well as the outcomes expected to be achieved in furtherance of the strategic plan (see Figure 12–2).

Strategy formulation consists of finding effective and efficient strategies for achieving goals and objectives. At this level, the organization must think "big." For example, a breakdown in many strategic planning processes is the failure to consider outside resources. Each fire department's response area is bordered by an adjoining department's response area. This presents the opportunity to evaluate intergovernmental or regional approaches to service provision. Even large departments—including the largest fire department in the United States, the New York City Fire Department—require mutual aid during a significant incident. A regional approach can take many forms. A mutual aid agreement provides for assistance from an adjoining department to a significant incident, upon request. An automatic aid agreement builds additional resources from a neighboring jurisdiction into the requesting department's run card. This may provide a cost-effective way of ensuring that adequate resources are on scene for minimal or no cost. (For more information on mutual and automatic aid agreements, see Chapter 16.)

Figure 12-2 An excerpt from the strategic plan adopted by Corvallis, Oregon, illustrates a table format.

1	Workforce Development: Improve development opportunities for the workforce.							
	Strategy 1.1: Encourage career development through support and formalized processes.							
		Lead	Partners	Time Frame	Frequency	Prioritization	Related Action Items Completion	Date
1.1.1	Establish a standardized annual performance review process for each employee, including semi-annual face-to-face feedback sessions and individualized benchmarks.	Fire Chief	Mgt. Team; HR; IAFF	Short	Annually	Med	1.1.3; 1.3.2	2012
1.1.2	Explore feasibility of an officer development program.	Training DC	Mgt. Team; IAFF; Other FDs	Short	N/A	Med	1.2.1; 1.2.2; 1.3.3	2010
1.1.3	Display performance benchmarks for crews at all stations.	Fire Chief	Mgt.Team	In Progress	Quarterly	High	1.3.2; 2.3.7	2009
1.1.4	Promote the core values of the department.	Fire Chief	All Members	In Progress	Continually	High	1.2.1; 2.3.7	Ongoing
1.1.5	Formalize selection process for special-duty assignments.	Fire Chief		Short	N/A	Low	1.2.1; 1.3.3	2012
	Strategy 1.2: Develop and maintain a training model and curriculum that meets the needs of staff and CFD.							
1.2.1	Reassess and enhance training curriculum in non-technical areas (e.g., conflict management, communication, time management, diversity and harassment, teambuilding, effective use of the chain of command, and sustainable practices.)	Training DC	HR; DPSST; NFA; Area FDs	In Progress	Annually	Med	1.1.2; 1.2.2; 1.2.3; 2.1.1; 2.3.4	2010
1.2.2	Provide more scenario-based training.	Training DC	Crews; DPSST; NFA	Short	Annually	High	1.1.2; 1.2.1; 6.1.1	2009
1.2.3	Host professional development opportunities locally.	Training DC	DPSST; NFA; GSRMC; Area FDs	In Progress	Annually	Low	1.2.1	Ongoing
1.2.4	Create opportunities to make up missed trainings.	Training DC		Long	Quarterly	Med	1.2.1	2013
1.2.5	Explore options to limit interruptions to training sessions.	Training DC		Long	N/A	Med	1.2.1	2014
1.2.6	Establish annual tours of large and multistory complexes to increase staff awareness of building layouts.	Fire Marshal	Training DC	Long	Annually	Low		2014
	Strategy 1.3: Promote a positive work environment by prioritizing morale.							
1.3.1	Communicate changes to CFD goals and policies as they occur.	Fire Chief	Mgt. Team	In Progress	N/A	High	2.3.2	Ongoing
1.3.2	Display CFD goals prominently throughout the department.	Fire Chief	Mgt. Team	In Progress	Quarterly	High	1.1.3; 2.3.7	Ongoing
1.3.3	Explore opportunities to increase team building within and among crews.	Training DC	Batt. Chiefs	In Progress	N/A	Med	1.1.2; 1.1.4	Ongoing

Source: Corvallis, Oregon, Fire Department, *Strategic Plan 2009-2014* (June 2009), 13, ci.corvallis.or.us/downloads/fire/CFDStrategicPlan.pdf.

Additional cooperation and financial advantages can be achieved through the use of a specialty team jointly staffed and funded by more than one department. Many HAZMAT teams and other special operations are the result of cooperation among multiple entities. Over the past several decades, many areas of the country have looked at the benefits of consolidation.

While each of these approaches is fraught with political issues, thoughtful implementation of regional programs can both enhance services and provide cost-effective delivery to the community. The strategic planning process can help identify opportunities within a particular community. These opportunities should be considered in the strategic planning process—even if the organization simply conducts an exploratory review or study of the issue.

Strategic plans provide an outline of how a program's performance can be measured against stated objectives so that variances from targets can be identified and explained. Essentially, departmental strategic planning allows the political and administrative functions of local government to review actual results and compare them against target results, rather than simply monitor inputs (costs). This review of results is part of the feedback loop that informs policy makers on where resources may be required.

It is this outline of performance measures that makes a strategic plan an accountability document. (For a fuller discussion of performance measurement, see Chapter 14.) The strategic plan also helps policy makers focus on results and on what has been planned but not yet accomplished, rather than on what is being done now.

Once a strategic plan is approved by the governing body, it is imperative that the department's chief officers assign responsibility for specific goals and objectives throughout the organization and monitor their progress. All too often, fine strategic plans simply collect dust because departmental leadership did not follow through on implementation. The result is often frustration and organizational drift from the agreed-upon mission. Since many strategic plans are created for a three- to five-year time frame, quarterly or semiannual progress reports should be required.

Executing change

Because fire and emergency service organizations are made up of people, the human component must be considered when changes are planned. Introducing new programs and initiatives during good times, and imposing program cuts and budget reductions during weak financial times, require leadership. Understanding the organizational and financial considerations necessary to successfully implement the strategic plan and budget is critical. Therefore, chief fire officers must consider successful implementation of their strategic objectives as part of strong fiscal management. In essence, there are two main considerations: organizational and financial.

Organizational considerations Most theories in organizational behavior recognize that there will be resistance to change. This is especially true in the fire and emergency services. Including members of the organization in the development of a strategic plan is the first step to overcoming that organizational resistance.

Communication is another important element in successful implementation. Resistance is often rooted in a lack of information. Thus, the department's strategic plan, budget, and overall financial picture should be readily available to anyone in the organization. The justification for new programs or the need for budget reductions should be explained to key stakeholders; insofar as possible, these stakeholders should be involved in the implementation of change, and efforts should be made to address any fears or concerns that they may have about their future. Involving stakeholders will help gain acceptance for the changes within the organization and increase the likelihood of success.

Finally, new initiatives or programs should be reviewed after a period of time—often six months to one year—to give stakeholders an opportunity to raise remaining issues or identify problems.

Financial considerations Fire department leaders must ensure that new program initiatives or other significant budget changes are fully analyzed. When developing new programs or initiatives, advocates will sometimes underestimate the actual costs in order to minimize potential budget impacts and increase the likelihood of acceptance by policy makers. However, leaders' credibility will be damaged if the program can be only partially implemented or if the department must go back to policy makers and ask for more funding.

For each program proposal, the department needs to identify all costs and add appropriate contingency factors to the budget for unexpected costs. It is not unusual to see a 10–15 percent contingency added to major program proposals. This practice helps protect those who advocate for and approve these programs.

Similarly, care should be taken when estimating the cost savings from reductions in program budgets. When governmental budgets contract and fire departments are forced to do more with less, agencies are required to propose program cuts with concurrent budget reductions. Many times these reductions are driven by a target set by the budget office. In this situation, there is a temptation to overestimate the savings that such program cuts may produce in order to just "get through" the budget development process. However, should policy makers decide to implement budget reductions and the projected savings do not materialize, chief fire officers will be asked to explain the deficit. A basic rule of budgeting is especially important in times of fiscal stress: underestimate your expected revenues and savings, and overestimate the anticipated costs for any program. Doing so will provide a small buffer to help ensure that your budget stays balanced.

Budgeting

As just discussed, a budget should be prepared in conjunction with a strategic plan. Historically, emergency response services have not generally been subjected to the same funding constraints in the budget process as have other local government departments. However, when debt loads increase, infrastructure decays, transfer payments from higher levels of government decrease, and the desire to lower property taxes makes itself heard, local governments become less willing to sacrifice other services in order to maintain emergency response services at existing levels. Fire and emergency service departments then face the same scrutiny as other local government departments.

Developing a department budget in conjunction with the local government budget is perhaps the single most important and time-consuming administrative activity of a fire and emergency service. The budgetary amounts for the current year, and the financial projections for the next several years, are set within the framework of the strategic plan discussed above (see Figure 12-3). The financial projections should accurately reflect the financial resources needed to accommodate the service levels (including the strategies for managing human resources, information technology, and physical assets) proposed to achieve organizational goals.

Choosing a budget approach

All local and state governments are required to adopt a balanced budget. (Only the federal government can adopt a budget that calls for deficit spending.) The revenues available to fund fire and emergency service operations and the expenditures of the various programs to be funded must be balanced. Numerous attempts have been made over the past several decades to develop budgeting processes that provide for greater accountability and efficiency. And while each attempt has yielded some positive elements, most local governments use one of two approaches—either a line-item budget or a program budget.

Whether for a small volunteer department or a career department in a large city, preparing a departmental budget is often a difficult task. Most departments find that the process requires considerable time, effort, and expertise. It generally begins in one of two ways: either (1) the elected officials or the local government administration establishes a fixed financial target or (2) the chief of the department determines the financial resources required to provide a level of service that has been established through a political or administrative process.

With the economic downturn, governments are increasingly electing to set a fixed financial target for budget development. Such a target requires the chief to determine what can be provided within the funding limit provided. Preparing a budget to meet a fixed target can be very trying; the department may be forced to do any or all of the following: reduce staffing levels, decrease levels and types of services, decrease response capability, and seek

Figure 12-3 A generic example of expenditure projections is shown here, illustrating the major categories of expenditures for the fire and emergency services department.

5-Year Expenditure Projections - Fire Rescue Department

DEPARTMENT	FY 2009	FY 2010	FY 2011	FY 2012	FY 2013	FY 2014
Fire Rescue						
Personnel Services	$ 14,585,755	$ 14,315,042	$ 16,080,794	$ 16,884,833	$ 17,729,074	$ 18,615,527
Health Insurance	$ 1,255,057	$ 1,380,563	$ 1,518,619	$ 1,670,481	$ 1,837,529	$ 2,021,282
Pension--General	$ 96,550	$ 120,688	$ 144,825	$ 159,308	$ 175,238	$ 192,762
Pension--Fire	$ 1,731,864	$ 2,164,830	$ 2,597,796	$ 2,857,576	$ 3,143,333	$ 3,457,666
Operating Expenses	$ 1,703,734	$ 1,757,913	$ 1,813,815	$ 1,871,494	$ 1,931,007	$ 1,992,413
Capital Purchases	$ -	$ -	$ -	$ -	$ -	$ -
Vehicle Replacement	$ -	$ 42,000	$ 43,336	$ 44,714	$ 46,136	$ 47,603
Computer Replacement	$ -	$ -	$ -	$ -	$ -	$ -
Non-Operating/Other	$ -	$ -	$ -	$ -	$ -	$ -
	$ 19,372,960	**$ 19,781,036**	**$ 22,199,185**	**$ 23,488,406**	**$ 24,862,317**	**$ 26,327,253**

Notes and Assumptions:

2.50%	Annual COLA Increases--Midyear Adjustments on March 31
2.50%	Annual Merit Increases--Midyear Adjustments on March 31
3.18%	Annual CPI Increases--Operating
3.18%	Annual CPI Increases--Non-Operating/Other
3.18%	Annual CPI Increases--Capital
3.18%	Annual CPI Increases--Vehicle Replacement
3.18%	Annual CPI Increases--Computer Replacement
10.00%	Annual Increases--Health Insurance Medical Trend
25.00%	Annual Increases--Pension Year 1
20.00%	Annual Increases--Pension Year 2
10.00%	Annual Increases--Pension Year 3
10.00%	Annual Increases--Pension Year 4
10.00%	Annual Increases--Pension Year 5

alternative methods of funding or of delivering services. However, the task can also be rewarding and informative: often the constraint of a fixed target acts as a catalyst for new and innovative service delivery methods that enhance the quality and effectiveness of the service.

Increasingly less common is the department-initiated budget. Generally such a budget is prepared after a risk assessment has been performed to determine the level of risk to life and property in the community (see Chapter 3). The levels of human resources, physical assets, and so forth that are necessary to respond to the identified risks are determined and costed, usually in a line-item budget format (see below).

Whichever approach is taken, the budget must be submitted to local elected officials for approval.

Line-item budgeting

The line-item budget focuses on inputs or individual expenditure categories (or lines), such as salaries, health insurance, fuel, and supplies. It lists items to be purchased and organizes them by department, division, or some smaller organizational unit. Dollars are appropriated for specific items (see Figure 12-4).

A line-item budget is quite simple to understand once the underlying structure is understood. This structure, which is often referred to as the chart of accounts, follows a specific format and numbering scheme for expenditure categories. Each category typically has a specific purpose and associated definition. Various funds may be established for

Figure 12-4 The Fire-Rescue Department budget from Sunrise, Florida, is an example of a line-item budget.

		ACTUAL FY 2007-2008	AMENDED FY 2008-2009	ADOPTED FY 2009-2010
FIRE RESCUE				
PERSONNEL SERVICES				
3201-522.12-01	Salaries	$9,831,512	$9,823,225	$10,412,554
3201-522.12-02	Incentive Pay	1,504,518	1,564,802	1,814,502
3201-522.12-03	Holiday Pay	463,756	456,438	492,953
3201-522.14-01	Time and a Half Overtime	351,466	143,000	143,000
3201-522.14-02	Straight-Time Overtime	20,009	21,000	21,000
3201-522.15-02	Special Detail Pay	60,377	51,020	55,102
3201-522.15-05	Clothing Allowance	27,000	28,200	28,600
3201-522.15-07	Sp. Detail Pay-Non-Reimbursable	16,151	30,000	32,400
3201-522.21-01	SS and Medicare Matching	882,391	929,061	967,431
3201-522.22-01	Pension-General	117,654	84,304	66,421
3201-522.22-02	Pension-Firefighters	2,137,263	1,627,737	1,866,020
3201-522.23-01	Health Insurance	1,009,673	1,184,173	1,129,395
3201-522.23-04	Statutory Life and AD&D Ins.	4,819	4,819	5,750
3201-522.24-00	Workers' Compensation	619,994	587,839	555,222
REQUESTED APPROPRIATION		**$17,046,583**	**$16,535,618**	**$17,590,350**
OPERATING EXPENSES				
3201-522.31-20	Medical Services	$32,495	$17,450	$50,000
3201-522.31-21	Medical Director	30,396	30,396	36,000
3201-522.31-30	Professional Services	30,567	19,965	169,966
3201-522.34-02	Records Retention	692	1,000	1,000
3201-522.34-04	Temporary Services	0	100	100
3201-522.34-05	Building Maint. Contracts	15,598	29,500	24,000
3201-522.40-01	Travel and Per Diem	6,209	2,952	2,962
3201-522.41-01	Telephone	106,189	103,352	103,362
3201-522.41-05	Data Line	0	70,608	70,608
3201-522.43-01	Electricity	171,756	189,920	190,000
3201-522.43-10	Water & Wastewater	57,143	57,390	80,346
3201-522.43-15	Stormwater	4,439	6,116	8,562
3201-522.44-02	Buildings- Rental	39,545	41,352	44,000
3201-522.46-10	Maint Auto Equipment	387,652	380,372	408,000
3201-522.46-11	Maint Office Equipment	0	250	250
3201-522.46-13	Maint Communication Equip	35,440	49,500	49,500
3201-522.46-16	Maint Computer Equipment	0	100	100
3201-522.46-29	Maint Other Equipment	54,539	65,000	74,200
3201-522.46-40	Maint Buildings	0	44,000	44,000
3201-522.47-01	Printing and Binding	2,447	5,000	5,000
3201-522.47-02	Photocopying Costs	1,681	2,000	4,000
3201-522.49-08	Permits & Licenses	640	9,000	1,000
3201-522.49-54	Vehicle Replacement Funding	0	0	1,049,890
3201-522.51-01	Office Supplies	7,542	8,950	12,294
3201-522.52-01	Gas & Oil	193,887	197,761	197,761
3201-522.52-03	Uniforms	39,907	30,451	34,000
3201-522.52-04	Protective Clothing	33,695	62,790	38,500
3201-522.52-10	Medical Supplies	151,265	145,090	150,000
3201-522.52-14	Building Maintenance/Supplies	58,728	0	0
3201-522.52-17	Small Equipment	68,967	8,548	10,000
3201-522.52-50	Haz. Mat'ls Supply & Exp	10,108	11,000	10,000
3201-522.52-51	Dive Team Supply & Exp	728	1,000	1,000
3201-522.52-52	Explorers Supply & Exp	629	750	500

specific purposes; revenues from various sources are defined; and expenditures are grouped by line item or purpose. The chart of accounts and other budget structures are often established at the state level, and most charts of accounts are similarly organized. One example is shown in Figure 12–5.

A line-item budget format has several advantages. Adding up lists of items purchased is relatively simple, so the total budget is easy to derive. Also, the level of operational detail enables departmental supervisors to monitor, revise, and control day-to-day operations and prepare and justify the next year's budget. And because the purchasing and payroll systems are linked directly to actual financial amounts within specific budgetary line items, budgetary control can be effected through the accounting control system.

Description	Fund	Department	Function and activity	Account class	Balance sheet accounts, revenue, sources, and expenditure objects
Fund codes					
General	100				
Special revenue	200-299				
Capital projects	300-399				
Debt service	400-499				
Enterprise	500-599				
Internal service	600-699				
Trust and agency	700-799				
General fixed assets	800-899				
General long-term debt	900-999				
Balance sheet: Assets and other debits					
Current assets				11	1000-4999
Non-current assets				11	5000-5999
Restricted assets				11	6000-6999
Capital assets				11	7000-7999
Other assets				11	8000-8999
Other debits				11	9000-9999
Balance sheet: Liabilities					
Current liabilities				12	1000-4999
Non-current liabilities				12	5000-6999
Liabilities payable from restricted assets				12	7000-8999
Balance sheet: Equities and other credits					
Other credits				13	1000-1999
Contributed capital				13	2000-2999
Retained earnings				13	3000-3999
Fund balance				13	4000-4999
Revenues					
Taxes				31	1000-9999
Licenses and Permits				32	1000-9999
Intergovernmental				33	1000-9999
Charges for Services				34	1000-9999
Fines and Forfeitures				35	1000-9999
Investment income				36	1000-9999
Contributions and donations				37	1000-9999
Miscellaneous				38	1000-9999
Other financing sources				39	1000-9999
Function					
General government			1000		
Judicial			2000		
Public safety			3000		
Public works			4000		
Health and Welfare			5000		
Culture/recreation			6000		
Housing and development			7000		
Debt service			8000		
Other financing uses			9000		
Expenditures/expenses					
Personal services and employee benefits				51	1000-9999
Purchased/contracted services				52	1000-9999
Supplies				53	1000-9999
Capital outlays				54	1000-9999
Interfund/interdepartmental charges				55	1000-9999
Depreciation and amortization				56	1000-9999
Other costs				57	1000-9999
Debt service				58	1000-9999
Other financing uses				61	1000-9999

Figure 12-5 The state of Georgia publishes a Uniform Chart of Accounts for use by local governments.

A major complaint about line-item budgets, however, is that unless the budget development process incorporates the priorities outlined in the department's strategic plan, chief fire officers, budget directors, and policy makers simply look at the previous year's revenues and expenditures and make minor, "incremental" changes for the upcoming year based on assumptions about increases in salary costs, projected fuel savings, the need to replace some hose, etc. This process, known as incremental budgeting, does not add value to the organization and fails the community because its scope is too narrow. It is driven by a limited view of the fire and emergency services department.

To prevent incremental budgeting, the budget process should start with an assessment of the priorities outlined in the strategic plan and the adjustments needed to fund or eliminate programs according to those priorities. The budget should reflect the priorities of the local government.

A line-item budget format has several other disadvantages. Although easy to balance, this format makes it difficult to cut expenditures because a cut in one line item may have ramifications throughout the budget. Most of the human and physical resources listed as line items in the budget are linked not to single strategic objectives but to a variety of objectives. Thus, when

Fund definitions, state of Illinois

FUND: An accounting entity with a self-balancing set of accounts in which financial resources, related liabilities and residual equity or balances, are recorded and segregated for specific activities or to attain certain objectives in accordance with regulations, restrictions or limitations. A government is not limited to the number of funds it may have, but should use the least number of funds possible. All of the funds used by a government should be classified into one of seven fund types as listed below . . . :

Capital Projects Fund: A fund created to account for financial resources to be used for the acquisition or construction of major capital facilities (other than those financed by proprietary and trust funds). Absent of a legal requirement, the use of a capital project fund is not required.

Debt Service Fund (Sinking Fund): A fund established to account for the accumulation of resources for the payment of general long-term debt principal and interest. Absent of a legal requirement, the use of a debt service fund is optional. Debt service funds are required if they are legally mandated and/or if financial resources are being accumulated (over several years) for principal and interest payments maturing in future years.

Enterprise Fund: (1) A fund established to account for operations financed and operated in a manner similar to private business enterprises (for example, water, gas and electric utilities; airports; parking garages; or transit systems). This method is used, where the intent of the governing body is that the costs of providing goods or services to the public on a continuing basis be financed or recovered primarily through user charges. (2) A fund established because the governing body has decided that periodic determination of revenues earned, expenses incurred and/or net income is appropriate for capital maintenance, public policy, management control, accountability or other purposes.

Fiduciary Fund: A fund established for governments to hold or manage financial resources in an agent or fiduciary capacity. A single trust and agency fund type is used to account for a government's fiduciary activities. This single fund type, however, is subdivided into five "sub-fund types" to account for various types of fiduciary obligations. These "sub-fund types" are the non-expendable trust fund, the expendable trust fund, the pension trust fund, the investment trust fund, and the agency.

General Fund: The fund used to account for all financial resources, except those required to be accounted for in another fund. All of a government's financial activities should be accounted for in the general fund unless there is a compelling reason to report them in some other fund types (e.g., legal requirements). A government may never report more than one general fund. The general fund can be composed of several different accounts. All accounts are general funds unless a specific ordinance provides that funds or accounts are restricted as a special fund. . . .

Internal Service Fund: A fund used to account for the financing of goods or services provided by one department or agency to other departments or agencies of that government, or to another government on a cost reimbursement basis.

Special Revenue Fund: A fund used to account for the proceeds of specific revenue sources (other than expendable trusts or major capital projects) that are legally restricted to expenditure for specified purposes. (NOTE: Gravel, oil, and special bridge funds are generally Special Revenue Funds. General Funds for Component Units also should be recorded under the Special Revenue Fund column. Although grants are commonly reported as special revenue funds, it is not appropriate to report capital grants as a Special Revenue Fund. If a grant is restricted to capital construction or acquisition for general government purposes, report it in a capital project fund type.)

Source: State of Illinois, "Chart of Accounts and Definitions" (n.d.), 3-4, ioc.state.il.us/ioc-pdf/LocalGovt/AFR2004/2004chartofaccounts.pdf.

arbitrary reductions are made (e.g., when the entire budget is reduced by a flat percentage), the consequences of cuts may be unforeseen; the budget itself will give no information on the implications of reductions for operational items such as fuel. If decision makers do not understand the complex nature of the fire and emergency services, they will not understand how cuts will affect the overall picture. In contrast, as discussed below, when decision makers make a cut in a program-based budget (as opposed to a line-item budget), they know how operations will be affected—that is, which specific program levels will be reduced.

A third disadvantage of the line-item format is that the emphasis is on the items of expenditure (inputs) rather than on the results (outcomes). A fourth disadvantage is that the level of detail tends to reduce operational flexibility: monies are appropriated for specific items, but if circumstances change significantly between the time that the budget is prepared and the time that it is implemented, moving monies between and among line items may require getting various approvals. Fifth, precisely because the line-item budget is easy to control, it invites overcontrolling and may stifle innovation.

Finally, line-item budgeting may encourage unnecessary spending. Any unexpended amount for the current fiscal year is lost to the department, and because failure to spend these funds can be interpreted as a lack of need for such monies, an equal amount is probably lost in succeeding years. Thus, it is almost inevitable that department leaders will try to spend all funds appropriated each year, whether they need to or not.

Program budgeting

An alternative to line-item budgeting is the program-based budget. Whereas the line-item budget focuses on inputs, a program-based budget focuses on outputs—on the programs provided by the local government (see Figure 12–6). Program-based budgeting can be defined as the allocation of activity costs on the basis of program cost centers, which represent the smallest segments or areas of responsibility for which costs are accumulated.

One of the first tasks in program-based budgeting is defining the program cost centers. A program cost center should be defined in a manner that (1) facilitates decision making, (2) is consistent with legislation, and (3) aligns the cost center with a specific set of goals or objectives for serving a specified target group or customer population. Program cost centers must also be aligned with the overall organizational mandate and should not be limited by functional groupings within the organizational structure.

Fire

Operating Budget Summary

Sort Description	*FY 07 Actual*	*FY 08 Actual*	***FY 09 Budget***	*FY 09 Estimate*	***FY 10 Budget***	***Percent Change***
Expenditures by Category Name						
Personal Services	$13,098,866	$15,033,771	**$17,072,726**	$16,750,156	**$16,400,241**	**-3.94%**
Contractual Services	$2,347,061	$3,379,963	**$3,806,353**	$3,694,918	**$3,132,993**	**-17.69%**
Commodities	$1,078,160	$713,490	**$848,114**	$823,102	**$580,537**	**-31.55%**
Capital Outlay	$173,776	$14,564	**$310,288**	$467,292	**$250,000**	**-19.43%**
Total :	$16,697,863	$19,141,788	**$22,037,481**	$21,735,468	**$20,363,771**	**-7.59%**
Expenditures by Division						
Fire Admin	$592,599	$773,497	**$872,657**	$844,724	**$709,079**	**-18.74%**
Fd Community Services	$1,275,790	$1,516,805	**$1,582,084**	$1,230,825	**$1,149,287**	**-27.36%**
Fire Support Services	$1,477,076	$812,519	**$872,177**	$1,054,027	**$583,336**	**-33.12%**
Emergency Medical Services	$96	$436,229	**$1,057,281**	$1,022,681	**$537,102**	**-49.20%**
Fire Training	$111	$287,767	**$590,979**	$543,246	**$528,518**	**-10.57%**
Emergency Management	$0	$134,612	**$473,457**	$430,282	**$216,912**	**-54.19%**
Fire Operations	$13,226,628	$15,142,744	**$16,526,746**	$16,551,298	**$16,301,437**	**-1.36%**
Fed Assist to Firefighters Grt	$0	$0	**$0**	$0	**$300,000**	**NA**
Homeland Security Grant - MMRS	$89,306	$0	**$0**	$0	**$0**	**NA**
Vol Firefighter Pension Trust	$33,781	$34,475	**$33,600**	$33,600	**$30,600**	**-8.93%**
Citizen Donations-Fire	$2,476	$3,140	**$28,500**	$24,785	**$7,500**	**-73.68%**
Total :	$16,697,863	$19,141,788	**$22,037,481**	$21,735,468	**$20,363,771**	**-7.59%**
Staffing by Division						
Fire Admin	6.00	6.00	**8.00**	7.00	**6.00**	**-25.00%**
Fd Community Services	13.00	13.00	**12.00**	10.00	**9.00**	**-25.00%**
Fire Support Services	7.00	7.00	**6.00**	6.00	**5.00**	**-16.67%**
Emergency Medical Services	0.00	2.00	**2.00**	2.00	**2.00**	**0.00%**
Fire Training	0.00	2.00	**2.00**	2.00	**2.00**	**0.00%**
Emergency Management	0.00	1.00	**1.00**	1.00	**1.00**	**0.00%**
Fire Operations	131.00	142.00	**142.00**	142.00	**142.00**	**0.00%**
Total :	157.00	173.00	**173.00**	170.00	**167.00**	**-3.47%**

Figure 12–6 The Operating Budget Summary from Peoria, Arizona, shows a format for a program budget.

Expenditures in program-based budgeting are listed by program rather than by department or division. A list of major programs for a fire and emergency services department might include

- Fire prevention/education
- Fire suppression
- Emergency medical services
- HAZMAT response
- Technical rescue response
- Communications/dispatch
- Administration
- Training.

The advantage of a program-based budget system is that it allows policy makers and chief fire officers to concentrate on the costs and outcomes from programs instead of on the dollars allocated (inputs) to various line-item objects, such as electricity or medical supplies. In this way, top officials can see the budget not as a pure control system but rather as a decision-making tool for implementing policy.

The disadvantages of a program-based budget are, first, that programs are often hard to define and, second, that the line-item detail useful for day-to-day management decision making is lacking.

Full cost accounting Budgets are ways of organizing costs, but costs can be defined in different ways. Accountants use cost accounting to link expenditures to specific programs. In essence, cost accounting is a means of identifying the total cost of providing a particular program at a specific level and of making clear the interrelatedness of budgetary items. There are various cost accounting techniques, but the one that is consistent with the philosophy behind program-based budgeting is full cost accounting.

Full cost accounting, or full costing, includes both direct and indirect costs. Indirect costs include administrative support and overhead; overhead includes managerial salaries, employee benefits, financing, interest, and other related costs. Only in the late 1990s did governments begin using full costing.

Initiating full costing for a program allows local government decision makers to shift their focus from arbitrary cuts in expenditures, which can have unforeseen impacts on programs, to the achievement of chosen outcomes at an acceptable cost. With full costing in place, elected officials can relate expenditures to defined levels of service. Accordingly, when they cut the budget, the officials will be aware of the reduced level of service that will result. Fully costed program-based information gives local elected officials a fuller picture of the programs that the tax dollars are purchasing and allows them to make informed decisions to enhance, cut back, or shed programs. Fully costed program-based information gives nonelected public servants a sense of clear direction and the freedom to exercise choice and expertise, and it gives elected officials true control over policy and level of service.

Collecting full-cost information does, however, involve challenges. Direct costs related to a program may be easier to identify than indirect costs. Utility costs for a fire station, for example, have to be apportioned among all the programs delivered from the station, using some sort of allocation formula. Possible formulas include taking a certain percentage of on-call volume, using average length of call, or combining the two in some way. Allocation of salaries may also be a challenge. If staff members are paid on an hourly basis, the payroll system may be able to allocate costs directly to the program, but if they are paid on a biweekly basis, an allocation formula is required. And some method of allocating downtime costs must also be taken into consideration.

Program budgeting requires a clear understanding of cost attributes (i.e., type of cost: fixed, semifixed, and variable). The behavior of each type of cost must be considered, managed, and influenced over a period of time. For example, variable costs can be affected by decision makers in the short term, but fixed costs can be affected only over the longer term. What this means is that if a financial target of a 5 percent expenditure reduction is set but 75 percent of the departmental budget consists of fixed or semifixed costs, the 5 percent reduction is tantamount to reducing the remaining costs (the variable costs) by 20 percent. Education about these concepts and a better understanding of them at all levels of the organization will produce a better understanding of the effects of decisions on programs.

Linking performance measures to costs As outlined above, the major benefit of program budgeting is that it gives decision makers the ability to understand the actual cost and revenues derived from any single program. But to be fully informed about the impact of money spent, decision makers need performance measures for each program. Therefore, program budgeting often presents specific output or outcome measures for each program. Using these measures, policy makers are able to see the specific benefits derived from the program and at what cost. Cost may be stated in a per-unit format—for example, cost to provide fire safety message per student, cost to treat and transport a single medical patient, or the cost to conduct an annual fire safety inspection. By comparing per-unit costs from year to year, decision makers can track improvements in the efficiency of local service delivery.

Program budgeting requires financial managers to make decisions about where to allocate costs and on what basis. By looking at similar costs in other benchmark agencies, policy makers can assess how their agencies compare in providing cost-effective services. Before drawing conclusions based on comparisons of program cost from one agency to another, however, they must be sure that the same methodology for allocating costs has been used in both cases. (For more discussion of the connection between performance management and budgeting, and the approach to budgeting known as results-based budgeting, see Chapter 14.)

Revenues

Funding influences the level of services that can be provided to the community. When funding for a fire and emergency services department is considered, the following questions need to be asked and answered:

- Who should pay for the service?
- Should the service be treated as insurance against community loss?
- Could user fees help pay for the service?
- Should this service be offered by local government as a public good?

More broadly, should firefighters compete in the marketplace, assume revenue-generating roles not typically part of their job description, or step outside the collective agreement (i.e., perform work beyond what the labor-management contract calls for—work for which the union will require additional pay)?

Answers to the above questions will help determine the level of diversification needed in local fire and emergency service revenue sources. Generally speaking, the department should seek to diversify the revenue sources used to fund day-to-day operations. Recent experience has shown that heavy reliance on a single revenue stream—for example, property taxes—can be disastrous if that particular source is severely reduced. Local fire service officials should consider using a number of different approaches in order to protect overall funding capabilities. The likelihood of many different revenue sources all being adversely affected simultaneously is less than the likelihood that all will vary significantly from year to year.

The question of who should pay raises the issue of regressive, progressive, or proportional taxation. A regressive tax puts a proportionally greater burden on the poor than on the rich. An example is the sales tax, which every purchaser must pay at the same rate, regardless of his or her income. By contrast, a progressive tax puts a greater burden on those with a greater ability to pay. The federal income tax is a progressive tax. In between these two are proportional tax systems, in which the tax rate is fixed and people pay based on the amount of the goods or services involved. In practice, proportional tax systems are not that common today. Most tax systems are generally argued to be either regressive or progressive.

The following section outlines a wide variety of funding mechanisms in use today in different fire and emergency service agencies across the nation. These funding mechanisms and their descriptions have been compiled from the Federal Emergency Management Agency's publication *Funding Alternatives for Fire and Emergency Services*,[3] as well as from other sources.

Most revenue sources described here must be authorized by the state legislature. State law may restrict the use of some of these opportunities. The local finance director or attorney can provide direction on any revenue-related issues.

Property taxes

Property taxes represent one of the major sources of revenue for fire and emergency service operations. Revenue generated locally through property taxes often represents almost a third of the local government's revenue. The term *millage rate* applies to the number of dollars collected per $1,000 of taxable value. For a home with a taxable value of $100,000 and a millage rate of two mills, the property tax is $200. Each state has its own rules for establishing the fair value/taxable value of properties, and many states also set a maximum number of mills that the local government can assess for services.

Assessments

Benefit assessments or special assessments are charges for services based on the estimated benefits that users are expected to derive from those services. Administered somewhat like property taxes, these charges are not determined by a millage rate formula. Instead, the assessment for fire and emergency services is based on the property type and/or size of the property that receives the benefit from those services. These assessments generally are not restricted by millage-based limits, and they also have the potential to collect dollars from properties that may pay little or no regular property taxes, such as churches and educational institutions. Some argue that using assessments in addition to regular millage-based property taxes makes the burden for funding fire and emergency services more equitable.

Sales taxes

Many jurisdictions either collect sales tax revenue directly or receive it as a pass-through from the state government. To help local governments diversify their revenue streams, some states (e.g., Florida) have adopted legislation that allows for a local option sales tax to be added specifically to assist in funding fire and emergency service operations.

Development impact fees

New developments may be required to pay for their impact on capital expenditures (e.g., building and equipping new fire stations). The premise behind impact fees is that new developments will place additional demand on the existing fire and emergency services system. Impact fees are often collected and held in a special fund until the local government constructs new facilities or purchases new apparatus needed for the expanded service. Impact fees cannot be used to fund day-to-day operational costs.

User fees

User fees range from small revenue producers to more lucrative ones. The former include permit fees for new construction, special events, and performance of hazardous activities (such as putting on fireworks displays, removing old underground fuel-storage facilities, or making explosives or highly flammable or toxic products); the latter include fees charged for emergency medical care and transport (see below).

Ambulance fees

Billing for EMS transportation is a common practice. Many fire departments contract the billing function to private contractors. Medicare, Medicaid, and insurance programs often pay for EMS transportation services at established rates depending on the level of care provided—basic life support (BLS) versus advanced life support (ALS). Departments that provide EMS transportation may recover anywhere from 33 percent to 50 percent of total EMS costs through ambulance fees. For departments that employ cross-trained firefighter paramedics, this revenue stream has the benefit of increasing the department's capability to respond to any kind of emergency, whether it is a mass casualty incident or a large structure fire.

Currently, medical insurance does not cover the cost for emergency medical services unless transportation to the hospital is provided by the department. Efforts to change this at the federal level for Medicare and Medicaid in recent years have been unsuccessful. Some local EMS transport providers (private or public) reimburse the fire and emergency services for some of the costs of providing first-responder emergency medical services; Pinellas County, Florida, for example, fosters a regional approach to EMS response, providing coordination and funding to local fire departments.

Fire inspection fees

Fees for required fire safety inspections generally cover the cost of performing the inspection and are established by the legislative body. Fees may be collected annually as part of the property tax bill or business tax license, or by some other method. Some agencies collect the fee at the time of inspection.

Alarm fees

Fire departments spend a significant amount of time responding to activated fire alarms. Typically these alarms are false. Many fire departments cover the cost of false alarms through fees.

Registration Many fire departments require businesses and homes to register fire alarm systems with the department. The purpose is to ensure that the fire department has current contact information for each key holder and owner. This registration may be a one-time occurrence or require renewal each year. The registration fee is to cover clerical and database management costs.

False alarm Improperly installed or maintained alarm systems generate many false alarms. Some buildings have hybrid systems that are prone to premature signal generation resulting in false alarms; responses to these alarms often prevent much-needed personnel and apparatus from responding to genuine emergencies. For building owners, having the local fire department respond—sometimes several times during a twenty-four-hour period—might be easier than repairing or replacing the system at a cost of several hundreds of thousands of dollars. Some departments charge a fee for each response beyond a predetermined acceptable number.

Contracting

Fire and emergency service departments are increasingly contracting to provide services beyond their core geographical jurisdictions. Most common is providing full fire and/or emergency

Palm Bay false alarm ordinance

The city of Palm Bay, Florida, passed an alarm system ordinance in 2000 to respond to the problem of excessive false alarms. The ordinance, which covers both fire and police alarm systems, affects all business and residential monitored system users. Requiring all commercial and residential monitored alarm users to obtain a permit for their alarm system, the ordinance addresses the problem through a program of permit registration, fines for excessive false alarms, and alarm awareness and education. An annual permit fee of $20 is charged each fiscal year. Alarm users get two "free" false alarms; after that, fines are imposed ranging from $50 to $200.

A report covering the period from 2000 through 2008 found that Palm Bay succeeded in reducing false alarm activation response by both the fire and the police department first responders, attaining a cumulative decrease of over 66 percent. Overall savings to all city taxpayers in fiscal year 2008 exceeded $300,000 in worker-hours and equipment usage.

Regional fire apparatus maintenance facility

Broward County is a metropolitan area of about 1.8 million residents in South Florida. With over twenty fire and emergency service departments and a hundred stations in the county, the demand for quality fleet maintenance is paramount for fire personnel. In the 1990s, the county made major upgrades to one of its several fleet maintenance facilities, geared to include specialized bays, equipment and training for fire apparatus, and ambulance repairs. Recognizing that a number of smaller agencies in the county do not have the same expertise or infrastructure, the county offers specialized fleet maintenance to all of its thirty-two municipalities.

This vehicle maintenance program includes scheduled preventive maintenance (PM); chassis repairs; pump repairs and replacements; and valves, aerial, engine, transmission, and various other warranty repairs. A fully outfitted service truck is on duty to perform daily road calls and PM at the fire stations. The fleet services function also provides after-hour service 24/7 in support of area fire departments.

The program provides other fire and emergency service departments with specialized apparatus services on a "per hour" basis–not unlike a local car dealership. With a cadre of over twenty-five certified mechanics, the county fleet maintenance facilities can provide municipal agencies with services whenever a specific problem exceeds those agencies' own in-house capabilities or if they should have a sudden spike in repair requests. This program is one of several in which Broward County provides fire and emergency support services on a regional basis. All participants enjoy cost savings because of economies of scale. In addition, these programs encourage greater uniformity in the vehicles and equipment used by different fire agencies throughout in the county.

medical services in neighboring jurisdictions. Other examples include the provision of selected or special services such as training, HAZMAT response, or technical rescue services. The economies of scale that result from providing services over a larger population base benefit the departmental budgets of both jurisdictions.

Large fire and emergency service departments that maintain their own diesel and heavy equipment may be able to market these services to other departments.

On a smaller scale, many departments service their own self-contained breathing apparatus (SCBA). But fire and emergency services are not the only users of such devices. Many industries and institutions are required to have these units on hand, with personnel adequately trained in their safe operation. The units require yearly inspections and servicing. Fire and emergency service providers that are certified to service their own SCBA may be able to market this service to other users.

Requests for building safety inspections generated by property sales can also generate fee income. Law and real estate firms often arrange safety inspections of buildings and properties up for sale, charging the customer for the service. Generally this service can be offered only by inspectors trained in the various building and fire codes—something that the fire department already has.

For most of the examples listed above, potential benefits outweigh the risks. Because the capital infrastructure and personnel are already in place, there is little additional cost. In fact, the fire service, when dealing in its core competency, does not have the setup costs that a private sector organization wishing to offer the same service will have.

Fire and emergency service departments receive numerous requests for services that could be revenue generating, but in many places, local or state law must be changed to allow a department to charge for such services.

Cost sharing (partnering)

As an alternative to direct contracting of services to or from an adjoining jurisdiction, many departments achieve the same economies of scale by sharing costs, or partnering, to pay for new facilities or services. Cost sharing reduces the burden on each party, especially when the facilities or services are not used frequently.

Regional communications

Regional dispatching has a considerable advantage over traditional dispatch models. Costs for the system can be borne by several departments. Patient transport is improved because a regional system has links to various medical centers or hospitals in the region that practice specific types of medicine. If a "bed registry" is incorporated into the system, patients with specific medical problems can be transported to the nearest facility that has both available bed space and the appropriate specialized medical treatment.

Shared regional communication systems facilitate much stronger use of mutual aid and automatic aid between neighboring agencies. In many parts of the country, the cost to provide dispatching services can be as high as $25–$30 per capita. Minimizing the cost to provide such services, while maximizing coordination with adjoining jurisdictions, often improves service while reducing costs.

Large fire and emergency service organizations require extensive equipment for communications and logging radio traffic. A trunking network (see Chapter 16) can serve many departments or agencies, providing upgradable state-of-the-art technology that can be used simultaneously by a large number of people for secure (private) two-way communication. Other departments or private sector partners can either share costs or pay a fee for time used. Trunking systems also achieve the goal of interoperability by allowing cooperating departments to use the same communications system.

Subscriptions

Subscriptions are essentially a form of insurance in which households pay a fixed fee per year for a service. Today subscriptions are most commonly used for emergency medical services. When a subscriber uses the service, the department waives or reduces any out-of-pocket expenses that may be due from the user—for example, a co-pay for medical transportation. Often the subscriber can then recover the fixed fees from a medical or homeowner's insurance carrier. When nonsubscribers need service, however, they must pay a fee that covers the entire cost of service each time they require it.

State and federal intergovernmental fund transfers

Local fire and emergency service departments obtain considerable funding from state and federal programs and grants. Many states provide direct funding, grant aid, or low-interest loans for capital improvement projects, and federal legislation enacted in 2009 made funds available for capital projects. These state and federal sources often require that funds be spent on specific categories or programs. The Assistance to Firefighters and the Staffing for Adequate Fire & Emergency Response grant programs have been especially good sources of funding for fire and emergency service departments in the United States. Increasingly, local agencies are employing professional grant writers in order to increase their chances of receiving awards. Local departments can research funding sources through state and federal agency websites.

Grant funding, from whatever source, often carries a significant responsibility for grants management. Agencies should ensure that their financial units, or those in the department who are applying for and using grants, are well prepared to manage the required paperwork after the grant is awarded. A full grant file should be set up immediately upon receipt of a grant, rather than waiting until an audit is requested after the grant has expired. The file should include the following components:

- Full copies of the grant application and grant award, with the proposed budget, in the front of the file
- Records of all disbursements made with grant dollars, including purchase orders
- Any correspondence relating to the grant, especially anything from the granting institution
- Any reports that are periodically filed and/or periodic progress reports
- A close-out report, documenting the final expenditure of funds and the results/impact of the grant.

Those handling the day-to-day grants administration must carefully follow all required reporting and management processes, and the department should use an accounting system to track all expenditures. The required retention period for grants records can be quite long.

Other sources of revenue

Public education programs on preventing accidents and fires can be made available on a user-fee basis or funded through sponsorships. These programs are now offered for free and in most cases are loosely organized. However, this type of service is in great demand, and many departments cannot keep up with the numerous requests from various civic organizations. Printing five-color pamphlets and acquiring videotapes and programs for children's safety can be extremely costly, although some of the costs can be recovered through sponsorships, donations, and user fees. The object is not to make a profit but at least to cover the costs associated with the efforts. If fire and emergency service organizations stopped this activity, several other organizations would fill the resulting void and they, too, would move at least to have their costs covered.

Public fire departments are increasingly establishing nonprofit foundations to solicit private donations. Volunteer fire and emergency services, especially, can often raise considerable funds from the private sector. The list of fund-raising and equipment-acquisition activities is endless. The local culture and context of each community will suggest appropriate types of activities.

Opportunities to generate revenue are certainly available. Taking advantage of them requires adopting a public version of entrepreneurship, which has the ultimate goal of saving taxpayers money. To involve the entire department in looking for opportunities to generate revenue, the local fire and emergency services department may want to return a percentage of revenues developed to the units that generated them, which would serve as an incentive to others to implement additional opportunities.

Borrowing

At times, it may be necessary for a fire and emergency services department to borrow funds for long- or short-term needs. If the organization is part of a local government, the finance department may well handle this function. If it is an independent fire district, its senior staff will need to be familiar with the steps required in financial borrowing. In either case, the expertise of financial professionals is needed. The fire chief's role is to assist in determining the need for capital expenditures and the expected useful life of the investments being funded. The chief must also ensure that all program costs are defined. Since borrowing is a long and complex process, forgetting to define all costs can be disastrous. Finally, if borrowing entails the use of a dedicated funding source to repay the debt, the fire chief may be asked to provide certain assurances that this revenue will be available for the time required to pay off the debt.

Fire prevention sponsorships

Like many fire departments throughout the nation, the La Junta Fire Department in Colorado places a high importance on public education. One focus is reaching school-aged children during Fire Prevention Week each October. In addition to presenting fire safety messages to all schoolchildren from kindergarten through third grade, the department provides educational outreach into preschool and day care centers. The program provides activity books, magnets, stickers, and fire hats to over 750 children.

The department covers the cost of this program by actively soliciting sponsorships from businesses and individuals each year. It sends letters to many of its local community leaders and businesses offering them an opportunity to sponsor a full or half school grade with educational materials. In 2009 the department's efforts secured support from over thirty sponsors to provide the educational materials. In total, this annual sponsorship drive provides almost 50 percent of the public education funding for the year. The program has a twofold benefit: the supplemental funding allows wide dissemination of the fire safety message, and the community is engaged in supporting fire prevention efforts.

For those chief officers managing independent districts, a basic understanding of borrowing is also essential to ensure that long-term costs are kept to a minimum. (For information on other approaches to funding capital needs, also see Chapter 13.)

Bonds Bonds are instruments sold to investors in order to raise funds for long-term capital improvements or major expenditures. The issuance of bonds requires experienced advisers with expertise in the tax and legal implications of such transactions.

Bonds are usually sold through various financial markets to investors who are seeking a guaranteed rate of return (interest) on their investment. Governments have the ability to issue bonds that are tax-exempt, which makes them more attractive for many investors. Bonds are typically issued for a twenty- or thirty-year time frame; their repayment, which is made annually by the issuing government, includes both principal and interest as determined at the time of sale.

Historically, government agencies wishing to issue bonds could do so when they identified a revenue stream that was sufficiently stable to ensure repayment on the bonds. To protect investors, the agency would normally also buy bond insurance to assure purchasers that the bond would eventually be repaid. With the changes in financial markets that occurred in 2009, most bond insurance companies left the business. Increasingly, government agencies wishing to issue bonds must be independently rated on the basis of their own financial strength—just as private sector issuers are. However, the costs and time necessary to be independently rated can be quite burdensome. Thus, agencies contemplating issuing bonds should work with qualified advisers well before funds are needed.

Short-term borrowing While bonds are used for long-term financing, agencies may also use short-term borrowing. Unsecured short-term loans ranging from one day to nine months, referred to as commercial paper, generally require the agency to be rated and have an excellent credit history. For governments that have dramatic swings in their revenue streams and require a short-term bridge between immediate expenditures and future anticipated revenues, commercial paper may be an option. Typically, the longer the term of these short-term loans, the higher the interest paid by the borrower.

Expenditures

Fire department budgets typically have three major expenditure components: personnel costs, operating costs, and capital costs.

Personnel costs

For fully career fire and emergency service departments, personnel costs typically represent 90 percent or more of the overall budget, excluding capital costs. These costs are not simply the salaries paid to department personnel; they include additional compensation paid to the firefighter in the form of incentive pay, holiday pay, overtime, etc. Personnel costs also include employee benefits such as social security, pension, health insurance, life insurance, and workers' compensation.

The wages and benefits paid to fire personnel may be governed by a collective bargaining (labor) agreement. Many states have comprehensive collective bargaining statutes, and the intricacies of labor negotiations are beyond the scope of this chapter. However, since the costs for personnel are such a large percentage of expenditures, chief fire officers should be well briefed on the fiscal impact of collective bargaining language and move carefully when considering changes. Understanding state law concerning collective bargaining and learning from the experiences of other agencies can help mitigate the fiscal impact related to personnel.

Salaries Salaries for career firefighters represent the single largest cost in the budget. Salaries alone, without other benefits, commonly make up 50 percent of the total fire budget. While salary levels vary widely across the nation, other personnel costs—including overtime, pension, and social security—are linked to the salary level paid to firefighters. It is not unusual for the total cost for each firefighter to be 125–150 percent of the salary paid.

Health care Health care costs have risen faster than most other commodities, increasing insurance costs for employers and employees alike. Most agencies that provide health insurance share costs with employees. However, in 2009 the total (shared) cost for health insurance was approximately $5,000 for a single firefighter and $14,000 for family coverage. The rate at which premiums for health insurance increase each year has consistently exceeded 10 percent for the past several years.

Retirement Retirement benefits generally fall into two major categories: defined benefit or defined contribution. The *defined benefit* plan guarantees firefighters a specific dollar amount once they reach retirement. Typically the amount is determined by a formula:

Number of years of service × percentage × salary = benefit for remaining years of life.

Thus, for example, if the percentage is 3 percent, twenty years of service ensures the retiring firefighter 60 percent of salary. Many defined benefit plans require that the firefighter contribute a fixed percentage of his or her salary toward the retirement plan. The government must contribute any additional funds necessary to keep the retirement plan sound, based on actuarial studies. During good economic times (when the stock markets are doing well), the employer's contribution is minimized. When the stock market performs poorly, the employer's contribution rises dramatically. The assurance of a defined benefit for the firefighter is offset by the uncertainty for the employer regarding contributions that must be made.

A *defined contribution* retirement plan simply places retirement dollars, usually a percentage of salary, into an investment plan. The value of that plan upon retirement is dependent on how well the stock markets have performed. In a defined contribution plan (e.g., a 401 plan), the employer's and employee's costs are known each year. However, depending on how well the investment plan does, the retiring employee may or may not have sufficient funds accrued to provide for the planned retirement. Most private sector employers have moved to defined contribution plans, many of which are structured so that the employer matches employee contributions up to a specific percentage. In light of recent economic downturns, more government agencies are considering defined contribution plans because they eliminate the uncertainty regarding the employer's future costs.

OPEB Other benefits are often structured outside of the pension plan but provide value to a firefighter once he or she leaves employment. For example, some employers provide a health insurance subsidy or direct health insurance once a firefighter retires. Others provide certain types of life insurance. These other post-employment benefits (OPEB) must now be reported under new accounting guidelines promulgated by the Governmental Accounting Standards Board (GASB). At a minimum, governmental entities must now report how these costs will accrue and create a liability for the government in the future. Ideally, OPEB costs should be funded through a fiduciary fund similar to a defined benefit pension plan.

Operating costs

Operating costs represent the day-to-day expenses of running the fire and emergency services department. These costs typically include medical and firefighting supplies, gasoline and oil to operate vehicles, and repair and maintenance of facilities and the fleet, along with uniforms, telephones, office supplies, and other associated costs. Almost every item not related to personnel costs and not exceeding a specific dollar amount (e.g., $1,000) would be considered an operating cost.

Operating costs can be reduced through the same kinds of best practices that individuals often use in their own homes—for example, buying in bulk; turning off lights or adjusting the thermostat to save energy costs; or simply being careful about day-to-day supplies. However, since operating costs represent only a small percentage of the overall department budget, significant dollar savings are unlikely.

Capital costs

Capital costs are those planned expenditures that typically exceed a certain threshold limit. Capital assets—for example, vehicles, radios, and even facilities—usually have a useful life well beyond the year in which they are purchased. However, computers that were once considered to be a capital expenditure are increasingly being treated as an operating cost. While there are no hard and fast rules, items considered a capital expenditure typically are accounted for separately and must be inventoried each year.

Capital expenditures are sometimes funded differently from day-to-day operating costs or personnel costs. Depending on the dollar amount involved, they may be funded through dedicated revenue streams or long-term borrowing such as bonds. (See Chapter 13 for more on budgeting for capital expenditures.)

Financial controls

State and local governments must function in a very open and transparent environment in order for the public to have confidence in their fiscal responsibility. The chief fire officer's responsibilities include accomplishing the organization's basic purpose (effectiveness), making good use of scarce resources (efficiency), complying with legal and policy-level restrictions on the use of those resources (compliance), and periodically demonstrating accountability for the use of those resources (reporting).

Accordingly, governmental accounting and financial reporting must include proper procedures and tools to ensure that these basic responsibilities are met. The Government Finance Officers Association defines this comprehensive framework as having five essential elements:

- A favorable control environment—one where managers are knowledgeable about internal controls and actively support their use.
- A continuing assessment of financial risk, both internal and external to the organization.
- An effective method for communicating financial information, including the format of such information and the frequency with which it is disseminated.
- Effective control-related policies and procedures—for example, how long should financial records be maintained? Managers must ensure that such controls are put into place and adhered to.
- Ongoing monitoring of the control-related procedures—essentially, assessing whether the above elements are working effectively.

Accounting standards

The standards governing the format and contents of public agencies' external reports are known as generally accepted accounting principles (GAAP). While not intended to provide all the information that any one group may desire, GAAP provides citizens and legislators with the basic information needed to assess an organization's finances. GASB establishes these standards.

Audits

While most of the foregoing discussion in this section has dealt with the responsibilities of the chief fire officer and other managers in the organization to ensure that proper internal controls are in place, it is also crucial that the organization subject itself to an external review of its financial practices and status. This external process is referred to as a financial audit.

Basically, financial audits are intended to provide users of the various financial reports with a reasonable, if not absolute, assurance that those reports are in fact reliable. Auditors select various financial transactions and reports at random and then independently verify their accuracy. Most governmental agencies require independent, external audits at least annually.

Reporting

The local government organization's basic financial reports and the auditor's opinions of these reports are compiled in a comprehensive annual financial report (CAFR). The CAFR

Figure 12-7 This basic financial report from Boone County, Missouri, shows revenues, expenditures, and changes in fund balances.

BOONE COUNTY, MISSOURI

STATEMENT OF REVENUES, EXPENDITURES AND CHANGES IN FUND BALANCES GOVERNMENTAL FUNDS
For The Year Ended December 31, 2008

	Major Funds					
	General Fund	Road & Bridge Fund	Law Enforcement Services Fund	One-Fifth Cent Sales Tax Capital Improvement Fund	Nonmajor Governmental Funds	Total Governmental Funds
REVENUES						
Property taxes	$ 2,951,281	1,208,922	—	—	—	4,160,203
Assessments	—	—	—	—	105,288	105,288
Sales taxes	11,460,782	11,815,984	2,860,622	4,577,324	234,060	30,948,772
Other taxes	179,159	—	—	—	—	179,159
Licenses and permits	295,491	14,027	—	—	51,428	360,946
Intergovernmental	2,560,964	1,269,787	—	—	566,378	4,397,129
Charges for services	3,429,987	23,914	—	—	1,672,433	5,126,334
Fines and forfeitures	14,791	—	—	—	26,376	41,167
Investment income	224,012	271,694	38,536	145,986	197,972	878,200
Interfund services provided	218,712	21,493	—	—	—	240,205
Miscellaneous:						
Hospital lease revenue	1,630,692	—	—	—	—	1,630,692
Contributions	—	—	—	—	15,000	15,000
Other	439,227	15,782	—	—	61,089	516,098
Total revenues	23,405,098	14,641,603	2,899,158	4,723,310	2,930,024	48,599,193
EXPENDITURES						
Current:						
Policy and administration	6,589,682	—	—	—	1,048,443	7,638,125
Law enforcement and judicial	14,182,667	—	2,573,119	—	606,825	17,362,611
Environment, public buildings, and infrastructur	46,218	13,928,261	—	—	379,259	14,353,738
Community health and public services	1,195,151	—	—	—	43,737	1,238,888
Economic vitality	66,000	—	—	—	—	66,000
Beautification and recreation	56,485	—	—	—	—	56,485
Protective inspection	1,094,470	—	—	—	—	1,094,470
Interfund services used	21,493	150,000	—	—	68,712	240,205
Capital outlay	321,429	305,487	304,399	7,337,624	363,572	8,632,511
Debt service:						
Principal retirement	280,000	—	—	—	186,000	466,000
Interest and fiscal charges	133,215	—	—	—	140,542	273,757
Total expenditures	23,986,810	14,383,748	2,877,518	7,337,624	2,837,090	51,422,790
REVENUES OVER (UNDER) EXPENDITURES	(581,712)	257,855	21,640	(2,614,314)	92,934	(2,823,597)
OTHER FINANCING SOURCES (USES)						
Transfers in	83,414	—	—	75,000	2,943,453	3,101,867
Transfers out	(127,614)	—	(15,000)	(2,360,002)	(599,251)	(3,101,867)
Insurance proceeds	21,193	5,630	—	—	—	26,823
Issuance of GO Bonds	—	—	—	—	1,700,000	1,700,000
Sale of capital assets	26,178	31,722	37,825	—	3,050	98,775
Total other financing sources (uses)	3,171	37,352	22,825	(2,285,002)	4,047,252	1,825,598
NET CHANGE IN FUND BALANCES	(578,541)	295,207	44,465	(4,899,316)	4,140,186	(997,999)
FUND BALANCES, beginning of year	8,014,864	8,748,203	1,464,751	7,089,020	6,461,920	31,778,758
FUND BALANCES, end of year	$ 7,436,323	9,043,410	1,509,216	2,189,704	10,602,106	30,780,759

should include at least three basic sections. The introductory section typically presents general information on the government, its structure, and the purpose and scope of the services it provides. The financial section contains basic financial statements as well as the independent auditor's report. The statements typically cover information from the prior fiscal year, showing revenues and expenditures—both budgeted and actual—by various categories and funds (see Figure 12-7). Finally, the statistical section provides a range of financial and demographic information—often provided with ten-year trends—that helps the reader assess the organization's overall economic condition.

The CAFR has essentially been the standard for local government financial reporting since the 1970s. If the fire department is part of a general-purpose local government, it typically does not have to worry about preparation of this document. Independent fire districts, however, are usually required by the local board or state law to prepare such a report each year.

Government Finance Officers Association and the Governmental Accounting Standards Board

The purpose of the Government Finance Officers Association (GFOA) is to enhance and promote the professional management of governments for the public benefit. GFOA accomplishes this by identifying and developing financial policies and practices and then promoting them through education, training, and leadership.

Also working to ensure public confidence in public sector financial management is the Governmental Accounting Standards Board, whose mission is to establish and improve standards of state and local governmental accounting and financial reporting so as to produce useful information for users of financial reports as well as to guide and educate the public, including issuers, auditors, and users of those financial reports.

Since its beginnings in the early part of the last century, GFOA has been committed to the transparency and reliability of public sector financial reports. Thus, it often publishes the guidance needed by public sector finance managers in order to promote the highest possible standards of accounting, auditing, and financial reporting as represented by generally accepted accounting principles (GAAP), generally accepted auditing standards, and *Government Auditing Standards* (GFOA, July 2007, gao.gov/new.items/d07731g.pdf).

Asset management

Compared with many other local government departments, the fire and emergency services organization (depending on its size and scale) manages physical assets that are quite valuable. One engine (pumper truck), depending on how it is configured with equipment, can cost as much as $650,000 (in 2009 dollars), and one aerial ladder truck can cost more than $1 million. Apparatus, rescue and medical equipment, protective clothing, buildings, property, and so forth all represent an extensive financial commitment. To manage and properly account for this accumulation of physical assets, the organization should commit to an asset management plan that ensures that the department budget will include all the activities and costs related to asset acquisition, preservation, replacement, and disposal.

An asset management plan makes certain that all the major assets used by the fire and emergency services, or for which the fire and emergency services are responsible, are properly recorded and valued, and that forecasts of each asset's remaining life and replacement need are properly recorded as well. The plan should also touch on measures for preserving the life and reliability of assets in a cost-effective manner, disposing of assets that will not be required, and acquiring new assets as needed to conduct the organization's business.

An asset planning framework therefore has four main components: the organizational strategy relative to the delivery of emergency response services, asset planning and acquisition, asset preservation, and asset replacement/disposal (Figure 12–8).

An assessment of a department's current portfolio of assets from the perspective of the department's public programs and services will identify additional needs as well as opportunities for disposal. (Items are often disposed of by the local government rather than by the department because the former can hold auctions of a large quantity of items from several departments, making the disposal process much simpler and transparent to public scrutiny and audit.) Once the mix of existing and required assets is known, the local government can identify maintenance and protection programs to preserve assets and can then either develop strategies compatible with time frames for replacement or anticipate a period of extreme asset needs (e.g., in the event of a disaster).

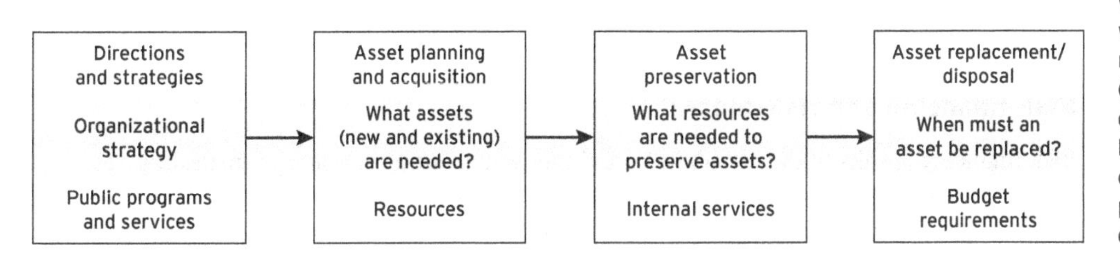

Figure 12-8 The asset planning framework includes several steps. The bottom line ("Public programs and services" in the first box) represents what must be considered when a statement is made about the top line ("Directions and strategies" in the first box). The boldface center heading or question indicates a process that flows from one box to the next.

Fire and emergency service providers that have significant responsibilities for facilities and other durable structures (e.g., stations, training facilities, communications sites and towers) should have systems in place, such as regular engineering or architectural inspections, to ensure the maintenance of these assets. Otherwise, funds devoted to this function will likely be inadequate.

Financial risk management

Financial risk management is the process of making and implementing—at a reasonable cost—decisions to (1) minimize the negative effects that accidental losses may have on the organization, (2) protect the organization's assets, and (3) ensure the organization's ability to meet objectives. In essence, financial risk management is the process of assessing and controlling the risks (in terms of financial exposure) that are inherent in any operation. The goal is to have the right balance between control and risk—to have effective control and an acceptable level of risk. Effective risk management provides reasonable assurance that the organization will achieve its objectives and that the level of residual risk of the organization's failing to meet its objectives is known and acceptable.

Most fire and emergency service organizations think of incident scene risk and personnel safety when they think of risk management. However, financial risk management is an important consideration for any organization. In fact, financial risk is often affected by operational risks. For example, an accident involving a piece of fire apparatus leads to repair costs, to the rental cost for a replacement apparatus, and even to the need to curtail service if a reserve is not available.

Massive exposure can lie in many directions, both internal and external. Internally, risk relates to the elements of an organization that, when taken together, support people in their efforts to achieve the organization's objectives—elements such as the organization's resources, systems, processes, culture, structures, and tasks. Externally, managers must always bear in mind the power and perceptions of the local elected and appointed officials, who are influenced not only by budgets (debt and deficit) but also by interest or pressure groups, the media, and the general public. The perceptions of the local elected and appointed officials are often no more than assumptions, but if acted on, those assumptions have the potential to seriously jeopardize a department's ability to function.

Thus, chief officers have a dual task: they must attempt as much as possible to educate the powers that be about the effects of their decisions while simultaneously ensuring that their own actions are not viewed as self-serving or empire building. In short, there is great risk in having financial decisions controlled by parties who are uneducated about the fire and emergency services.

Traditionally, the fire service has approached risk management by reducing its exposure to tort litigation and loss of financial resources. However, there are other areas of potential loss that can also have significant consequences for the organization. Aside from physical losses, financial risks can include loss of a mandate or program that is vital to the organization's ability to realize its goals and objectives; loss of customer satisfaction and support, or what is known in the private sector as market share; loss of public support as a result of actions, inaction, or unintended consequences that may flow from financial decision-making processes; loss of suppliers; reduction of budget; increases in supplier costs; and failure to realize or take advantage of opportunities. These are only examples. In fact, the areas of possible risk may be beyond anyone's capacity to enumerate.

How then can a fire and emergency services organization establish a balance between control and risk and approach the analysis of negative outcomes sensibly? The first step is to obtain knowledge about the working environment with a comprehensive SWOT analysis, determining internal strengths and weaknesses and external opportunities and threats (the same SWOT analysis that is conducted in connection with strategic planning).

Risk financing and risk control

Risk financing speaks to the concept of providing some sort of measure or insurance against negative financial effects on the organization. Such measures can take the form of reserve funds (many local governments have substantial financial reserves or expense budgets through which they can basically self-insure, i.e., retain risk internally); self- or third-party insurance (risk can be transferred to external life and property insurance companies or to hold-harmless agreements and waivers); transfer grants or relief from other levels of government; or well-designed training programs to prevent loss. Alternatively, one can do nothing at all (ignoring the presence of risk and hoping it will go away). Financing risk involves paying for losses that may or may not occur (in effect, paying to prevent risks from materializing: again, the steps taken to reduce risks entail some expense).

Risk controls are actions set in place that, once loss begins to occur, help to identify problem areas and prevent further damage to the organization. Total risk control is virtually impossible: as mentioned above, the nature of the services provided by the fire and emergency services organization means that the number of active variables is infinite. Therefore, engaging in risk/loss prevention is more appropriate than trying to achieve total control.

Traditionally, fire and emergency service departments have organized risk management, or risk control, by using fairly rigid processes, which are referred to as hard controls. Because hard controls consist of various rules, regulations, and policies, they are relatively easy to quantify and can provide an instant yardstick for measuring performance. A substantial degree of risk management can also be achieved with the application of soft, or informal, controls, but the difficulty of quantifying any tangible evidence that could relate directly to performance measures makes these types of controls hard to implement; in addition, implementation is often blocked by an organization's culture and values.

Analyzing risk: Risk management models

Decisions to reject or accept risk (i.e., to control it or choose not to control it) must be conscious. A risk that is taken unconsciously or inadvertently (or that cannot be measured) cannot be managed. Most significant risks can be analyzed in conjunction with one or more appropriate models. Both visually and conceptually, models help clarify risk and therefore can help educate people about potential exposures and areas of vulnerability; models can also identify options for controlling risk. Although knowledge is often gained from "lessons learned," the only way such knowledge will lead to better risk preparedness is if an enabling process is in place.

There are a number of risk management frameworks, or models, that represent systematic methods not only of identifying risks associated with the achievement of objectives but also of analyzing, assessing, treating, and monitoring risks and communicating information about them to the organization. These models were originally designed with the corporate environment in mind. More recently, they are coming to be applied to the public sector. Discussed here are two such models that indicate how a risk management process could work: the Committee of Sponsoring Organizations model, and a more intuitive Liability Self-Assessment Checklist.

Committee of Sponsoring Organizations (COSO) The COSO model was developed by major accounting and auditing professional organizations in North America. Similar efforts exist in Europe as well. Known as enterprise risk management (ERM), the model is designed to illustrate the interrelationship between corporate or organizational activities, the environment, and the ways in which risk can be managed.

ERM provides a powerful way to integrate risk management into all aspects of fire and emergency services management. As depicted in Figure 12–9, the COSO model has eight interrelated components operating at four strategic levels within the organization:

1. *Internal environment:* The internal environment takes into account the organization's risk management philosophy, cultural values, and ethical values.
2. *Objective setting:* Management must select objectives, such as a response time goal, fire loss target, or reduction in employee injuries.
3. *Event identification:* Management must identify the internal or external events that affect the achievement of objectives, distinguishing between those that present risks and those that present opportunities.
4. *Risk assessment:* Risks are analyzed as to their likelihood and impact in order to determine the most effective management focus.
5. *Risk response:* Management selects responses to avoid, reduce, or share risk. These responses are consistent with the organization's willingness to take risks.

6. *Control activities:* Policies and procedures are established to ensure that risk response activities are followed.
7. *Information and communication:* Relevant information is collected and communicated throughout the organization.
8. *Monitoring:* The organization's risk management process is monitored using various performance measurement tools, and adjustments are made on the basis of previous successes, changes in the environment, or changes in the organization's risk tolerance.[4]

The ERM process, which is increasingly being adopted by governments, must be applied from the lowest subunit to the overall organization as a whole. Within a local government, the fire and emergency services organization is considered a "business unit" or "division." The "entity level" is the municipal or other level of government to which the fire and emergency services organization reports. (For more information on ERM, see coso.org.)

Quoting from an article in *Internal Auditor,* the advantages of ERM are that it

- "Takes note of the interrelationships and interdependencies among risks
- Offers improved ability to manage risks within and across business units
- Improves the organization's capacity to identify and seize opportunities inherent in future events
- Considers risk in the formulation of strategy
- Applies risk management at every level and unit of an entity
- Facilitates communication by providing a common risk language
- Takes a portfolio view of risks throughout the enterprise."[5]

The Liability Self-Assessment Checklist All individuals and organizations are exposed to potential legal liability. Liability claims for failure to provide a "duty of care," or a "standard of care," can be damaging not only to the fire and emergency services organization but also to

Figure 12-9 The COSO model for enterprise risk management has eight components that must be considered on four levels.

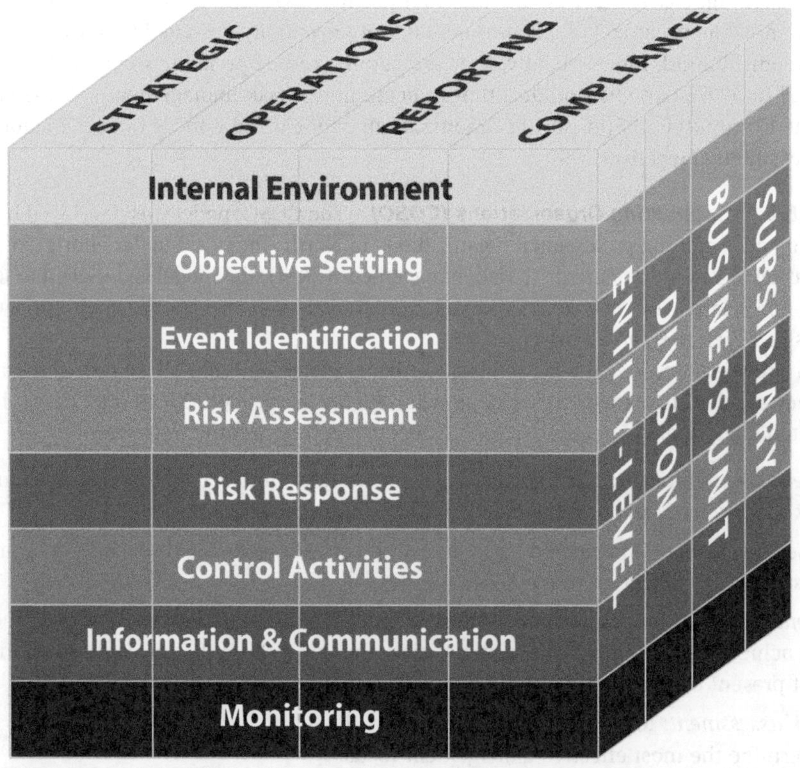

Source: Committee of Sponsoring Organizations, "Enterprise Risk Management–Integrated Framework: Executive Summary" (September 2004), 5, coso.org/documents/COSO_ERM_ExecutiveSummary.pdf. Reprinted by permission.

its local government. To minimize exposure to litigation, fire and emergency service providers should fill out the Liability Self-Assessment Checklist (see Figure 12–10). Developed by attorney Terry-Dawn Hewitt, the checklist is a questionnaire about the department's activities, standards, processes, and policies, requiring yes and no answers; Hewitt maintains that answers such as "no" or "I don't know" indicate work to be done on the development of a risk management program, of which financial risk is an inherent component.[6] (For more on legal liability in the fire and emergency services, see Chapter 10.)

Conclusion

A common mistake for chief fire officers is to focus on operational issues and assume that financial management doesn't deserve the same attention; often they relegate the task of ensuring strong financial management to others. But financial resources—just as in fire-ground staffing—must be linked to the task at hand. An assessment of community risk followed by the development of a strategic plan to guide the development of a budget that will provide the financial resources needed to address local risks are the first steps. All this should be done well before the first alarm bell sounds.

Figure 12-10 Liability Self-Assessment Checklist

- ☐ Does your department have copies of all legislation, regulations, bylaws, codes, and standards that are relevant to your department's operations?
- ☐ Has your municipality passed a fire bylaw? If so, was it tailor-made to suit the particular needs of your department? Does it accurately reflect both the duties imposed on your members by provincial or state legislation and the discretionary powers actually exercised by your department?
- ☐ Do you know how policies in place at the time of an incident can afford a defense to a civil liability action?
- ☐ Does your department have written policies?
- ☐ Does your department have Standard Operating Procedures (SOPs) for the implementation of department policies? If so, were they tailor-made to suit the particular needs of your department?
- ☐ Is there a mechanism for the review of the SOPs on a regular basis to assess them and implement changes?
- ☐ Are members from the fire floor (i.e., the general firefighter population, the operational rank and file) involved in the development of department policies and the SOPs?
- ☐ Does your department provide instructional programs, either in-house or through an outside agency, to train department members in the operational standards required by the SOPs?
- ☐ Does your department have methods of recording and maintaining information that may be needed for defending a liability action or an occupational health and safety (OH&S) prosecution?
- ☐ Does your department have a public information officer? Is he or she adequately trained to effectively deal with the media? Does your public information officer understand the legal liability implications and risks inherent in his or her duties?
- ☐ Do your firefighters, officers, and incident commanders customarily prepare written reports as soon as possible after a call (whether or not it was a false alarm)? Are the reports prepared in such a way as to make them useful as evidence in a legal action? Are they systematically retained?
- ☐ Does your department have mutual aid agreements with neighboring communities?
- ☐ Have your chief and senior officers met with neighboring municipalities and addressed problems of mutual aid—for example, incompatible equipment or emergency communications in the event of a disaster?
- ☐ Have your department's mutual aid agreements been reviewed for potential traps from a legal liability perspective?
- ☐ Have you developed a relationship with one or more lawyers who are knowledgeable in the fields of civil liability of fire services and OH&S liability and who can provide your department with the necessary guidance concerning your liability risks and potential and pending legal actions? Have you educated your lawyers respecting issues of particular concern to the fire service generally and to your department specifically? Have you reviewed your fire bylaw, SOPs, and fire service agreements with a lawyer knowledgeable about fire service liability?
- ☐ Do you understand the details of the liability insurance coverage covering your department? Do your department members understand their duties to the insurer and how the municipal liability insurance will respond in the event of a legal action against your municipality respecting the actions or omissions of your department?

If you answered either "no" or "I don't know" to any of the questions posed above, you have work to do.

Source: Adapted with minor revisions from Terry-Dawn Hewitt, *Fire Loss Litigation in Canada: A Practical Guide* (Scarborough, Ontario: Carswell, 1993), 27-28. Reprinted with permission of Carswell Publishing through the Canadian Copyright Licensing Agency (CANCOPY).

Assuring the public that its tax dollars are being spent wisely will allow the fire and emergency services organization to earn and maintain public support—an essential element in a democracy. This confidence will translate into the public's support for fire department programs and initiatives. Chief fire officers have a responsibility to build and maintain that support.

Notes

1. Bruce Moeller, unpublished raw data on fire department demographics (2007).
2. Adapted from Gail Stephens, Robert P. Gannon, and William H. Clark, "Fiscal Management," in *Managing Fire and Rescue Services*, ed. Dennis Compton and John Granito (Washington, D.C.: International City/County Management Association, 2002), 168.
3. Federal Emergency Management Agency, *Funding Alternatives for Fire and Emergency Services* (Washington, D.C.: Government Printing Office, n.d.), 1-2 to 1-5, usfa.dhs.gov/downloads/pdf/publications/fa-141.pdf.
4. Committee of Sponsoring Organizations, *Enterprise Risk Management—Integrated Framework: Executive Summary* (September 2004), 3–4, coso.org/documents/COSO_ERM_ExecutiveSummary.pdf.
5. Christy Chapman, "Bringing ERM into Focus," *Internal Auditor* (June 2003): 29–30, theiia.org/download.cfm?file=28663 (accessed June 6, 2010).
6. Terry-Dawn Hewitt, *Fire Loss Litigation in Canada: A Practical Guide* (Scarborough, Ontario: Carswell, 1993), 27–28.

CHAPTER 13

Capital Resource Management

Kevin M. Roche

This chapter provides an understanding of

- The definition of capital resources in the context of fire and emergency service operations
- Steps in the procurement of capital equipment and facilities, and emergency vehicles
- The importance of capital resources to the operation of fire and emergency service departments
- The importance of user involvement in the selection and purchasing of capital equipment, apparatus, and facilities
- The importance of life cycle costing in the evaluation of best value
- How to manage for effective maintenance and accountability.

Capital resources are the equipment, vehicles, and facilities that enable firefighters to deliver services to their customers. For many communities, the equipment, vehicles, and facilities that the fire and emergency services department uses in doing its work can be among the most costly expenditures of their type. However, the cost of providing fire and emergency services is often small compared with the costs involved in providing other municipal services; the costs of public service facilities such as roads and wastewater treatment plants, for example, can easily overshadow the cost of a new fire station. Yet very few public facilities are more closely integrated into the fabric of a neighborhood than the local fire station.

Valid generalizations about capital resource management are very hard to make because fire and emergency service departments differ, sometimes significantly, in the services they deliver to their communities and in the means of delivery. The profile of emergency service delivery in each community is a product of history, finance, politics, standards, personalities, and community expectations. Thus, the information presented here does not necessarily apply in full to the specific situation of every fire department in the United States and Canada, much less to that of every fire department around the world. But by focusing on the processes used to procure, maintain, account for, and replace capital resources, the following discussion should help most fire departments manage these resources. And since most fire and emergency service departments in North America perform some emergency medical service (EMS) functions, the information provided here incorporates capital considerations for those operations as well.

The emphasis in much of this discussion is on accommodating the legitimate needs of the user of the equipment, vehicle, or facility—the person who delivers the actual service. In fire and emergency service departments, that person may be the firefighter, the inspector, the educator, the staff person, or the manager who has direct contact with the customer. The job of a support person, such as someone who provides equipment, apparatus, and facilities, is to provide front-line workers with the tools they need to do their jobs: this is the reason that support services exist.

The first section of this chapter defines what is meant by capital resources; the subsequent three sections discuss the procurement of, respectively, capital equipment, emergency vehicles, and capital facilities. Because procurement is closely tied to the decision to replace a capital resource, these sections include a discussion of the factors that contribute to such a decision. Specific purchasing procedures, however, are not detailed because the actual methods that a community uses to procure capital items largely depend on state laws, local ordinances, and operating procedures. The chapter then provides a section on maintenance and another on accountability, followed by a brief conclusion.

Capital resources defined

There is little doubt that a piece of fire apparatus or a fire station meets any standard definition of a "capital" resource, but the definition of the equipment that qualifies as capital varies widely from jurisdiction to jurisdiction. Some communities define capital equipment as any item costing more than $100 and having a service life longer than one year, whereas others use a higher purchase cost and longer service life for the definition. In this chapter, the term *capital equipment* refers only to the most expensive individual items of capital equipment, as well as to tools, such as hose, that individually have low unit prices but collectively represent a significant cost. More specifically, this chapter defines three kinds of capital resources:

1. *Fire and EMS equipment:* Firefighters use a very broad array of tools and equipment to deliver fire protection and emergency medical services. Most of these tools are relatively inexpensive (unit prices below $200) and are not discussed in this chapter. The equipment that is addressed here includes such items as hydraulic rescue tools, defibrillators, hose, self-contained breathing apparatus (SCBA), and power tools such as saws.

This chapter is a revised and updated version of Chapter 7, "Capital Resource Management," by Kevin M. Roche, in the 2002 edition of this volume.

(a) Photo by Ron Jeffers

(b) Photo by Ron Jeffers

(c) Photo by Ron Jeffers

(d) Photo by Ron Jeffers

(e) Photo by Kevin M. Roche

(f) Photo by Kevin M. Roche

Figure 13-1 Fire department emergency vehicles: (a) a pumper (engine), equipped with a water tank, pump, ground ladders, and hose, used for fire attack; (b) a ladder (truck), not equipped with a pump; (c) a quint, combining the features of a pumper and a ladder; (d) a heavy rescue, which usually carries vehicle extrication equipment, rescue rope, portable lighting, firefighting tools, and firefighters specially trained in special rescue activities; (e) a tanker, also called a tender, used in areas that lack fire hydrants to deliver firefighting water to the scene of an emergency; (f) an airport rescue firefighting (ARFF) apparatus, equipped with a large water tank and firefighting foam systems to fight fires involving aircraft.

2. *Emergency service vehicles:* Only the specialized fire and EMS vehicles used for delivering emergency response services to the community are discussed here: apparatus (pumpers, ladders, quints, heavy rescues, tenders [see sidebar on next page]); EMS vehicles (squads, ambulances); and emergency support vehicles (command, aircraft, and specialty vehicles) (see Figure 13–1). All of these are included in most of the generally accepted definitions of capital resources. Not addressed here are other capital vehicles, such as sedans, vans, and pickups, which are not unique to the fire and emergency services department.
3. *Emergency service and support facilities:* Fire stations are the basic facility from which fire, emergency medical, and hazardous materials services are delivered. Although some communities have experimented with EMS systems that deploy ambulances to various positions in the service area on the basis of computer models (such deployment is called system status management or mobile deployment), most communities provide fire and emergency medical services from fixed locations, such as fire stations. Addressed in this chapter are fixed service delivery facilities (e.g., fire stations, combined fire/EMS facilities, and EMS base stations) but not administrative facilities unless the latter are co-located with service delivery facilities. Administrative facilities are not specific to the emergency response service, and adequate information on planning and operating them can be found in architectural and planning texts.

Fire and emergency service vehicles

Pumper (engine) A pumper is the type of fire apparatus most commonly operated by a fire department. It carries a water tank, pump, ground ladders, hose, and other fire and EMS equipment. The main mission of the firefighters who staff this type of apparatus is to secure a water supply—for example, by laying a hose line from a fire hydrant to the fire—and to put water on the fire. A pumper may also be referred to as an engine, a squad, or a wagon.[1]

Ladder (truck) A ladder is a large firefighting vehicle that incorporates an aerial device, such as an aerial ladder, tower ladder, or platform. Along with equipment that is used for firefighting, forcible entry into buildings, rescue, and ventilation, the vehicle also carries other support equipment. The main missions of the firefighters who staff this type of apparatus are search and rescue, and removal of smoke and hot gases from structures. Many ladder companies also provide other rescue services, such as extrication of car crash victims. Ladders may also be referred to as trucks, aerials, towers, sticks, bobtails, and hook and ladders.

Quint A quint is a combination of pumper and ladder, although the full capabilities of these two types of vehicles cannot be completely accommodated in one vehicle. Quints incorporate a water tank, hose, pump, ground ladders, and an aerial device, and may be used as ladders or as pumpers in many situations.

Heavy rescue A heavy rescue (called a rescue company) is a large firefighting vehicle that carries rescue equipment and firefighters but usually no appreciable water supply or large ladder. Rescue company firefighters are highly skilled in firefighting and rescue and may be considered the specialists of their departments. Many rescue companies also provide technical rescue capability, such as diving and lifting heavy objects. The number of firefighters assigned to a heavy rescue is usually higher than the number assigned to a pumper or a ladder. Heavy rescues may also be referred to as squads or tactical units.

Tender A water carrier, known as a tanker on the East Coast, is commonly called a tender in the western United States. A tender must carry at least 1,000 gallons of water and may be designed to deliver water by gravity or be equipped with a pump. Tractor-drawn tenders can exceed capacities of 5,000 gallons.

1 The term *squad* is used in different communities to mean different things.

Procurement of capital equipment

Fire and emergency services equipment is used under the most extreme circumstances imaginable. Tools must work well in extreme heat and extreme cold, in extremely wet and extremely dry conditions, in situations of low visibility, and in atmospheres contaminated with toxins. Equipment that may work perfectly well for most home and business uses will not survive the rigorous use it will receive at the hands of firefighters working in emergency response situations.

In addition, all fire and EMS equipment requires an extremely high degree of dependability. Firefighters can ill afford saws that will not cut, hydraulic spreaders that will not spread, or defibrillators that will not deliver a shock. Failure of these devices in the field can have drastic consequences. The importance of this fact is hard to overstate. These tools literally make the difference between life and death for firefighters and the customers they are serving. Moreover, when an equipment failure affects the outcome of an emergency, significant civil liability is possible.

This section discusses establishing the need for the purchase, assessing the existing equipment, complying with standards, seeking input from local and other users of the equipment, weighing costs (not only the cost to purchase but also the cost over the entire life of the equipment, the cost of standardization and of training in the absence of standardization, and the cost of—or savings from—vendor support), evaluating the safety of the equipment to be purchased, and considering possible ways of funding the purchase.

Establishing the need for purchase or replacement

The first step in any planned procurement process for equipment is establishing the need for the purchase. When a needed piece of equipment has been lost, stolen, or destroyed, a formal process that establishes need is unnecessary; the need is obvious. The need is also obvious when a new unit or program is activated and requires equipment. But in other cases, establishing the need is more difficult. Some items of fire and EMS equipment, such as hose adapters, will last for decades before wearing out or becoming obsolete, whereas others, such as defibrillators, are overtaken by obsolescence within a few years.

One important source of data for decisions about replacement is equipment maintenance records that are properly maintained. Equally important are the observations of the firefighters who use the equipment. Their feedback, reflecting hands-on experience, can help department managers identify specific pieces of equipment that have proven unreliable or identify trends that might suggest the replacement of a piece of equipment on a department-wide basis. With regard to obsolescence, information on the state of the art in equipment is readily available from trade publications, seminars, direct mailings, and—of course—fire equipment dealers.

Assessing existing equipment

Once the need to replace a piece of equipment has been established, an examination of the positive and negative aspects of the equipment being replaced is often very useful. Maintenance records should be examined for recurring problems that can be eliminated when the new equipment is specified. Here, too, the users should be consulted on what should be changed to improve the equipment's usefulness and on what should not be changed. Two important considerations are weight and size. A new defibrillator that is twice the weight of the old one is not likely to strike the user as a change for the better, regardless of any new features it might have.

Complying with standards

Increasingly in the United States, Canada, and the European Union, standards exist that establish minimum performance, construction, and certification norms for fire and EMS equipment. In many cases, compliance with these standards is completely voluntary. For example, standards produced by the National Fire Protection Association (NFPA) do not generally carry the force of law (see sidebar on next page). In the United States, however, Food and Drug Administration (FDA) standards governing medical devices and National Institute for Occupational Safety and Health (NIOSH) certification of SCBA are mandated by law.

In addition, within the homeland security realm, standards for reliability and interoperability of communications and protective equipment are referenced in federal funding and performance assessments. Many federal grants require compliance with these standards in the purchase of equipment. Compliance is also an expected criterion for assessment of emergency preparedness. Chapters 15 and 16 on information systems and communications, respectively, have more information on these trends.

Local government managers and fire chiefs who choose to purchase equipment that is not in compliance with voluntary or mandatory standards assume a higher level of potential liability and risk. Even though voluntary standards carry no compliance requirement, they have been used in litigation to establish a level of care for fire and emergency medical services. Should the situation arise in which a manager chooses to ignore a component of a standard, the manager should document the reasoning behind the decision at the time the decision is made and should file the documentation properly, thus possibly gaining some measure of protection if the decision is questioned in the future.

Seeking input from local and other users

The actual user of the equipment—the person who will be expected to put the tool to use once it is received—should continue to have a voice in the purchasing process. In some cases the way to gather user input may be as simple as visiting the fire stations where the existing tool is in use, discussing the replacement with the firefighters there, and providing the firefighters with information on the proposed purchases. For more expensive purchases or for purchases of critical safety equipment such as SCBA, a committee comprising fire department users, managers, and administrators should be consulted. For the largest purchases, an ad hoc committee of users and managers should be formed to research the products available in the market, decide which are best for the community in terms of their usefulness and cost, and recommend appropriate replacement equipment to upper management. In combination fire departments (those that use the services of career and volunteer firefighters), input should be included from all firefighter groups. All members of the committee should be free to express their opinions without fear of recrimination or retribution; otherwise, discussions may be inhibited.

When the purchase of new or replacement equipment is contemplated, there is no point in reinventing the wheel. Other fire and emergency service departments and users can provide very valuable information, and it is common for firefighters to compare notes about the performance of equipment. Other departments should be consulted about their experience with a particular brand or model of equipment, with maintenance, with parts availability, and with support from the manufacturer. Very often the equipment manufacturer will, if asked, supply the names of other fire departments that use a piece of fire equipment. One should keep in mind, however, that the list is being supplied by the person who is trying to sell the equipment, so it is important to seek other sources of information. Also, firefighters tend to feel a certain measure of passion about their equipment. A tool that is not liked in one community may work perfectly well in another community: this is why they make vanilla, chocolate, and strawberry ice cream.

A source of information that is tapped less often is users from outside the fire and emergency services. A lumberjack, for example, would be an excellent source of information about the reliability of a chain saw under heavy use. Likewise, an asbestos removal contractor or a hazardous-waste cleanup company would probably provide useful information about the durability and reliability of an SCBA under heavy-duty use. Too often these sources of information are ignored.

NFPA standards for equipment

The National Fire Protection Association (NFPA), a nonprofit educational and standards development organization, produces consensus standards for use by the fire service. (On NFPA standards and the standards-making process, see also Chapter 10.) NFPA standards exist for almost every piece of fire equipment, including hose, nozzles, hydraulic rescue tools, SCBA, and ground ladders. The proper development of NFPA standards depends on the quantity and quality of input provided to the standards-making process. Participation in this process can take several forms.

First, fire service and local government personnel are encouraged to participate actively as members of NFPA technical committees, if they can. Such participation typically requires attending an average of one to two meetings per year somewhere in the United States or Canada. Expenses for participation are the responsibility of the committee member or his or her sponsoring agency.

Second, those who are unable to participate as committee members have ample opportunity to propose new standards, suggest changes to existing standards, and comment on documents proposed for adoption. NFPA regulations require that every proposal and comment submitted on a given standard be addressed and an answer published. The vehicles for these discussions are a Report on Proposals and a Report on Comments, both of which are available from NFPA on the organization's website (nfpa.org). (Also available on the website is information about the NFPA standards development process and a listing of the standards published to date.)

Finally, there is also an opportunity to address the issues of a standard at a technical committee report session where the standard is presented for action by NFPA's members. Such sessions are held annually in conjunction with multifaceted NFPA meetings (where, in addition to action on standards, there are educational sessions and exhibits by vendors).

NFPA works very hard to maintain an appropriate balance on its committees: committee members include representatives of user groups, manufacturers, regulatory organizations, and others. However, given budget and travel restrictions, it is often difficult for fire and emergency service members to attend, so it is not uncommon at committee meetings related to fire service equipment for a high percentage of attendees to be manufacturers. The access provided during the proposal and comment phases of standards development is intended to level the playing field for the various vested interests.

By whatever method, fire service input to the standards-making process is critical. The quality, affordability, and safety of all types of equipment hang in the balance.

Weighing costs

The initial purchase price of equipment is only one of the costs that should be considered. Others are the cost of the equipment over its lifetime of service, expenses related to standardization (or its lack) and the need for training, and vendor support over the long term.

Life cycle costs

The Bugtussle Heights Fire Department has completed a two-year process and is now about to select a new self-contained breathing apparatus (SCBA) for the department. Two bids have been received from reputable manufacturers. The SCBA committee has determined that each SCBA meets the department's specifications and that each would be a good, safe unit for Bugtussle Heights. Twenty units are to be purchased.

After much research, the SCBA committee has determined that the new SCBA will have a ten-year life span. The committee has also determined, in advance of the bid, that the parts of the SCBA that are most often replaced are the facepiece, the shoulder straps, and the cylinder retention system.

SCBA #1 SCBA #1 has been offered at a unit cost of $2,500, with a 10 percent discount off the list price for parts and with free initial and annual training for the firefighters who maintain and repair the units. The manufacturer recommends that SCBA #1 units be checked by a technician three times a year and that an overhaul be performed every three years. Parts for the overhaul cost a total of $200 after the discount has been applied. The standard package of replacement parts outlined by the SCBA committee has a total cost of $1,500, including the discount.

SCBA #2 SCBA #2 has been offered at no charge, with a 20 percent discount off the list price for parts. Initial training is free for the Bugtussle Heights's SCBA maintenance team, and annual recertification training is offered for a flat fee of $300 per year. The manufacturer recommends that SCBA #2 units be checked by a technician twice a year and that an overhaul be completed once a year. Parts for the overhaul cost a total of $500 after the discount has been applied. The standard package of replacement parts outlined by the SCBA committee has a total cost of $2,500 including the discount.

Below is a life cycle cost comparison of the purchase, with all cost factors taken into account:

	SCBA #1	SCBA #2
Initial cost per unit	$2,500	Free
Total initial purchase price (20 units)	$50,000	Free
Initial training for firefighters	Free	Free
Annual recertification training for four technicians		
SCBA #1: Free	Free	
SCBA #2: $300/year for 10 years		$3,000
SCBA checks, labor only, at $60 per hour, one hour per check		
SCBA #1: 20 units × 10 years × three 1-hour checks/year × $60/hour	$36,000	
SCBA #2: 20 units × 10 years × two 1-hour checks/year × $60/hour		$24,000
Overhauls, three hours labor plus parts		
SCBA #1: 20 units × three 3-hour overhauls/year × $60/hour labor	$10,800	
SCBA #2: 20 units × ten 3-hour overhauls/year × $60/hour labor		$36,000
SCBA #1: Overhaul parts, 20 units × $200 × three overhauls/year	$12,000	
SCBA #2: Overhaul parts, 20 units × $500 × ten overhauls/year		$100,000
Standard replacement parts list		
SCBA #1: 20 units × $1,500 for parts	$30,000	
SCBA #2: 20 units × $2,500 for parts		$50,000
Total life cycle cost	$141,300	$213,000

If all other factors were equal, SCBA #1 would be the better buy despite the much lower initial price of SCBA #2.

Life cycle costs Fire departments that are procuring new or replacement equipment should give some thought to the total cost of the equipment—both the initial cost and the cost of keeping the unit in service for its expected service life. Life cycle costs consist of the original purchase price, any applicable sales tax, and the cost of parts and labor for repairs and preventive maintenance. An unscrupulous equipment vendor may offer its product at a deep discount only to charge high prices for parts in the future. When life cycle costs are considered, the competing equipment that had a higher initial price may be a better value.

Standardization and training costs Fire and EMS equipment is used in time-sensitive, high-stress situations. Establishing familiarity and practicing with equipment in advance of the emergency will make the firefighter more efficient in these situations. It is incumbent on the fire and emergency services department to provide equipment operation training for anyone who is expected to use a tool. Standardization on one piece of equipment minimizes the need for training and the associated expense. In some cases, it may be less expensive overall to pay a little more for a piece of equipment that firefighters are already familiar with than to save money on the purchase price of a new or modified tool only to spend funds later for training. (Standardization is also discussed below under "Evaluating Safety.")

Costs and vendor support The relationship between a fire and emergency services department and the supplier of some types of equipment can be very long term, so a consideration of costs should include the support that the equipment manufacturer and the local equipment distributor will provide after the sale. The vendor will generally be most attentive to the department at the time of the purchase, so this is an excellent time to establish a contract for the purchase of parts and services related to the equipment. For example, a component of a purchase agreement for defibrillators might be a five-year contract that provides a standard percentage discount off the manufacturer's suggested retail price for parts and a set hourly labor rate for nonwarranty work. Before a purchase is completed, the procedure to be used for warranty repairs, as well as the process for ordering and receiving parts, should be clear to everyone involved. Vendors are typically very much in love with their customers prior to the issuance of the purchase order. Love can fade after the equipment is delivered, so it is best to work out support details during the courtship.

Evaluating safety

Firefighting itself is among the most hazardous of occupations, but fire and EMS equipment should not be hazardous to the health of firefighters. NFPA, FDA, and NIOSH standards and certifications provide some measure of protection by giving assurances that equipment has met those minimum safety standards. In addition, before purchase, each piece of equipment should be assessed for its effect on the safety of firefighters.

Certain critical pieces of fire and EMS equipment—for example, SCBA and defibrillators—should be replaced on a systemwide basis at one time rather than incrementally. Because SCBA provide safe breathing air in hazardous atmospheres, they are used in situations that are defined as immediately dangerous to life and health (see Figure 13–2). Accordingly, their importance to the firefighter cannot be overstated. Each fire department should use only one type and model of SCBA (or units that are extremely close in configuration and operation) so that firefighters are required to remember only one set of emergency operating instructions. This precaution ensures that if things go wrong in an emergency situation, when the firefighter is already under extreme stress, he or she will not be forced to remember which type of SCBA is in use and what the proper emergency procedures are for that brand or model. Extreme emergencies involving the SCBA are rare, but when they do happen, knowing and immediately performing emergency operations can mean the difference between life and death for the firefighter.

Defibrillators allow trained firefighters to read heart rhythms and deliver electrical shock to convert abnormal rhythms to normal or restart a nonbeating heart. Using only one make or model of a defibrillator (or units that are extremely close in configuration and operation) will simplify training and ensure that all firefighters are familiar with the unit being used. Unlike SCBA emergencies, heart attacks and trauma are not rare, but they still require the firefighter

Photo by Kevin M. Roche

Figure 13-2 Self-contained breathing apparatus (SCBA) is a critical part of firefighter personal protective equipment, and the purchase and regular maintenance of SCBA are a key component of capital budgeting.

to work with great speed and skill. The patient (the customer) should not have to wait for the firefighter to recall which defibrillator is in use and how it is operated. This knowledge should be instinctive, and the provision of a standard piece of equipment ensures that there are no delays caused by unfamiliarity with the equipment. Standard units also simplify the stocking of supplies since only one type of pad and one type of leads (wires) have to be stocked.

Considering various funding sources for services

Funding sources for fire and emergency services vary widely from community to community, but the most common source of funding for career fire and EMS equipment is the community's operating (noncapital) budget. Funding sources for volunteer fire departments vary widely: some departments are supported solely by donations, others are supported by dedicated property taxes, and still others contract with local communities to provide their services.

Depending on local laws and procedures, funds for major purchases can be rolled from one fiscal year into the next so that sufficient funds accumulate. Some states, such as Florida, have statewide grant funds that can be used for the purchase of specific EMS equipment. Major purchases that cannot or should not be incrementally implemented, such as the replacement of a department's SCBA inventory, should be considered for bond program funding or lease purchase (defined in a later section). Often civic organizations, businesses, local foundations, or individuals are willing to provide certain types of equipment that a fire and emergency services department needs but cannot afford. One example of private funding is the grassroots efforts that have purchased infrared cameras for local fire departments. (By allowing firefighters to see through smoke, these cameras speed up rescue and firefighting activities.)

A source of funding for firefighting equipment and protective clothing since 2002 is the Assistance to Firefighters Grants (AFG) program. This program delivered almost $2.7 billion worth of fire apparatus, fire equipment, and protective clothing into the hands of local fire departments in its first five years. The program, administered by the U.S. Fire Administration (USFA)—part of the Federal Emergency Management Agency (FEMA)—has an annual application process. The USFA provides initial guidance, discussing grant priorities for the year and guiding fire departments through the application process. Grants are submitted online and evaluated by firefighters and others to ensure program priority compliance. In most cases, these grants require a local fund match on a sliding scale depending upon the size of the community applying for the grant.

FEMA has other grant programs that assist in fire safety research and public education as well as providing funding for firefighter staffing.

Procurement of emergency vehicles

The primary mission of fire apparatus and emergency vehicles is to provide service to the customers (residents, commuters, and visitors) within the community, so the maintenance and reliability of these vehicles are critical. These vehicles are more than a means of conveyance and service delivery; they are also a source of pride both to citizens and to the firefighters who use them. They are the most visible symbol of the fire and emergency services department in the community.

The procurement of apparatus and emergency vehicles involves the same steps as the procurement of equipment. With vehicles, however, the development of specifications is of particular concern and so is obsolescence.

Establishing the need for purchase or replacement

The need to purchase a new vehicle for a new fire station or for a new program is fairly easy to establish. The decision about *when* to replace a vehicle is much more difficult. Emergency vehicles, especially engines (pumpers) and trucks (ladders), are extremely expensive pieces of equipment, and no matter how large the community, the cost is significant. Thus, managers should keep each vehicle in service as long as possible (to get the maximum benefit from it) while at the same time bearing in mind that all emergency vehicles must be extremely reliable.

Traditionally, pumpers were retained in service for up to fifteen years and ladder trucks for up to as many as twenty years. Changes in the fire apparatus industry and in the fire service itself have pushed that convention in both directions: on the one hand, new apparatus is capable of longer service life than apparatus manufactured in the past, but on the other hand, the inclusion of emergency medical services has dramatically raised activity levels for many fire departments. Even in departments where the wear and tear on fire apparatus is at lower levels, new technology makes older apparatus obsolete before it wears out. In the past, a pumper or ladder with more than 100,000 miles on the odometer was unheard of. Modern apparatus reaches this milestone regularly.

Generally, volunteer fire departments serve smaller communities with lower emergency activity levels and thus less frequent use of fire apparatus. Even with lower-use intensity, however, fire apparatus and emergency vehicles are overtaken by new technology—for example, improved safety equipment, important to the firefighter and everyone else on the road with the fire truck—and become obsolete. NFPA 1911, Standard for the Inspection, Maintenance, Testing, and Retirement of In-Service Automotive Fire Apparatus (2007 ed.), includes guidance on retirement criteria for fire apparatus. However, there is no national standard governing the replacement of emergency vehicles. The decision is left to each locality and represents a balancing of numerous factors: fire department activity levels, maintenance cost and history, individual vehicle reliability, funding availability, technological changes, firefighter safety, and vehicle use (see sidebar on facing page). Fire apparatus must be replaced before it becomes unreliable, but it must be held in service for as long as possible to maximize the benefit of the large initial investment.

The purchase of fire apparatus should be defined in a local replacement plan: fire department managers and firefighters, fleet maintenance managers and technicians, and local government managers should meet and develop a long-term plan for the replacement of fire apparatus and emergency vehicles. Three successful replacement plans are outlined in the sidebar on page 374. The variety of carefully considered approaches shows that there is no one way to structure a long-term fleet replacement plan; unless some plan exists and is implemented, however, the department will eventually face an accumulation of unreliable emergency vehicles and the associated effect on the budget of a large vehicle-purchase package. (For more on asset management, including replacement, see Chapter 12.)

Service life of emergency vehicles

Comparing fire department fleets with other fleets is difficult. One readily available indicator of use is mileage. Local service delivery trucks, buses, and refuse vehicles can have service lives that extend into the hundreds of thousands of miles. Over-the-road trucks (e.g., eighteen-wheelers) can have service lives that last more than a million miles. So why is it that fire apparatus and other emergency vehicles cannot last that long? The answer lies in three fundamental differences between fire department fleets and these other fleets.

First, a large percentage of the road miles placed on fire and emergency vehicles are incurred when the vehicles are responding to emergencies. Any emergency response requires repeated cycles of rapid acceleration and deceleration, hard turns, and quick stops—a type of use that places extreme demands on a vehicle. For fire apparatus engaged in pumping and/or aerial operations, long periods of stationary operations at high engine speeds are common.

The second difference between fire department fleets and other fleets is the need for reliability. Although with a refuse truck, a failure to start is not unimportant (especially to people with their trash on the curb), the effect of that failure can be addressed by assigning another vehicle in the same yard to perform the broken vehicle's duty or by making some other accommodation. The worst thing that happens is that the trash stays on the curb a little longer.

In the United States and Canada, if a fire truck or an ambulance fails to start, there is almost never another similarly equipped vehicle sitting next to it that can be rapidly deployed. In those two countries, the general practice is for fire and emergency service departments to deploy a thin layer of emergency response resources in a large number of locations around the community. In Europe and elsewhere, however, the number of fire stations present in the community is small, but multiple resources are concentrated in these stations. Compare, for example, Berlin, Germany, with Houston, Texas: the Berlin Fire Brigade protects more than 3.4 million people spread over 340 square miles with thirty-two staffed fire stations, whereas the Houston Fire Department protects about 2.2 million residents spread over 600 square miles with ninety fire stations.

In the U.S. deployment model, very few—if any—of the numerous fire stations have multiple response units of the same type. If the primary unit fails to start or is unable to function for some other reason, backup can be sent quickly from the next-closest fire department facility, but the travel distance from the other station can add minutes to the response. In fire and EMS situations, it is not an overdramatization to say that these additional minutes can be the difference between life and death.

Photo by John Cochran

Departments that house all their response resources in one location, as is the case for many volunteer and smaller career fire departments, are less affected by the failure of one unit to start because another vehicle is probably available and equipped to act in its place. But once a piece of equipment is at the scene of the emergency, its failure affects all fire departments to the same degree, regardless of their deployment methodology.

The third difference between fire department fleets and other fleets is that fire apparatus are fully loaded at all times, with vehicle components constantly bearing their maximum load. Over-the-road trucks, delivery trucks, refuse vehicles, and buses spend a significant part of their service life below maximum load. Suspension systems, driveline and power systems, and brakes are more taxed by full than by partial loads. This constant extreme use shortens the service lives of components on fire apparatus compared with components on vehicles that are used differently.

Assessing existing vehicles

As is the case for fire equipment, examination of the positive and negative aspects of current apparatus and emergency vehicles forms a solid basis for developing specifications for a vehicle's replacement. Maintenance records can provide key information, as can input from the users of the vehicles.

Complying with standards

A great deal of information about specifications can be gathered from a review of current standards for fire apparatus and emergency equipment. NFPA manages the development of—and publishes—voluntary standards on many types of fire apparatus, including pumpers, ladders, tankers, wildland firefighting vehicles, and airport rescue firefighting (ARFF) vehicles. These standards do not usually have any regulatory force (although in some states, such as Texas, they may be adopted on a statewide basis), but they are considered generally accepted industry standards. Moreover, they are minimum standards, so using them as a basis for the development of any purchase specification is prudent.

However, two standards do have regulatory force. The first is the General Services Administration's (GSA) KKK-A-1822 standard related to the construction and performance of ambulances. The Triple-K ambulance standard is used as a basis for most state EMS ambulance certification requirements. Ambulances that do not meet this standard generally cannot be

Three successful vehicle replacement plans

The communities of Plano (Texas), Phoenix (Arizona), and Clifton Park (New York) have different but well-thought-out solutions to the problem of planning for the replacement of regular apparatus and emergency vehicles.

Plano, Texas The Plano Fire Department provides fire and emergency medical services to the 270,000 residents of Plano (near Dallas) from twelve fire stations distributed over seventy square miles. In conjunction with the city's fleet maintenance department, fire department management determined an expected service life and expected replacement costs for every vehicle type in the fleet. The replacement cost for a piece of apparatus was divided by the item's service life, and an annual replacement cost was derived. Each year, the department budgets this amount for each apparatus covered by the plan, and the funds are deposited in an interest-bearing holding account. When the apparatus reaches the end of its expected service life, the funds should be available to replace it. The final decision on the need to replace an individual piece of apparatus takes into consideration its condition, its reliability, and the cost of maintaining it.

Phoenix, Arizona The Phoenix Fire Department provides fire and emergency medical services to 1.5 million residents from fifty-eight fire stations distributed over 518 square miles. In the late 1990s the department found that its fleet of engines (pumpers) was deteriorating to the point that keeping all engine companies in service each day was difficult. In the previous seven years, only two pumpers a year, on average, had been replaced. After analyzing the cost of maintenance and the reliability of the aging pumpers, management determined that this type of apparatus should be replaced when it had accumulated 150,000 miles. A large spreadsheet was created that first estimated the annual accrual of miles on every pumper in the fleet over a period of ten years, and then analyzed the cost and consequences of several replacement plans. In the end, management decided that the best way to keep the fleet healthy while also controlling costs was to replace five pumpers per year.

Clifton Park, New York The Clifton Park Fire Department, a volunteer organization, provides fire and emergency services to a suburban fire district located fifteen miles north of Albany; the fire district is home to an estimated 20,000 people in fifteen square miles. The department operates a heavy rescue, a ladder tower, and two pumper/tankers. In the early 1980s, the district commissioned a comprehensive analysis of the department's resources, including its apparatus. A component of the final report was a recommended replacement time frame for each piece of fire apparatus. Replacements were spaced to allow the district to accumulate funding in advance and avoid getting into a situation in which all department apparatus would need to be replaced at the same time. Using the plan as a template, the district began saving funds in sufficient amounts to make the plan a reality. This plan continues to serve the district and allows for the regular replacement of apparatus in a manner that ensures that funds are available when needed.

licensed or permitted for use. The August 2007 edition of this specification is titled KKK-A-1822F, *Federal Specification for the Star-of-Life Ambulance.*[1] In 2009, NFPA began the development of a standard that may eventually replace the Triple-K standard.

The second standard that has regulatory force is the Federal Aviation Administration (FAA) advisory circular that sets minimum standards for the construction and performance capability of ARFF vehicles: AC 150/5220-10D, *Guide Specification for Aircraft Rescue and Fire Fighting Vehicles* (September 2007).[2] If the vehicle is to be funded fully or partly by the FAA, it will have to meet this standard. But even if FAA funding is not to be used to purchase an ARFF vehicle, the advisory circular provides valuable information for developing a purchase specification and is considered an industry-acceptable standard.

Seeking input from local and other users

Involving local users in developing the specification for the purchase of a new emergency vehicle is extremely important. Because users are the people who will operate this vehicle in the course of their work, their practical perspective on the vehicle's capabilities and features will prove very valuable. Many fire departments establish either standing or ad hoc apparatus committees to bring together the interests of users, management, and maintenance personnel in developing specifications (discussed in detail below). In volunteer departments or departments serving small to moderate-sized communities, the fire chief or the fire district may appoint an apparatus committee, whose function is usually to research the needs of the department and the community; develop purchase specifications; and manage and track the apparatus throughout the design, construction, and delivery process. In larger fire departments, where direct access to all users is difficult, user surveys are an excellent means of gathering information and input.

As with purchases of equipment, information related to other departments' experience with the apparatus and vehicles should be solicited. This information can help a local fire and emergency services department avoid mistakes already made by others and develop an improved product for local use.

Developing specifications

The development of performance or construction specifications for the purchase of emergency vehicles is highly recommended and, in many communities, may be required by local purchasing rules. The process should start with an assessment of local needs and operating conditions. Building on successful specifications from another department that has similar operating conditions can be a good starting point. The specifications should be open enough to allow manufacturers to address the needs of the purchaser in different ways with engineered solutions, yet restrictive enough to protect the purchaser from an inferior product. Draft or suggested specifications are available from most manufacturers; along with the appropriate standard, they can provide a basis for a purchase specification. In most locales, assistance from a governmental purchasing agent can be helpful in developing language to protect the fire and emergency services organization and provide an avenue for resolution of concerns later in the procurement process.

After the contract to construct a piece of apparatus has been executed but before construction starts, the manufacturer and representatives of the fire department should meet and discuss the specification in detail. If possible, this meeting should be held at the apparatus manufacturer's production facility, where immediate access to engineers, managers, and production experts is possible.

Because there are relatively few manufacturers of fire apparatus and emergency vehicles, chances are that the apparatus being built for a community will not be constructed within or near that community. Thus, a final inspection of the apparatus before it leaves the manufacturer's facility is a good investment of time and resources. Problems with the apparatus that are discovered at the plant can be rapidly addressed by manufacturer's staff who are familiar with the vehicle. Once the vehicle leaves the factory, getting service becomes more difficult and may lead to long delays before the new unit can be deployed. Final inspection trips should be conducted by fire department members and others who are very familiar with the original purchase specifications and with any changes that were made during the design and construction process.

Weighing costs

As with capital equipment, the purchaser must consider not only the initial outlay but also costs over the whole life cycle, costs relating to standardization and training, and vendor support.

Life cycle costs Fire service and fire apparatus publications often feature advertisements from manufacturers selling new fire apparatus at extremely low prices. These apparatus very often meet the minimum national standards and may be suitable for use in low-activity areas, but they are not generally constructed or equipped for use in communities that place severe demands on their apparatus. It may be obvious that the shiny touches (such as chrome) and the necessary but not required systems (such as air conditioning) that are present on many pieces of vehicular fire equipment are missing. However, also missing may be some features, such as supplemental braking devices, that may extend the life of the apparatus, minimize maintenance costs, or improve firefighter safety.

When a department is developing specifications and comparing proposals from different manufacturers, it should give thought to the costs of operating and maintaining the vehicle. The addition of a heavy-duty drive train component may extend the life of a vehicle or reduce maintenance costs throughout its life. A minimal initial investment can help reduce ongoing costs throughout the life of the apparatus or emergency vehicle.

Standardization and training costs Because of the long service lives of emergency vehicles, it is difficult to provide units that have standard ways of storing and using equipment and standard operational methods. But to the extent possible, fire apparatus and other emergency vehicles should have standard layouts, and the equipment stored in a particular location should be similar from unit to unit. Standardization in storage and layout will minimize time spent searching for a piece of equipment by firefighters who are unfamiliar with the exact layout of a unit from another location or who work in different locations from day to day.

Operational standardization, too, is important; the need for additional training can be minimized if pumps and aerial devices have similar operational controls and characteristics. Achieving operational standardization is complicated, however, by advancements in technology that incrementally improve operational control and capability as well as by variations from manufacturer to manufacturer.

Costs and vendor support The fire apparatus and ambulance manufacturing industries have a long history of very old and reliable companies failing, and of new companies being developed and becoming successful—and then failing. The survival of any one apparatus manufacturer cannot be absolutely guaranteed for the life of the warranty, much less for the service life of the vehicle. However, fire departments and local government managers can take several steps to minimize this risk.

First, they can develop a good purchase specification. It should be based on local needs and requirements, national standards, and the experiences of those inside and outside the local fire and emergency services department. A well-thought-out purchase specification can go a long way toward providing a vehicle that will serve the community and perhaps outlast those who created it.

Second, to the extent possible, a department should not use apparatus components that are handmade or bought on special order. Later in the life of the vehicle, these parts and components will become scarce or impossible to procure. In addition, whenever possible, it is best to use components and configurations that are not unique to the fire service. If a component is in general use in the trucking industry, it will probably be available when needed in the future. If a department has a mission-critical component that may be unavailable in the future, it should purchase a spare one.

Third, the department should get an "as-built" electrical diagram of every vehicle. Electrical problems are one of the most common afflictions of fire apparatus and emergency vehicles—and among the most time-consuming and difficult problems to solve. The diagram will be expensive, probably costing thousands of dollars, but it will pay dividends over the life of the vehicle. Any changes made after the vehicle is placed in service should be documented on this diagram to keep it current, which can help speed up the diagnosis of problems.

Hard-wired vehicles are now being replaced with vehicles that have computerized electrical controls, such as multiplexing, which may be more difficult to repair. (*Multiplexing* refers to an electrical control system whereby wires can power multiple components under the control of data links that communicate with each other and with controllers to perform the functions previously performed by relays or circuit breakers. It has become very common in recent years. Advantages of multiplexing include fewer electrical wires that must be run through a vehicle and easier troubleshooting of electrical problems.)

Finally, the department should require the vendor to provide high-quality service manuals. The purchase specification should also require documentation for the servicing and use of every major component of the vehicle.

Evaluating safety and obsolescence

Concern for the safety of firefighters and of the people who live their lives around fire and emergency service vehicles should be central to the purchasing process. In most parts of the United States, if not most of the world, laws grant special permission or allowances to the operators of emergency vehicles responding to an emergency. In many cases these operators are allowed to drive at speeds above the posted speed limit, travel in opposing lanes of traffic, proceed through red traffic signals after stopping, and engage in other higher-risk driving behavior. Since these activities occur on every emergency response, they present some of the highest liability and life safety risks to the fire and emergency services department. According to USFA data from 2008, 20 percent of firefighter deaths occur while firefighters are responding to or returning from alarms.[3] And firefighters are not the only ones at risk. In vehicle collisions involving fire apparatus and civilian vehicles, the driver and occupants of the civilian vehicle almost always suffer worse consequences than the firefighters.

Risks encountered in responding to an emergency rescue call can be minimized by vehicle operator training, response procedures, and traffic preemption devices. Although monumentally important, these risk management procedures are outside the scope of this chapter. But other ways of minimizing the risks encountered during an emergency response can be addressed here. NFPA, FAA, and GSA standards directly affect the safety of fire apparatus, ARFF vehicles, and ambulances, and these standards should be used as the basis for any purchase specification. They lie behind a number of positive safety changes in the fire apparatus industry, among which are noise attenuation, emergency-vehicle conspicuity, and requirements for fully enclosed passenger compartments and for minimum load ratings of aerial ladders.

But the same changes that improve safety may also hasten obsolescence. In the 1990s, fire apparatus and other emergency vehicles changed in many ways, and many of these changes not only improved the safety of firefighters but also accelerated the obsolescence of existing apparatus. For example, aerial ladder standards at the beginning of the twenty-first century set minimum weight capacity for aerial ladders, improving their stability and therefore their safety. Departments began to remove many older ladders not capable of meeting these minimums and not as stable as the newer equipment, replacing them with new, more advanced ladders offering more operational capability and higher levels of safety for firefighters.

Another example of a change that both improves safety and accelerates obsolescence is the addition of compressed air foam systems (CAFS) to fire engines (pumpers). These systems, which introduce air and foam concentrate into the hose stream, have been found to increase firefighting efficiency and limit water damage. The systems are not inexpensive—most cost more than $25,000—but retrofitting many existing pumpers with them is difficult or impossible. Thus, the desire to add CAFS capability to firefighting apparatus has accelerated the replacement of some apparatus.

Considering various funding sources for vehicles

Apparatus and emergency vehicles are funded by a variety of mechanisms, including the operating budget, capital purchases through bonds, lease-purchase arrangements, sinking funds, and leasing. Larger communities may be capable of funding the replacement of apparatus and emergency vehicles as a recurring cost in their annual budgets. Some communities choose to fund apparatus through voter-approved bond issues. With lease-purchase arrangements, communities can pay for purchases in much the same way that many people buy their family cars—that is, by making monthly or annual payments and paying interest for the use of the funds.

Some communities view replacing vehicles as a process rather than an event and have thus developed sinking funds, a pay-as-you-go means of replacing apparatus and vehicles. Sinking funds are specially dedicated monies that are tied to a replacement plan for apparatus and emergency vehicles. Every vehicle in the fleet is assigned a service life and a replacement cost estimate. The service life is based on the replacement plan, and the cost estimate accounts for inflation and projected cost increases. That cost is broken down into payments that are based either on the passage of time (payments made monthly, quarterly, or annually) or on vehicle use (payments by the mile or by the hour). The payments are deposited into an account, where they accumulate until it is time to fund the purchase of replacement apparatus and other vehicles. Depending on local laws and regulations, these accounts may or may not be capable of earning interest as a hedge against inflation. The accounts provide funding for replacements only, not for additions to the fleet. Fleet additions are usually paid for by some other funding source; after their purchase, however, contributions are made to the sinking fund to pay for their eventual replacement.

The replacement plan must also make some accommodation for vehicles that are destroyed or rendered useless before their planned service life has expired. Either the plan itself (i.e., the sinking fund) may absorb such unscheduled expenses, or another source of revenue may be called on to fund the replacement of destroyed and damaged vehicles. These other sources may be, for example, insurance, funds recovered from the responsible party, or the operating or capital budget.

One shortcoming of sinking funds is that they eventually reach a significant size and may therefore become the object of attention when fiscal conditions send local government managers in search of sources of quick cash. In some cases, funds have been withdrawn from sinking funds on the understanding that the withdrawals will be replaced when the economy turns upward again. But despite everyone's best intentions, these replacements cannot always be made. Although some local charters or government bylaws do not allow funds of any kind to be insulated from any legal use determined by the local governing body, steps should be taken to shield these funds from well-intentioned raids that will impair the funds' ability to function as intended. The other side of the equation may come into play as well: the fire chief who wants to purchase a 200-foot ladder when the plan contemplated only a 100-foot ladder may need to look outside the sinking fund to find the monies to pay for the difference in cost.

Fire apparatus may also be leased. The terms of the lease agreement are similar to those for the lease of a car. Payments are based on the difference between the original purchase price and an estimate of the residual value of the apparatus at the end of the lease period, at which time the department surrenders the apparatus and returns it to the vendor. Some leases contain a provision that allows for the purchase of the apparatus at a set price at the end of the lease, if desired. Positive aspects of lease arrangements include lower initial costs, regular replacement of apparatus, and, if a piece of equipment presents trouble, the ability to dispose of it in a shorter period of time. Negative aspects include the need to return or purchase the vehicle at the end of the lease period and the associated need to either find funding for a purchase or arrange another lease.

As had been mentioned, fire apparatus may be eligible for AFG funding. In the first years of the AFG program, competition for fire apparatus grants was the most competitive part of it.

Procurement of capital facilities

Fire department capital facilities consist mainly of fire stations, which are exposed to some of the most intense and demanding uses of any public facility. Career stations are occupied literally around-the-clock, and volunteer stations are occupied for significant amounts of time each week. In addition, many fire stations contain meeting rooms and rooms for other public uses. These capital facilities must not only accommodate the severe uses to which they are put but also be capable of serving for decades.

Establishing the need to replace an existing station and procuring a replacement are closely related actions, and both actions—closing an existing fire station and siting a new or replacement facility—are among the most contentious issues that public sector managers can address. Fire stations are an integral part of the fabric of the community they serve. They are constants in a changing world. Once a fire station is constructed, it may serve at that very spot for more than a hundred years (see Figure 13-3). Firefighters assigned to a fire station identify very closely with the residents of "their" area (often called a company's first-due area), and they feel strongly about their duty to serve that area. In turn, the citizens living in proximity to an existing station often have strong feelings about the need to retain the station in its existing location. Faced with a station's closure or relocation, the neighbors may express concerns about levels of service and the fate of "our firefighters" and, most especially, about the response to their emergencies and the fate of the building that is vacated. When a new station is to be constructed, members of the new community are generally very happy about the prospect of having firefighters nearby but are concerned about the effect a fire station will have on their neighborhood in terms of traffic, noise, and light. For all these reasons, caution and a deliberative decision-making process are called for in any decision to close or relocate a fire station or open a new one.

The key to preventing community distrust and anger when a decision is made to close, relocate, or construct a fire station is communication. If the need to change fire station deployment is explained to the community truthfully and early, the decision will probably find more support than if the news is delivered in the morning paper or through a local blog.

The need to open a new fire station or relocate an existing one should be based on a fire station deployment plan that takes into account shifts in population, annexation of additional areas into a jurisdiction, and other factors. The deployment plan is often part of a fire department's or community's overall master plan—a massive planning effort that can set the tone for fire department deployment for decades. This chapter does not discuss the master planning effort, but it does examine not only the decision to remodel or relocate an existing fire station but also some components of the process used to site and construct a new facility. The final decision on remodeling or replacing an existing facility does not follow any formula. Local government managers must take all the factors discussed here into consideration before making their decision. (Also discussed here are fire station specifications and related matters.)

(a) Photo by Kevin M. Roche

Figure 13-3 Fire stations can vary greatly depending on age, mission, history, and civic culture. In older communities, fire stations may be architecturally distinguished or of historic value (a). Newer stations may be utilitarian (b) or may reflect a community's desire for a "signature" facility (c).

(b) Photo by Kevin M. Roche

(c) Photo by Kevin M. Roche

Closing or opening a fire station

The process of closing or opening a fire station can be a public relations nightmare. Local government and fire service officials need to be prepared for the fact that regardless of how citizens feel about the department itself, their views on the proximity of fire stations may be quite varied and may be expressed quite vociferously.

The officials of a small community in the southwestern United States had planned for years to close an undersized and poorly placed fire station. When funds finally became available, the matter became news when it was placed on the city council agenda. Two groups of citizens asked to be heard at the council meeting.

One group of citizens was from the quiet old neighborhood that had hosted the station since the 1920s. These citizens were outraged that the city would consider moving the facility. They pointed out that their neighborhood had many aging structures and was in a renaissance mode, with many young families moving into the area. They also complained that instead of being sold, the historic old structure should be remodeled and used for its intended purpose. The group was loud and well organized and did not take comfort in verbal assurances from the fire department that the new facility, to be located about 0.7 mile away, would provide very adequate protection within the specified norms for the city.

The other group of citizens represented the new, upscale neighborhood that was located a short distance from the intended site of the new station. These citizens made it clear that they liked the fire department and thought the service it provided was good and extremely important. However, they did not want a fire station near their neighborhood. It was certain to be noisy, smelly, too bright, too large, and a probable blight on property values. They invoked the diesel smoke, the noise of sirens, and the perceived threat that speeding fire apparatus posed to children playing in the area. Although they wanted a fire station as close as possible, they did not want it close enough to impinge on their environment.

The debate went on for months and even became an election issue. As a result of the turmoil, the inadequate old station was superficially remodeled and remained in service. Expansion of the city boundaries, however, was limited by the fact that adequate fire services were not readily available in one particular direction.

When asked later how he might have approached the matter differently, the fire chief made it clear that he had felt unprepared. Missing from his defense were critical specific and scientifically supportable data on response areas and on the environmental impact of a fire station. Certainly the emotional issues will always be a consideration, but good, substantiated information will often help allay the fears of well-meaning citizens.

The actual decision to remodel or replace an existing fire station is based on the following:

- The condition and serviceability of the existing station—that is, the physical condition of the facility itself and of its major systems, and the ability of the station to serve the current and anticipated needs of the community as they relate to the services to be provided from the station
- The availability and acceptability of other sites
- The availability of funding
- Other factors, such as the level of political and community interest in the siting process.

Physical condition and serviceability

The physical condition of the facility can be assessed by fire department staff, other government workers, or contractors. In a large or extremely talented fire and emergency services department, this review could be conducted entirely in-house, but most departments will need to rely on the expertise of other agencies or contractors for some or most of it. The review must include assessments of (1) the physical condition of the structure and its major systems, (2) the station's livability from the point of view of its occupants and visitors, and (3) the station's deployment and service delivery capability.

Structure and major systems This is the assessment that is most often beyond the fire department's ability to provide. In many jurisdictions, professional building maintenance and

Standards and accommodation

New fire stations are required to accommodate both men and women, including those with disabilities, and the assessment of an existing station must keep these new requirements in mind.

Many fire departments, if not most, now have both male and female members. But the need to accommodate both sexes in fire stations is relatively new, and most older stations were built to accommodate only men. Accommodating women generally involves converting or adding restroom and locker room facilities for women. Except in smaller stations where space is at a premium, such accommodations can generally be made without too much difficulty.

The Americans with Disabilities Act (ADA) has also affected assessments of fire stations, for the need to accommodate persons with disabilities was not given much consideration when stations were designed in the past. Even if applied only minimally, the ADA requires that the public access areas of a fire station be designed and configured to accommodate people with physical disabilities. Fire stations equipped with elevators, once an unimaginable building component for such facilities, are becoming more common.

engineering expertise can be secured through the public works or facility maintenance function. Another source of this type of expertise is private sector engineering firms.

The review needs to address the physical condition of the station's structural components (floors, bearing walls, roof); the operability of the building's systems (heat, air conditioning, water, gas, wastewater, steam, communications); and compliance with local, state, and national codes. Although in many cases compliance with codes is not required until the building is modified, the local jurisdiction may choose to comply with codes at any time. For example, a community may desire to make its buildings more accessible to people with physical handicaps (see sidebar above). This part of the review should include an estimate of the cost of resolving any identified problems and an overall professional recommendation about the decision to remodel or replace.

Occupant and visitor livability Occupant and visitor livability is the assessment that is most often within the fire and emergency services department's ability to provide. Nobody understands the weaknesses and strengths of a building better than its occupants and visitors.

The occupants should be solicited for input about the station's comfort and capability. For example, should an individual dorm room be provided for each on-duty firefighter rather than the large bunk rooms that were standard in the past? Is there a need to provide space for physical fitness equipment, such as stationary bikes and treadmills, in response to an increased emphasis on firefighter wellness? Is more separation needed between the station's living areas and its apparatus storage areas in order to address concerns about safety and health? Given the increased role played by many fire departments in providing emergency medical services, is an additional storage room or a designated space needed where equipment and clothing can be decontaminated?

The needs of station occupants who are not members of the department must also be addressed. Many fire stations serve as meeting places for community groups and as local contact points for other services. Often, for example, on-duty firefighters will provide community residents with blood pressure checks at the station. In addition, many communities in Texas have regulations (partly as a means of revenue generation) that require trash to be contained in an approved bag, and the approved trash bags are sold through the local fire stations. And many volunteer fire departments operate social halls, which they use for fire department functions and often rent out for other occasions. Thus, the public's access to the facility must be addressed.

Deployment and service delivery capability A major part of the decision to remodel or replace a station is the ability of the existing facility to support fire and emergency services department deployment. Fire apparatus has grown in size over time, and an older station may not be able to house new apparatus, especially aerial apparatus. Departments that provide emergency ambulance service may need additional space to house ambulances and staff. Moreover, shifts in population or in emergency incident loads may require additional staffing and equipment in an area that did not need it in the past. Although many of these concerns will have been addressed in the development of the fire station deployment plan mentioned previously, consideration must also be given to the ability of the existing site—both the building's internal space and the land available—to accommodate needed functions as well as to the availability (or nonavailability) of acceptable alternative sites.

Acceptability of other sites

Consideration should be given to the size of the lot or land that is secured to site a new or replacement fire station. The general location of the site will be driven by the department's deployment plan, but the exact site chosen should be large enough to accommodate the anticipated uses of the station now and far into the future. Placing a fire station on a postage stamp–sized lot will save money in the short term but will limit that site's future usefulness.

For volunteer fire departments, decisions about where to locate a fire station should also give consideration to where firefighters live and what response routes lead into the station. Unlike career fire stations, volunteer fire stations are usually not constantly staffed, and firefighters must respond from their homes or places of work when an emergency occurs.

Funding and community interest

When possible, fire station sites in developing areas should be purchased before the wave of construction begins, even if funding for the station's construction is not yet available. The sites for these future stations should be supplied with signs, as large as local ordinances permit, that announce "Future Site of Fire Station Number XX." These signs inform home and commercial buyers that a fire station will eventually be their neighbor and may lessen the force of any future NIMBY (not in my back yard) movement.

In 2009, the American Recovery and Reinvestment Act provided $210 million for fire station construction in the United States. Each project application was limited to $5 million, with no more than $15 million to be awarded to any jurisdiction. In late 2009 and early 2010, this program funded over 100 fire station construction projects. It is unknown at this time whether this grant program will be repeated.

Specifications, working with architects, and safety

Fire stations are unique in that their living and sleeping quarters must be kept very close to apparatus storage areas and that their level of use is so high. Thus, some architects working on fire station designs end up learning as they go. A fire and emergency services department that prepares a standard fire station specification, similar to an apparatus specification, and provides it to the architect at the beginning of the process will be helping to eliminate a lot of rework, which will therefore speed up the design process. The station specification should (1) set out the number of firefighters to occupy the station, (2) describe living arrangements, (3) provide rough estimates of square-footage uses for each activity, and (4) describe the standard features and fixtures that are expected but may be unfamiliar to architects (e.g., those that address NFPA standards on infectious disease control or safety issues related to diesel exhaust management).

The specification should give primary consideration to firefighter safety: the provision of proper walking surfaces, minimization (when possible) of the use of stairs and fire poles, infection control and hazardous-waste disposal, diesel exhaust management, proper lighting, and safe movement of apparatus. These issues are very familiar to members of the fire and emergency services but need to be effectively communicated to architects (as well as to public works officials, upper government managers, and customers).

Excellent examples of the type of specification discussed here have been developed by the Fairfax County (Virginia) Fire and Rescue Department; the Miami-Dade (Florida) Fire Rescue Department; and the Phoenix (Arizona) Fire Department. A body of literature, mainly in the form of journal articles, gives guidance on station design. And an excellent resource on safety in the design of fire stations is *Safety and Health Considerations for the Design of Fire and Emergency Medical Services Stations*, a free publication prepared by the USFA.[4]

The processes used by most governments to design and construct public buildings can be slow and expensive. Many times, these processes are in place to prevent undue influence in the selection of contractors. In the past decade, several new processes have been developed to save time and money. One process, called design/build, calls for the selection of a single contractor to design and build a structure. Another process, called Construction Manager at Risk (CM@Risk), puts management of the building process in the hands of a private contractor; the fee for the project is set at the start so the cost of any change orders during the process is the responsibility of this contractor.

Maintenance and accountability

Once the fire department's capital equipment, emergency vehicles, and facilities are procured, they need to be maintained so that their readiness is preserved and a long service life ensured. What follows are maintenance recommendations and suggestions for managing accountability for these capital assets.

For capital equipment

This section does not provide guidance on such details of equipment maintenance and accountability as the recommended frequency for testing ladders. It does, however, provide information on overall maintenance and accountability programs, the effect of these programs on service delivery, sources of information, and general guidelines for managers.

As mentioned previously, firefighters use a very broad array of tools in performing their work. At one extreme, some of these tools have not changed in a hundred years and generally do not require much maintenance beyond routine lubrication and painting. At the other extreme, some tools are so complex—for example, the cardiac monitor/defibrillator used by paramedics and the automatic external defibrillators used by other firefighters—that very few fire and emergency service departments have the expertise, inventory, or inclination to fully maintain this type of equipment. Instead, many departments choose to have such equipment routinely maintained and repaired by the manufacturer or by a manufacturer-authorized service center.

Maintenance In two respects, maintenance requirements for fire equipment differ from those generally applicable to equipment in every industry. First, given the emergency circumstances in which fire equipment is used, extremely high rates of reliability are necessary, as has already been discussed. An SCBA, for example, needs to have the highest level of reliability because its correct functioning literally means the difference between life and death for the firefighter. Similarly with a cardiac monitor/defibrillator: its correct operation—every time—is critical to the survival of cardiac customers.

For such equipment, therefore, periodic tests are a vital part of an adequate maintenance program. SCBA and defibrillators, for example, should be checked by career firefighters at the beginning of each shift to ensure reliability. In volunteer departments, equipment checks should be performed on a regular basis—at least weekly—to ensure readiness. In addition to periodic checks by the user, many items of fire and EMS equipment must be checked periodically by technicians trained in maintaining them (as discussed below under "A Support Function").

The second respect in which equipment maintenance is different in the fire and emergency services from that in other industries is the role of inventory. Given the fire department's need to plan and be prepared for both natural and man-made disasters (see sidebar at the top of page 384), inventory levels for fire equipment (spare equipment that is on hand to temporarily replace equipment that is broken or in the maintenance cycle), as well as for parts for that equipment, are often maintained at higher levels than the casual observer might think appropriate.

Maintenance of fire and emergency services department equipment generally involves the active participation of at least four players: the firefighter, a support function of the department, the manufacturer, and NFPA. An overall maintenance plan that involves all four of these players, and any others as required at the local level, provides a good basis for equipment readiness.

Civil disturbances, terrorism, and strategic reserves

The disabling disasters and civil disturbances—not to mention the attacks by domestic and international terrorists—of the last two decades have served as a reminder that fire departments need to maintain a strategic reserve of equipment for these situations, however infrequent. The civil disturbances in Los Angeles in 1992 left that city's fire department with missing and damaged fire equipment and apparatus that had to be immediately replaced to ensure continued service to the community. Similarly, the terrorist attacks on New York City's World Trade Center on September 11, 2001, led to the destruction of a huge amount of fire equipment and apparatus as well as to the deaths of 343 firefighters and large numbers of law enforcement personnel and civilians. Proper prior planning by the New York City Fire Department allowed spare and reserve apparatus and equipment to be rapidly placed in service. For most agencies, mutual aid agreements can also address "loan" of fire apparatus to fulfill temporary needs. Some vendors and fire apparatus sales companies will also lease fire apparatus on terms of varying duration.

The firefighter Firefighters routinely perform daily, weekly, and monthly checks of equipment as prescribed by policies developed within each department and by the maintenance plan. As mentioned, in career departments the operation of equipment is generally checked at shift change; in volunteer departments, during weekly training days or nights. Firefighters also perform more detailed checks less frequently—generally weekly or monthly.

A support function The support function of the fire and emergency services department performs maintenance beyond the minor maintenance performed by firefighters; it also repairs broken or damaged equipment and manages the department's inventory of tools and parts. This support function may be provided in a number of ways, depending on the size of the department, the range of the equipment to be maintained, and local considerations.

One way is to have the function provided by fire department members working in a department support operation or by firefighters assigned to fire stations who are trained and equipped to perform maintenance. A second way, and one used by many fire departments, is to employ firefighters or civilians whose sole function is to provide equipment maintenance and repair. Third, still other departments develop "specialties" for their stations and provide these stations with the necessary training, tools, equipment, and parts (see sidebar below). A fourth option is to contract with outside vendors to provide such services, although the use of outside contractors does not relieve the fire department of all maintenance responsibilities. Program management and such details as equipment collection and delivery to the vendor still need to be addressed.

The manufacturer Equipment manufacturers are an excellent source—most often the only source—of maintenance information. The manufacturer's literature that comes with fire equipment needs to be retained and held in a reference library for use in the development of maintenance plans and for general reference. Manufacturers of some pieces of fire equipment,

Support service without support staff

The Poudre Fire Authority serves Fort Collins, Colorado, and the surrounding Poudre Valley Fire Protection District. The department operates ten career and three volunteer fire stations with a total in 2009 of 168 career and 40 volunteer members, protecting 235 square miles and a population of 189,000. When the department found itself without sufficient resources to devote full-time staff to many support services, Chief John Mulligan initiated an imaginative system of specialty fire stations to perform emergency and support duties. One station specializes in hazardous materials incident response (along with responses to its regular fire and emergency medical service call load), and another specializes in the maintenance and repair of safety equipment such as self-contained breathing apparatus. Each station has some specialty that contributes to the strength of the organization.

such as SCBA and hydraulic rescue tools, provide maintenance schools and certifications for their equipment. These programs often cost little or nothing. Manufacturers may also provide service for their equipment.

NFPA NFPA publishes standards for the maintenance of fire equipment items such as ground ladders and hose (see Chapter 10). These standards provide information on maintenance frequency, testing, maintenance methods, records retention, and practices for specific classes of equipment. For example, NFPA 1962, Standard for the Inspection, Care, and Use of Fire Hose, Couplings, and Nozzles and the Service Testing of Fire Hose (2008 ed.), prescribes testing of hose and nozzles, record keeping, and testing procedures. Other NFPA standards are in place or under development to guide the maintenance of ladders and protective clothing. Although NFPA standards generally do not carry the force of law, they are often referenced by manufacturers and are considered industry standards of care for equipment.

Accountability To manage their inventories, fire and emergency service departments should have equipment accountability systems in place. The basis of these systems should be the local asset-inventory reporting requirements and whatever system is used to keep records on equipment maintenance. Each piece of equipment should be marked to identify its proper owner or assignment. These markings may include retroreflective stickers containing the name of the fire department and the name or number of the station or unit to which the tool is assigned; or they may include inventory numbers that are painted on or tamped into the equipment, or bar codes that are chemically etched into the metal. Bar coding systems can simplify and automate many labor-intensive inventory-related activities.

To maintain public trust, fire departments should use generally accepted accounting standards, such as those of the Governmental Accounting Standards Board or the American Institute of Certified Public Accountants, to ensure that assets and liabilities are tracked in a standard and transparent way. A system should be in place to report and document the absence (due to loss or theft) of a piece of equipment. Because fire equipment is most often purchased with public funding, an accurate and timely accounting for the location and use of all equipment is called for. When equipment is lost, stolen, or destroyed in the course of its life, proper documentation must exist to ensure the integrity of the accountability system and to provide a basis for requesting replacement equipment.

For emergency vehicles

The same basic concern and cast of players that relate to fire equipment relate to emergency vehicles. The basic concern is that the vehicle and its systems must exhibit extremely high levels of reliability if service is to be delivered effectively. The cast of players consists of the firefighters, who perform routine maintenance and checks; the fire department support function, which manages more complex or involved maintenance and repair; manufacturers, who provide support; and NFPA, which develops standards that address periodic testing and maintenance of vehicle components, such as aerial ladders and pumps.

Unlike equipment maintenance and repair, vehicle maintenance and repair are very often performed by a division of the larger governmental body, such as a city or county fleet management function. In these situations, the fire department support function coordinates service and the movements of vehicles. A large number of fire departments, however, perform their own maintenance, with civilian or uniformed members of the department providing the service.

Maintaining adequate reserve vehicles and an adequate parts inventory is more costly than maintaining adequate reserves and parts for fire equipment. Reserve vehicles are needed to ensure that a service-ready vehicle is present to replace a vehicle that is unavailable because it is in maintenance, has broken down, or is being tested. The term *reserve* is actually a misnomer as it is used throughout the fire and emergency services to describe a vehicle that is not permanently assigned to front-line duty but may be regularly called upon to serve in that capacity. The number of vehicles required to maintain an adequate reserve depends entirely on the size of the fire department fleet, the department's level of activity, the cycle time for vehicle maintenance and repair, the overall health and age of the fleet, and other local considerations. The Insurance Services Office, still considered by some to be the authority for fire department evaluation, recommends one reserve pumper for every eight pumpers (or portion thereof) needed in service, and one reserve ladder, or aerial, for every eight ladders (or portion thereof) needed in service.

The importance of regular vehicle checks cannot be overstated. In career departments, daily operational checks of apparatus are the norm, usually performed by the oncoming shift at shift change. In volunteer departments, regular checks often occur on weekly training nights or on some other regular basis. Catching a failure during a regular check may mean preventing a failure in service delivery.

Accountability for vehicles may be more or less of a challenge than accountability for equipment. Although a fire engine is harder to lose than an ax, it must be accounted for in the same way: as prescribed by local asset-tracking rules and as tracked for maintenance record keeping. Collisions involving fire department vehicles should be well documented, and when the damage created in these collisions is assessed, the impact of the collision on fire department-related components of the vehicle needs to be included. For example, if an aerial ladder is involved in a collision with another vehicle, the body of the truck may have received damage that a local body shop can adequately assess; however, if a component of the aerial system, such as an outrigger (or jack), is involved, the services of an engineer employed or authorized by the aerial manufacturer may have to be secured in order to competently evaluate any negative impact on the aerial system.

For capital facilities

Facility maintenance and accountability involve mostly the same concerns and cast of players discussed above. Reliability is a concern with facilities: critical systems within the fire station, such as heat, water, sewer, gas, and air conditioning, need to work without fail. Standard everyday station maintenance is almost always provided by firefighters, although some communities use other government workers (such as parks employees) or contractors to perform landscape maintenance. Many volunteer fire departments employ or contract with maintenance workers to handle day-to-day chores.

What is different about capital facilities, though, is that fire stations are among the most heavily used of government buildings, as has been noted. They are occupied around-the-clock or for significant periods each month. Volunteer fire department stations in particular are very often the focus of many non-fire-department functions, and career fire stations are now emulating volunteer fire stations in providing community rooms to integrate the fire station more closely into the community. These rooms can be used for meetings of local homeowners associations or of Boy Scouts and Girl Scouts, and for other social functions. In the normal course of use, things in a fire station will break and wear out, so planning in advance for the eventuality will make everyone's life more pleasant.

Provisions should be made to enable emergency repairs to be performed at any time: contracts and/or after-hours contact information should be in place before a service is needed so that the fire department is able to contact maintenance and repair providers after hours and on holidays. Although the average home could make it through a weekend with no hot water, for example, a fire station could not. Unless firefighters can cook, clean, and maintain personal hygiene (e.g., take showers), the station will not remain functional.

Certainly, much of the information needed to manage facilities properly is not unique to the fire service. An annual operational assessment of all fire department facilities by a qualified individual will identify problems before they lead to system failures. Preventive maintenance on such systems as heating and air conditioning can dramatically extend the lives of those systems.

Very few fire and emergency service departments provide all of their own facility maintenance services (beyond taking care of chores and minor maintenance). Most departments do not usually employ construction workers and the like who do remodeling, electrical work, plumbing, and other trade work. Rather, they contract out some services or have another governmental agency perform the work. An individual or a position within the fire department should be identified as the department's facility manager. In smaller organizations, this role can be adequately performed by a single individual; in larger organizations, a staff may be called for.

Many governments carry or list their facilities as assets, and in these cases, local rules governing annual or periodic reporting must be followed, as with equipment and apparatus. Improvements or remodeling since the previous reporting period should be detailed in the current period's report.

Conclusion

The fire and emergency service's customers demand that the service be a good steward of their money. They also demand that the tools, apparatus, and facilities used to provide fire and emergency services work when they are needed. In the future, a still higher level of scrutiny by the public and the press can be expected. This scrutiny will certainly have a strong effect on capital resource management. A structured maintenance program for capital equipment, vehicles, and facilities ensures that funds are spent wisely and that these essential resources are available when needed.

Technology, too, promises to have a major effect on capital resource management. Already the computerization of records and inventories has made the fire and emergency services more accountable and efficient, and the application of technology in tracking equipment, operating fire apparatus, managing facilities, and maintaining all three types of capital resources can be expected to have a like effect.

Notes

1. U.S. General Services Administration, *Federal Specification for the Star-of-Life Ambulance* (August 1, 2007), deltaveh.com/KKK-A-1822F.htm.
2. This airport rescue firefighting vehicle advisory circular is available at faa.gov/regulations_policies/advisory_circulars/.
3. U.S. Fire Administration (USFA), *Firefighter Fatalities in the United States in 2008* (Washington, D.C.: Federal Emergency Management Agency, U.S. Department of Homeland Security, September 2009), 14, usfa.dhs.gov/downloads/pdf/publications/ff_fat08.pdf.
4. USFA, *Safety and Health Considerations for the Design of Fire and Emergency Medical Services Stations* (Emmitsburg, Md.: USFA, May 1997), usfa.dhs.gov/downloads/pdf/publications/fa-168.pdf.

PART FOUR

Critical Support Systems and Functions

CHAPTER 14

Performance Management

David T. Endicott

This chapter provides an understanding of

- The various types of performance measures
- The three levels of performance in an organization and the three performance needs at each level
- How to select appropriate performance measures and capture data to measure performance
- How to analyze and communicate performance data at all levels of organizational activity
- How performance data can be used to improve performance.

In theory, improving the performance of a fire and emergency services organization is simple. It requires only four basic things: that the organization

1. Have a clear picture of where it wants to go (i.e., of its desired state), which requires the organization not only to understand what its mission is in the broader context of the governing body's strategic plan, but also to have a departmental strategic plan setting forth the programs, activities, and processes necessary for achieving the desired state
2. Perform a gap analysis to measure where it currently is in relation to where it wants to go
3. Set realistic goals and objectives for an implementation plan to close the gap between existing performance and the desired state
4. Put the implementation plan into practice, and measure performance with respect to the required programs, activities, and processes.

Although simple in theory, improving organizational performance is in fact a complex process that entails six stages and the use of sophisticated analytical and management tools. First, a strategic plan, which is a vital component of organizational improvement, should be developed, drawing on the perspectives of all stakeholders—management, labor (career and volunteer alike), citizens, and the business community—and identifying the goals and objectives of performance measurement. Second, performance measurement tools must be determined, which also involves many people—this time from different levels within the organization. Third, the organization must collect and then analyze the necessary data and report the findings. Fourth, the organization must investigate and evaluate reasons for high or low performance levels and use the findings to consider needed changes. Fifth, after a department has established the existence of performance gaps, explained them, and considered changes, it must develop strategies for changing performance and must then implement and evaluate them. Lastly, the results should be reported and factored into the repetition of the cycle.

Performance *measurement* captures data about programs, activities, and processes, and it displays the data in fairly standardized ways that are useful for managing programs to their peak performance. Performance *management* takes performance measurement to the next level. It identifies the causes of gaps in performance and explains the effects that changes in business practices, staff deployment, and additional budgetary expenditures or reductions will have on achieving performance goals and objectives. Performance management has been used to significantly improve how government agencies in general, and fire and emergency service departments in particular, set and refine goals and achieve results.

One may well ask what makes performance management such a powerful agent for change and why all that work is worth doing. Simply put, what gets measured gets done. If a fire and emergency services department measures the right things and regularly and accurately reports the results to managers and first-line supervisors so they can track performance, the people in a position to make needed changes will be aware of what is happening and will be able to take steps to affect it. But if the wrong things are measured and reported—or, worse yet, if nothing is reported—managers and supervisors will not have the information they need to make performance-optimizing adjustments.

Indeed, the hardest aspect of performance measurement is measuring the right things in the right ways. Fire and emergency service departments have measured many activities for many years, but often the items measured have not been related to the performance of core business functions or have not described the results (outcomes) of the activities. Measuring what really matters

- Maximizes the benefit to the department by allowing scarce resources to be used in the most productive ways possible
- Gives managers a sense of where the organization, work unit, or individual is in relation to performance expectations
- Allows managers and work-team leaders to focus their time and efforts where they are most needed to improve performance

---

This chapter is a revised and updated version of Chapter 10, "Performance Measurement and Organizational Improvement," by David T. Endicott, in the 2002 edition of this volume.

- Provides information for budget justifications in language that budget developers, reviewers, and policy makers understand and use, giving the organization a chance to compete effectively for limited budget dollars
- Provides important input into internal performance and quality improvement processes.

This chapter, which begins by reviewing traditional criteria against which fire and emergency service departments are often measured, presents work done in the last decade in using performance measurement to improve organizational performance generally and process performance in particular. The first section surveys broad-based efforts to establish performance measurement criteria. The second section discusses the use of performance measurement to identify, manage, and resolve performance problems at three levels—organizational (strategic), process (tactical) (with particular attention paid to process mapping as a tool for measuring processes), and job/performer (individual). The third section explains basic types of performance measures and how they are used to manage performance at the organizational and process levels, focusing particularly on process mapping. The fourth section discusses how to collect, analyze, and use performance data—in, for example, results-based budgeting. The chapter concludes with sections on determining the causes of poor performance and approaching performance management as a team effort, a quick summary, and a look into the future.

Establishing performance measurement criteria: Broad-based efforts

During the last decade of the twentieth century, several projects were undertaken to establish more usable criteria for performance measurement. The projects described here were undertaken by the Center for Public Safety Excellence, Inc., which oversees the accreditation process of the Commission on Fire Accreditation International (CFAI);[1] the Governmental Accounting Standards Board (GASB), which produces research reports on government performance measurement; and the International City/County Management Association (ICMA) (in conjunction with the Urban Institute), which set up the Center for Performance Measurement (formerly, the Performance Measurement Consortium).

Accreditation by the Commission on Fire Accreditation International

One method of measuring fire and emergency service departments against established criteria is the CFAI accreditation process, which is currently in widespread use. The International Association of Fire Chiefs, in conjunction with ICMA, worked with CFAI to develop this process, one component of which is a thorough self-assessment. An organization measures itself against criteria within ten categories prescribed by CFAI (see sidebar on the next page); when the organization believes it meets the criteria, an independent evaluation team visits it and audits the results.

Self-assessment and accreditation provide fire and emergency service organizations with opportunities to develop both baseline and benchmarking information. Thus, the accreditation process helps them define their levels of service. Furthermore, self-assessment is not a one-time event but an evolving, iterative process that often leads fire organizations to develop a range of products—from strategic plans to short-term plans of action to support documents for day-to-day operations—all of which are necessary foundational components of performance management.[2]

The Governmental Accounting Standards Board

The GASB of the Financial Accounting Foundation studied the use of performance measurements by state and local governments. The study's results were presented in the GASB research report *Service Efforts and Accomplishments Reporting: Its Time Has Come,* which establishes five categories of measurement: input indicators, output indicators, outcome indicators, efficiency (and cost-effectiveness) indicators, and explanatory information.[3]

Each of these categories takes a slightly different view of fire and emergency service department operations, providing a perspective not only on what the community is putting its money toward but also—and more important—on what results are realized from that expenditure. Definitions of the GASB categories, or performance indicators, appear in Table 14–1.

Third-party assessment

An accreditation program for local fire departments is administered by the Center for Public Safety Excellence (CPSE) through its Commission on Fire Accreditation International (CFAI). (CPSE also administers the Commission on Professional Credentialing, discussed in Chapter 9.) The accreditation process is designed to help a local department determine community risk and safety needs, evaluate its own performance, and establish a method for achieving continuous organizational improvement.

Regardless of size, fire departments that wish to be accredited must complete a detailed self-assessment that asks managers to examine more than 200 separate performance indicators, about 100 of which are considered "core," or required, competencies. The performance indicators fall into ten categories:

- Assessment and planning
- Essential resources
- External systems relations
- Financial resources
- Goals and objectives
- Governance and administration
- Human resources
- Physical resources
- Programs
- Training and competency.

After CFAI reviews the completed self-assessment, a team of site evaluators visits the fire department to verify and clarify the information provided in the self-assessment. The evaluation team recommends either final accreditation or additional work.

Each department can expect to devote several hundred hours to the process of self-assessment and is responsible for the cost of the site visit as well as for a sliding-scale fee based on the size of the population it serves. CFAI encourages interested fire departments to register for a three-year preparatory period before beginning the rigorous accreditation process; during this period, department leaders may attend CFAI workshops and gather advice from departments that have already been accredited. For more information, see publicsafetyexcellence.org/agency-accreditation/about-accreditation-cfai.aspx.

These indicators provide a framework within which fire and emergency service organizations can look at—and make some sense of—the data they are capturing; how they can use the data is explained in another section of this chapter.

The ICMA Center for Performance Measurement

ICMA has been a leader in developing practical uses for performance measurement. In 1994, in conjunction with the Urban Institute, ICMA initiated a project to bring together working managers from cities and counties with populations of 200,000 or more to develop useful

Table 14-1 The five GASB performance indicators

Category	Definition
Input indicators	These are designed to report the amount of resources, either financial or other (especially personnel), that have been used for a specific service or program.
Output indicators	These report the number of units produced or the services provided by a service or program.
Outcome indicators	These are designed to report the results (including quality) of the service.
Efficiency (and cost-effectiveness) indicators	These are defined as indicators that measure the cost (whether in dollars or employee hours) per unit of output or outcome.
Explanatory information	This includes a variety of information about the environment and other factors that might affect an organization's performance.

Source: This table, from Harry P. Hatry et al., eds., *Service Efforts and Accomplishments Reporting: Its Time Has Come* (Norwalk, Conn.: Governmental Accounting Standards Board, 1990), 10, copyright by the Financial Accounting Foundation (FAF), 401 Merritt 7, PO Box 5116, Norwalk, CT 06856-5116, has been reproduced with permission. Complete copies of the report are available from the FAF.

comparative measures for critical services. Originally called the ICMA Performance Measurement Consortium, the project later came to be called the ICMA Center for Performance Measurement (see icma.org/performance/); and by the end of the first decade of the twenty-first century, over 220 cities and counties of all population sizes were participating in the program, tracking and comparing their data against both the data of other communities and time-series data for their own jurisdictions.

Representatives from participating fire and emergency service departments (initially there were forty) began meeting in 1994 to discuss and select measures. During the group's first several meetings, participants were trained in performance measurement and began the process of identifying meaningful measures for their study areas. They identified the critical functions that should be covered in their efforts—fire suppression, emergency medical services, fire prevention, and public education—and began the laborious process of developing and defining recommended measures. It quickly became clear that the group would also have to collect community descriptors so that users of the data would be able to discern the presence of significant differences (if any) among jurisdictions and organizations.

The fire group spent a significant amount of time developing definitions of all the data elements. For each function, it created templates of measures and agreed-upon definitions. The templates help the departments identify what data have already been collected and where they reside; determine how to collect what has not already been collected; and begin the process of collection and recording. Much of the information collected is in the National Fire Incident Reporting System (nfirs.fema.gov/); however, additional information on process times needs to be captured to accurately reflect system performance from a customer perspective.

Early in the process of developing outcome measures, the fire group encountered a significant problem. Reductions in the number of deaths and injuries and in the size of dollar losses from fire are desired outcomes of fire and emergency services department prevention and response activities; in many communities, however, the low frequency with which death, injury, and (to a lesser degree) dollar loss occur makes it difficult to measure changes from year to year. Many smaller jurisdictions experience few fires each year and perhaps a fire death only once every few years or even every few decades. Consideration of this problem ultimately led to the realization that there are short-term outcomes, intermediate outcomes, and long-term outcomes that should be measured. Thus it was decided to concentrate on short-term, intermediate, and long-term (or end) outcome measures to track progress on factors that are believed to directly affect fire loss or other outcome measures.

Some short-term measures are response times for all components of the system's response process. Response times are short-term measures because the expectation is that the faster that properly trained and equipped emergency responders are dispatched, arrive, and deploy at the emergency, the more likely it is that the specific actions they are able to take will mitigate the negative consequences—deaths, injuries, and fire losses—of the event. By tracking changes in short-term measures—that is, response times and their critical subcomponents—an organization can see the effects of changes in the response process more quickly and begin to judge whether the changes are having the desired results. (Response times are discussed in much more detail later in this chapter.)

Model for performance measurement

As already noted, a significant body of research and literature has been geared toward improving the quality of organizational performance, both in business and in government. One way to begin improving performance is to measure it. In business literature, the topic of performance measurement is generally handled under the larger headings of "total quality management" and "continuous process improvement." Public sector literature addresses performance measurement as the critical first step in effectively using either benchmarking or results-based budgeting to improve organizational performance. (On budgeting, see Chapter 12.)

Geary A. Rummler and Alan P. Brache developed a model for assessing business sector organizations and improving performance that is directly applicable to fire and emergency service organizations.[4] They view an organization as a system, which makes it possible to better understand the relationships among the various components and the ways in which changes in one part may affect the operations of other parts. They then identify three levels of performance

Performance measurement in Prince William County, Virginia

In Prince William County, performance measurement is a critical element of successful strategic planning, budgeting, service planning and evaluation, and departmental and employee goal setting. A four-year strategic plan is developed with each newly elected Board of County Supervisors. Citizens play a pivotal role in strategic planning as they collaborate with staff to craft objectives designed to accomplish board goals. As part of this work, the community identifies key public safety outcome measures to evaluate both the effectiveness of the objectives and the success of the Fire and Rescue Department in attaining them. The outcome measures make the strategic plan real.

Performance measures enable the fire chief to create a "contract" with elected officials and the community for new initiatives presented in the budget process. The budget that the county executive presents to the board includes each proposed initiative, its cost, and its expected return on investment. Performance measures provide a tool with which current performance can be contrasted with performance that will be achieved if a proposed initiative is approved. The elected officials thus have detailed information to use throughout the annual budget and capital planning cycles when evaluating where to invest new funding.

Measurement also supports the county staff's service planning and evaluation activities. The Prince William County budget process includes two phases. Phase I establishes accountability for commitments made in the prior fiscal year and begins the service planning and forecasting efforts for the upcoming fiscal year. Prior-year performance is reviewed against the established "performance contract," and deviations are explained. Typically, after a few years' experience with results-based budgeting, Phase I review shows close compliance with projections. Phase I thus advances service planning by creating a baseline projection for performance in the upcoming fiscal year that is based on a review of past performance trends.

Phase II of the budget process focuses on the allocation of resources and includes new initiatives and, when necessary, program downsizing alternatives. Performance measures are used to demonstrate the effects of resources allocated as compared to the status quo.

Throughout the course of the year, the use of performance targets and regular reports on progress toward them means that "face time" between the county executive and the fire chief is devoted to strategic and tactical decision making instead of to nonproductive debates about whether service delivery is going well or poorly. Even more important, the tracking of key measures allows county leaders to explore growing trends before a crisis emerges and to take corrective action to avoid it. The county executive and the fire chief can focus on the important long-range issues facing the fire services and not simply react to the latest crisis.

To develop annual goals, the Fire and Rescue Department prepares an annual mission achievement plan (MAP), providing further details about how department resources will be applied to accomplish organizational goals that contribute to the strategic plan. Each station and work site develops an annual work plan for its team that contributes to the achievement of MAP goals.

Finally, the county's employee performance management system establishes measurable performance goals for each employee that contribute to achieving department and county government performance goals. For employees, performance measures communicate departmental goals and expectations in a way that promotes common purpose and individual employee goal setting. Their individual goals provide a line of sight from the employee through the department's annual goals on to the community's multiyear strategic goals.

Involving citizens with department staff in the strategic planning process truly advances democracy at the local community level. Using performance measurement to establish and communicate strategic goals, allocate resources, evaluate services, and drive employee performance supports the development of a successful community. And by linking all the activities of the county government to the community's goals, this performance-based approach becomes integral to the ethos of the county government.

Source: Craig S. Gerhart, county executive (ret.), and Kevin J. McGee, chief, Prince William County Fire and Rescue Department.

in organizations and three performance needs that are necessary at all three levels. The three levels of performance are the organizational (or strategic) level, the process (or tactical) level, and the job/performer (or individual) level. The three performance needs are goals, design, and management.

The organizational (strategic) level is concerned with the basic functions of the organization and its relationship to the external world. The organization's outputs and outcomes are produced through work processes that involve contributions from many different organizational units. The process (tactical) level is concerned with meeting both the customer's and the organization's requirements for products and services. The job/performer (individual) level is the level at which employees meet the organization's goals as they perform their jobs, creating products and providing services. Each level should be evaluated. When the three performance levels and the three performance needs are combined into a matrix, the result is nine performance variables, as shown in Table 14–2. This matrix offers a framework that organizations can use to target areas for organizational improvement.

The measures selected should provide managers with the basis on which to communicate not only performance expectations but also feedback that identifies performance successes

Table 14-2 Rummler and Brache's nine performance variables

The three levels of performance	Performance needs		
	Goals	**Design**	**Management**
Organizational level	• Has the organization's strategy/direction been articulated and communicated? • Does this strategy make sense, in terms of the external threats and opportunities and the internal strengths and weaknesses? • Given this strategy, have the required outputs of the organization and the level of performance expected from each output been determined and communicated?	• Are all relevant functions in place? • Are all functions necessary? • Is the current flow of inputs and outputs between functions appropriate? • Does the formal organization structure support the strategy and enhance the efficiency of the system?	• Have appropriate function goals been set? • Is relevant performance measured? • Are resources appropriately allocated?
Process level	• Are goals for key processes linked to customer/organization requirements?	• Is this the most efficient/effective process for accomplishing the process goals?	• Have appropriate process subgoals been set? • Is process performance managed? • Are sufficient resources allocated to each process? • Are the interfaces between process steps being managed?
Job/performer level	• Are job outputs and standards linked to process requirements (which are in turn linked to customer and organization requirements)?	• Are process requirements reflected in the appropriate jobs? • Are job steps in a logical sequence? • Have supportive policies and procedures been developed? • Is the job environment ergonomically sound?	• Do the performers understand the Job Goals (outputs they are expected to produce and standards they are expected to meet)? • Do the performers have sufficient resources, clear signals and priorities, and a logical job design? • Are the performers rewarded for achieving the job goals? • Do the performers know if they are meeting the job goals? • Do the performers have the necessary knowledge/skill to achieve the job goals? • If the performers were in an environment in which the five questions above were answered "yes," would they have the physical, mental, and emotional capacity to achieve the job goals?

Source: Geary A. Rummler and Alan P. Brache, *Improving Performance: How to Manage the White Space on the Organization Chart* (San Francisco: Jossey-Bass, 1995), 27.

and gaps. In addition, the measures selected should inform individual employees specifically about what is expected of them while allowing self-evaluation (as well as feedback from managers). Rummler and Brache argue that it is critical to measure the right things and that what turns performance measurement data into "intelligent action" (i.e., improved performance) is the management process, or the control mechanism.

The rest of this section outlines how to do performance measurement and performance management at the organizational, process, and job/performer levels, with emphasis on some examples of outcome indicators. Detailed discussion on how to use performance measures is presented in the next section.

Organizational-level (strategic) performance indicators

Organizational goals (like organizational strategies and objectives) are usually found in the strategic plans of the jurisdiction and the department. Because these goals are usually very broad and general, the performance measures that would indicate progress toward accomplishment need to be at a macro level. An example of an organizational goal might be to "use innovative techniques to maintain effective fire and emergency service response times as population and community density grow." An appropriate intermediate outcome measure of system performance would be one that identifies the overall "system response time" and could be compared for changes from one reporting period to the next.

Organizational design—how an organization is structured—has a direct effect on the organization's ability to perform. Performance measures for this area address the outcome, effectiveness, or efficiency of the structural design, or the effectiveness of how business is conducted among the individual organizational components. These measures should enable one to evaluate several alternative placements for the performance of a critical function or should be used to estimate the effect of a proposal to consolidate or separate functions or divisions. For example, an organizational design question might be, Where in the city or county organizational structure is it best to locate the building/construction plan review function for fire protection purposes? The resultant decision—whether to locate it with the fire marshal or with the building official—might benefit from an evaluation of measurements of (1) the quality of the reviews of the fire protection system plans, (2) the quality of the reviews of the building construction plans, and (3) fire loss caused by fire protection or building defects.

Measures of organizational management should address, at the macro level, key management tasks or specific management issues. When employee morale is a management issue, for example, one measure might be the frequency with which disruptive, significant personnel actions (grievances) occur and the amount of staff time spent dealing with them. Other possible organizational management measures that might be addressed are the timeliness and quality of management decisions (did these decisions, when implemented, have the expected results?).

Process-level (tactical) performance indicators*

In the case of fire and emergency services, process goals and priorities for emergency response to fires generally include protecting life, protecting the environment, stabilizing the incident, and conserving property. Measuring progress toward achieving these goals involves ensuring that the process is producing results based on and directly meeting customers' needs.

Outcome measures of process goals might include the availability of the "first-due" unit to respond, extent of losses incurred, stage or size of the emergency when control occurs, time taken to achieve each goal, sequence in which each goal is achieved, number of customer complaints filed, and rate of customer satisfaction with the results of the process. If the process is to achieve a positive result, the process goals must be acceptable from the customer's perspective.

Process design involves establishing the sequence of steps to be performed and the flow of tasks and activities among various work groups or individuals. Measures of process design include the time taken to accomplish a component task or activity, quality of the product of the task or activity, variance in the performance of the task or activity, and variance in the result of the process compared with the result of alternative designs for the same process.

---

*Information in this section is adapted from *Handbook for Basic Process Improvement: Tools for Basic Process Improvement* (Washington, D.C.: Total Quality Leadership Office, U.S. Department of the Navy, 1992).

Process management requires that process measurement systems be developed and established, ensuring that accurate and complete data are captured, reported, analyzed, and interpreted in a timely fashion to target problems of variance. Solutions to these problems of variance might involve training staff, redesigning the steps of the process, or reengineering the available tools and equipment used to perform the tasks so as to improve performance. Outcome measures of process management might include measurements of process variance, improvements in process efficiency, improvements in error rates, and so forth.

Job/performer-level (individual) performance indicators

Measures for job performance as it relates to the individual or work team are also critical. Immediate supervisors should be held accountable for individual and work-team performance and should be able to use process or activity performance measures to identify whether the team is performing adequately. When there is a variance from the expected performance, the supervisor must evaluate each member's performance or contribution to the team effort and identify any individual performance problems that exist.

Some problems are obvious, such as when a pump operator fails to charge an attack line on time. That kind of performance error immediately stops the firefighting crew's activity, which stays stopped until the problem is corrected. Other performance problems are less obvious. Thus, changes in performance measures need to be tracked over time. These tracked changes indicate to the supervisor where to concentrate attention in order to identify the performance issues, practices, and individuals that might be causing the changes. Some useful measurement tools (e.g., Pareto charts and run charts) and their applications are discussed later in this chapter.

Measuring and managing performance

A number of methods are used to measure and manage performance in fire and emergency service organizations. After taking a closer look at the kind of information that must be collected and analyzed, this section discusses several approaches to measuring and managing performance at the organizational and process levels. Each department must decide on the approach that best suits its own needs.

Performance measures established at the organizational and process levels should be reflected in performance measures for individual members of the department and integrated into the department's system for evaluating employees' performance. (For a discussion of employee evaluation, see Chapter 8.)

The basics

As mentioned earlier, GASB defines five categories of measurement information: input indicators, output indicators, outcome indicators, efficiency (and cost-effectiveness) indicators, and explanatory information (see again Table 14–1). Before considering methods of performance measurement, this section looks at each category of information and shows how it is related to the others.

Input indicators Inputs measure the monetary and nonmonetary resources expended or consumed to produce outputs of the department's activities. Obviously a basic measure of monetary input is the dollar amount expended for fire and emergency services department functions. Likewise, a way of measuring inputs that the money buys is to address the major equipment necessary and/or the number of staff hours expended in performing services. For yearly comparisons, the staff hours of effort devoted to a function are normally expressed as full-time equivalent positions (FTEs); for shorter durations, the actual number of hours may be used.

Many organizations already report both the number of staff assigned to various divisions and the costs associated with those divisions' activities. However, organizations often use staff from one program area to perform activities in other program areas (e.g., fire suppression unit staff may also respond to medical emergencies, perform fire inspections, or conduct public fire education programs). To allocate the costs correctly, an organization should track the amount of time spent on individual program activities (see sidebar at the top of the next page).

A word of caution on cost allocation

When data are collected and reported as described in the text, inexperienced analysts could conclude—incorrectly—that a shift in program activities would result in cost savings proportional to the full-time equivalent positions (FTEs) affected. If, for example, 20 percent of the field operations program dollars (or the same percentage of the program's FTEs) is allocated to performing fire inspections, an inexperienced analyst might presume that moving the inspections somewhere else could save 20 percent of the fire suppression budget. But this logic is flawed because it ignores two critical points.

First, shifting the fire inspection workload to another agency usually means adding additional FTEs at the receiving civilian agency, and even though civilians usually work for a lower compensation package than firefighters, funding is still required and reduces the apparent initial savings. Second, firefighters perform these inspection duties while they are on standby for emergency response. In other words, they perform inspections as an ancillary duty, but whether the inspections are performed or not, the firefighters must still be available to respond to and control emergencies as this is the primary reason for fire suppression positions. Thus, the reduction in monies with the consequent 20 percent reduction in field operations staff might well have a drastic negative effect on operational effectiveness at emergency incidents. The perceived "go-away" cost savings of moving the inspections activity function might therefore be nonexistent or actually end up as a cost increase.

Output indicators Output measures count the number of activities produced as a result of the expenditures: for example, the number of incidents responded to, inspections performed, violations detected, car safety seats checked, and training programs conducted.

Outcome indicators The most important and most difficult measures to capture are outcomes, for they address the effect that the program, process, or activity has had. Strategic-level outcomes for fire prevention and suppression activities are the deaths, injuries, and dollar losses from fires that the community experiences. Experience has shown that it is important to develop some short-term, intermediate, and long-term measures for outcomes. Examples of outcome measures, presented in Figures 14–1 and 14–2, cover the range of major program areas and present an approach for documenting and reporting fire and emergency service department–initiated saves.

Efficiency (and cost-effectiveness) indicators Efficiency measures are useful for managers to track changes in the cost of a process over time and to compare one organization with another.

Some important distinctions

Differentiating inputs from outputs

Inputs are what you put into the process to perform work. For fire and emergency medical service (EMS) agencies, the typical input measurements are the amount of money budgeted and expended or the amount of human effort provided to do something, usually expressed in full-time equivalent positions. It is simply what is provided in the hopes that something gets done.

Outputs are the levels of activity that result from the inputs being expended. For fire and EMS organizations, the typical outputs are the number of incidents of various types (e.g., fire, emergency medical, hazardous materials, technical rescue) responded to, public education classes performed, fire inspections performed, prefire plans completed or updated, certification levels obtained or refreshed, and the like.

Differentiating inputs and outputs from outcomes

Inputs are what is expended, in either dollars or time, to achieve a result. Outputs are the activities that result from the expenditure of time or money. Outcomes are the changes in expected results of the activity. Measuring how many fires or EMS calls were responded to does not measure results. A fire and emergency services department responds to fires in an effort to minimize the losses in deaths, injuries, and dollars. Therefore, *changes* in the numbers of fire deaths and injuries and in the amount of dollar loss are measures of outcome.

Overall objective: To minimize losses to persons and property by helping to prevent fires from occurring and to reduce losses from fires that occur.

Objective	Quality characteristic	Specific measure	Data collection procedure
Overall loss minimization	Civilian casualties	1. Number of civilian (a) injuries and (b) deaths related to fires, absolute and per 1,000 population.	Incident reports, census
	Firefighter casualties	2. Number of firefighter (a) injuries and (b) deaths per 100 firefighters.	Casualty reports
		3. Number of firefighter (a) injuries and (b) deaths per 100 fires.	Casualty reports
	Property loss	4. Direct dollar loss from fires (a) per $1,000 property protected and (b) per 100,000 population.	Fire department or insurance company estimates
Prevention and deterrence	Reported fire incidence	5. Number of fires reported per 1,000 population, (a) overall and (b) by property type.	Incident reports
	Reported building fire incidence	6. Number of building fires per 1,000 occupancies, by (a) property type and (b) fire size.	Incident reports, planning department records
	Reported household fire incidence	7. Total number of household fires (reported and unreported) per 1,000 households.	Household or user survey
	Inspection effectiveness	8. Percentage of fires in which the affected property was inspected within the 12 months prior to the fire (a) for all occupancies and (b) by property type.	Fire inspection files linked to incident reports
	Deterrence effectiveness for arson	9. Number of intentional fires per 1,000 population.	Incident reports, police and court records (for arson motive)
	Apprehension outcomes for fire-related crimes	10. Clearance rate for intentional fires.	Fire incident and inspection data linked to police arrest records and fire department case records
		11. Conviction or other acceptable outcome rate for arson arrests for (a) juveniles, (b) adults, and (c) all offenders.	Incident reports, police and court records, census
		12. Percentage of arson offenders who receive treatment or are incarcerated that reoffend within perhaps one or two years (recidivism rate) for (a) juvenile and (b) adult offenders.	Police records, juvenile treatment program records
	Inspection violation clearances	13. Percentage of building violations resolved within a specified time period (e.g., one week, one month, one year).	Inspection records
	Detector/sprinkler usage and maintenance	14. Percentage of homes with working smoke alarms.	Household survey
		15. Percentage of (a) homes or (b) businesses with working sprinklers.	Inspection records, utility company permits
	Prevention outreach	16. Percentage of residents reached by at least one fire prevention education message.	Household survey
Suppression and mitigation	Property loss control	17. Average dollar loss for fires not out on arrival, by property type.	Incident reports
		18. Percentage of fires confined to room or area of origin (or a specified area expressed in square feet).	NFIRS fire reports
		19. (a) Number and (b) percentage of fires that took more than a specified time period (e.g., 30 minutes) to control or extinguish.	Fire department records
	Response time	20. Percentage of response times that are less than a specified amount (e.g., four minutes).	Incident reports
		21. Percentage of fire calls where the first-due complement arrives on the scene within a specified time period (e.g., five minutes).	Incident reports
	Rescue effectiveness	22. Number of civilian lives saved per 100,000 population.	Incident reports, census
Citizen satisfaction	Citizen satisfaction	23. Percentage of residents receiving direct fire department service who reported the service as satisfactory.	Household or user survey
Emergency medical services		24. Percentage of patients for whom agreed-upon medical protocols are followed.	Incident reports, hospital records
		25. Percentage of cardiac patients who reach the hospital alive.	Incident reports, hospital records
		26. Percentage of cardiac patients who leave the hospital alive.	Incident reports, hospital records

1 The term "occupancy" refers to a piece of property in terms of its use,—for example, detached houses containing only one household, apartments, drug stores, or warehouses. There may be more than one type of occupancy in one building, and some occupancies—for example, garbage dumps and piers—are not buildings at all.

2 For example, fires started by flammables stored near ignition source or in buildings with fire code violations relevant to the fire start would be "relatively preventable." Fires started by hidden equipment defects not common to that equipment would be relatively "unpreventable."

Source: Harry P. Hatry et al., *How Effective Are Your Community Services? Procedures for Performance Measurement*, 3rd ed. (Washington, D.C.: ICMA and the Urban Institute, 2006), 82.

Figure 14-1 This chart of suggested outcome measures for fire protection services presents individual measures and the data collection procedures for each.

Figure 14-2 As this example of a fire saves report (data from 17 fires) shows, each save should be documented with specific information.

	Victim mobility	Number and types of saves						
		Unable to walk		Can walk only with assistance	Can walk			
		Unconscious	Other		Pinned/ trapped	Path blocked	Unaware of fire	
Fire hazard for victim	**Fire department action**	**Carried**	**Carried**	**Aided**	**Released**	**Provided path**	**Directed**	**Totals**
1. Fire in room		1	1	2		1		5
2. Fire on same floor								
a. Smoke/heat hazard in room				1		10	9	20
b. No smoke/heat hazard in room							2	2
3. Fire on next floor below								
a. Smoke/heat hazard in room		1				24	2	27
b. No smoke/heat hazard in room						2	2	4
4. Fire more than one floor below								
a. Smoke/heat hazard in room					3	13	7	23
b. No smoke/heat hazard in room						2		2
5. Within danger zone of hazardous materials fire							1	1
6. Below fire floor								
Totals		2	1	3	3	52	23	84

Source: Harry P. Hatry et al., *How Effective Are Your Community Services? Procedures for Performance Measurement*, 3rd ed. (Washington, D.C.: ICMA and the Urban Institute, 2006), 94.

Service efforts and accomplishments (SEA) reports often use efficiency measures as a basis of comparison among like jurisdictions.

Efficiency measures for fire and emergency services department programs can be expressed in two ways: as unit costs (input dollars divided by output, or input dollars divided by outcome) or as units of output or outcome per input (output or outcome divided by either costs or some other measure, such as FTEs). Cost-effectiveness measures are determined by dividing the cost of either output or outcome by the number of units of output or outcome.

Efficiency measures for outputs might include the operating cost per incident, per capita protected, per $1 million of property value protected, or per inspection. Another measure for outcomes might include the operating cost per fire code violation corrected.

Historically, departments have done a very good job of counting inputs and outputs, and some departments have developed good efficiency measures. But fewer departments seem to have been able to measure outcomes in a meaningful way, or to link outcome measurement with resources and accurately gauge how changes in resources or business processes affect outcomes.

Explanatory information When performance measures are reported, explanatory information should be included wherever necessary to draw attention to variations from expected results in data displays, or to changes in measurement results that are caused by modifications in the way data are defined or collected or by the removal or addition of data elements. It is important to explain to the reader what special circumstances might have had an impact on the performance measure. Footnotes should connect the explanatory notes to the relevant data elements.

Performance management at the organizational (strategic) level

Several approaches to strategic performance management are being used and refined by fire and emergency service departments in North America. Regardless of the approach chosen, it is important to identify and understand the key program areas (major groupings of activities that provide services to the public or internal customers), develop standardized ways to measure what is being done, and employ effective ways to display and share the information.

Incident time line and key intervals An incident time line can help a fire and emergency services department identify key program areas and analyze its performance. Response to emergency incidents encompasses most of the major activities of a department, and the flow of activities for these incidents contains at least eleven critical time points (as shown in Figure 14–3):

A. Incident occurs

B. Incident is detected

C. Incident is reported (911 rings)

D. Call is answered

E. Call is transferred to dispatcher
F. Call is dispatched
G. Unit(s) respond(s)
H. Unit(s) arrive(s)
I. Unit(s) set(s) up and begin(s) work
J. Incident is under control
K. Incident ends.

When deciding what emergency response time measures to collect, the department should recognize that identifying and tracking all the components that make up the response process are critical, even if some of those components—such as the call-processing time in dispatch—are not under the department's control. The only way to accurately represent how the service is being provided to the customer is to record and report the response time for each component from the customer's perspective.

The time intervals for each segment (A–B, B–C, etc.) are named as shown in Figure 14–3. Using standardized names for the intervals is essential. One of the most difficult things about using performance measures for benchmarking against other departments is that some departments use different definitions (start and stop points) for system response time, unit response time, and other critical intervals.

For each interval the department should establish performance expectations as appropriate, and should track the times to understand what is happening in the process. National Fire Protection Association (NFPA) Standards 1710 and 1720 contain recommendations for measuring some of the process intervals in Figure 14–3, as does CFAI's Standards of Cover document. The model proposed in Figure 14–3 differs slightly from both of those approaches, however. It is designed to represent more accurately the critical components of the process that need to be measured from a customer's perspective rather than those components that are easy for the department to collect.

Customers are not concerned with who operates the 911 center or how the call gets processed as long as the service is competent, polite, and effective. Customers call 911 to activate emergency response, period; their response time "expectation clock" starts when they pick up the phone and dial. Fire and emergency service departments should start their process clocks at the earliest possible point that can be captured: ideally, when the 911 phone begins to ring at the public safety answering point (PSAP).

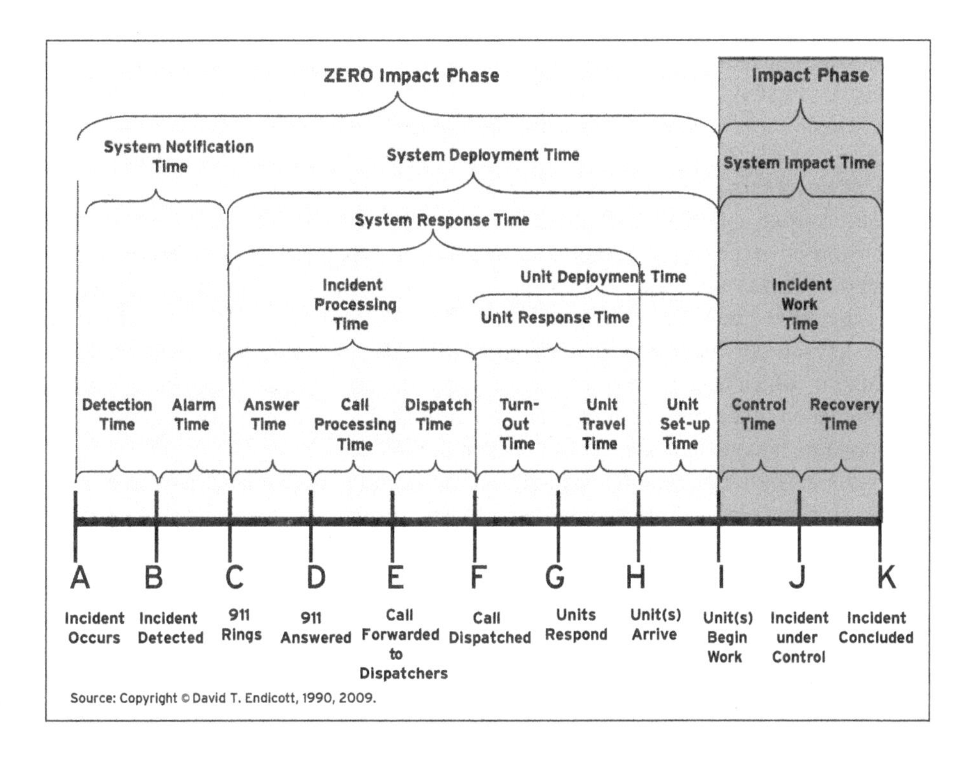

Figure 14-3 This diagram represents a sample emergency incident response time line and response intervals.

Ideally, if a department uses the customer-based incident time line shown in Figure 14–3, the collection of data on fire and emergency system response times should begin when the emergency itself begins. Unfortunately, usually no accurate record of the time can be made until the response system is activated by someone dialing 911 to call the PSAP. But although performance in the areas of detection and notification cannot be accurately recorded, it can be inferred from analysis over time of the number of fires that have spread beyond the area or room of origin before response units arrive. Information about the times of occurrence and notification can often be gathered and reconstructed from witnesses and is collected as a normal part of the fire investigation process; however, that information is rarely captured in a form that lends itself to easy analysis.

In many jurisdictions the fire and emergency services department does not control the 911 call receipt or dispatch processes. In those jurisdictions, the department should work with the PSAP manager to specify what performance measures and standards are expected. The department is the PSAP's internal customer and depends on the timely processing and/or dispatch of emergency calls in order to meet its own customers' expectations. It cannot ensure good service unless all the components that make up the service provide accurate performance measurements.

For specific types of incidents, the variables within each segment should be more detailed. For an EMS call, for example, the set-up and control-time intervals should be subdivided to capture other critical times, such as "at patient," "patient extricated," "patient transported," "at hospital," and "available for another call."

In defining the precise points at which the measurements will start and stop, a department should consider when in the process delays might occur and what effect these delays might have on each starting and stopping point. For example, if the start of the clock for "call received in communications" is defined as when the telephone is answered rather than when it starts to ring, the definition does not allow accurate capturing of the "ring time," nor does it allow a determination of how long the customer had to wait for the telephone to be answered—a key component of customer satisfaction.

Using the incident time line, an agency can assign responsibilities (see the section on tactical assignments and process mapping further on in this chapter), develop measures for each interval, and address strategies for improving each interval either independently or in groupings that make sense. For example, overall system performance is the responsibility of the chief of the department. Figure 14–3 charts out all the time line intervals that make up overall system performance. The entire time line comprises three combinations of intervals: system notification time (points A to C), system deployment time (points C to I), and system impact time (points I to K). As an indicator of overall system performance, these macrolevel performance factors can be reported regularly to the city or county manager, the local elected body, and citizens in a variety of ways.

Balanced scorecard The balanced scorecard (BSC) is a methodology for aligning strategy with performance objectives and measurement, and for ensuring the development of tangible strategic objectives and corresponding measures that support the strategy. The concept was originally created in 1987 at Analog Devices through the efforts of Arthur M. Schneiderman;[5] it was later refined by Robert S. Kaplan and David P. Norton.[6] Initially developed for business, the BSC has four areas of focus (finance, customer, internal business process, and learning and growth), which have been redefined for use in the public sector. It is a tool to aid in the implementation of the organizational strategy through development of strategic objectives and corresponding measures in each of the four areas of focus.

Charlotte, North Carolina, for example, has adopted the BSC to help develop and implement its strategic plan and show progress on the things that are important to the city. Charlotte's fire department uses the methodology to align department performance with organizational strategy in four areas: serving the customer, running the business, managing resources, and developing employees (see Figure 14–4). Balancing performance measurement within the four areas ensures that one area is not perceived as more important than another. The department develops strategic objectives within each area, with key performance indicators for each objective. It then tracks and regularly reports those indicators.

Figure 14-4 The Charlotte (North Carolina) Fire Department uses a balanced scorecard, as shown here.

KBU-Balanced Scorecard Report

Reporting Period: July 1, 2010 to June 30, 2011

	Corporate Objective	KBU Initiative (* indicates Focus Area Initiative)	Measure ($ indicates incentive pay measure)	Prior Year Actual	Lead or Lag	Performance Data: Target	Performance Data: YTD	Performance Data: Status	Comments/Explanation (To be completed at mid-year and year-end reporting)
Serve the Customer	C1. Strengthen Neighborhoods	Strengthen and prepare the community	Percent of CMS 3rd grade classrooms that receive fire education programs $*	71%	Lag	80%			
	C2. Increase Perception of Safety	Provide emergency services (fire suppression, hazmat, etc.)	Percent of Telecommunicators answering phone within 3 rings or 10 seconds	99.4%	Lag	90%			
			Percent of alarms first-due fire companies will be on scene within 6 minutes of telephone call*	80.2%	Lag	80%			
			Percent of first alarms to which an effective firefighting force will be on scene within 9 minutes	85.9%	Lag	80%			
		Provide effective public safety services (code enforcement)	Percent of fire code inspections conducted within state-mandated frequencies*	88.4%	Lag	85%			
		Provide effective public safety services (fire investigation)	Percent of arson cases investigators will clear	31.7%	Lag	34%			
Run the Business	B1. Optimize Business Processes	Provide up-to-date systems to support emergency and essential public safety service delivery	Procure a consolidated E911 System by 6/30/2011	N/A	Lag	100%			
			Implement phase II of the Charlotte Operations-Based Response Analysis (COBRA) project by 6/30/2011	N/A	Lag	100%			
Manage Resources	R1. Deliver Competitive Service	Monitor budget expenditures to ensure they are within budget appropriations	Fire Department's SBE utilization goal	5.16%	Lag	5%			
		Maintain optimal staffing requirements	Percent of time minimum staff of 255 on fire companies will be maintained $	100%	Lag	95%			
		Maintain resource availability	Percent of fire companies in service during daylight hours Monday-Friday $	91.4%	Lag	80%			
Develop Employees	E1. Recruit and Retain Skilled, Diverse Workforce	Maintain certifications	Number of active firefighters that will maintain EMT certification	100%	Lag	99%			
		Maintain diverse workforce	Turnover rate for African American/ minority firefighters	1.1%	Lag	<1%			
	E2. Achieve Positive Employee Climate	Support physical fitness	Number of firefighters who participate in annual fitness evaluations $	97.8%	Lag	95%			
			Distribute wellness message in department newsletter $	100%	Lag	100%			

Status:

1. Use a "+" (plus) sign to indicate all is well.
2. Use a "-" (minus) sign to indicate that the status is not where expected or the current status is in trouble. Provide explanation.
3. Use an "x" to indicate this target will not be or is not met. Provide explanation.

Source: *Charlotte FY 11 Strategic Operating Plan, Final,* charmeck.ci.charlotte.nc.us/city/charlotte/Budget/Documents/Charlotte%20Fire%20Department.pdf, 18-20 (accessed November 15, 2010).

"Stat" systems The first successful "Stat" system was COMPSTAT, developed by Jack Maple, former deputy commissioner of the New York City Police Department.[7] COMPSTAT requires four key strategies: (1) accurate and timely data, (2) effective tactics, (3) rapid deployment, and (4) relentless follow-up.

In Maryland, adaptations of the process were applied to an entire city government with "CityStat," which then Mayor Martin O'Malley of Baltimore developed in 1999, and "StateStat," which O'Malley adapted for the state level when he became governor. Fire and emergency service departments across the country have since moved to adopt similar systems.

In every "Stat" system, agency program managers first develop performance measures that are meaningful and then analyze, report, and manage the causes of performance that does not meet the targets set. This performance management approach is most successful when

Monitoring performance in Miami-Dade County

For fiscal year 2006, the county of Miami-Dade reported that 84 percent of all one- and two-family residential structure fire incidents were confined to the room of origin, compared to an average of 57 percent for all jurisdictions. Miami-Dade County promotes timely response and fire confinement by regularly monitoring service performance:

- Twice each month, division fire chiefs meet to discuss fire events and look for and address emerging trends across the county.
- Once each month, county staff review the types and locations of the fire rescue calls, again seeking trends that may require attention.
- Once each quarter, progress against goals in the county's balanced scorecard is reported and assessed.
- The fire department conducts monthly business review meetings and annual strategic planning workshops with executive staff, division chiefs and managers, and bureau chiefs and managers to review departmental and division goals and outcomes.

Source: Center for Performance Measurement, *What Works: How Local Governments Have Made the Leap from Measurement to Management* (Washington, D.C.: ICMA Press, 2008), 62-63.

it is pushed down to the lowest levels, as the people closest to where the work is performed often have the best solutions for how to improve the work processes. It is also most successful when meetings to discuss progress toward targets take place on a regular basis. Some solutions take months to plan and years to implement.

SEA reports and benchmarking Local government policy makers are using the GASB measurement categories discussed earlier to develop SEA reports (see Table 14–3). SEA reports make macrolevel snapshot comparisons of critical governmental functions across similar jurisdictions and are therefore a form of benchmarking. The fire and emergency services department is often one of the first agencies in a jurisdiction targeted for the initial SEA reporting process. Figure 14–5 on page 408 shows some sample pages from a 2008 SEA report from Des Moines, Iowa, which has been using SEA reports for several years.

Performance management at the process (tactical) level

Process-level performance measurement and analysis generally lead to the greatest amount of improvement in outcomes and efficiency. This section discusses the need for process performance measurement, the use of performance measurement at the process level, the assignment of responsibility for process improvement, and process mapping—a specific technique for devising and analyzing process performance measures.

The need for process performance measurement Continuous process improvement (CPI) was developed for use in improving business operations.[8] CPI uses judgmental and analytical problem-solving techniques to improve work processes. Critical data are gathered at set points in a work process to provide feedback to those who perform and manage the process, ensuring that they understand what is happening and can keep the process operating at full capacity. Work steps that do not add value are eliminated. To improve efficiency, managers measure variables such as time, cost, and conformance to control limits (specifications).

Managers focus on the process's activity rather than on its output. Focusing on activity reduces variation in the product at the earliest possible point, whereas waiting until the end to inspect for variance is too late: by then the damage is already done. The need to focus on the activity is even more valid in a service setting than in a manufacturing or business setting:

> In nonmanufacturing processes such as those found in service type industries, focusing on the process is even more critical. Why? Because if the process steps are not well defined, clearly explained, and totally understood, the process becomes very "people dependent." When that occurs, you have a high probability that process output cannot be accurately predicted which leads to process variation. And, that's exactly what you want to avoid.[9]

Table 14-3 GASB service efforts and accomplishments (SEA) report indicators

Categories of indicators	Measures
A. Indicators of service efforts	1. Inputs: Dollar costs of the service period for service efforts and accomplishments a. In "current" dollars b. In "constant" dollars–that is, adjusted for price-level changes. 2. Inputs: Amounts of *non*monetary resources expended, especially the amount of work time expended during the period (for the service). These might be expressed in such units as full-time-equivalent years or employee hours.
B. Indicators of service accomplishments	1. Outputs: Amount of workload accomplished 2. Outcomes: A numeric indicator of program results. This category includes indicators of service quality (such as timeliness), effectiveness, and amount or proportion of "need" that is (or is not) being served.
C. Indicators that relate service efforts to service accomplishments (These can also be labeled efficiency indicators, which for the purposes of this report include both input/output and input/outcome indicators.)	1. Amount of input related to (divided by) amount of *output*. "Input" can be any of the variations included under Section A, and "output" refers to B.1, not to B.2. 2. Amount of input related to (divided by) amount of *outcomes* or *results*. Again, "input" can be any of the variations noted in Section A. "Outcome" refers only to B.2, not to B.1. 3. Productivity (or efficiency) *indexes*. These traditionally have been used in reporting national productivity trends. Indexes are calculated by relating the ratio of productivity in the current year to that of a preselected base year. These indexes have the advantage that the productivity ratios for different activities for services, or across services, can be combined by weighting each ratio by the amount of input for each activity.
D. Explanatory information This is a term used to cover a variety of information relevant to a service that helps users understand the performance of the SEA indicators and factors affecting an organization's performance. The explanatory information should be grouped into two categories [shown at right].	1. Elements substantially outside the control of the public agency, such as demographic characteristics. 2. Elements over which the agency has significant control, such as staffing patterns.

Source: This table, from Harry P. Hatry et al., eds., *Service Efforts and Accomplishments Reporting: Its Time Has Come* (Norwalk, Conn.: Governmental Accounting Standards Board, 1990), 12-13, copyright by the Financial Accounting Foundation (FAF), 401 Merritt 7, PO Box 5116, Norwalk, CT 06856-5116, has been adapted with permission. Complete copies of the report are available from the FAF.

In other words, in the provision of services such as fire and emergency services, outcomes depend on individual performance. To ensure that those services meet the customers' needs, departments must pay attention to the details of processes (how the critical tasks are performed—i.e., the manner in which services are provided) in order to make sure that all personnel are prepared to perform at expected levels.

The Rummler and Brache model for measuring the goals, design, and management of processes, discussed earlier in this chapter, offers a way for fire and emergency service departments to meet performance standards and minimize the variations among, for example, different engine companies' or different shifts' ways of performing the same tasks. Anyone who does not think such comparisons among units are necessary should consider how often one hears something like, "When we operate on incidents together, it seems as if we are from _____ [*insert the number of stations/battalions/districts/shifts*] separate fire departments."

Some may claim, "We can't plan for or measure firefighting because no two fires are alike." In reality, though, most fires are substantially the same. Physics is physics, no matter

Figure 14-5 Shown is a sample page from the *2008 Performance Report* from Des Moines, Iowa.

Percent of Residents Who Feel Safe in Their Neighborhoods

83%

According to the 2008 Resident Satisfaction Survey, 72% of residents are satisfied with the quality of public safety in the City of Des Moines. The departments most often associated with public safety are the Fire and Police Departments, but many departments play a role in public safety. Public Works is responsible for reacting during floods and snowstorms. The Permit and Development Center makes certain structures are built safely. Engineering keeps traffic signals and signs in good working order to prevent accidents.

The Fire Department responds to calls for fire, hazardous materials incidents, emergency medical assistance and other specialized rescue – including high angle rope, water, trench and confined space rescue. Firefighters also work to prevent fires through a comprehensive fire inspection and education program, and are highly trained and skilled full-time employees. All firefighters are not only required to be certified as firefighters, but the majority of them are also trained paramedics. This standard of service requires additional tax dollars for training but also makes sure that fully qualified professionals are available to respond to life-threatening situations. In 2008 the City spent 29.7 million dollars ($368.92 per household) for fire/rescue service.

SAFETY
quality of public safety

The Police Department provides public safety by responding to and investigating crimes. Two categories of crime are tracked by the Police Department – property crimes (burglary, larceny, theft of motor vehicles and arson) and violent crimes against people (murder, rape, robbery and aggravated assault). The number of crimes reported in both categories is not only lower than the average for other Midwestern and national cities but Des Moines also has a higher clearance rate. In 2008 the City spent 53.7 million dollars ($667 per household) for police services.

37% of the residents surveyed felt that the number one area that should receive the most emphasis from the Police Department during the next two years is increased visibility in neighborhoods. Residents also felt it was important for both the Fire and the Police Departments to put an emphasis on improving how quickly they respond to emergencies.

Gary Wilson
Downtown Des Moines | Ink, watercolor

flatrocket@yahoo.com

Born in Los Angeles, Gary Wilson has sketched and scribbled from an early age, achieving recognition for his unique presentation. In 1991 he reversed his family's 1930 trek from the Midwest with a destination, Des Moines. The deep seasonal changes make his new home a source of artistic inspiration.

Painting modern art watercolors is Wilson's stress relief. This artwork portrays our city as a dynamic and visually exciting destination. The skyward structures and dramatic diagonal lines give drama to the cars and figures.

Fire fighters work to contain a residential fire.

25

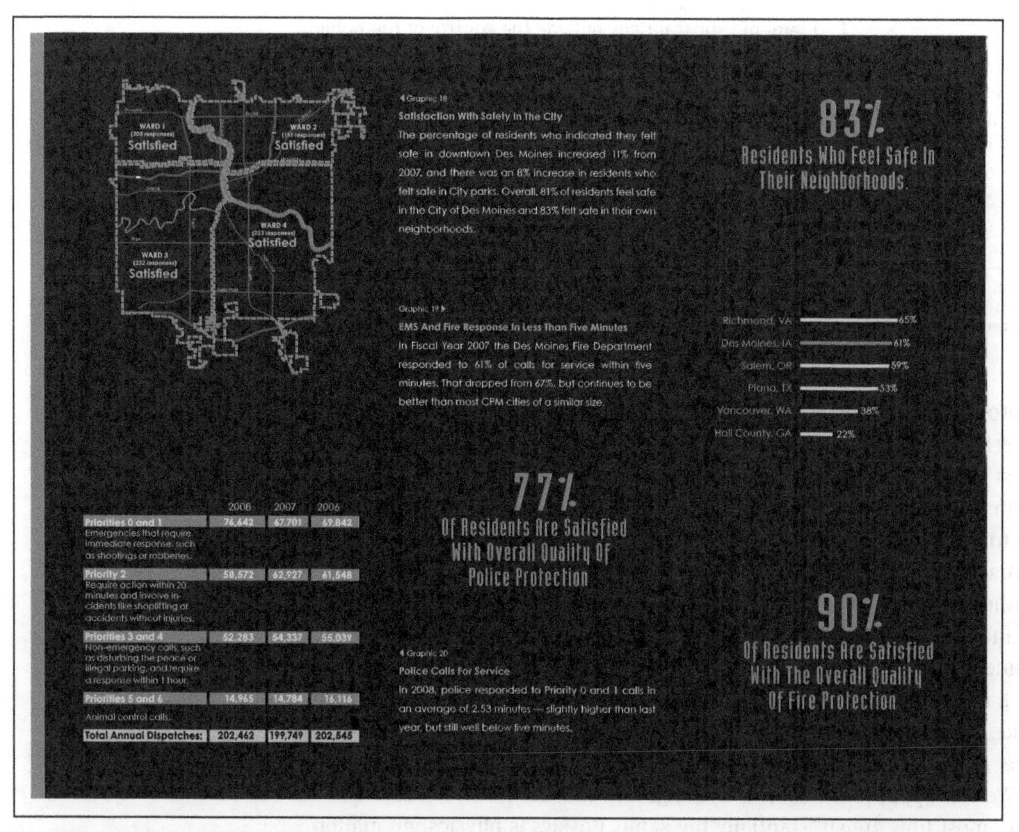

WARD 1 (205 responses) Satisfied
WARD 2 (155 responses) Satisfied
WARD 3 (232 responses) Satisfied
WARD 4 (223 responses) Satisfied

◀ Graphic 18

Satisfaction With Safety In The City

The percentage of residents who indicated they felt safe in downtown Des Moines increased 11% from 2007, and there was an 8% increase in residents who felt safe in City parks. Overall, 81% of residents feel safe in the City of Des Moines and 83% felt safe in their own neighborhoods.

Graphic 19 ▶

EMS And Fire Response In Less Than Five Minutes

In Fiscal Year 2007 the Des Moines Fire Department responded to 61% of calls for service within five minutes. That dropped from 67%, but continues to be better than most CPM cities of a similar size.

83%

Residents Who Feel Safe In Their Neighborhoods.

Richmond, VA	65%
Des Moines, IA	61%
Salem, OR	59%
Plano, TX	53%
Vancouver, WA	38%
Hall County, GA	22%

	2008	2007	2006
Priorities 0 and 1 Emergencies that require immediate response, such as shootings or robberies.	76,642	67,701	69,842
Priority 2 Require action within 20 minutes and involve incidents like shoplifting or accidents without injuries.	58,572	62,927	61,548
Priorities 3 and 4 Non-emergency calls, such as disturbing the peace or illegal parking, and require a response within 1 hour.	52,283	54,337	55,039
Priorities 5 and 6 Animal control calls.	14,965	14,784	16,116
Total Annual Dispatches:	202,462	199,749	202,545

77%

Of Residents Are Satisfied With Overall Quality Of Police Protection

◀ Graphic 20

Police Calls For Service

In 2008, police responded to Priority 0 and 1 calls in an average of 2.53 minutes — slightly higher than last year, but still well below five minutes.

90%

Of Residents Are Satisfied With The Overall Quality Of Fire Protection

Source: City of Des Moines, *Raising the Bar: 2008 Performance Report*, 25-26, dmgov.org/Departments/CityManager/PDF/2008PerformanceReport.pdf.

where you are. True, there is variation in where a fire starts within a structure, where it has spread to by the time the fire and emergency services department arrives, and whether there is anyone needing rescue. That variation is the reason that the National Incident Management System (NIMS) Incident Command System (ICS) was developed. The ICS is a method of bringing consistency to the process of assessing the situation upon arrival, planning a course of action, implementing that action plan, and continuously managing the process.

Once the specific nature of the situation has been determined, the incident commander develops a plan of action and orders standard tactical assignments—search, fire attack, search and rescue, ventilation—to meet the needs of the particular incident, and the responding companies execute the assignments. Firefighting process managers must ensure that each company's crew operates within the ICS and can execute the standard tactical assignments correctly and within the process limits (with respect to time and safety) set for each. Measuring the ability of responding crews to perform *before* the emergency is a necessary step toward ensuring consistent performance *during* emergency incidents. As has so often been said, "You fight like you train." Model procedures for various types of incidents have been developed by the NIMS Consortium (see NIMS-Consortium.org).

Performance measurement at the process level Up until now, too little of the performance measurement work for fire and emergency service departments has focused on measures at the process level. Each separate program or major activity for the department should develop and diagram its own internal chronological work flows and measures for critical tasks and activities.

EMS systems have typically done this: The physician serving as the system's medical director establishes medical protocols that identify specific requirements for the performance

Lean Six Sigma

Six Sigma and Lean are each methods of continuous process improvement (CPI). Six Sigma, developed by Motorola to eliminate defects,[1] focuses on the problems that cause errors.[2] Six Sigma (meaning 3.4 defects or errors per million) applies W. Edwards Deming's data-driven system process controls to eliminate variation in design and manufacturing processes.[3] Lean, a way of thinking developed by Toyota to eliminate waste and improve business process flow,[4] focuses on the customer, delivering value while minimizing errors. Over the years the two methodologies have evolved into Lean Six Sigma.

Although developed in the manufacturing sector, Lean Six Sigma can be used to improve speed, quality, and cost to provide services in fire and emergency services as well as in other public sector organizations.[5] To maximize its results, CPI must become a way of doing business rather than a special program for quality improvement. It takes a conscious effort to understand and think statistically about the processes that support providing the services that customers expect. Different people may perform those processes differently, which can lead to errors, but inherent in processes themselves are data that can be measured to explain any variability and help managers focus on ways to minimize errors, thereby improving quality and work flow and reducing waste to lower costs.

Lean Six Sigma can be applied within all facets of the fire and emergency services organization: operations, prevention, logistics, human resources, finance, and administration. The ultimate goal is to change the organizational culture and way of thinking so that CPI is a way of life. This means that employees are aware of the importance of their work and of how it contributes to the organization's mission, provides value to the customer (both internal and external), and eliminates waste.

1 Presentation, Tina Huesing, Motorola, October 2008, 6sigmaexperts.com/presentations/Six_Sigma_Through_the_Years.pdf. See also Motorola's Six Sigma online tutorials at motorola.com/Business/US-EN/Motorola+University/Free+Six+Sigma+Lessons (both accessed July 26, 2011).

2 Geoffrey Tennant, *Six Sigma: SPC and TM in Manufacturing and Services* (Hampshire, England: Gower Publishing Ltd., 2001), 6.

3 Ron Basu, *Implementing Six Sigma and Lean: A Practical Guide to Tools and Techniques* (London: Butterworth Heinemann, 2008), 19.

4 Lean Manufacturing and the Toyota Production System, Ronald M. Becker, Society of Automotive Engineers, sae.org/topics/leanjun01.htm (accessed July 26, 2011).

5 More information on using Lean Six Sigma in the public service sector is available at ocw.mit.edu/OcwWeb/web/home/home/index.htm (search for Lean Six Sigma); see also Forrest Breyfogle, *Implementing Six Sigma: Smarter Solutions Using Statistical Methods*, 2nd ed. (New York: John Wiley & Sons, 2003).

of advanced life support (ALS) procedures by emergency medical technicians and paramedics in the field. Usually a formal system is in place to review and evaluate whether the protocols were followed, whether they worked, and if they did not work, what changes are needed in either the protocol or the performance of teams or individuals.

An equivalent process of developing specific process-performance protocols and improving quality should be instituted by the "fire doctor" (the fire chief) for fire suppression, hazardous material activities, technical rescue, fire inspection activities, 911 call receipt and dispatch processes, and every other critical activity or process in which the department is engaged.

Another excellent example is the firefighter training and certification program used in Montana, developed by that state's fire training organization on the basis of standard tactical assignments performed by crews in a real-world setting. The scenarios are designed to meet both the requirements of NFPA 1001, Standard for Fire Fighter Professional Qualifications (2008 ed.), and the operational needs of the firefighters in the field operating under NIMS ICS. Each standard tactical evolution has the process steps laid out in chronological order with time parameters where appropriate.

To do performance measurement at the process level, the emergency response function should report performance measures for each significant component of a process, depending on how the service is delivered. If the department has separate tactical units (engine, truck, heavy rescue, or ambulance/medic companies), stations, and/or shifts, the data should be collected by each unit and then combined into station-, shift-, and division-level information that fits the needs of the organization. If the organization has multiple stations that make up geographic battalions or districts, the data should be reported at the lowest level (unit, station, etc.) that performs the activity and then aggregated at the battalion or district level. This is important because the only way to clearly identify where the variance is occurring is to separate out the data to the significant level for each process—in this case, the level of the tactical unit, station, shift, or battalion.

Identifying process managers As noted previously in this chapter, an incident time line like that shown in Figure 14–3 can help an organization assign responsibilities for crucial processes. Battalion or district commanders are responsible, within their assigned geographical or functional areas, for the unit deployment time (points F to I) and for the system impact time (points I to K)—that is, for coordinating the activities of multiple response units to quickly achieve positive outcomes at incidents. The district chief might be made responsible for developing a battalion management plan to focus on the problem within a residential community of above-average times for accessing the system (points A–C). Analysis might show that district personnel need to direct their efforts at smoke detectors, either having them installed or having the batteries replaced to ensure that detectors in residential properties are operational.

How the call receipt and dispatch functions are conducted will determine who is responsible for the call-processing time interval (points C or D to E) and the dispatch time interval (points E to F). For example, if the PSAP is handled by a separate agency that processes (handles) the 911 call and then transfers information to the fire and emergency services department for dispatch, the PSAP manager is responsible for the answer time and the call-processing time interval of system response time, which includes determining the required information (i.e., a valid computer-aided dispatch address, call type, and callback number). The department dispatch center manager is then responsible for the dispatch time interval. When the PSAP both answers the call and dispatches the fire and emergency services department, the PSAP manager is responsible for the entire incident processing time (points C to F).

Field unit commanders (e.g., engine company officers) are responsible for their units' response times (points F to H) and set-up times (points H to I). These commanders should be held accountable for their assigned crews' ability to turn out rapidly and safely, travel to incidents, deploy themselves and their equipment, and operate at the scene of emergencies. Battalion or other district commanders are responsible for those same measures for all the stations assigned to the district—that is, from a battalion perspective. Similarly, the operations section chief needs to measure those time components for all the battalions aggregated to the section level.

If a company has a higher-than-expected unit response time (points F to H), the station officer might be made responsible for developing a station management plan, a goal of which would be to reduce the station's unit response time. The officer would look at the two components of the time line that are under his or her direct control: turn-out time and unit travel time. Closer examination might reveal one potential reason for the high response time: that to perform physical fitness training each day, the company travels to the extreme dead end of its first-due area (i.e., the area within which it is the first company due at a fire). In this case, reengineering the work environment to provide adequate physical fitness facilities closer to the center of the company's response district may have a significant and positive effect on the unit's travel time. Similarly, changing the work process by analyzing the time of day at which calls are occurring and then scheduling the physical fitness training at the time of lowest probability for a call may also have a positive effect.

Figure 14-6 presents considerations for improving response time performance for each time line interval during which time spent is excessive. The point is, one cannot tell what is not going well unless performance is measured, and solutions cannot be developed unless a problem is identified. The methods used in developing solutions should involve people at all levels in the organization. People closest to the problem often have the best ideas.

Tactical assignments and process mapping For each standard tactical assignment to be performed by an individual or response crew, a process map should be prepared. That is, each critical process should be mapped out, and the mapping should identify what chronological steps must be completed to achieve the desired result, who does what, and what tools are used (see Figure 14-7). The process map should then become the basis for (1) the teaching and evaluation of standard training evolutions (tactical scenarios or assignments) during recruit and certification training, (2) periodic evaluations of crew performance, and (3) the assessment of actual on-scene performance during postincident analysis.

The process map can take any number of forms, from a list of sequential activities to a process flowchart of how the task should be performed. Several worthwhile examples of process mapping and evaluation can be found in the National Highway Traffic Safety Administration's booklet *A Leadership Guide to Quality Improvement for Emergency Medical Services (EMS) Systems.*[10]

Analyzing and using performance data

Analysis and use of performance data to explain what is happening should take place at three levels: the internal customer/tactical level; the department senior management level; and the elected officials and public level. Ideas for each level are presented below.

	Detection time	Alarm time	Incident processing time	Turn-out time	Unit travel time	Set-up time	Stabilize time	Recovery time
POTENTIAL OPTIONS	Citizen CPR Automatic detection systems Neighborhood Watch Police patrols	Citizen CPR Citizen 911 training Public awareness programs Automatic alarm systems	Technology changes Training Modify procedures Increase staffing in dispatch center	Station design Modify procedures Apparatus design Training	Road network Interparcel connectors Training Add response units to meet workload Add stations to shorten responses	New procedures New equipment More staff arrive earlier Training	More staff early in incident Crew training New methods New technology New tools	Provide relief staffing New methods New technology New tools

Figure 14-6 Numerous potential options exist for reducing time intervals between key points.

Figure 14-7 This sample process map of vertical ventilation tasks assumes a crew of three on scene and wearing personal protective equipment, including self-contained breathing apparatus except for facepiece when starting.

	Officer activity	F/f 1 activity	F/f 2 activity
Primary responsibilities →	Observe conditions Complete task Ensure crew safety	Back up f/f 2 Saw operator	Sound roof Backup saw operator Clear opening
Tasks			
1 Receive and echo tactical order	Listen to radio and receive order Echo tactical order back to command Time starts		
2 Give task order to crew	Tell crew assignment and location	Acknowledge order	Acknowledge order
3 Collect tools and transport them to task area	Monitor crew performance and radio	Carry ladder butt, saw	Carry ladder tip, sounding hook
4 Establish ladder access to roof	Observe conditions Monitor crew performance and radio	Heel ladder, tie off	Raise and set ladder
5 Don facepiece and climb to roof with tools	Don facepiece Second up ladder Monitor crew performance and radio	Don facepiece Foot ladder while others climb Third up ladder with tools	Don facepiece First up ladder with tools
6 Sound roof	Ensure f/f 2 sounds roof Monitor crew performance and radio		Sound roof before stepping off Hold ladder tip
7 Select cut location and proceed to cut area	Select cut location and communicate to crew Walk only where sounded Monitor crew performance and radio	Back up f/f 2 while sounding Walk only where sounded	Lead and sound path to cut area and entire cut work area Walk only where sounded
8 Make inspection cut	Select cut location Monitor crew performance and radio	Start saw Cut inspection opening	Back up saw operator
9 Decide whether to proceed	Decide based on area scan and conditions in inspection opening Communicate decision to crew	Acknowledge receipt of decision	Acknowledge receipt of decision
10 Make cut	Observe conditions Monitor crew performance and radio	Cut 4' x 8' opening with louvered panels	Back up saw operator
11 Clear hole	Observe conditions Monitor crew performance and radio	Back up f/f 2 while clearing hole	Clear hole of cut wood and sheetrock below
12 Radio status to command	Radio command that vent hole is cut and crew is exiting roof		
13 Exit roof	Move to ladder, walk only where sounded, hold ladder tip while others climb Monitor crew performance and radio Climb down ladder third	Back up sounder Move to ladder, walk only where sounded Climb down ladder second with tools	Sound roof Move to ladder Climb down ladder first with tools Foot ladder when down
14 Report status to command	Radio command that crew is clear of roof and ready for reassignment Time stops		

Collecting and analyzing process data

Program managers (i.e., the operations chief and prevention chief) and the managers of major subcomponents (station, battalion, or division commanders in operations; inspection, investigation, and public education managers in prevention) and processes that feed into another program or agency's work products (PSAP and dispatch centers, land use and construction plan review) should develop performance measures and collect performance data for their respective pieces of the puzzle. The format for display of the data needs to drill down to the level of the work unit being evaluated. The "Stat" process can be adapted to provide the performance information for managers at each meaningful level: "UnitStat," "StationStat," "BattalionStat."

The next step is to analyze the process data collected. This step, called process evaluation, is a foundation of quality assurance, total quality management, and other process improvement methodologies. The following sidebars—the Pareto chart, the run chart, and the histogram—discuss three specific ways of displaying process data to help the numbers "make sense" and to aid in meaningful interpretation. When these three tools are used to display a large number of data points, the analyst can begin to identify meaningful patterns, which in turn may suggest that a single "special cause" or several special causes are at work in the process. ("Special cause" refers to a sporadic or one-time event that influences a process, as opposed to a common cause that is a chronic or inherent quality of the system or process.) Again, the tools do not explain why the pattern is there but merely reveal that it exists and that further study is needed to identify the cause.

Analyzing departmental performance

Senior-level managers are concerned with analyzing the overall performance of major divisions within the organization, and the organization as a whole against the major goals and objectives set for it. This analysis is used to identify significant changes in resource levels needed to improve performance. Those resource changes are critical components in the development of the fire and emergency services department budgets, both operating and capital. A natural progression in the use of performance measurement is to develop performance- and results-oriented budget proposals (see the two sidebars on page 416).

The Pareto chart

A Pareto chart displays data in a series of bars arranged in descending height from left to right. The name comes from the Pareto Principle, which states that a small number of causes account for most of the problems. The display of data in this way breaks a big problem into small pieces, identifies the most significant factors contributing to the problem, and shows which areas are likely to respond most to changes and therefore which uses of limited resources are likely to be most productive.

An example is a situation in which there are delays in system response time. The data captured indicate that the delays are generated in several areas of the response process (Table A). To prepare a Pareto chart for this or any other situation, first order the data elements from largest to smallest (see Table B) and then place them into a Pareto chart, as shown. The X axis is the categories, the Y axis is the number of occurrences, and the Z axis is the cumulative percentage.

Table A

Point of occurrence	Number of occurrences
Call-handling time	5
Dispatch time	25
Turn-out time	16
Unit response time	4

Table B

Point of occurrence	Number of occurrences
Dispatch time	25
Turn-out time	16
Call-handling time	5
Unit response time	4

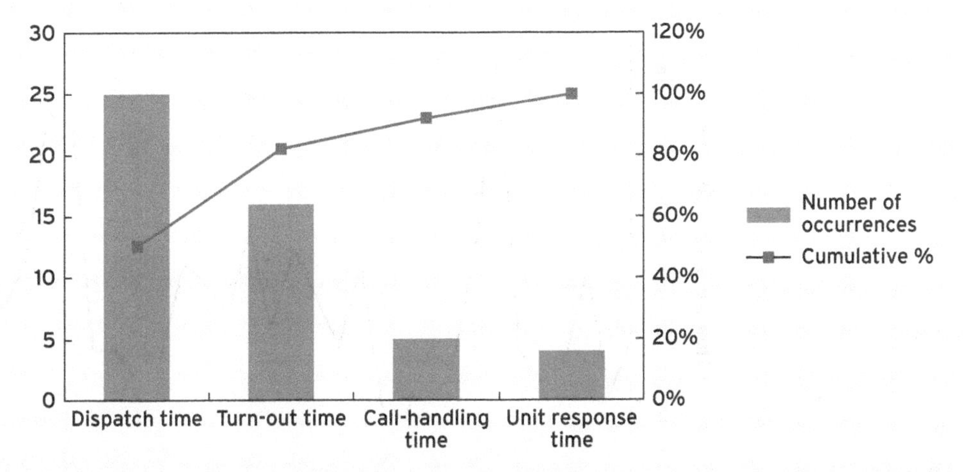

In this case, two bars are significantly taller than the others: both the dispatch segment and the turn-out segment of the process experienced a high number of delays. The cumulative percentage of the bar values is indicated by a single line. The first two bars, dispatch and turn-out, account for more than 80 percent of the total. The differences in bar heights between the first and second bars and between the second and third bars are much larger than the difference between the third and fourth bars. These dramatic differences in height are called the break points. The first break occurs after the dispatch bar; the second, after the turn-out bar. Another way to spot the break is to note the break point(s) where the slope of the percentage line lessens significantly.

The objective of the analysis is to find the break points and focus attention on the factors to the left of them. If the reasons behind the delays in the two largest categories can be identified and corrected, 80 percent of the causes for delays, or variation in performance, can be eliminated. As previously mentioned, Pareto charts allow one to focus one's efforts where they are likely to be most effective. If no break points are evident, one should evaluate other factors to see if a distinct pattern develops. For example, if all the process components have approximately the same number of delays, it might be useful to identify the length of delays in each category to concentrate on reducing the delays in the category where they are longest.

The run chart

A run chart is a line graph that plots data points on process performance in chronological order. The data points can be measurements, counts, or percentages of process outputs. One uses the run chart to detect trends over time, to understand whether unusual variation exists in a process, and, if it does, to help identify what might be causing it. One also uses the run chart to monitor process performance over time and to communicate information about that performance to others.

Some variation in performance is expected. Run charts look for unusual or excessive variation as indicated by the existence of a trend, run, or cycle. Such variation indicates the presence of special causes. Because the variation can be for better or for worse, its causes can be either positive or negative. But either way, it must be brought under control before more sophisticated analysis can be performed to fine-tune the process performance. Once statistical control of the process is achieved (i.e., once there is no trend, run, or cycle in at least 100 observations), additional analysis can be done.

The chart can also be used to measure change in a process after the process is redesigned.

Although the presence of a trend, a run, or a cycle indicates that there is a special cause (which must be investigated) for the unusual variation in the process, the absence of a trend, a run, or a cycle does not necessarily mean that the process is without variation. Before one can say that the process is in statistical control, the run chart should be done over a period of 100 observations without any signal of a special cause. Additional information on run charts can be found in the *Fire Data Analysis Handbook*.[1]

Once statistical control is achieved in a process, more sophisticated analysis can be conducted with the use of control charts, which establish upper and lower limits of the process specification and thereby enable the variations above and below those limits to be analyzed. Control charts are not addressed in more detail here, but the suggested readings for this chapter at the back of this book provide more information.

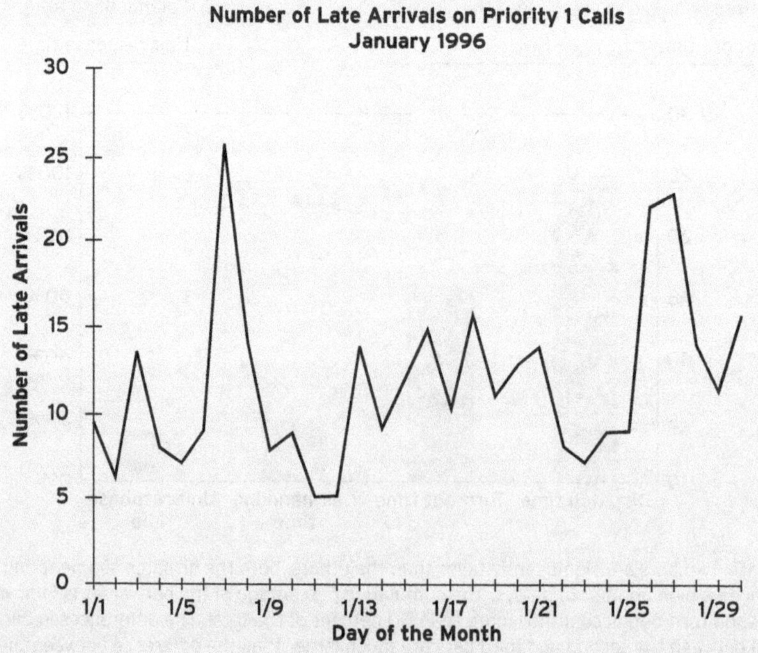

Source: U.S. Department of Transportation, National Highway Traffic Safety Administration, *A Leadership Guide to Quality Improvement for Emergency Medical Services (EMS) Systems* (Washington, D.C., July 1997), nhtsa.gov/people/injury/ems/leaderguide/ (accessed July 26, 2011).

1 Federal Emergency Management Agency, U.S. Fire Administration, *Fire Data Analysis Handbook*, 2nd ed., FA-266 (Washington, D.C., January 2004), usfa.dhs.gov/downloads/pdf/publications/fa-266.pdf.

The histogram

A histogram is a vertical bar chart that displays the distribution of a set of data. It provides a snapshot of a process at a moment in time rather than the process's performance over time (as in the run chart). A histogram is used when one wants to summarize a large data set in graphical form, compare process performance with process limits, communicate information in a readily understandable format, and have a decision-making tool.

A histogram comprises vertical bars placed on the X axis, which shows the scale for the values of the measurements. Each bar's width represents the length of the interval represented by the bar. The bar's height is measured against the Y axis and represents the number of occurrences within the X axis interval. A legend is used to explain the source of the data. To construct a histogram,

1. Count the number of data points to be displayed
2. Summarize the data points on a tally sheet and compute the range
3. Determine the number of intervals to use
4. Compute the interval width
5. Determine the interval starting point
6. Plot the data
7. Add the title and legend.

As mentioned earlier, histograms are graphical representations of summarized data. One can interpret histograms to determine whether performance meets expectations and what type of variation occurs during the performance period. From the distribution of the data, or groupings, one can tell whether the performance is within specification limits. In the histogram shown here, the performances of most of the responses are grouped to the left of the target time of 8 minutes, but several exceeded the maximum time and are shown tailed off to the right.

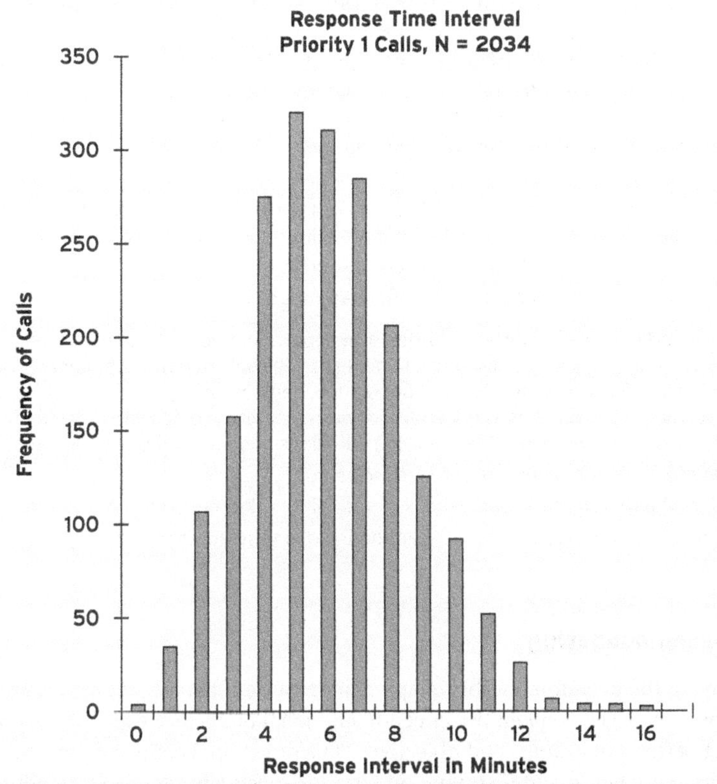

Source: U.S. Department of Transportation, National Highway Traffic Safety Administration, *A Leadership Guide to Quality Improvement for Emergency Medical Services (EMS) Systems* (Washington, D.C., July 1997), nhtsa.gov/people/injury/ems/leaderguide/ (accessed July 26, 2011).

Eleven suggestions for improving the usefulness of information

1. Address service quality and outcomes explicitly when reviewing services and programs.
2. Ask program managers to set a target for each performance indicator. Assess progress regularly against these targets.
3. Provide performance data in a timely manner.
4. Calculate key breakouts of the data for each indicator.
5. Include indicators of both "intermediate" outcomes and "end" [long-term] outcomes in the performance measurement process, but clearly identify both types of indicators.
6. Ask programs to provide explanatory information with each performance report.
7. In agency training programs, routinely provide information on performance measurement and its uses to supervisors and managers.
8. Incorporate outcome-related performance requirements into contracts wherever feasible.
9. Consider including service quality and outcome progress information as part of the performance appraisal process for internal employees, especially supervisors and managers.
10. Use information on service quality outcomes in formulating and justifying budgets.
11. Finally, avoid expectations that outcome information will indicate the causes of the outcomes.

Source: Harry Hatry, Craig Gerhart, and Martha Marshall, "Eleven Ways to Make Performance Measurement More Useful to Public Managers," *Public Management* 76, no. 9 (1994): S15-S18.

Asking questions

The chief can ask the following questions when examining performance data to gain insight into the department's performance:

- What is the call processing time and how do I compare with other departments?
- What is my turn-out time? What is my total response time? How does it compare with times in other departments? Is my response time better in some areas than in others?
- How many structure fires are there in my jurisdiction? What are the causes of these fires?
- How many vehicle fires are there? When are they occurring? Where are they occurring?
- Should I expect the occurrence of specific types of incidents to be related to specific weather conditions? If yes, how can I best use my limited resources?
- How many calls are false alarms? How many are system malfunctions? Are these false alarms seasonal? Are these false alarms weather related?
- What incident types predominate?
- Where are my resources being used? When are my resources being used? How long are my resources being used per incident? Will better training or different training bring the figure down?
- What can I do to get more from my current resources?
- Do I have any problems that need immediate attention?

When benchmarking the performance of the local department against the performance of another department, it is necessary to examine disparities between the communities served by the two departments (size of area, size of population, demographics, etc.) and difference in the activities related to the services in question. For example, when comparing performance data for emergency medical service calls, the following questions about definition should be asked:

- How does each department characterize incidents?
- Do different jurisdictional organizations dictate different definitions?
- Does one geographic region use different definitions from another?

Results-based budgeting

As mentioned at the beginning of this chapter, an important benefit of performance measurement is helping managers explain the effect of additional budgetary expenditures or reductions on achieving performance goals and objectives. The direct application of performance measurement in preparing and justifying budgets for specific programs or activities is called results-based (or outcome-based) budgeting.

Results-based budgeting is a process whereby the performance measures are used to quantify and explain the impacts of budget increases or decreases in terms of changes in service delivery. In results-based budgeting, one develops budget requests by addressing specific community or organizational needs that have been identified by the community's strategic plan or the department's service improvement plan. To identify the areas needing improvement, one uses performance measures. One also uses performance measures to estimate the effect of the budget increases or decreases on closing the performance gap: the same properly crafted performance measures and thoughtful analysis that made clear where the problems were will also provide the means of analyzing the effect of any corrective changes.

For example, if the performance gap is in the system's or the unit's response times to emergencies, the budget request should propose solutions that will close the gap. The request should identify not only the cost of the solutions but also the expected changes in the performance measures of the affected services. The clearer a department is about the specific improvements it expects, the more likely that the budget request will be approved. Conversely, the same methodology can be used to clearly assess the impact of budget reductions on critical levels of service to the overall community or to a specific neighborhood.

Shown in the sidebar below is an extract from a results-based budget that proposes converting a career medic unit from daytime-only staffing to twenty-four-hour-a-day staffing. This proposal involves adding two additional shifts of personnel for a total additional cost of $801,095. What is the community going to get for that increase in expenditures?

The budget document establishes a direct link to the county's strategic plan and provides background allowing the request to be understood in the context of that plan. The section on budget additions (not shown) contains narrative and data tables to clarify the need for, and effect of, the funding improvement.

The response-time improvements in the "service-level impacts" table show the expected improvements for important measures. The "FY XXXX base" column indicates what percentage the measure is expected to attain with no service improvement; the "FY XXXX adopted" column shows the percentage expected with the new funding level. The percentage of responses in Medic X's first-due area that will meet the service delivery goal of ALS within

Sample results-based budget justification for 24-hour medic unit staffing

Medical intervention

The medical director estimates that approximately 50 percent of our advanced life support (ALS) responses fall into interventions that are immediately lifesaving, that result in a significantly better outcome than sickness and death, and that will shorten the critical disease stage that could result in death. This equates to 298 patients annually whom the proposed medic unit from this station will treat to preserve the "chain of survival."

Strategic plan

The request for two additional shifts is applicable to the public safety strategy goal and, more specifically, to the objective that "fire stations adequately respond to the needs of the community 24 hours per day." By expanding the existing daytime medic unit to a 24-hour medic unit, the county is ensuring that the needs of the community are being adequately responded to 24 hours a day.

Desired community and program outcomes from budget request:

- Improve response time for ALS by 4 percent
- Improve response time for basic life support (BLS) by 5 percent
- Maintain citizen satisfaction with emergency medical service at 97 percent.

Service-level impacts	FY XXXX base, %	FY XXXX adopted, %
Improve ALS response time during volunteer hours in Medic X first due (90% target level)	35	75
Improve BLS response time during volunteer hours in Medic X first due (90% target level)	58	75
Improve ALS response time during volunteer hours in high-density areas countywide (90% target level)	73	75
Improve BLS response time during volunteer hours in high-density areas countywide (90% target level)	80	81

eight minutes is expected to more than double, rising from 35 percent to 75 percent. (For ALS response in high-density areas, the expected increase countywide is expected to be about 2 percent because the high-density area overall is so much larger than the first-due area.)

The importance of capturing and reporting good data is evident in this budget request. Good data make it possible to show clear improvement in performance and to explain the effect of that improvement in human terms. In this example, the case is made that a total of 298 patients will receive lifesaving treatment with the additional shifts in place. This information is important in enabling citizens, the governing body, and senior governmental officials to understand what they will be getting for the money they are being asked to spend. When everyone understands, everyone wins, including the fire and emergency services department.

Informing elected officials and the public

Reporting performance information at the neighborhood level is an effective way of reaching the public with pertinent information about city or county services. It is a way to use geographical variance in critical measures to raise awareness. Displaying information using a geographic information system (GIS) is especially useful in communicating to people how their neighborhood (or election district) is being served and how it compares to others. Some examples of useful GIS displays are

- Response time maps (Figure 14–8). People always find their houses on the map and ask what the response time is for them. That is true for citizens and elected officials.
- Actual response-to-incidents maps (Figure 14–9). These maps show where incidents have occurred and been responded to during a period. An enhancement would be to use dot map symbols to indicate the actual response time range for each response location.

Using multijurisdictional data

The ICMA Center for Performance Measurement (CPM) and the SEA report initiatives have inspired local departments to work together to develop performance measurement tools for SEA reporting and benchmarking. Such departments have identified similar departments within their regions of the country and agreed to meet periodically, exchange performance measurements, and evaluate their underlying business processes. It is a way for departments to share knowledge and experience relative to performance measurement and benchmarking, ultimately improving their own operations. As shown in the examples in Figure 14–10 (see page 421), Bellevue, Washington's fire department has developed a list of "vital signs" to evaluate its performance and also compares its performance data against data from other cities in its CPM consortium.

SEA reports give citizens, elected officials, and senior government and department executives comparison data on a few critical areas to highlight how well each department is doing relative to others like it. In the process, usually the jurisdiction's auditor or staff collects data from preselected comparison jurisdictions each year. (For each targeted service, the items compared often include measures of efficiency and outcome.) The side-by-side comparison of jurisdictions on points of critical data shows areas of strength and weakness and provides guidance for policy makers and departmental management.

When selecting comparison jurisdictions, it is imperative that the fire and emergency services organization be involved from the beginning. Otherwise, a jurisdiction selected for comparison may be an incredibly close match for the purpose of comparing finances or such services as police and transportation but may not be a close match at all for fire and emergency services. And this could pose a problem because in SEA reporting, the goal is to use measures to compare like services, and when the organizations or services do not match, the report must include explanations of differences that affect the measures. But the explanations are made in footnotes, which readers may not take the time to read. If the numbers shown make it look as though a jurisdiction is underperforming, SEA report users who do not read the explanations may conclude that the department is in fact underperforming even though the variance in performance has a rational explanation. (It is also possible that the compari-

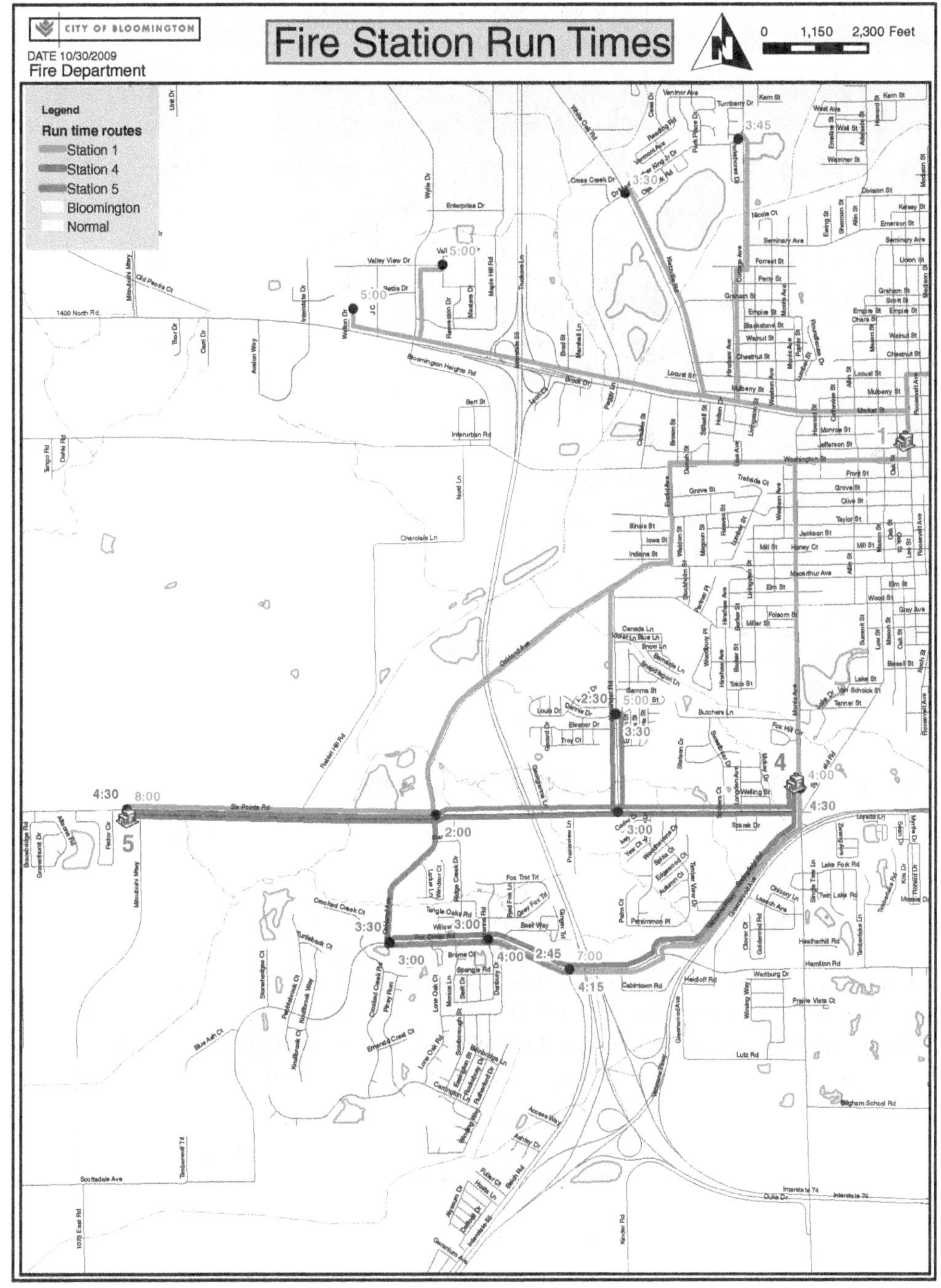

Source: City of Bloomington, Illinois, cityblm.org/spotlight/file.axd?file=2009%2f11%2fFireRuntimeMaps.pdf.

Figure 14-8 This GIS display shows fire station run times.

son jurisdictions are exceptionally high performers and that while a local department may seem to be underperforming in comparison to them, it is nonetheless performing at a relatively high level.)

Improving poor performance

Neither performance measures nor analysis explains why the performance problem exists. To discover the cause of the problem, one needs other tools.

People closest to the problem need to be involved in determining what is really causing it. Using cause-and-effect analysis tools such as fishbone diagramming (see the sidebar on page 422) will help the work team make sure that all possibilities are considered.

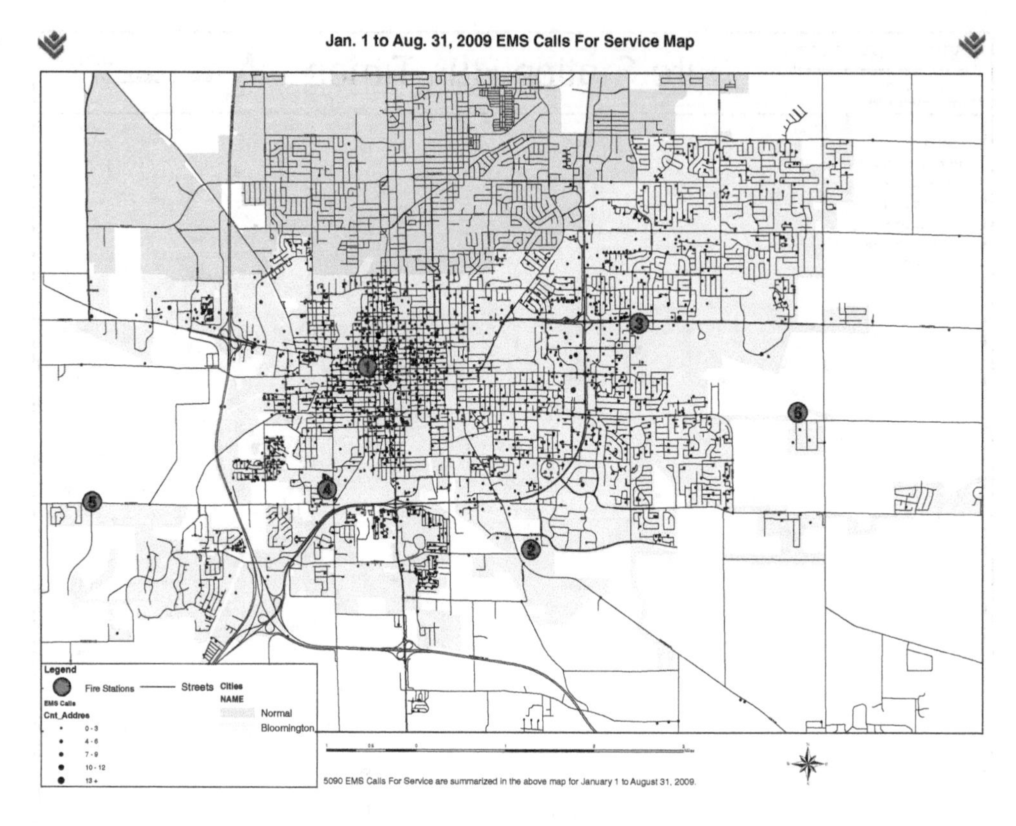

Figure 14-9 This GIS display shows calls for emergency medical services.

Source: City of Bloomington, Illinois, cityblm.org/spotlight/file.axd?file=2009%2f11%2f2009EMSCalls.pdf.

Once the team knows what the problems are and has determined their cause, it can focus on changing performance. Performance problems usually turn out to stem from the physical or psychological work environment, ineffective operating procedures, or failure to follow established procedures. When staff members fail to follow procedures, the reason is usually either that they have not learned the correct procedure or that they have deliberately chosen not to follow it.

For performance problems not caused by deliberate acts, strategies for change generally focus on three areas: the work environment, operating procedures, and training.

- *The work environment:* The work environment can be reengineered to eliminate the impediments, both physical and psychological, that have been identified. Reengineering may include changing or updating the tools and equipment available for performing the tasks. A task analysis of the process or an organizational/cultural analysis may be called for, depending on the severity of the problem.
- *Operating procedures:* Operating procedures can be modified to take maximum advantage of the physical environment (tools and equipment, either existing or updated) and of staff capabilities.
- *Training:* Staff can be trained, retrained, or coached in how to do the job correctly.

Solutions to performance problems often involve some or all of the areas listed above. If analysis shows that neither the environment nor existing procedures need to be changed, the training solution is the only one applicable.

However, if the performance problem results from deliberate acts of omission or commission on the part of fire and emergency personnel, a strategy for change must be developed that starts with training or verification that the correct process steps are understood and that the importance of following the steps is also understood. The training must be followed by monitoring, coaching, and, if necessary, counseling and progressive discipline to correct the behavior (see sidebar on page 423).

City of Bellevue Vital Signs	2005 Actual	2006 Actual	2007 Actual	2007 Target	Target Met Or Exceeded
Public Safety					
Patrol response times to critical emergencies from dispatch to arrival	3.7 min	3.4 min	3.9 min	4.2 min	✓
Percent of fires confined to room of origin	90%	88%	82%	85%	
Cardiac arrest survival rate	50%	63%	64%	45%	✓
Number of violent & property crimes committed per 1,0000 population	42	40	36.7	42	✓

11. PERCENT OF FIRE SUPPRESSION CALLS WITH RESPONSE TIME OF FIVE MINUTES AND UNDER

2006 Fire Data
(End Outcome Indicator)

Measure Definition: Percentage of fire incident calls responded to within five minutes or less. Measurement is from receipt of call by fire dispatch to arrival at the scene and contains both emergency and non-emergency response time averages.

Key Conclusion: Bellevue Fire continues to be challenged in its efforts to meet response time standards.

Current Year Performance and Trends:

- Since 2003, the ICMA average for percentage of Fire Suppression Calls with response time of five minutes and under has improved slightly. During this same time period, the percent of fire suppression calls with response time of five minutes or under for Bellevue has improved slightly but continues to be below the average of ICMA comparable cities.

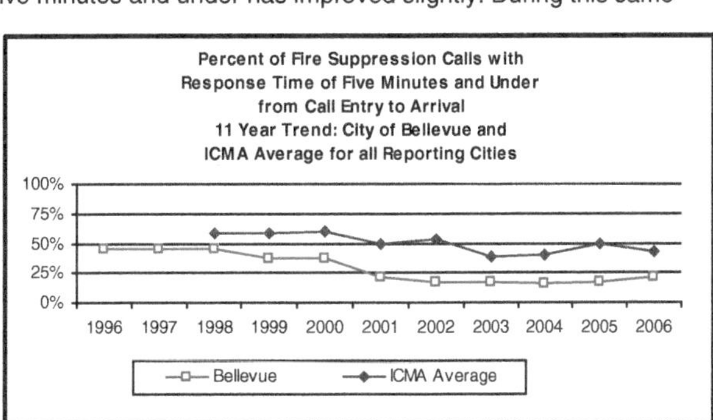

- Population density has a significant impact on the travel time component of response times. Johnson City, Tennessee, is slightly larger in area than Bellevue, has a population of approximately 61,000, and has 8 fire stations.
- In contrast, Bellevue is one of the fastest growth communities in the State of Washington. There are a number of factors experienced in growing communities that influence response times. These factors include: increased call volume, increased traffic congestion, and increased building and road construction activities.

Figure 14-10 Shown are sample pages from the City of Bellevue, Washington's *Report to Our Citizens* and *2006 Comparative Cities Performance Report*.

Source: City of Bellevue, Washington, *A Report to Our Citizens* (n.d.), 2, bellevuewa.gov/pdf/Finance/Report_to_bellevue_citizens.pdf, and *2006 Comparative Cities Performance Report,* 38, bellevuewa.gov/pdf/Finance/Entire_Document_for_website.pdf.

Performance management as a team effort

The usefulness of performance measurement information is directly related both to the accuracy and completeness of the data collected and to the analytical skills of those interpreting the data. The data collected and the analyses performed become the bases of judgments about the effectiveness of programs and activities—about what is working and what is not. With complete and accurate data and sound analyses, the judgments are more likely to be good ones. Thus, efforts to improve performance require strong commitment, both formal and informal, by all the organization's leaders. If the fire and emergency services chief is not involved and committed, the efforts are likely to fail because subordinates will recognize that the goal is not considered important. The same is true for the chief's boss.

The fishbone diagram

The fishbone cause-and-effect diagram (so named because when completed, it resembles the skeleton of a fish) is particularly useful for analyzing the causes of a problem or a bottleneck in a work process. The diagramming focuses attention on the underlying assumptions of an analyst's work. However, the diagram only helps identify possible causes of problems. With the fishbone, the analyst divides the possible causes (there is generally more than one, and they are often interrelated) into groups, or categories. This allows users to evaluate the true part played by each cause, which thereby broadens their understanding of the problem situation.

The figure below shows how a fishbone diagram might be used to identify the reason(s) for a vehicle getting poor gas mileage. The centerline points to the statement of the problem. Main branches lead to four categories of causes: methods, machinery, people, and materials. Specific causes are grouped under the appropriate major category. The problem-solving team's analysis of each variable will enable the team to identify the root causes of the problem and decide on priorities for those causes that should be pursued.

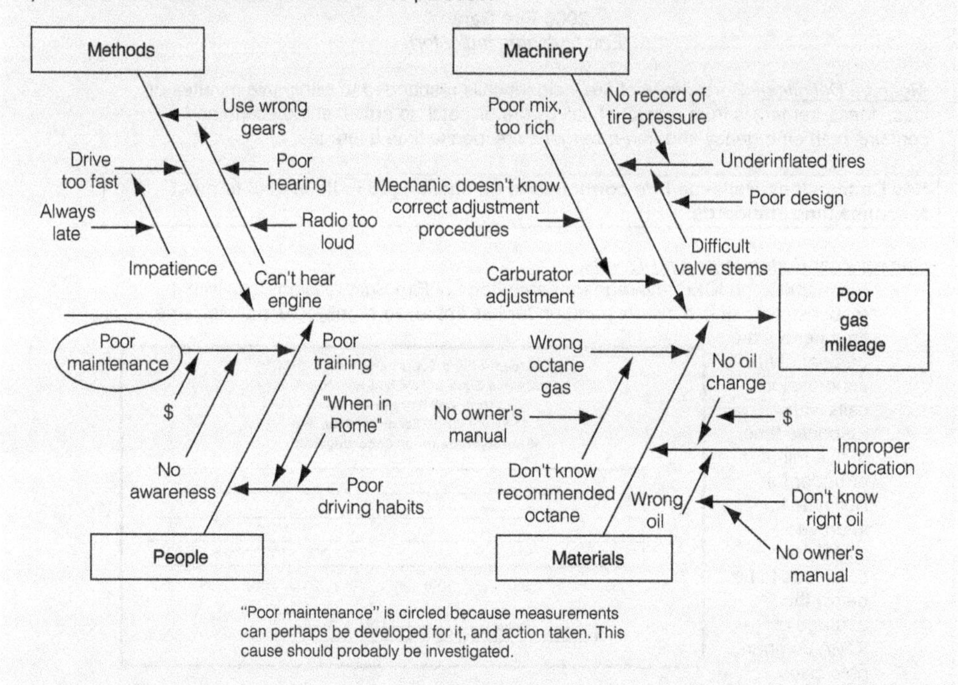

"Poor maintenance" is circled because measurements can perhaps be developed for it, and action taken. This cause should probably be investigated.

Source: David T. Endicott, "Performance Measurement and Organizational Improvement," in *Managing Fire and Rescue Services*, ed. Dennis Compton and John Granito (Washington, D.C.: ICMA, 2002), 328.

Similarly, for the data and analyses to be of high quality, the people capturing and analyzing the data must take the effort seriously and must have the requisite skills. This means that career and volunteer members of the organization should be involved in the process because they are the ones who capture and report the basic performance data. If they do not understand the reasons for the effort—or, worse, if they oppose it—the likelihood of success is reduced. And process and activity team managers should be involved because they are the ones who analyze the data and take corrective action if needed.

In short, unless everyone in the organization understands the purpose and effect of collecting the necessary information, there may be confusion and divisiveness. Without highly visible and consistent support from the top, the effort is likely to fail under the perceived weight of the additional workload.

Finally, it is important not to be caught unawares when people—and there may be some—try to use the data and analyses against the organization. Concern about criticism is not a legitimate reason for failing to collect the data and report the information. The positive gains in improving organizational performance and explaining what the community is getting for its money far outweigh any potential repercussions from high-quality collecting and reporting.

Using performance measures: Gilbert Fire Department staffing redeployment

During fiscal year 2009 (FY09), the Gilbert (Arizona) Fire Department allocated approximately $1.2 million for overtime to be used for filling fire operations positions that were vacant because of leave use (vacation, sick, military, injury, special assignments). For FY10 the overtime allocation was reduced to $229,000 because of a significant budget deficit.

Department management and labor group representatives met to determine what service-level impact would result from the loss of $1 million in overtime money and to identify potential staffing changes to compensate. The product was a plan that, in the short term, would accommodate the reduction in funding and, it was hoped, prevent significant consequences to emergency services. The plan, captured in an algorithm, included permanently redeploying an entire engine company (twelve personnel, four per shift) to a rover pool and identified subsequent companies for redeployment if necessary to meet budget and staffing requirements. Several stations had multiple response units housed in the same station, so redeploying an engine company out of the station to react to a lack of staffing in another station did not strip all response capability from the station.

Research was conducted prior to the change, and a number of measures were identified that would help fire department staff members monitor the effect of the staffing changes. Those measures included

- Biweekly overtime use reports
- Monthly review of first- and second-due response times
- Monthly review of incidents and locations
- Use of geographic information system modeling to track incident type and location and to create response time projections
- Monthly review of training hours and topics
- Monthly evaluation of leave use.

Average response times were computed and then plotted on a graph for analysis.

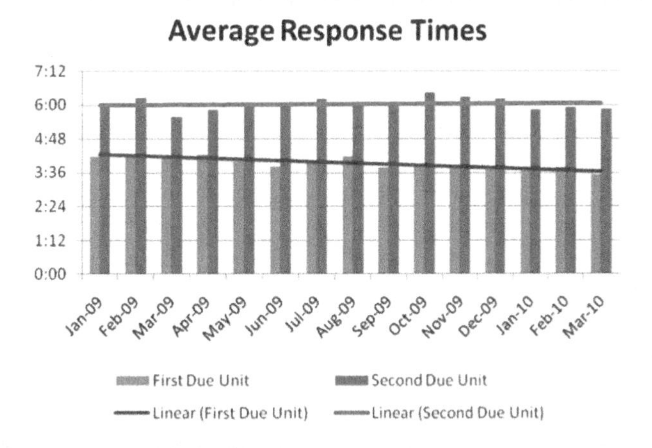

The analysis indicated that average response times for second-due units did not appear to change significantly after the initial unit was redeployed, and the first-due response times actually seemed to decrease when viewed on a summary graph.

This highlights the danger in using an average response time as a month-to-month performance measure. It is better to capture and display the response data in intervals such as shown below:

	First-due unit		Second-due unit	
Response times	**No. of incidents**	**Percentage of incidents**	**No. of incidents**	**Percentage of incidents**
< 2 minutes				
2-4 minutes				
4-6 minutes				
6-8 minutes				
>8 minutes				

This will allow for a more detailed and accurate picture of response time performance changes and for a clear depiction of how many incidents received service within our response time standards.

(continued)

Another factor analyzed was how often a unit from the first-due station was able to respond to a call. Using 2007 data as a baseline provides a way to compare the reliability as a percentage of the time the first-due station handled first-due calls:

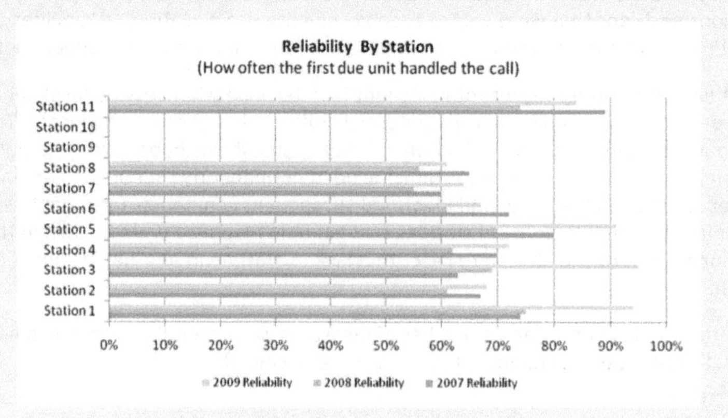

Summing up and looking ahead

Regardless of whether an organization is large or small, career or volunteer, performance measurement is a valuable tool for improving organizational performance. It is the foundation for improving and monitoring an organization's programs, activities, and processes; the foundation for benchmarking with similar organizations to identify best practices and improve operations; and the key ingredient in results-based budgeting, enabling managers to explain how improved resources or new program initiatives will result in changed outcome measures. So while using performance measurement involves a substantial amount of work, the payoff is worth it.

The measures should be tied to the goals and objectives outlined in the jurisdiction's and the department's strategic plans. All stakeholders must be involved in developing the measures, and the things that get measured should be the most important things that contribute to goal and objective achievement.

Measures should be developed at three levels—organizational (strategic), process (tactical), and job/performer (individual)—and, at each level, for each of three needs—goals, design, and management. At every level (but especially that of the work team at the process level), supervisors and managers must have access to the performance measures, and must use them to identify and correct unwanted variances in outcome by engaging the people involved in crafting changes to the process. The work team will often realize the most dramatic improvement.

In the future, as more jurisdictions learn how to use performance measurement, fire and emergency service managers—whether career, combination, or volunteer—will be held increasingly accountable for their organization's performance or lack of it. Middle-level managers will have to become comfortable with and proficient at performance measurement, which cannot remain an activity of concern only to office staff. Work unit leaders will have to learn how to use quantitative measurement and analytical methods to describe and improve the performance of their work units.

In short, successful fire and emergency service managers of the future will be as proficient in developing and interpreting run charts and other quality assurance and improvement tools as they currently are in working with prefire plans. As a result, benchmarking and process improvement work teams need to become the norm instead of the exception.

Learning how to measure performance, analyze the data obtained, and use the data and analyses to manage the improvement of operational outcomes is the challenge facing all supervisors and managers in the fire and emergency services today. There is much to be learned and much to be gained by practicing performance management.

Notes

1. Center for Public Safety Excellence, Inc., Commission on Fire Accreditation International, publicsafety excellence.org/.
2. To help fire and emergency service departments continue with the improvement process, CFAI produces documents, references, and training materials, all of which are available at public safetyexcellence.org/Accreditation/tabid/54/Default.aspx.
3. Harry P. Hatry et al., eds., *Service Efforts and Accomplishments Reporting: Its Time Has Come; An Overview* (Norwalk, Conn.: Governmental Accounting Standards Board, 1990).
4. Geary A. Rummler and Alan P. Brache, *Improving Performance: How to Manage the White Space on the Organization Chart* (San Francisco: Jossey-Bass, 1990).
5. Arthur M. Schneiderman, "Analog Devices: 1986–1992 The First Balanced Scorecard©," schneiderman.com/ (accessed November 15, 2010).
6. Robert S. Kaplan and David P. Norton, "The Balanced Scorecard—Measures That Drive Performance," *Harvard Business Review* (January–February 1992).
7. Jack Maple, *The Crime Fighter: Putting the Bad Guys Out of Business* (New York: Doubleday, 1999).
8. George D. Robson, *Continuous Process Improvement: Simplifying Workflow Systems* (New York: The Free Press, 1991).
9. Ibid., 110.
10. National Highway Traffic Safety Administration, *A Leadership Guide to Quality Improvement for Emergency Medical Services (EMS) Systems* (Washington, D.C.: U.S. Department of Transportation, July 1997), nhtsa.gov/people/injury/ems/leaderguide/.

CHAPTER 15

Information Systems

Wm. D. Morrison

This chapter provides an understanding of

- The basic components and functions of an information system
- The role of the National Fire Incident Reporting System in information management for the fire and emergency services
- Data elements to be considered for collection and analysis
- Ways in which data can be used to improve performance and efficiency in the fire and emergency services
- Guidelines for data retention
- The importance of ensuring data quality and techniques when using data for decision making
- Hardware and software acquisition issues.

Fire and emergency service managers must have good information to do the best possible job of reducing fires and related losses and providing the best emergency response service with the resources available. They also need good information to explain and defend their decisions to local government managers, budget directors, the media, and citizens. Like other agencies and public interest groups, the fire and emergency services must be prepared to make the case for its priorities.

Because the range of problems facing fire and emergency service departments today is formidable and the range of activities they engage in is broad, the amount of information that managers have to assimilate is huge. Even the smallest department can have any of ten thousand chemicals spilled at its door, can fall victim to arson, must deal with a variety of medical emergencies, and must account for hundreds of different tools, equipment, and supplies. No one can remember it all, and in fact no one has to try.

This chapter outlines the basic principles of how to design and maintain a management information system (MIS)—a system for storing and processing data (the raw material for the information managers need). Written for the fire and emergency services manager who may have limited familiarity with computers, this chapter explains what a management information system, data system, and the National Fire Incident Reporting System are. It lists the data elements of some common fire service database systems; lays out some of the uses of data; discusses the importance of ensuring data quality, analyzing data, and presenting information effectively; and ends by looking at management issues involved in designing and purchasing an MIS.

The discussion applies to fire and emergency service departments of all sizes and types. Even though the size of the MIS and its degree of computerization may vary, as may the sophistication of the data analysis, the basic principles and considerations are similar for all departments.

Data and management information systems: What are they?

Merriam-Webster's Collegiate Dictionary defines *data* as "factual information . . . used as a basis for reasoning, discussion, or calculation." Basic facts collected about fire and emergency service activities—for example, incident number, incident date, and incident time—are called data *elements*. Data are generally considered to be unprocessed information, often measurements or counts. When data are processed, ordered, analyzed, or evaluated using statistical or other methods, they can be considered information. The key distinction is that *information* is useful for making decisions while *data* may not be useful.

As the raw material for the information needed by managers, data elements have to be stored and processed. Systems that do this, usually using computers, are called management information systems (Figure 15-1). Sometimes the term *management information system* refers to simple computerized systems that store data in separate files from which the desired information can be retrieved. More commonly the term refers to systems of greater complexity

Figure 15-1 An information system manages and analyzes data from throughout the department.

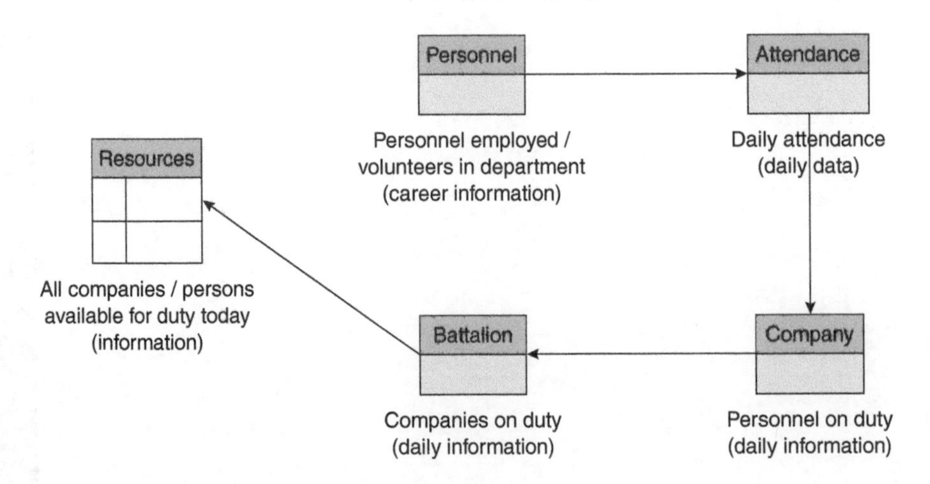

This chapter is a revised and updated version of Chapter 14, "Information Management," by Wm. D. Morrison, in the 2002 edition of this volume.

that allow data from several files to be manipulated and intermixed or relationally connected (i.e., organized by a common relationship, such as address, census tract, or any other administrative or geographic area).

When data elements having to do with a single occurrence or incident are collected and brought together, the analyst or interpreter can form a picture of the situation and of the steps taken to mitigate it. When data elements about all incidents of a particular type are collected into a common grouping, or *database*, analysts can form an even clearer picture of incidents that have similar characteristics. In Figure 15–2, the table INCIDENTKEY defines the primary data elements required for any incident. The table IN_BASIC defines the next most important layer of data for each incident. The data elements FDID, FDIDSTATE, IN_DATE, and IN_NUM create a unique identifier for each incident in this database and connect to the other tables by the value of INCIDENTID.

A fire and emergency services department can construct databases to collect data elements in the following general categories, among others: fire dispatch, fire incidents, hazardous material (HAZMAT) incidents, urban search and rescue, fire prevention and inspections, tactical inspections, fire hydrant maintenance, emergency medical service (EMS) patients, geographic information, 911, personnel, and vehicle location. In addition, databases may be organized, indexed, and interconnected for further analysis.

```
DATABASE – NFIRS – contains multiple records

    TABLE – INCIDENTKEY – record containing data
        INCIDENTID *
        IN_RELEASE
        IN_STATUS
        FDID
        FDIDSTATE
        IN_DATE
        IN_NUM
        IN_EXPOSURE
        IN_STATION
        IN_NFIRSVERSION
        IN_VENDORID
        IN_SO FTWAREID
        IN_LASTUPDATED
        IN_LASTUPDATEDBY
        IN_CREATED
        IN_CREATEDBY
        IN_NFIRSLOADVERSION
        IN_LASTEXPORTED

    TABLE – IN_BASIC – record containing data
        INCIDENTID *
        IN_TYPE
        IN_ADDRONWILDLAND
        IN_MUTUALAIDFLAG
        IN_ALARMDATE
        IN_ARRIVALDATE
        IN_CONTROLLEDDATE
        IN_LASTUNITCLEAREDDATE
        IN_SHIFT
        IN_ALARMS
        IN_DISTRICT
        IN_RESOURCEFORMUSED
        IN_APPARSUPP
        IN_APPAREMS
        IN_APPAROTHER
        IN_PERSSUPP
        IN_PERSEMS
        IN_PERSOTHER
        IN_INCMUTAID
        IN_LOSSPROPERTY
        IN_LOSSOTHER
        IN_LOSSTOTAL
        IN_VALUEPROPERTY
        IN_VALUEOTHER
        IN_FATALFS
        IN_FATALOTHER
        IN_NONFATALFS
        IN_NONFATALOTHER
        IN_DETECTOR
        IN_HAZMATRELEASED
        IN_MIXEDUSE
        IN_PROPERTYUSE
        IN_FIRECAUSE
        IN_FATALEMS
        IN_NonFatalEMS

    * common connection key
```

Figure 15-2 A database (shown here: that of the National Fire Incident Reporting System, or NFIRS) contains records (shown here: INCIDENTKEY and IN_BASIC), and each record contains data elements. In this example, the value "INCIDENTID," the name given to the incident number within the database, connects the contents of the two records.

A more advanced MIS may use computer models to help with decision making and may incorporate the logic and information of experts in the form of "expert systems" that imitate highly experienced advisers. Often a department's MIS is a collection of many programs that set up and maintain files, provide specialized analysis, and govern output report formats. This kind of MIS may consist of more than a hundred separate programs or several large programs that work together under an executive computer program. The system may be designed to be user friendly so that people with little training can interact with it directly, or it may be designed so that only programmers/analysts or specialists trained in the use of the system can use it, or it may be designed so that both types of users may use it but often for different purposes.

In short, the fire chief has choices as to the type and capabilities of the department's MIS. The system can be manual or computerized and, if computerized, can be at any level of complexity and cost. The chief can store information in a simple set of paper ("hard copy") files or can use computers to store and retrieve data for analysis. The chief who is so inclined can even use expert systems to support management decisions.

The National Fire Incident Reporting System

The need for the fire service to collect data was realized and identified in 1973 with the publication of *America Burning* (see also Chapter 1), which recommended "that a national fire data system be established to provide a continuing review and analysis of the entire fire problem."[1] This and other recommendations in *America Burning* led to the creation of the U.S. Fire Administration (USFA), the agency that evaluates the nation's fire problem. One of the duties of the USFA is to provide for a nationwide exchange of standardized information pertaining to fire and life safety; another is to have the capability of collecting, storing, retrieving, and disseminating data and analytic reports.

The National Fire Incident Reporting System (NFIRS) was developed beginning in the mid-1970s, and the first NFIRS Users Conference was held in 1975. In 1999, USFA implemented NFIRS version 5.0, which is still the national standard for fire incident reporting. Version 5.0 was the culmination of a long review process that began in 1988. Input was received from more than two hundred fire departments, the National Fire Protection Association, the Consumer Product Safety Commission, the International Association of Fire Chiefs, the International Association of Fire Fighters, the National Association of State Fire Marshals, the National Highway Traffic Safety Administration (NHTSA), and the National Volunteer Fire Council.

Periodically the USFA will release changes being made to the NFIRS system. The latest release is version 5.7. The USFA website (nfirs.fema.gov/documentation/) should always have the latest documentation.

NFIRS allows for the collection and comparison of information gathered by reporting fire departments at several levels (national, state, and local) and in many jurisdictions. With NFIRS version 5.0 used as the standard, records will contain the data elements listed in the accompanying sidebar. The current NFIRS includes a simplified coding structure, a modular construction, and an "all-incident" reporting system that includes EMS, HAZMAT response, and technical rescue reporting capabilities. Because of the system's modular design, additional modules can be added to meet the changing needs of the fire service.

State agencies collect NFIRS fire incident data via the Internet and forward the data to the USFA's national database. Java (a programming language designed for use with Internet browsers) was selected for NFIRS because it is platform independent: it will run under several operating systems (Microsoft Windows 2000/XP/Vista/Windows 7, Mac Operating System, LINUX, and UNIX).

Data elements for use with NFIRS version 5.0

Basic incidents

Incident number
Incident date and time
Location of the emergency
Type of incident
Action taken (up to three)
Aid given or received (mutual aid or automatic aid [see Chapter 16])
Times for the following: alarm, on location, control, last unit cleared
Shift working and number of alarms
Resources used (apparatus and personnel for these categories: suppression, EMS, other)
Casualties (fire and civilian)
Property use
Property owner
Person or entity involved in the incident (owner, occupant, etc.)

Fires

Property details
On-site materials or products
Ignition details, including cause
Factors contributing to ignition
Human factors contributing to ignition
Equipment involved
Fire suppression factors
Mobile property

Structure fires

Building data (structure type, status, height, ground-floor area)
Fire origin (location, spread, damage, factors contributing to flame spread)
Detector data (presence, type, power supply, effectiveness)
Automatic extinguishment equipment (presence, type, operation, effectiveness, reason for failure)

Civilian casualties

Casualty personal data
Cause of injury
Human factors contributing to injury
Nonhuman factors contributing to injury
Activity when injured
Location at time of injury
Primary symptom and area of body injured

Firefighter casualties

Firefighter personal data
Primary symptom, cause, object involved, area of body injured, factor contributing
Location where injury occurred
If protective equipment contributed to injury, equipment involved and type of failure

The increased use of personal computers throughout the fire service has given new meaning to data interoperability and encourages the quick transfer of data files. With continued government support, this use is expected to increase so that the backbone infrastructure between the major common carriers can be expanded to handle rising demand.

Data elements of selected fire service database systems

This section lists the data elements for the following databases: computer-aided dispatch (CAD); EMS patients; fire inspection, site orientation, and related tactical information; fire hydrants; and personnel records.

Computer-aided dispatch

An especially critical system within the fire and emergency services department is CAD (see Chapter 16). This system should interrogate other systems that may provide useful information to emergency operations personnel from global positioning/automated vehicle location systems, special location files, fire hydrant maintenance systems, tactical information systems, and geographic information systems. By gathering information from these databases, the CAD system can dispatch the closest available unit and provide field personnel with vital information. Any CAD system must also be able to pass data elements to the incident reporting system, thereby eliminating the need to reenter data—an activity with the potential for introducing errors. In a combined CAD system, police and fire dispatch data will be intermingled. This is not a major issue because fire data can be reported separately; more important is the fact that some types of incident require both fire and police response.

At a minimum, the CAD system should record the following data elements for purposes of dispatch:

- Incident number
- Date and time the call was received by CAD
- Date and time the incident was dispatched by CAD

EMS

Time arrived at patient
Symptom or provider assessment
Personal data (age, race, sex, ethnicity)
Body site of injury
Type of injury
Procedures used (aid provided)
Equipment involved
Cardiac arrest data
Level of provider care
Patient status and disposition

HAZMAT

Chemical identification
Container data (type, capacity, release state)
Released-area data (population density, area affected, area evacuated, persons and buildings evacuated)
Cause data (cause, factors contributing, factors affecting mitigation)
Equipment involved
Mobile property involved
Disposition

Wildland fires

Location specifications
Fire cause, human factors, suppression factors, heat source, mobile property, equipment involved
Weather data
Property data (buildings ignited, buildings threatened, acres burned, crops burned)
Property management
Fuel model data
Person involved
Fire behavior data

Apparatus or personnel

Apparatus identification
Apparatus type
Date and time of dispatch, arrival, clear
Action taken by unit
Personnel identification number
Action taken by each person

Departmental demographics

Fire department name, address, phone number, fax number, e-mail address, and Federal Information Processing Standard code
Number of stations
Number of career firefighters, volunteer firefighters, firefighters paid per call
Number of civilian employees or administrative volunteers, Civilian Emergency Response Team members

- Location of emergency: address, street name, street type (e.g., dead end, divided road), cross street
- Type of incident (i.e., fire or medical emergency)
- Medical self-help provided to caller by dispatch
- Phone number of the party making the emergency call
- 911 data supplied by the local phone company (Automatic Number Identification/Automatic Location Identification.)
- Any comments that were supplied by the caller (e.g., description of the situation, location within a building, name of building)
- Assignments (e.g., units assigned, date and time assigned)
- Times for the following occurrences: assignment, en route, on location, clear
- Identity of the first-arriving unit or company, date, and time
- Identity of the first-arriving engine company, date, and time
- Identity of the first-arriving chief, date, and time
- If vehicle location data (supplied by mobile data computer units mounted in the vehicles) are used for dispatching the closest unit, unit location at date and time of dispatch.

Emergency medical service patients

For many fire departments, information on EMS patients can be as important as incident data. The National EMS Information System (NEMSIS) has developed standards for the collection of EMS patient data built around a revision of the NHTSA Uniform Prehospital Dataset.[2] Each state and/or jurisdiction's medical director is responsible for each jurisdiction's control of these data requirements. The EMS data listed in the sidebar on pages 430–431 is a minimal set of data. For departments that charge patients for services rendered, that listing contains the data necessary for billing, whether by the incident or by a cost itemization. A more detailed list of EMS data elements is as follows:

- Incident number
- Date and time the call was received
- Date and time the incident was dispatched
- Date and time of arrival at the address and at the patient
- Location where service was rendered
- Type of medical emergency
- Medical self-help provided to caller by dispatch
- Patient's medical history
- Medication history
- Primary symptom
- Aid provided
- Drugs provided
- Pulse, blood pressure, and respiratory rate, and date and time of each
- Cardiac data
- Obstetric data
- Fee assessment (where the charging of fees is permitted), including the accounting data necessary to comply with auditors' requirements.

Fire inspection, site orientation, and related tactical information

A tactical information system should contain planning data helpful to the emergency operations personnel while they are en route to the scene of an emergency. It should store structure or occupant information that may or may not be obvious to the first-arriving company officer, and it should contain information about the storage of hazardous materials, the location and description of other types of potential dangers, the location and description of fire alarm and fire extinguishment systems and specific reset/testing instructions, the presence and location of any people who are physically impaired, and so forth.

In departments whose CAD systems interface with mobile data computers (MDCs) installed in the emergency vehicles, field personnel can receive vital tactical information while en route. In departments that do not have MDCs, this information can be printed ahead of time and stored in a loose-leaf notebook. (In this instance, terminals may be either intelligent workstations/computers or dumb workstations able to perform only specific tasks. *Mobile* implies that the device is communicating in real time with a central host computer. Most MDCs communicate with the host computer via radio transmissions, over a private radio network or a broadband cellular network.)

Some departments have facsimile (fax) receivers in stations, to which brief site-specific data are sent for "tear and go" response help (i.e., tear it off the printer and go get on the engine, truck, or other vehicle). With the higher-capacity hard drives available for MDCs today, it may be possible to store a local copy of the preincident, hazardous locations information so that the only additional planning necessary is to schedule periodic updates of this information.

The following is a list of possible tactical information data elements:

- Structure address
- Building name, alternative names
- Building owner(s)/representative: name, mailing address, and phone number (cell or land line)
- Building owner's emergency contact: name and phone number
- Building characteristics (e.g., height in stories, ground-floor area, construction type [truss construction, etc.], date of construction, date of last remodel)
- Business name, phone number, and hours
- Business emergency contact: name and phone number (and alternative name and phone number)
- Type of business
- Location of the closest fire hydrants in all four directions
- Location of standpipe connections
- Drawings (e.g., floor plans, when appropriate; HAZMAT locations; locations of incapacitated or homebound individuals)
- Plans/methods to gain entry while minimizing damage
- Security codes, etc.
- For structures with multiple occupancies: similar information about the different occupants
- Hazardous materials: identity, description, location, and guideline number
- Tactically significant problems: identity, description, and location
- Incapacitated or homebound individuals living in structure or visiting: special needs or assistance (identity, description, location)
- Underground storage tanks: location, tank capacity, date installed, date of last inspection
- Permits required for special equipment, materials storage, etc.
- Inspection history: date of last inspection, violations found in last inspection, date of next-to-last inspection, violations found in next-to-last inspection, next scheduled inspection date
- HAZMAT response data
- Court cases pending
- Fee assessment (where the charging of fees is permitted), including the accounting data necessary to comply with auditors' requirements
- Complaint history: date, type, and resolution
- Fire protection features: standpipe types and locations, sprinklers, detectors
- Alarm system description and history.

Courtesy of the Alexandria (Virginia) Fire Department

Figure 15-3 Information on locations of and flows available from fire hydrants is useful to emergency response.

Fire hydrants

A fire hydrant system is used to collect data about the condition and status of each hydrant (Figure 15-3). This information can and should be shared with fire suppression/emergency operations personnel. For departments with CAD systems that interface with MDCs installed in the emergency vehicles, responding crews can receive real-time hydrant status information while en route.

A hydrant system should contain all the following data elements, even though not all the information would be provided to responding units:

- Location of hydrant (hydrant A): street address
- Next-closest hydrant: direction, distance from hydrant A
- Make and model of hydrant A
- Outlet type
- Color code identifier: water main size, pressure, flow
- Date of last test
- Current repair status, date of last status change.

Personnel records

All departments keep some data about their current and past personnel. This should include training information, certifications, skill sets, and capabilities. In particular, exposure records are an important means of tracking a person's history of exposure to hazardous or toxic materials and to potentially contaminated body fluids. The most important aspect of personnel data is security: privacy should not be violated.

A typical personnel record system can include the following:

- Individual employee data: training history (physical fitness levels, firefighter certification levels, EMS certification levels, training scheduling), medical history, exposure history (fire, hazardous materials, emergency medical), personal data, education history (including major areas); disciplinary or other infractions should also be noted
- Personnel rosters: current assignment, previous assignments, language or other special skills
- Work or "on-duty" scheduling: workdays, shift planning, vacation planning, staffing levels
- Work history.

Uses of data, including identification of a department's fire problem

Once all the databases discussed above (and any others that a department may be using) have been created, organized, and populated, they can be used as summarized in the sidebar on the facing page, which presents a bird's-eye view of data uses. And if those databases are then grouped and organized by a common relationship (e.g., address or census tract), they are capable of generating information that is useful for

- Dispatching the proper type and amount of equipment to the correct location
- Analyzing the relationship between incidents that occurred and resources (e.g., engines, trucks, and personnel) dispatched
- Developing annual budgets
- Analyzing and modeling the placement of facilities or individual resources in relation to time of day, day of week, traffic patterns, etc.
- Summarizing and analyzing annual activity.

Information generated by databases that are organized by common relationships may also be useful in connection with

- Changes to the building codes
- Changes to the fire protection codes

- Departmental operation standards
- Departmental personnel safety standards
- Departmental training standards
- Apparatus and equipment maintenance policies
- Equipment standards and geographical analysis for long-range planning and forecasting
- Common measurements of productivity, 911 call analysis (which provides a view of the department's workload)
- Specialized studies
- Legal responses
- Public relations.

In planning annual budgets, for example, fire and emergency service managers can use summaries of relevant data to justify expected expenses and to prevent unwarranted cuts in personnel and purchases of equipment. Or managers can use summarized incident data for identifying the seriousness of the fire problem and the range of demands on the local fire and emergency services department. More particularly, every department can identify its fire problem by analyzing the "what," "where," "who," "when," and "why" questions about its fires, casualties, and losses.

Strangely, however, this rich array of incident data elements—which is at the heart of many aspects of prevention, suppression, and other public service programs—is largely underused. To be sure, by the time most officers rise to the position of chief, they are familiar with and have learned to make use of a wide range of management data (albeit not necessarily within the context of a formal MIS): personnel information, training schedules, shift scheduling, inspection scheduling, hydrant maintenance scheduling, and other day-to-day operational issues. And it would seem natural to assume that the category of fire incident data would be among them. Yet experience shows that it is not. Although officers generate incident data for most of their careers, this class of management information reports, which provides a usable picture of local hazards and risks, remains underused. Departments must begin tapping this wealth of information to assist in all aspects of its operations: budgeting, personnel needs, fire station planning, inspection planning, hydrant maintenance, and the like.

Bird's-eye view of uses of data

Fire incident data can be used to summarize activity by incident type and to calculate response times, time out of service, dollar loss, and so forth.

Company resource data can be used to calculate staffing statistics, total time on scene, action performed by company, and so forth.

Fire service injury data can be used to study injuries and develop safety standards, equipment standards, and training.

Fire hydrant data can be used to verify the serviceability of fire hydrants and to track maintenance problems by hydrant type.

Vehicle maintenance records can be used to identify problems early so that preventive maintenance can reduce the cost of some repairs.

Tactical information can be used to identify structures and occupancies that present a tactical problem or a hazard for fire service personnel, who can retrieve this information while en route to an incident.

911 data can be used to summarize calls and identify the times when call volumes are highest.

EMS patient data can be used to analyze patient care protocols (for fire departments that provide local ambulance service).

Vehicle location data provided by global positioning satellites can be used to analyze and predict the travel times to each incident dispatched.

For a department that wishes to better understand its fire problem by analyzing its fire incidents, some of the necessary questions and the data elements needed to answer them are presented here.

- *What type of property burned?* Specify structures (by type of construction, number of stories, etc.), vehicles (cars, trucks, trains, planes, etc.), outdoor materials (forest, grass, brush, etc.), other.
- *What type of occupancy?* Specify residential, stores and offices, institutions, schools, places of public assembly, industrial facilities, storage, vacant, under construction, other.
- *Where did the fire occur?* Specify census tract or area, and whether a central business district or residential or commercial neighborhood.
- *Who suffered losses?* Specify owners and occupants (e.g., residents, shoppers, people sleeping, etc.), with dollar loss, civilian casualties, firefighter casualties.
- *When did the fire occur?* Specify time of day, day of week, month, year.
- *Why did the fire, casualty, or loss occur?* Specify cause, contributing factors, human factors, automatic detection equipment, automatic extinguishment system.
- *What environmental factors affected the fire?* Specify temperature, humidity, etc.
- *Why did the fire spread?* Specify contributing materials and factors (open doors, clutter, flammable interior furnishings, etc.).

Other information is also needed:

- Suppression factors: long response time, special problems
- Casualty circumstances: activity at time of injury, condition before injury
- Extent of the loss: direct property loss, extent of damage, number of buildings
- Indirect losses: person-days lost from work, person-days displaced from home or business
- Use of resources: incident type (i.e., fire, nonfire), property use at time of incident (in case of an unreported change of occupancy—e.g., the local garage owner may have rented the empty tailor shop to store his tires and batteries without reporting the new use).

Finally, proper use of good statistics can help managers identify potential problems, develop public education programs, and build a positive image of the fire department (see the accompanying two sidebars).

Use of data by a small fire department

In a relatively small fire department, collecting data and predicting trends can be difficult because of the smaller numbers of incidents. This should not discourage departments from collecting and using their data when making decisions about their operations and planning for the future. Even with a small number of incidents, records should be collected and incident reports compiled.

Such "hard" information can be critical in establishing need and justifying resources for fire and emergency services. Monitoring of information on attendance, response times, and numbers and types of incidents can help identify the need to plan for sharing or even consolidating services or for entering into an automatic aid agreement (see Chapter 16).

For example, village officials in Ossining, New York, were concerned about a possible decline in participation in their all-volunteer fire department. Working with local data on incidents, attendance, and response times, the department was able to document that attendance to calls was timely and consistently met local standards. It was also able to confirm that new members were continuing to join the department.

Combining data from several adjacent small departments might also reveal trends more readily than looking at only a small data sample. For example, small increases in malicious false alarms or fire alarm malfunctions might indicate a growing problem, calling for a renewed emphasis on public education. Cooperation is especially valuable because most local media outlets and many school districts encompass communities that are served by separate small fire departments. By working together, small departments can gain attention for their needs more effectively.

Data and cooperation between the fire and planning departments

A growing city in the upper Midwest collects a good bit of data through its computer-aided dispatch system as well as through its long-term and committed use of the National Fire Incident Reporting System. Working with a very progressive planning department, the fire department identified some potential uses for its data that were not necessarily traditional.

The community was in a constant process of reviewing and modifying its subdivision ordinance. In this process, the fire and planning departments identified some questions that could be addressed using comparisons of the fire department's data with demographic information from other sources. Among the questions were these:

- Are there definable relationships between subdivision covenants and fire loss or emergency medical impact?
- Are there definable relationships between the size of homes and the demand for advanced life support (ALS) services?
- Do retention/detention ponds for surface-water drainage affect the frequency or severity of calls for fire services?

The answer to all these questions was yes. For instance, when the subdivision covenants permitted in-ground swimming pools, calls for emergency medical services increased. When houses were required to have a large percentage of brick on their exteriors, the percentage of property loss went down. When covenants prohibited combustible roofs, fire loss (predictably) decreased.

The trend in the demand for ALS services was subtle and might be difficult to substantiate. The hypothesis, however, was that homes with higher value tended to be occupied by slightly older citizens. Accordingly, the likelihood of heart attacks and strokes in neighborhoods with more expensive homes seemed to be higher, whereas the overall incidence of emergency medical service calls was lower.

Finally, this community had a serious soil percolation problem that required subdividers to provide substantial ponds to hold surface-water runoff from developed land. The data indicated (although the statistical basis was not huge) a trend in drownings or near-drownings that required special and substantial resources from the fire department.

Although this type of information may not directly affect the placement of emergency service resources in a community, it does help to predict trends in service demand as planners look at the short- and long-term development of a community. Fire and emergency medical services are part of the system that responds to demands created as a result of the socioeconomic makeup of a community. Both demographic and response data play an important part in predicting what services will be needed as a community grows or changes.

Records retention

Record retention policies are typically determined by the needs of the fire chief and/or the city or county manager of the jurisdiction, in conjunction with legal counsel. These policies cover a wide variety of data. For example, they might include the following stipulations:

- 911 telephone voice recordings and TDD (telecommunications device of the deaf) messages should be kept for some period of time.
- Dispatch data should be kept for some extended period of time so that they can be used for planning and analysis.
- Incident data (NFIRS) should be kept for some extended period of time so that they can be used for spatial analysis, reporting, and planning.

As hard drives have become larger and cheaper, exceeding 1 terabyte, all the data described in this chapter can be stored on a hard drive or drives and easily retrieved for future use. (See sidebar on page 438 for definitions of technical computer terms and abbreviations.)

All database systems have the capability to create a backup copy of the files that can be stored on a compact disc/digital video disc (CD/DVD) or on a tape or flash drive. DVD technology will provide larger capacities for data backup, raising the current 700-MB (CD) standard to a 4-GB or greater standard. Future technology will provide an even greater capacity to store data, sound, and video. Given the current cost of hard drives, it is now possible to maintain historical records for twenty years or longer. Aging data not used in the agency should be archived or donated to a library rather than destroyed.

Backups should be done daily to minimize the loss of data; the last one of the week should be considered the weekly backup and the last one of the month should be considered the monthly backup. The weekly and monthly backups should be stored at a site away from the location of the servers (see sidebar below).

Data quality, analysis, and presentation

If the data captured in an information system are not accurate, complete, and unambiguous, the information produced and the conclusions drawn will be neither accurate nor meaningful. In themselves, data are not meaningful; rather, they must be analyzed, and the analyses

Basics of an information system

Components of an information system

- **Data:** Data elements are like the columns of a spreadsheet and each row represents a complete record.
- **Hardware and software:** Hardware can be servers, desktops, or mobile (laptop) computers. Software includes operating systems (e.g., Windows Server 2008), business application software (e.g., Microsoft Office), and web browsers (e.g., Internet Explorer, Firefox).
- **Procedures and policies:** Procedures specify a series of actions or operations that have to be executed in the same manner in order to always obtain the same result under the same circumstances; policies lay out broad guidelines for acceptable action. Together they describe a deliberate plan of action to guide decisions and achieve rational outcomes.
- **Purpose or goal:** Managers must understand the intent behind or the intended result of an action. If the goal of the system is to provide better medical first-responder support for the community, the system design should allow for the evaluation of data to test the outcome of changes.

Common computer terms and definitions

- **Bluetooth:** Wireless technology, a short-range communications technology intended to replace the cables connecting portable and/or fixed devices while maintaining high levels of security.
- **Broadband:** Data transmission speeds exceeding 768 kilobits per second (Kbps), or 768,000 bits per second (bps), as per the U.S. Federal Communications Commission in 2009.
- **DVD:** Digital versatile disc or digital video disc, an optical disc storage media format.
- **GB:** Gigabyte or 1,024 megabytes, descriptive of computer memory, hard drive capacity, DVD capacity, or data file size.
- **LCD:** Liquid-crystal display, a method of displaying readings continuously.
- **MB:** Megabyte or 1,024 kilobytes, descriptive of computer memory, hard drive capacity, DVD capacity, or data file size.
- **NIC:** Network interface card, computer hardware component designed to allow computers to communicate over a computer network.
- **Operating system:** A set of software programs found on most any device that can run more than one computer program. Operating systems control how the machine functions and regulate other software that can run on the computer. Application software must be written for compatibility with a specific operating system.
- **RAM:** Random-access memory, a form of computer data storage.
- **Server:** A computer in a network that provides services to other computers in the network.
- **TB:** Terabyte, a form of digital information storage equal to 1,000 GB.
- **USB:** Universal Serial Bus, a specification to establish communication between devices and a host controller.
- **WiFi, 802.11 standard:** A communications standard for wireless networking; the original standard was followed by variations noted by different letter designations (ex. 802.11g).

of various databases can help managers make various important decisions. In addition, how information that results from this analysis is presented plays a major role in how effectively it communicates.

Ensuring the quality of the data

A database is subject to the principle enunciated by the old adage, "Garbage in, garbage out." *Garbage* refers to inaccurate or unhelpful data, and eliminating it is what is meant by *ensuring the quality of the data.* Garbage can be introduced in three ways: firefighters input inaccurate or incomplete data, they use the wrong category (often because the system is not flexible enough to allow for different situations), or the data collection system is too complex to allow users to make sense of the data collected. Ensuring that data are of high quality means ensuring that a true and accurate representation of the situation is recorded. The database should be free of both contextual errors (e.g., the wrong type of occupancy) and relational errors (a reported lack of advanced life support transport capability when, in fact, only basic life support transport was necessary.)

The only way to verify data quality is to look with a critical eye at the reports generated from the database. The manager can create cross-tabulation reports against the database and look for anomalies inconsistent with previous values in the reported cells. When an anomaly is found, a little research into the data entry process will help determine whether the anomaly is a deliberate attempt to bypass the coding system (by either omission or commission) or the first appearance of a new situation. Another way to find anomalies is to search for data extremes, or outliers (values that are outside the normal range, either high or low)—for example, a dollar loss greater than $999,999 or a response time of 60 minutes. For most departments, a million-dollar fire is pretty rare; so, too, is a response time greater than 10 minutes.

Analyzing the data

A fire and emergency services department collects a tremendous amount of data. Reports generated from the databases can provide insight into the department's daily, weekly, monthly, and annual activities. The numbers and types of incidents (see Figures 15-4 and 15-5) and the average response times will be reported, but the fire chief must make sure that they are always reported by day of the week, hour of the day, or month of the year. The bar graph in Figure 15-4, which was developed using data from the CAD and NFIRS data systems, shows data elements combined to reveal patterns of occurrence. The number of incidents reported by each system is displayed by hour of day; the two bars show reported structure fires as dispatched versus actual fires, determined by incident reports from personnel on scene. (For more information on CAD and records systems, see Chapter 16.)

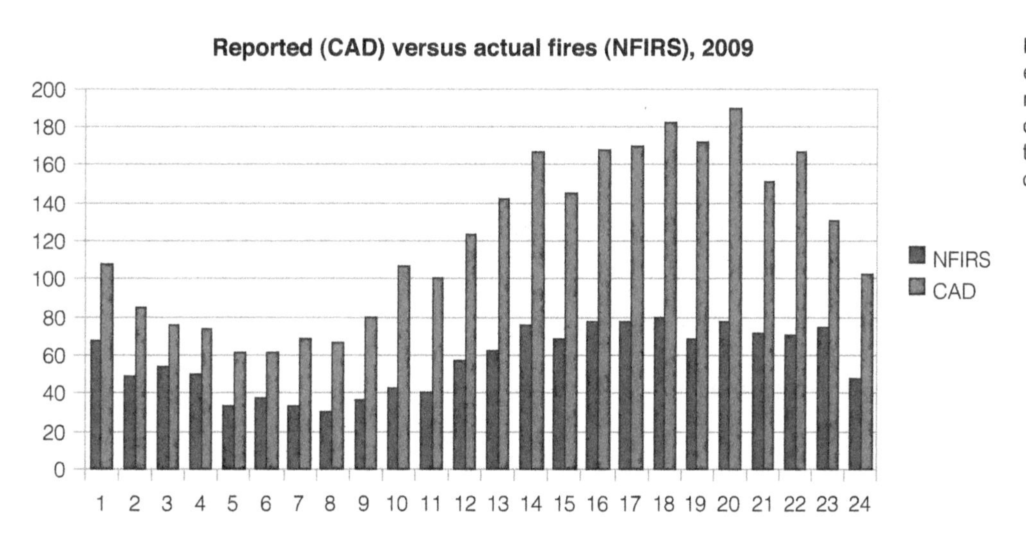

Figure 15-4 Data elements (time of day, nature of incident) can be combined in bar graphs to reveal patterns of occurrence.

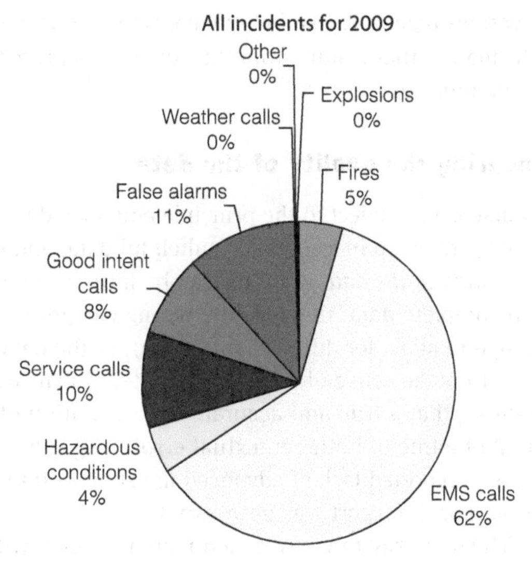

Figure 15-5 This pie chart, which presents incidents by type, illustrates a basic step in the analysis of incident data. Small percentages of incidents for weather, explosions, and other appear as zeros because values have been rounded for this display.

There are at least four good reasons for fire and emergency service managers to look more closely at their data: (1) to gain insights into the pressures that various types of incidents place on the department, (2) to improve the allocation of resources to correspond to the demands of the jurisdiction, (3) to identify training necessary for meeting these demands, and (4) to identify potential problems with equipment or vehicles before the problems become real issues.

For example, a statistical analysis of EMS calls can enable the chief to improve the allocation of resources (the second reason for looking more closely at the data): the analysis can show both the effect of adding an additional ambulance unit in the field and the best place to berth it. The addition of just one unit, if that unit is placed correctly, might reduce the average response time from 5 minutes to 3.5 minutes, for example. This reduction would mean better medical coverage across the jurisdiction.

The same type of analysis can help determine the correct locations for fire stations. Growth or changes in a jurisdiction's building patterns may affect the department's response times in a specific geographic area. Accordingly, a decision might be made to either add a new fire station or replace an inadequate one.

An analysis of current incident data may indicate that the training curriculum should be expanded to include first-responder medical training, vehicle extrication, basic HAZMAT training, or other skills not previously identified.

To do these analyses, one does not have to be a professional statistician; however, a basic understanding of statistical processes can be very useful, improving the quality and acceptability of one's information. Many instructional books are available in the marketplace, including the *Fire Data Analysis Handbook,* produced by the USFA.[3] A basic guide to statistical analysis, it was written specifically for fire service personnel and uses fire service examples throughout. And among the several statistical software programs available, two of the more popular are SAS (originally, Statistical Analysis System) and Predictive Analytics Software (PASW).

Initial questions as to why certain numbers are large or small will suggest still other questions, and those questions and their answers will form the basis for planning and evaluating the fire and emergency services protection for the community. (See Chapter 14 for information on analyzing data to identify trends or relationships among various data elements and to measure current performance against past performance.)

Presenting the information

Data analysis results in information that can be presented in many formats: textual recommendations, histograms (see Chapter 14), charts (bar, column, line, pie, dot), maps, or any combination of these. A decision on how to break out the data most meaningfully must be based on the staff's analytical skills and an understanding of the community. When information is assembled, it can become an annual report describing the department's activity and accomplishments. This document can be made up of both monthly reports (which graphically display the occurrence of incendiary fires, car fires, or structure fires, for example) and special reports (which could help with the search for patterns). If locations of the incidents being reported are shown on a map of the local jurisdiction, over time the annual reports may indicate a pattern of fires. When assembling data into a report format, one should remember that a picture (histogram, chart, or map) can be worth a thousand words (see sidebar on pages 442-443).

Designing and purchasing a management information system

Management issues in designing and purchasing an MIS include how the data are to be organized, who the users of the system will be, what the security requirements are, whether software should be bought off the shelf or be custom written, whether some tasks should be outsourced, what the proper acquisition steps are, and what computer hardware should be bought. Licenses are needed to support two and preferably three environments, one each for production, training, and test; in small departments, a training and test may be combined in one environment. Since some of these systems need to run 24/7, the test/training setup is very important. At the very least, making a change without testing it could prove embarrassing; at the worst, it could take down the entire system.

Organization of the data

Before data are organized, two major viewpoints should be considered: the potential user's and the programmer's. Accordingly, as a system is being designed, the fire chief and staff must have a dialogue with the programmer who will fulfill their requests. Often the user specifies needs first and then lets the programmer design the organization of the information. The programmer may ask detailed questions about how the data will be used and how frequently.

Users of the system

Who will use the system directly and who will use it indirectly? Of the many users of fire department information, direct users include the fire chief, assistant and battalion chiefs, other departmental officers, the local government manager and staff, the local government legislative body, and other local government departments. Indirect users of the data may include the local media, the insurance industry, the state fire marshal, the USFA, the Consumer Product Safety Commission, and the public. Some users may have to use the system more frequently than other users. In addition, fire department analysts must have direct access to the data files for quality assurance, but secondary users will have access to the data only after the data have been quality checked. Managers and local media may have access only at the summary level rather than at the record level. It is important to identify these different types of users and the different ways in which they will be interacting with the system.

Security requirements

The answer to who is allowed access to the data will depend on the types of data and the local jurisdiction's open records laws (see Chapter 10 for a discussion of open records laws). To protect patient confidentiality, access to records that deal with emergency medical services provided by paramedics should be very restricted. The Health Insurance Portability and Accountability Act of 1996 may apply to certain types of incidents, and some incidents may also need to be treated as part of a criminal investigation that may lead to prosecutions. This means that whatever NFIRS and investigations data are collected must be restricted and not released to open records requests without the approval of the department's legal representative. Access to records on fire cause and origin investigation for suspicious or set fires should also be very restricted. To meet state requirements, records describing juvenile fire setters or suspects must be highly protected. A department should follow the guidelines used for all criminal investigations.

GIS for fire and emergency services

A geographic information system (GIS) is a computer software program that can access, process, and display data from multiple sources visually according to their location. Although referred to as mapping software, GIS is a powerful tool for display, analysis, and presentation of information tied to location. Using GIS allows fire and emergency service organizations to use data from other government organizations and display their own data as well.

GIS users start with a "base map" that usually consists of topographical features, streets, waterways, and parcels or buildings. These features typically are developed by a county or regional level of government, although many larger cities may have established their own base maps. Additional features or data sources can then be added as "layers" to this base map; these layers would include fire/EMS incident data, response times, population counts and characteristics, and census data. These other data sources are referred to as layers because they can be used when necessary but also hidden from view when they are not needed for a particular project or purpose.

Additional data used to develop layers on a GIS map might include

- Fire hydrants and water mains
- Electrical or gas utility networks
- Fire stations
- Police stations
- Hospitals
- Schools
- Satellite images
- High-hazard occupancies
- Planned roadways.

Each layer has data elements associated with its use; these are called *attributes*. Attributes for a high-hazard occupancy layer would include address, building height, HAZMAT inventory, presence of detection or suppression systems, and even emergency contacts.

For multiple-station departments, GIS can be valuable for display and analysis of response times, calls for service, and compliance with local response-time or level-of-service goals. Many large agencies or communication centers serving multiple departments are capable of bringing GIS into the field to assist in the management of large incidents.

Other uses of GIS software include

- Tracking unit locations
- Planning for moving or adding facilities
- Identifying areas of high demand
- Providing a platform for preincident plan information.

GIS can be deployed at a single workstation, via a network throughout an entire building, or as an enterprise software system running on desktop and mobile computers. It is increasingly becoming more closely aligned with CAD and dispatch functionality. GIS lies at the heart of efforts on the

Personnel data will, in part, be held as confidential. Some portions of the data on buildings should be considered confidential because they describe alarm systems, HAZMAT storage locations, and the presence and location of incapacitated or homebound individuals living in the occupancy. However, hydrant records and incident records from the CAD system may be available to anyone upon request.

For online records, security should be set up with the following permissions: read only, add, change, delete, special update (outside of normal time frame), print option, password required, specific day of week, time of day.

Software: Off the shelf or custom written?

What are the pros and cons of buying software off the shelf as opposed to using custom-written software?

Off-the-shelf software Off-the-shelf software is available to perform many noncritical tasks, such as creating reports from databases and from spreadsheets, and to facilitate computer

national level to enhance situational awareness and aid in incident management through initiatives such as the U.S. Department of Homeland Security's "Virtual USA."[1]

GIS is particularly useful for fire and emergency services because its displays are clear and understandable. Although GIS software requires specialized training and experience, routine processes can be automated, meaning that regular reports can be produced without great effort. Additionally, there are software packages that are targeted at the fire service user and programmed to perform common tasks.

Number of incidents by fire box area, city of Alexandria, Virginia, 2008

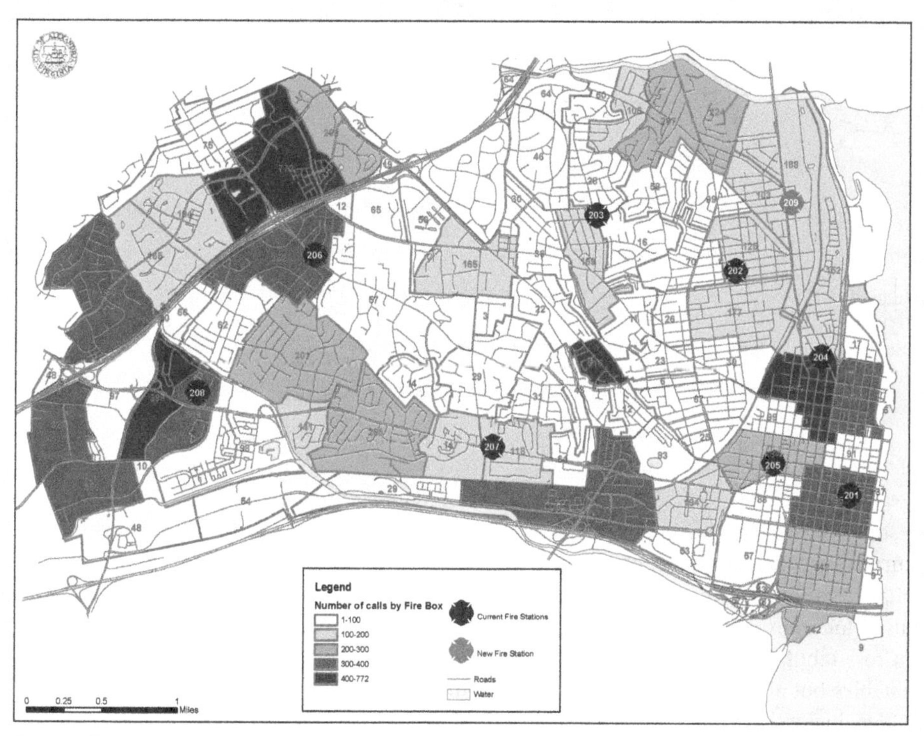

Figure courtesy of the Alexandria (Virginia) Fire Department

Assistance in preparing GIS maps can be found in other local government departments and even at many institutions of higher education. When an outside agency is assisting with preparation of maps and analyses, it is critical that the fire and emergency services organization have someone available who is knowledgeable about its data and operations and able to verify assumptions made in presenting the data.

1 For more information on Virtual USA, see firstresponder.gov/Pages/VisualUSA.aspx.

mapping, cross-tabulations, and statistical analysis. Generally, off-the-shelf products are useful only when the instructions are simple and the data requirements are neither complicated nor restrictive.

Office suites such as Microsoft Office and Corel WordPerfect Office offer an array of programs that many fire and emergency service departments use, including a word processor, a spreadsheet package, a database package that can help the user organize and index data to make them more easily accessible, and a presentation software package.

Most of the report-writing software available (e.g., Crystal Reports, Hummingbird, or any of the SQL [Structured Query Language] products) will work with database files and support "query by example," a query language that is supported in some form by most databases and helps the user construct queries; some databases refer to query by example as "wizards." Report-writing software is excellent for both standard periodic (weekly, monthly, and annual) and ad hoc reports.

Computer mapping programs are an excellent way to display information spatially (see sidebar above). For most types of fire and emergency data, a spatial representation of raw data, connecting incident information to geographic location, produces a better analytical

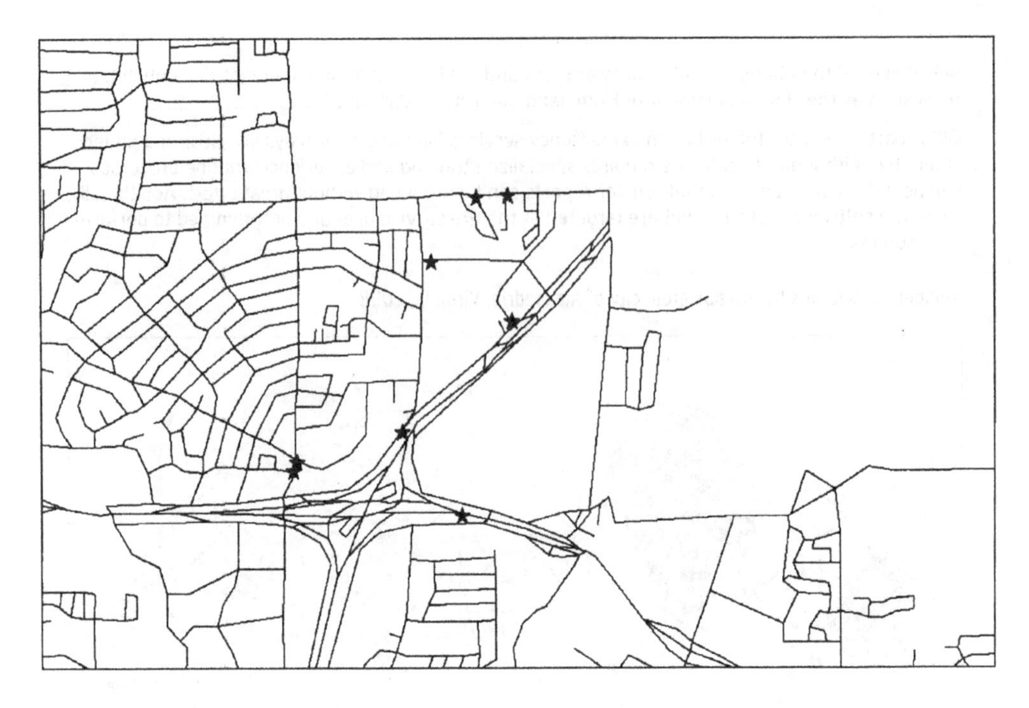

Figure 15-6 This computer-generated map shows areas with potentially high emergency response times. The stars identify intersections where traffic is heavy.

tool. The map shown in Figure 15–6, which identifies an area with potentially high response times due to traffic congestion, was produced with MapInfo Professional; ArcGIS and Intergraph are some other currently available mapping programs. Mapping can be used to study the occurrence of structure fires, car fires, assist-ambulance calls, alarm system malfunctions, or similar situations. Computer mapping programs that locate the demand for services can also be used for analyzing and locating fire department facilities.

Cross-tabulation software is also used for data analysis. This software not only creates tables but also produces print-ready multidimensional cross-tabulation reports from flat files, hierarchical files (files containing different data records that must be processed in a predefined order), and Oracle/SQL databases. Cross-tabulation programs can be used to determine how many incidents occurred on each day of the week, during each hour of the day, or during each month of the year. When the raw numbers are too overwhelming, a basic understanding of statistics is very important. For instance, average response time—used as a common measure of productivity—can be made more meaningful when it is compared with the median response time.

Another very important issue to keep in mind when buying off-the-shelf software is the need for (and availability and cost of) training. The fire and emergency services spend a great deal of time on training, not just for rookies but also for the more experienced firefighters and (as far as computer support is concerned) for civilian members of the department. Most training classes provide some additional techniques for achieving better results. Moreover, as new versions of operating systems and application software are released, more training will be necessary.

Open-source software Since the last edition of this book was published in 2002, open-source software has begun to be more widely used by public agencies. *Open source* describes practices in production and development that promote broad access to the end product's source material—typically, its source code. The code is available to the public at no cost, enabling anyone to copy, modify, and redistribute it without paying royalties or fees. Open-source software evolves through community cooperation and encourages sharing of innovations within the public sector. Examples of open-source software include

- FreeBSD, an operating system derived from Unix
- Linux, an operating system based on Unix
- Eclipse, a software framework for "rich-client applications"

- Apache Tomcat, a web server, available at tomcat.apache.org/
- Moodle, a course management system, available at moodle.org/
- Mozilla Firefox, a web browser, available at mozilla.org/
- Mozilla Thunderbird, an e-mail client, available at mozilla.org/
- Open Office, an office suite, available at openoffice.org/.

There are also open-source GIS packages available, although none is currently widely adopted by fire and emergency service organizations.

Custom-written software Custom-written software can have advantages over off-the-shelf products if the department has the funds for contracting out or for the in-house personnel to design, document, write, test, and implement the system. The greatest advantage of custom-written software is that as the department's needs change, the software can be modified to accommodate the new policies, whereas when off-the-shelf software is used, departmental policy must conform to the software's design rather than vice versa. The greatest disadvantage is that the modification process may require a long time for programming, testing, and implementation. Another disadvantage may be the cost of a custom-written code. Standards must be in place to protect the investment in time for any software developed inside the department or by a consultant.

Regardless of whether a department chooses to use off-the-shelf, open source, or custom-written software, if the software does not need to be changed over its life, it is not really being used. For budgeting purposes, a department should allocate money to perform annual maintenance on off-the-shelf software or to make the necessary changes to custom-written software. And given that the data are the most valuable part of its investment, the department should also remember to back up the database.

Outsourcing: Good or bad?

Outsourcing is subcontracting a service, such as software design, development, or maintenance, to a third-party company. For smaller departments, outsourcing may provide access to expertise not available on staff, or it may free up staff time for higher-level tasks, such as data analysis and strategic planning. The larger the department, the easier it is to justify primary and backup persons dedicated to information management.

The strategic use of outside resources to perform activities traditionally handled by internal staff and internal resources may be appropriate, but before deciding to outsource, a department should consider the following five factors because they have cross-functional implications:

- Cost of purchasing the service (can the department afford to spend the money?)
- Quality level of the service provided
- Effect on the organization's culture
- Ways of measuring the service provider's performance
- Ways of managing the service provider (e.g., through a service-level agreement, which specifies what is expected).

To reduce risks associated with outsourcing, a department should also consider the following questions:

- If other systems must be integrated, can the vendor provide the necessary connectivity? Who accepts accountability for interface problems?
- Can the vendor always respond in a timely manner regardless of the contractual agreement?
- If the vendor's business should fail, what protection or recourse is available to the local fire department (what happens to the source code and its ownership, and how can the department gain access to it)?
- In the case of a custom-written code, who owns it?

It is the department's responsibility to design, write, and execute a test plan to verify that all software works as specified.

Acquisition issues

When preparing to outsource or contract for custom-written software, a department should take the following steps:

- Define in a general way its expectations of the system.
- Identify the data elements that will be necessary for reaching the desired goals.
- Study the data elements: will the coding scheme produce the answers to only one question, or can the data be used to explore multiple questions? Is this scheme flexible enough to anticipate future needs?
- Analyze the relationship between the data elements and the respective codes to determine any relational edits necessary for producing the desired goals.
- Determine the implementation time lines and establish the necessary milestones.
- Define the acceptance testing procedures to be followed.
- Never make partial payments for products or work that has not been completed. Only when the product or work passes the acceptance test and has been proven to work as advertised should the department pay for it. Spending less than the full amount on a product that does not do the job and for which a full refund cannot be obtained does not save the department a nickel.

The process of defining and specifying will take a lot of time, so managers should not be in a hurry.

Computer hardware, present and future

Computer hardware, whether desktops, laptops, or servers, is probably fully useful for only about three years, so when purchasing hardware, always get a four-year service agreement to cover the equipment while replacement machines are being purchased. Remember that processors, RAM (random-access memory), and hard drives are relatively inexpensive compared to software and staff time.

A few recommendations for hardware specifications can be offered, but readers who need to use this kind of information should be careful to update their knowledge periodically as the technology changes:

- *Servers.* A server should have dual-power supplies, dual NICs (network interface cards) of at least 100/1,000-GB capacity, and an internal and external RAID (redundant array of inexpensive disks) interface with at least five hard drives, which allows for high reliability from lower-cost storage devices.
- *Desktops.* Every desktop should have a DVD drive, a 100/1,000-GB NIC, as much RAM as possible (4 GB or more), and the largest hard drive that the department can afford. For easy viewing, desktops need a 20- or 22-inch-diagonal LCD (liquid-crystal display) monitor.
- *Laptops.* A laptop that is to be used as a desktop workstation and as a portable office computer should have at least a 15-inch-diagonal LCD screen, at least 4 GB RAM, a DVD drive, three or more USB (Universal Serial Bus) ports, a built-in 802.11G or higher wireless card, and a bluetooth interface. If the laptop computer is to be used for critical high-availability access to the server and/or user network, a built-in wireless broadband (cellular) interface card should be included, as well as a port replicator so that in the office it can be attached to a wired network and large screen monitor.
- *MDCs.* Computers that are to be mounted in a mobile environment (engine, truck, rescue, battalion chief) should be hardened or ruggedized. They should also have touch screens for ease of use when wearing gloves, 4 GB RAM or more, and a built-in wireless card (802.11G or higher) so that software updates and data updates don't require a hard-wire connection. If real-time communication with a dispatch center is desired, a built-in wireless broadband card (which requires a monthly financial

commitment per card) is desirable. Again, the largest hard drive available, 500 GB or more, is needed.

Ruggedized laptops are designed to absorb the vibrations of road travel, even on unimproved roads. These laptops, which are configured with touch screens and are easily viewable in bright sunlight, cost between $3,300 and $5,000, depending on the configuration. Consumer laptops are considerably less expensive, costing between $800 and $2,000, but their plastic cases are not designed to tolerate the vibrations and potentially unfriendly environmental conditions to which they are exposed in the fire and emergency services. It is also very difficult to press keys on the keyboard while bouncing down the road. Adding touch-screen capability can increase the cost of consumer laptops. Repair costs for laptops are often higher than those for desktops, and the most expensive part is the screen, which is the most fragile part of the laptop.

Any laptop used in a vehicle must be locked down into a dock station (around $1,000) so that it does not become a projectile in case of an accident. However, mobile dock stations are designed to secure and immobilize laptops, which will accentuate any vibrations through the vehicle to the laptop.

In 2010, Microsoft was still the dominant operating system software vendor in the industry for both servers and desktops. Today Microsoft Windows XP Pro (Business and Government where security is important) is the most popular, and Windows 7 is likely to become the predominant desktop system of the future. In the server world, Windows 2008 in one of its forms (Standard, Enterprise, Datacenter) will provide all the necessary capabilities needed.

UNIX-based software (including LINUX and its variants) is becoming very popular as the basis for both desktop and server operating systems because of its price and performance. Some versions of LINUX are available in open-source configurations. Some of the large computer manufacturers are now providing LINUX as an option. Other operating systems for servers are FreeBSD (open source) and Solaris (proprietary).

"Virtual machine" operating systems can allow a single computer to be configured as multiple servers. This allows a single piece of hardware to fulfill the functions of multiple servers. Each server application operates like an independent machine. Each virtual machine can run a different operating system, such as LINUX or Windows Server, and the operating systems run at the same time. A virus that infects one virtual server generally will not infect the others. Virtual machine software allows for more efficient use of servers than would be possible if each application was operating on its own dedicated hardware.

Conclusion

This chapter has provided a glimpse into the ever-changing world of computers and data management, sketching out various possibilities for using technology in the fire and emergency services. A fire and emergency services organization, now and in the future, should view technology as a tool that will help it fulfill its mission of protecting citizens. At the same time, it should try to be creative in using the new technologies that are available.

Information technology can be used to collect, analyze, and present financial, administrative, and performance data from the organization for use in preparation of budgets and grant applications and in communicating results to the community and other stakeholders. The question that fire managers should constantly ask themselves in developing and using information technology is, how does this help us better serve our customers? The answer should be, through either more efficient or improved service.

To ensure that the protection provided to citizens is as good as it can possibly be, the fire and emergency services organization must approach technology proactively. It is appropriate for the organization to keep up with technological advances, which it can usually do by adopting technologies and software upgrades and additions once they have accumulated some field use experience among early-adopting organizations. However, risks in technology innovation are real, so unless a fire and emergency services organization has considerable in-house expertise, good support from its governing body, and sufficient funding, most departments should avoid pioneering applications and new technologies.

Computers and software are becoming critical components of most fire and emergency service organizations' critical administrative support systems. An important lesson to remember is that nothing lasts forever: a department should plan to replace its computer hardware about every four years and to upgrade its software (databases, operating systems) as recommended by the manufacturer. A weekly or monthly time period should be allocated in which to perform these upgrades. Organizations should consider not only the cost of acquisition but also the essential need to maintain technologies as they are adopted. Maintenance costs should be identified before acquisition, and necessary funds for required maintenance, licensing, and upgrades, as well as for training, should be identified and supported throughout the life cycle of new technologies.

Notes

1. National Commission on Fire Prevention and Control, *America Burning* (Washington, D.C., 1973), 9, usfa .dhs.gov/downloads/pdf/publications/fa-264.pdf (accessed June 7, 2010).
2. At the time of publication, Version 3 draft documents for NEMSIS are available for review at nemsis.org.
3. Federal Emergency Management Agency, *Fire Data Analysis Handbook,* 2nd ed., FA-266 (Washington, D.C.: U.S. Fire Administration, January 2004), available at usfa.dhs.gov/downloads/pdf/publications/ fa-266.pdf (accessed July 11, 2010).

CHAPTER 16

Communication Systems and Emergency Communication Centers

Charles R. Jennings and Steve Souder

This chapter provides an understanding of

- The history of public safety communications and 911 systems
- The radio spectrum and methods of signal propagation
- The role of communication systems and centers in fire and emergency service organizations
- Computer-aided dispatch systems
- Records management systems
- The challenges of managing human resource functions in a communications center
- Consolidation and communications center management
- The need to maintain awareness of technology and plan for upgrades.

Communication systems are a critical component of fire and emergency services. However, such systems often do not receive the necessary attention from management and personnel within the organizations they serve. This chapter gives a very brief history of emergency communications and then discusses their major components: the 911 system, the public safety communications center, computer-aided dispatch systems, records management systems, and communications hardware. It also discusses performance measures for dispatch and communication, operational issues associated with fire and emergency service communications, new systems acquisition, project management, and future trends in communication systems.

Communication systems play such a large role in fire and emergency services that they are often taken for granted. But one of the hallmarks of a well-functioning fire and emergency services department is a well-managed and effective communications system and operation. A communications system is critical for receiving alarms, selecting and alerting the proper units, ensuring reliable on-scene communications, and capturing the incident-related information needed to document and learn from responses. It is difficult for a fire and emergency services department to achieve greatness if its communications system is not functioning properly. Postincident analyses following major events and events involving injuries to personnel often indicate that communication issues play a role in negative outcomes.

Communications technology is advancing, and the regulatory environment and operating practices are changing to accommodate new services. Communication upgrades and related projects are costly, and often require financial support from capital budgets or bond issues with oversight from elected officials. Thus, it is essential that fire and emergency service managers understand communications technology, its capabilities, and its limitations.

A brief history of fire and emergency service communications

For the earliest settlers in the United States, fire was a constant threat to life and property. Citizen volunteers patrolled cities at night to spot fires early and sound the alarm using various noise-making devices. The red cottage–style fire alarm box was introduced and over time was located on virtually every street corner. It was eventually replaced by the telephone. In 1958 the concept of a single three-digit nationwide phone number to call to report emergencies was initiated by the National Association of Fire Chiefs, which later became the International Association of Fire Chiefs; on February 16, 1968, the first 911 call was placed in Haleyville, Alabama. Then computer-aided dispatch (CAD) systems were introduced, and "technology" came to the fire service.

In the early 1700s, officers of fire brigades began using brass or pewter speaking trumpets as a means of communicating orders and giving direction to personnel pulling and operating hand-drawn and hand-operated pumpers and hoses made of leather and rivets. Hence, the symbol of fire officer rank was born. Two hundred years later, trumpets were replaced by radios, and fire and emergency service communications have continued to evolve. Today, they serve the same functions that they did three centuries ago, but the execution depends on a sophisticated system of policy, procedure, technology, and incident command designed to serve the public and protect firefighters.

The 911 system

The 911 system is the cornerstone of fire and emergency service communications. Uniform emergency reporting numbers date back to the 1930s in England and other countries; at that time there were recommendations for the establishment of a national emergency reporting number in the United States as well. When a 1967 report of the Presidential Commission on Law Enforcement and Administration of Justice recommended a national number for contacting police,[1] AT&T and other telephone companies, with support from other emergency services, moved quickly to implement the recommendations. By 1968, there were municipal 911 systems running in Alabama, Alaska, and Illinois. Today the use of 911 as an emergency reporting number is nearly universal in North America.

Portions of this chapter have been revised and updated from Chapter 15, "Communication Systems and Emergency Response Centers," by Timothy R. S. Campbell, in the 2002 edition of this volume.

Interestingly, some of the concepts advanced by telephone companies during the conception of the 911 system envisioned significant consolidation of dispatching functions and the creation of true "public safety" dispatch centers uniting fire and emergency services with police and emergency medical service (EMS) transport.

Basic 911

Early systems were known as "basic 911." Calls were routed using a three-digit telephone exchange. A problem arose, however, in the processing of these calls: because the service boundaries of telephone company central switching offices do not often coincide with those of government jurisdictions, calls were not necessarily routed directly to the appropriate 911 center. As a result, many dispatchers had to handle calls from citizens in other jurisdictions while calls from citizens within their jurisdictions were answered by a neighboring community's 911 system. Most communities resisted adopting 911 because of concerns that the lack of boundary alignment would slow down responses to calls.

The next innovation came in mid-1970s, when automatic number identification (ANI) made it possible to direct 911 calls to a call center based on the landline's location, not its telephone exchange. This was a major breakthrough because, as noted, most communities were reluctant to adopt 911 when calls might not go to the appropriate answering point. ANI gave the calling-party number to the telecommunicator in the 911 center and queried a 911 address database to give the dispatcher the address of the calling telephone as well. The telecommunicator could then send the call to a different call center, if necessary.

It was not until 1980 that telephone systems offered the services now known as Enhanced 911. In addition to previous features, these services enable automatic location identification (ALI) using the account address. They also include capabilities for what is called selective routing, in which a routing code is assigned to each address in the community, and the telephone system uses the code to ensure that the call automatically reaches the correct public safety answering point (PSAP).

Although implementation of 911 enhanced systems has improved service to citizens, there are still problems with 911. Determining the caller's location when the call comes from a telephone located in an office on a campus or in a high-rise building served by a private telephone system or switch can be difficult. Telephone companies often provide service to multiple locations in a metropolitan region from a telephone switch located in another state. Calls from numbers served by this switch may give just a street address for a ten-story building or the main office location for an organization with sixteen geographically separate offices. Another problem is locating the caller who uses a cell phone to report an emergency or who uses "voice over Internet protocol," both of which situations are discussed in the next two sections.

Wireless (cellular) 911

The explosion of cellular telephones created a major problem for 911 centers. Because users move around, cell phones are not tied to particular locations. Moreover, people reporting emergencies on a cell phone may not know their precise location, and using the location of the closest cell tower to determine a caller's location is not always accurate enough for emergency response. In 2010 the Federal Communications Commission (FCC) reported that up to 50 percent of incoming calls to 911 systems were estimated to come from wireless callers.[2] In response to this problem, it required wireless phone service providers to report certain data for their customers calling 911. In 2001 telephone companies began offering so-called Phase I and Phase II wireless 911 services. These services allow for the determination of both the calling number and the approximate location of the calling party.

VoIP telephony

Voice over Internet protocol (VoIP) technology offers considerable cost savings and additional features for the public. VoIP services, through the interconnection of computer equipment to the public switched telephone network, handle calls in a completely new fashion: rather

Federal Communications Commission wireless 911 service requirements

The Federal Communications Commission (FCC) has set forth the following rules, which "apply to all wireless licensees, broadband Personal Communications Service (PCS) licensees, and certain Specialized Mobile Radio (SMR) licensees:

"Basic 911 rules require wireless service providers to

- Transmit all 911 calls to a public safety answering point (PSAP), regardless of whether the caller subscribes to the provider's service or not.

"Phase I Enhanced 911 (E911) rules require wireless service providers to

- Within six minutes of a valid request by a PSAP, provide the PSAP with the telephone number of the originator of a wireless 911 call and the location of the cell site or base station transmitting the call.

"Phase II E911 rules require wireless service providers to

- Within six minutes of a valid request by a PSAP, provide more precise location information to PSAPs; specifically, the latitude and longitude of the caller. This information must be accurate to within 50 to 300 meters depending on the type of technology used."

The FCC has mandated that by September 11, 2012, all licensees must provide even more precise location information—specifically, information that is accurate to the closest PSAP. The commission has also established a five-year phase-in period to allow wireless service providers more time to develop this capability. Those providers must report to the FCC annually on their progress.

Source: Federal Communications Commission, Consumer and Governmental Affairs Bureau, "Wireless 911 Services," fcc.gov/cgb/consumerfacts/wireless911srvc.html.

than using a dedicated channel created for each particular call, VoIP routes a call through the computer network in packets, and each packet may take a different path. But this service has created a new wave of problems for 911 center operators. VoIP telephone services are not necessarily fixed to a particular location. In fact, because they use networking equipment and software protocols, VoIP services can be tied to a mobile device, such as a laptop computer, or even to a handheld device, and these devices have the capability to place and receive calls from the same number regardless of their location. That is, a number with an area code from California could actually be located in Illinois. Moreover, VoIP calls may appear to be coming in from "normal" landlines, and the address that comes up in the 911 center may not be accurate.

Users of fixed interconnected VoIP telephone services must register their locations with their service providers. However, while this process should route calls dialed from the affected line to the appropriate 911 PSAP, all the location and identification features of a landline call may not be available. Users of portable devices must be able to provide their location to properly route a 911 call.

Funding Legislation in many states permits the state, counties, and even some municipalities to fund 911 systems through fees or taxes for 911 services. Revenues are commonly used to buy or replace equipment infrastructure and pay for upgrades to 911 enhanced capability and Phase I and II wireless services. Ironically, in some states, wireless phone services are exempt from taxes and fees for 911 service. As the proportion of wireless lines increases, this exemption may create revenue shortfalls for 911 systems.

Public expectations and resource limitations Another 911 issue is public expectations. Much as the television show *Emergency!* promoted the spread of prehospital emergency medical systems, television shows such as *Rescue 911* helped to convince the public and elected officials that 911 was needed. But these shows also portrayed a world where people rarely died if they called 911, operators saved lives over the telephone and were rarely overloaded by multiple calls, units responded very quickly and never got lost, and there were no interagency problems.

Television dramas portrayed the best possible world, and the public mistook it for the norm. But as many well-publicized cases gradually revealed, service varied across the United States. In many places, 911 operators were poorly trained, inadequately supervised, and poorly compensated and equipped. In some places, citizens were advised to bypass 911 and contact agencies directly. Often the real problem was a lack of sufficient field resources for all the calls but 911, and operators were blamed for this although it was totally beyond their control. To the public, 911 constituted the entire public safety system; people were unaware of the decentralized system of independent agencies and the limited resources available to police, fire, and EMS. (Some solutions were found in training, organization, and technology.)

Another issue arose when many cities, on implementing the 911 system, discontinued their previous seven-digit emergency telephone numbers and told citizens to call 911 if they needed any public safety service whatsoever. As a result, many nonemergency calls clogged the 911 system, which was advertised as the citizens' lifeline. Troubled, understaffed, underfunded, or poorly managed 911 systems undermine public confidence and create challenges for fire and EMS organizations reliant on the centers and their personnel. To remedy this situation and improve customer service, many communities have now introduced 311 for nonemergency public safety or public service calls. (See sidebar on 311 centers on page 461.) A longer-term solution lies in planning for Next Generation 911 (see sidebar below).

The public safety communications center

This section examines the role and function of the public safety communications center (PSCC), a term favored by progressive communication professionals. The section reviews the distinctions between a single-discipline and a multidiscipline PSCC; it also addresses facility design issues, key utilities, management and staffing, operating procedures and training, the role of CAD and records management systems in the work of the center, and consolidation.

Next Generation 911

Existing 911 systems grew from technology designed to work on traditional wireline phones. But these systems are unable to accommodate increasingly popular new communication technologies—for example, voice over Internet protocol (VoIP), text messaging, and data-based services—with the same level of integration and reliability that exists for wireline phones.

The term "Next Generation 911," or NG911, was coined to describe the activities associated with the design and construction of a new public emergency reporting network. The effort began in 2000 under the leadership of the National Emergency Number Association (NENA) and involves federal legislation; the development of standards; and the participation of federal agencies, national associations, and numerous equipment vendors.

Once it is operative, NG911 will be a national, secure, emergency services IP-based communications network that allows public safety answering points (PSAPs) and emergency responders to receive calls originating from wired or wireless phones and devices, as well as from Internet-based communications such as text, video, and sensor-based services (e.g., automatic crash detection). NG911 will also enable such data as floor plans or precise caller location to be transmitted among PSAPs and even to responders.

The future of NG911 depends on local leadership, the availability of funding, and the development of technical standards. To provide funding, state and local authorities will have to levy fees on telecommunication services and properly plan and budget for design, construction, and maintenance of the required infrastructure. Standard operating procedures and technical standards must be developed to ensure reliability, accessibility, and interoperability. The move to NG911 is likely to cause a new round of consolidations among communication centers and service sharing among agencies to both reduce costs and increase efficiency. In the meantime, pioneering centers may adopt IP-based architectures, which will put them on the road to NG911 in the near future.

More information on NG911 is available from NENA at nena.org/ng911-project, the Federal Communications Commission at fcc.gov/pshs/services/911-services/nextgen.html, and the U.S. Department of Transportation at its.dot.gov/ng911/.

Organization

Building a new dispatch facility is an opportunity to locate and create a facility that will be free of vulnerabilities and capable of meeting the needs of the jurisdiction being served for at least twenty years into the future (see Figure 16–1). Preparation should include an environmental scan and discussion with neighboring or nearby centers and organizations about the feasibility of sharing services.

PSCCs are organized around three key dimensions. The first is its range of responsibility—that is, whether the center is responsible for only one discipline or for more than one. For example, many organizations maintain separate centers for police and fire and emergency dispatch. Where fire services do not provide EMS transport, these may be handled by another organization or from an independent communications center.

The second key dimension of a PSCC's organization is its range of service—that is, whether it serves a single agency or multiple agencies, and whether these agencies are outside the political entity that operates the center. Centers can be small, serving a single agency, or they can be countywide, serving numerous agencies and performing complex dispatch functions. If the political jurisdictions extend beyond one county, such centers can be described as joint or regional (see the section later in this chapter on consolidation). A city fire and emergency communications center may also serve other municipalities under contract or other arrangement. Table 16–1 illustrates these various configurations. As centers move from the upper left corner of the table (single agency, single discipline) toward the lower right corner (regional, multiple discipline), they tend to become larger and are more likely to use specialized communications personnel. PSAPs parallel this framework but may be independent of the organization of a particular discipline's communications center.

One of the drivers in determining the "best" approach for a city, county, or region to take is cost. Generally speaking, the more duplication, the higher the cost. Additionally, duplication often means less standardization, less resource sharing, and less interoperability at many levels.

The final dimension of a PSCC's organization is the nature of the personnel who staff and operate it. These personnel can be uniformed members of the agency that is dispatched (firefighters or police officers), or they can be civilian personnel hired solely to do communications work. They can be employees of a particular agency, or the center can exist as an independent agency. There are numerous variations, all of which are based on local conditions and history.

A general distinction can be made in terms of the training and assignment of personnel in the PSCC. Sworn personnel are usually police or fire service staff who have received basic

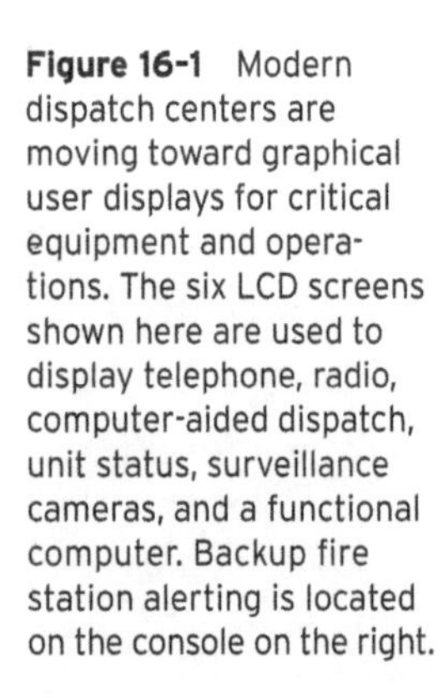

Figure 16-1 Modern dispatch centers are moving toward graphical user displays for critical equipment and operations. The six LCD screens shown here are used to display telephone, radio, computer-aided dispatch, unit status, surveillance cameras, and a functional computer. Backup fire station alerting is located on the console on the right.

Photo by Charles R. Jennings

Table 16-1 Public safety communications center organization

	Single-discipline client, e.g., fire and emergency services only	Multiple-discipline public safety clients, e.g., fire and emergency services and police services	Multiple-discipline clients, including non-emergency services such as parks or public works or transportation
Single-agency provider			
Municipality as provider			
County as provider			
Regional (more than one county) center as provider			

training in their discipline and perhaps some experience in field assignments before being assigned to the communications function. In some places, sworn personnel enter directly into the communications job function and spend their careers within this promotional and rank structure. Nonsworn (civilian) personnel, on the other hand, usually come directly into the function without the same level of training in the public safety disciplines.

The distinction between sworn and nonsworn personnel can be overdrawn and should not be interpreted as a slight to "civilian" telecommunicators. However, because of the relatively lower hazard and physical requirements of the telecommunicator positions, sound personnel management has produced a situation in which pension and benefit plans for civilian telecommunicators are often not the same as they are for uniformed (police officer or firefighter) personnel.

Design of the facility

A new PSCC can include, besides the communication consoles, a training room, a break room, administrative offices, locker rooms, showers, sleeping space, and physical fitness facilities (see Figure 16–2). The facility should be able to maintain self-sufficiency, including meals and space for personnel to work extended shifts in the event of a disaster.

Security concerns for PSCCs have come full circle. Earliest standards for these facilities came from municipal fire insurance underwriters. To avoid the hazard of conflagration, dispatch facilities were located in parklike settings away from neighboring buildings. During the Cold War, facilities in major urban areas were designed in anticipation of a nuclear attack. Some of these facilities were constructed underground with thick walls and ceilings, and some had blast doors and were designed to be self-sufficient for a period after an attack. Later their design became more open, with aboveground facilities featuring windows and more amenities for dispatch personnel. However, concerns following the attacks of September 11, 2001, have again pushed security to the forefront in the design of facilities.

Figure 16-2 Fairfax County, Virginia, moved into its new emergency communications center (left) in 2009. This facility combines public safety operations with a regional transportation operations center. The fire and emergency services dispatch area (right) has a large display screen at the right.

Photos by Charles R. Jennings (left) and Steve Souder (right)

While blast-resistant facilities are not the norm, ideally PSCCs should be located outside of floodplains and away from hazards; a security survey should be conducted of proposed sites. Parking adjacent to the center should be restricted to employee-owned vehicles. (After centers have been constructed, all vehicles admitted to parking areas should be checked periodically.)

Of the many lifelines in the community, the one most critical to emergency operations is communications. Thus, hardening and redundancy of communication systems are basic mitigation activities. Fire protection and safety and security standards for a communications facility should exceed the minimums required in local building codes. The federal government publishes standards for the protection of diplomatic and government facilities that can be used as a guide for standoff distances, resistance to explosives, and general construction detailing. Local project managers should contact appropriate federal agencies for guidance. A qualified blast engineering company must design any structure intended to be blast resistant.

Every PSCC must have a backup facility should an event—for example, an incident of workplace violence, a natural disaster, a fire, contamination of the facility, or an electronic or mechanical failure affecting critical equipment—cause the facility to become unusable. While most communities do not have the resources to maintain a fully redundant capability, a minimum communications capacity should be retained in a separate location unlikely to be affected by the same event that disables the main facility.

As communications technology becomes increasingly computerized, strategies for backup that rely on redundant servers and equipment linked by data lines make off-site backup and system reliability more achievable. Neighboring jurisdictions can host "live" backup equipment, along with some "surge" capability for housing additional PSCC personnel should they need to relocate to continue their operations. Hosting arrangements need to be considered when a new communications facility is in the planning stage (see Figure 16–3).

Attendance at national meetings of organizations such as the Association of Public-Safety Communications Officials (APCO) International can be invaluable for identifying best practices and recent examples of well-regarded facilities. Site visits to other recently constructed facilities are also worthwhile. Staff making these visits should take detailed notes and bring home documentation to present to other members of the team tasked with designing the new facility.

Key utilities

To ensure the reliability of the PSCC, designers must clearly understand the routing and backup arrangements for key lifelines such as telephone service and electricity. Identifying the current arrangement, particularly of underground utilities, will require the participation of the local utility and phone companies.

Generally, multiple sources should be used wherever possible so that failure of a single facility outside the 911 center will not bring the system down. Working through these issues

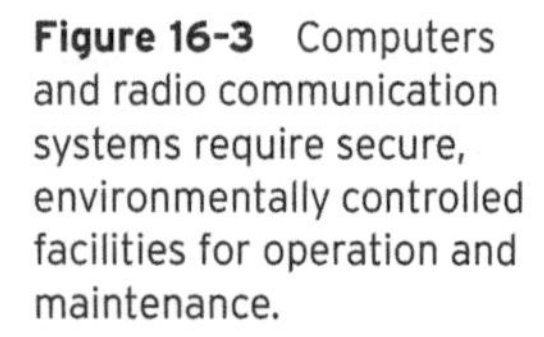

Figure 16-3 Computers and radio communication systems require secure, environmentally controlled facilities for operation and maintenance.

Photo by Charles R. Jennings

will likely require time and the commitment of top-level management to get definitive answers and documentation from the local phone company or other service providers. Once issues are identified, solutions may be costly to implement, but the value in terms of enhanced system reliability should be considered, especially over the life of the facility.

Redundancy for the physical 911 system equipment and incoming lines should also be considered. In many of the 911 systems that have been put in place, the failure of a single point can cause the whole system to collapse. Managers should conduct the equivalent of a process safety analysis to see where the risk exists. If 911 lines are all routed through a single location or through one set of switching and processing equipment, the system is vulnerable to failure. The telephone network that we use every day is inherently redundant for all lines except the one linking our own location to the local central office. From the local office to the central office that serves the person we are calling, the system uses multiple pathways to ensure that calls go through. The 911 system should be equally redundant.

In addition, the manager must ensure that the 911 system has priority in restoration efforts. There is a national priority system for telephone-related restoration of service. To set what will be fixed first, the system uses a code applied to the records of designated customers, and telephone companies have no choice but to restore service to those customers first. If a 911 system has not been designated a priority, repairs will wait until service to all priority customers has been restored. To ensure that mission-critical telephone services are designated for priority restoration, 911 managers, along with emergency operations center (EOC) managers and officials of agencies with emergency missions, must work with telephone company personnel. There is an additional cost for this service, but it must be viewed as an essential cost of doing business.

Management

Management of a PSCC requires a diverse skill set. Successful managers must be competent in human resource management and technology management, and must understand their organization's mission and operation as well as the missions and operations of other organizations they serve. Moreover, they need support from top management. This section is not intended to review general management principles, which can be found in other chapters of this text, but to describe the management environment and the challenges of PSCC operations.

The components and core processes of the PSCC are shown in Figure 16–4, which also shows the diverse influences on the communications function. Starting from the left, "suppliers"—including vendors, public safety personnel, and other government staff—provide the inputs that enable the center to function. Feedback for the input process comes in the form of electronic tracking systems for call monitoring and processing, customer feedback, and internal quality review procedures. The core processes are call taking and dispatch for emergency and

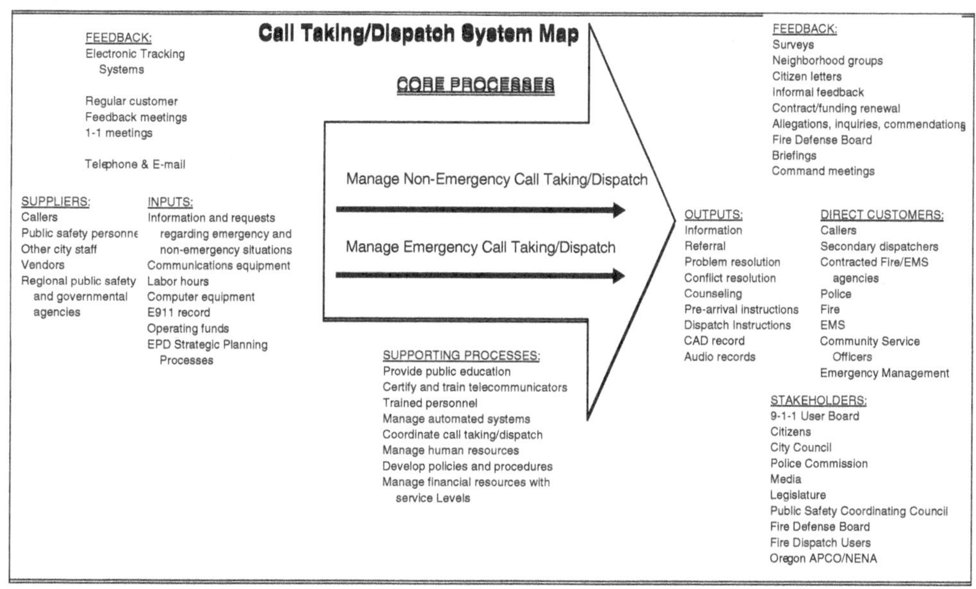

Source: Eugene Budget Committee "Call Taking/Dispatch" in *Citizen Subcommittee Service Profile Review* (November 29, 2006), 37, eugene-or.gov/portal/server.pt/gateway/PTARGS_0_2_236883_0_0_18/2006-11-29ServiceProfileUpdate.pdf.

Figure 16-4 A 911 call-taking dispatch system process map from Eugene, Oregon, illustrates the complexity of call center operations.

nonemergency calls. The outputs of call processing and dispatch include information (provided to callers and responders), problem resolution, referral, prearrival and dispatch instructions, CAD records, and audio files or records. The direct customers of the center include callers, secondary dispatchers (from allied organizations), and emergency response agencies served. Feedback on this side of the diagram includes surveys, neighborhood groups, contract or funding renewal, and command meetings. Finally, stakeholders on the output end of the diagram can include the 911 user board, citizens, elected officials, media, the legislature, and fire dispatch users.

In this complex environment, the PSCC director must be able to obtain and use feedback, develop and revise professional development objectives, share information, encourage networking, promote awareness of and compliance with legal requirements, practice a process for managing liability, and facilitate change. APCO publishes recommended core competencies for communications center managers and directors.[3]

Staffing

Despite all the equipment and no matter how hardened or redundant the communications system, the reliability of the entire operation comes down to the people who operate it: the call takers, dispatchers, and other telecommunicator who staff the PSCC. They are the most critical component of public safety communication systems, and their institutional affiliation, hiring, and training are central. It is also important that they clearly understand the role of the center and the operating agencies that it serves.

How communications personnel are recruited, selected, trained, mentored, compensated, and recognized has a direct correlation to the quality of service provided by the communications center. A PSCC is one of the most mission-critical facilities—if not *the* most critical facility—in a community, providing 911 and the dispatch of public safety services to citizens. However, for various reasons, these facilities are seldom provided with the care and attention they should have, and communications personnel are often considered the proverbial "red-haired stepchild" of public safety.

Staff for PSCCs can be dedicated civilian specialists or uniformed members of constituent agencies serviced by the center. Years ago, many centers, particularly in smaller communities, were staffed by law enforcement personnel. Initially, this made great sense, as the majority of calls for service were related to law enforcement, and often law enforcement personnel were the only paid force available on a twenty-four-hour basis. But as training requirements for call taking and dispatching increased and a need for greater economy in operations affected all government organizations, it became difficult to defend the use of sworn, armed personnel for dispatcher duties.

A multitude of staffing patterns and organizational affiliations exist across the nation. Successful centers operate with all uniformed personnel, with a mix of uniformed and civilian staff, and with all civilian staff. What these centers have in common is strong leadership, good policies, training, equipment, and a process for obtaining feedback and improving on service delivery through a review of calls for service and regular input from agencies being served.

Scheduling for personnel is a challenging task for most centers. More personnel are commonly assigned during peak hours, which can vary from place to place, depending on whether the 911 center also answers administrative phone lines for the agencies it serves. General practice for personnel engaged in dispatch is to limit shift duration to twelve hours in order to maintain alertness.

In addition to covering for normal absences, management must be able to quickly pull in extra staff during major events and extended emergencies. In large centers, off-duty staff may be recalled, but an alternative may be to maintain a cadre of trained personnel who can fill a "relief" role to provide greater flexibility. If these personnel receive the same training that core staff receive to achieve competence in necessary areas (e.g., tactical radio operations), they can enhance the quality of service and the quality of life for the core staff by reducing "forced" overtime.

Operating procedures and training

Because of the highly demanding environment in which PSCCs operate, it is absolutely essential that policies and procedures for daily center operations and activities be well defined.

Consistency is especially important in the operation of these centers. All calls for service should be classified and dispatched according to uniform criteria.

The telecommunicator's job is demanding, and training requirements are increasing, especially as centers pursue accreditation and implement advanced technologies. Proper recognition of the skills and expertise of telecommunicators is important, as these personnel are the backbone of a successful PSCC. Agencies that do not recognize their skills and abilities as well as their need for ongoing training risk higher turnover and less effective operations (see sidebar below).

The foundation of service in the communications and 911 centers is the initial training of telecommunicators. Training available for dispatch personnel is well established, and a number of nationally recognized organizations offer certification programs for telecommunicators. APCO International defines minimum standards for public safety telecommunicators.[4]

All of the professional organizations offer strong, job-validated courses in a number of subjects. Most of these courses have gotten longer as the complexities of communication operations have increased. Classroom training is supplemented by simulation training on consoles

Project RETAINS

In 1999, the Association of Public-Safety Communications Officials (APCO) International, with sponsorship from the National Institute of Justice, began a project known as Responsive Efforts to Address Integral Needs in Staffing (RETAINS) to examine staffing and retention issues in public safety communications centers (PSCCs) and provide center managers throughout the country with tools and strategies needed to increase the effectiveness of their own management practices in areas of

- Staffing
- Overtime and retention
- Recruitment, screening, and selection of qualified staff
- Shift management and employee satisfaction
- Turnover and retention rates
- Job complexity
- Compensation and benefits
- Working conditions
- Center performance
- Orientation and training
- Recognition and appreciation.

Initial research results and an *Effective Practices Guide*, as well as a *Staffing and Retention Toolkit*, were released in 2008.

A 2009 Project RETAINS study identified the importance of supportive management and perceived recognition to reducing psychological stress and turnover among PSCC personnel. Although the centers differed widely in terms of size, location, and type, several patterns emerged in the study findings that are relevant for local communication centers:

- The overwhelming majority (83 percent) of centers saw an increase in the number of dispatched calls from 2005 to 2008.
- Staffing pressures were found in PSCCs of varying sizes, although in different ways. Small and medium-sized centers were especially likely to report an increase in dispatch volume, but small centers were less than half as likely as large centers to report an increase in staffing levels. On the other hand, directors of large centers reported much more difficulty in keeping their authorized positions filled throughout the year.
- The average retention rate for PSCCs was 81 percent, two percentage points lower than the rate calculated in 2005. Variation in retention from center to center had increased.

Another APCO Project RETAINS report released in 2009 examined how the economy, salary, psychological distress, staffing of dispatcher positions, consolidation, and leadership development can affect staffing and retention. Project RETAINS intends to reevaluate its information every four or five years to keep pace with technological developments and update the online toolkit.[1]

1 All APCO Project RETAINS reports and tools are available free to APCO members. To learn more about APCO Project RETAINS, visit apco911.org/about/911/retains/ and apcointl.com/new/commcenter911/retains-faq.php.

like the one that the successful candidate will be expected to operate. Critical components of basic training are time on the job under the direct supervision of a coach and "ride-along" programs with field forces.

In addition, "train-the-trainer" programs are available that allow agencies to develop internal training programs (see Figure 16–5). Many major vendors are willing to allow telecommunicators to attend their training programs. Training in a private industry environment can help emergency service telecommunicators develop an understanding of PSCCs as customer service agencies with many different customer bases.

Computer-aided dispatch systems

CAD serves as a resource for the dispatcher, and speeds the processing and dispatch of calls for service. A database of street addresses, place names, business names, and other commonly used identifiers must support the CAD system. For each location or small area that the dispatcher enters into the system, the computer will search for the closest units according to the nature of the emergency and any other rules created by and unique to the agency. However, the system must be flexible enough to allow dispatchers to input incidents using informal place names or locations that may not have a commonly known address. In several documented cases, dispatches were considerably delayed because the dispatchers did not have a street address for a known location, and the CAD system would not permit the dispatcher to create a file for an incident and dispatch responders without this information. Modern CAD systems use mobile data systems and global positioning systems (GPS) to dispatch responders to incidents and support decision making in the field.

Early CAD systems took incident location data that had been manually input by a dispatcher and recommended a response. A dispatcher input and maintained the status of available units using radio transmissions from the field. Newer systems have made it possible to transfer responsibility for status changes to the field units when those units are equipped with simple data status units, mobile data terminals, or mobile computers. With this transfer of responsibility, airtime that had been taken up by a routine change in unit status has been freed up for critical communications, and dispatchers can spend more time monitoring field operations or providing support services, such as placing telephone calls, more expeditiously.

In addition, newer CAD systems interface with enhanced 911 systems (those that show the location of the caller) and with governmental computer systems. This interfacing allows access to vast amounts of information that, if properly managed, can be of assistance to emergency responders. Information about location-specific hazards or about previous activity at an address, for example, can improve responder safety. However, fire and emergency service managers must consider carefully what data should be made available to system users in various roles, so as to avoid data overload and ensure that sensitive information is not needlessly disseminated.

Modern CAD systems are the basis for information that is stored in records management systems. An area of evolving interest is the linking of CAD systems to enable information to be exchanged automatically. Working with law enforcement organizations and agencies, the Department of Justice and the Department of Homeland Security (DHS) have developed the

Figure 16-5 A class is being conducted in a dedicated training room, using equipment identical to that on the dispatch floor. Larger centers typically include facilities where employees can train on functional equipment without interfering with "live" dispatch operations.

Photo by Charles R. Jennings

311 centers

The inundation of 911 systems with nonemergency calls led to the development of an alternative system to provide nonemergency assistance. Baltimore was the first city to use a 311 system, which it deployed in 1996 as a police nonemergency number. The Baltimore 311 system now fields complaints and concerns regarding traffic signs, housing violations, rodent problems, and a host of other issues. Dedicated personnel (police personnel or civilians hired specifically for the call center), as well as a cadre of staff drawn from other city call centers, answer the 311 calls. If they cannot handle an issue, they can transfer the call to the police department district stations, which are staffed on a twenty-four-hour basis, or to emergency dispatch. At any time, if the officer determines that there is a need, the call can be transferred to 911. With 311, a major part of the previous 911 call load in Baltimore has been removed from the emergency system.

In 1999 Chicago expanded the idea to create a comprehensive 311 system that citizens can call not only for nonemergency public safety services but also for assistance or information from any city department or service. Within a few years, with encouragement from the federal government, many other communities concerned about 911 overload adopted 311 either for public safety nonemergencies or for all city services, and these systems are generally producing positive results. Greenville, South Carolina, makes it even easier for citizens to use 311 to report problems or request services by making available a free 311 "app" for iPhone and iTouch users.[1]

311 is most appropriate for large municipalities with complex government structures and a heavy demand on the 911 system. However, these duties cannot simply be added to the public safety 911 center. Implementation of 311 requires planning and, usually, additional personnel and the creation of a facility for operating the center. Comprehensive 311 systems may be located outside the public safety departments.

A concern in setting up a 311 system is helping citizens understand what is an emergency and what is not. Actual experience shows that citizens usually do distinguish between emergencies and nonemergencies; for example, in those communities where existing seven-digit numbers for public safety services were kept in service after the implementation of 911, citizens were told to use 911 for emergencies and the seven-digit numbers for nonemergencies. Some calls that should have come in over 911 did not, as citizens used their own criteria for making the determination, but 911 did not get overloaded, and citizens generally routed their calls correctly.

Some communities will benefit from 311 and others will not; 311 is not a cure-all. Fire and emergency service managers must evaluate the 911 center's handling of calls, and must then participate in the municipality's decision whether to use 311 and how to configure the service.

1 "Greenville Unveils iPhone Application," *WYFF4.com*, February 8, 2010, wyff4.com/news/22504009/detail.html (accessed October 27, 2010).

National Information Exchange Model (NIEM; niem.gov/) as a user-driven set of standards to facilitate data exchange among different agencies' electronic systems. Users stretch across the public safety community to include fire, rescue, EMS, law enforcement, and allied agencies.

Records management systems

A records management system (RMS) is not the same as a CAD system. Usually invisible to the end user, an RMS supports CAD by capturing essential data on calls for service and how they are handled, on the response of units, and on the disposition of incidents. The Bureau of Justice's Law Enforcement Information Technology Standards Council is an excellent resource for specification of requirements for CAD and records management systems.

An RMS for fire services should be designed specifically for fire service use and be compatible with National Fire Incident Reporting System standards for export of fire incident data to state and federal levels. The RMS is more than just a repository for the department's data; it is also the heart of the department's ability to collect, analyze, and relate CAD and incident information from various sources and functions for management and performance measurement purposes. It should not only readily accept data but also facilitate processing that data for the department's needs. Numerous vendors offer fire-specific or public safety records management systems.

An RMS should be able to track dispatch data, incident reports, building information and preincident plans, permits for hazardous conditions or materials in buildings, training records,

Performance measures for a public safety communications center

The information below suggests categories of information that need to be collected to measure the performance of the PSCC. Measures can be in raw counts, percentages, time, etc.

Telephone system statistics

Emergency 911*

- Wireline**
- Wireless**
- Voice over Internet protocol (VoIP)**
- 911 calls for which the caller hung up/disconnected before the call could be answered

**Does not include calls that were disconnected before the call was answered.*

***Includes 911 calls that were disconnected before the call was answered.*

Ten-digit emergency number
Nonemergency number
Nonemergency tow line
Calls from the media (includes print, TV, radio, Internet, etc.)
Calls for which the caller hung up/disconnected before the call could be answered*

**Includes all calls for which the caller hung up/disconnected before the call could be answered.*

Total calls received from the public*

**Emergency 911, ten-digit emergency number, nonemergency number, nonemergency tow line, and calls from the media.*

Percentage of 911 calls answered within 10 seconds*

**In compliance with the National Emergency Number Association (NENA) standard 56-005 that states "Ninety percent (90%) of all 9-1-1 calls arriving at the Public Safety Answering Point (PSAP) shall be answered within ten (10) seconds during the busy hour (the hour each day with the greatest call volume, as defined in the NENA Master Glossary 00-001)."*

Percentage of 911 calls answered between 11 seconds and 20 seconds*

**Denotes the longest length of time a caller waited before being answered.*

Number of times the prerecorded "All 911 Lines Are Busy" message played for callers
Average speed to answer (Emergency 911) in seconds
Average speed to answer (ten-digit emergency number) in seconds*
Average speed to answer (nonemergency number) in seconds
Average speed to answer (nonemergency tow line) in seconds

**Includes private alarm companies and other local area PSCCs.*

fire hydrant locations, and inspection or public education reports. Integration of records with geographic information or an interface with geographic information system (GIS) software is a desirable feature as well.

Performance measures for dispatch and communications

As with other aspects of fire and emergency service department operations, measurement of performance for the communications or dispatch function is important. A key aspect of this performance measurement is quality and customer service. Unlike the performance of some other fire and emergency service activities, that of an individual telecommunicator can be closely measured and directly linked to the quality and timeliness of service provided. Capabilities for tracking and recording performance data can be included in CAD/RMS systems.

Performance measures for PSCCs include telephone system statistics, CAD statistics, radio transmission statistics, quality assurance statistics, and operations statistics (see sidebar for examples in each category).

Consolidation

A way to reduce costs and improve the professionalism of the communications system is to create a joint communications center by consolidating two or more existing centers.

Calls transferred to other agencies
Calls requiring *language line* interpretation

- Average length of language interpretation calls in minutes
- Hours spent using language interpretation

Calls for which emergency medical dispatch/pre-arrival instructions (EMD/PAI) were provided

Computer-aided dispatch (CAD) system statistics

Fire-emergency services department events entered by call takers/dispatchers
Fire-emergency services department events initiated by fire-emergency service units in the field and controlled by dispatchers
Average call/dispatch processing time (location verification to unit dispatched)
Total number of advanced life support (ALS) and basic life support (BLS) events created and controlled

- Average call/dispatch processing time for ALS events
- Average call/dispatch processing time for BLS events

Radio transmission statistics

Total radio transmissions made to fire-emergency service units
Total radio transmission time in hours

Quality assurance statistics

Number of EMD/PAI reviews conducted*

**In compliance with American Society for Testing and Materials (ASTM) Standard 1560 that mandates that an agency quality assurance program shall review, at a minimum, 7 to 10 percent of EMD calls.*

Number of high-risk/low-frequency EMD reviews*

**A subtotal of the total number of EMD/PAI reviews conducted; high-risk/low-frequency EMD events include cardiopulmonary resuscitation, shooting, stabbing, assault with weapon, drowning, and suicide.*

Operational statistics*

Childbirth delivery calls received
Choking calls received
CPR administered by call takers

**Statistics are generated by Event Search query within the event remarks; therefore, occurrences are approximate based on correct spelling of specific keywords.*

Source: Suggested categories and measures based on Fairfax, County, Department of Public Safety Communications, *Monthly Productivity Report* (March 2011), fairfaxcounty.gov/911/docs/march_2011.pdf.

(*Regionalization* is another term for consolidation.) The same results can be achieved by contracting for communication services from another agency.

Joint facilities are not without problems, however. Responder agencies may feel that they have lost control of a key part of their response capability. Police officers and fire department personnel may each want the joint center to give their department priority. Finally, if a joint center is cooperatively administered by two or more departments, there will be ongoing debates over whether the communications function should be put under a public safety agency to ensure appropriate management, or be split up and returned to decentralized management by the cooperating departments.

How can the turf wars over joint communications be controlled? One way is to create an oversight committee with members from each of the agencies served and from the public. Established to address issues and concerns about the communications system, this committee would be charged with finding solutions, not discussing problems endlessly or assigning blame. Consensus decision making can be used to ensure that issues are resolved in a fashion that benefits the public. Problems that the cooperating agencies cannot resolve through the oversight committee would have to go to the elected officials for resolution because those officials are the FCC licensee and control the funding. Accordingly, there must be protocols for presenting both sides of the issue to the elected officials or their designees. Without a fair and balanced way to settle differences, individuals and agencies may lose confidence in the communications system.

Consolidating the communications function: Charlottesville-Albemarle County, Virginia

The Charlottesville-UVA-Albermarle County (Virginia) Emergency Communications Center (ECC) serves public safety agencies across three separate jurisdictions under an interlocal agreement between the County of Albemarle, the City of Charlottesville (independent city), and the University of Virginia (UVA) (Commonwealth of Virginia). The agencies served by the ECC include the Charlottesville City Police Department, the Albemarle County Police Department, the UVA Police Department, the Albemarle County Fire Department (a career department, seven volunteer fire departments, and three volunteer rescue squads), Charlottesville-Albemarle Airport Public Safety, and the Charlottesville Fire Department (CFD).

Housed within the county government, the ECC began as a combined public safety answering point (PSAP) for the city and the county to dispatch police and emergency medical services. In 2006, it took the first step toward consolidating fire dispatch by assuming fire dispatch responsibilities for Albemarle County. Within the county, this step was significant because for almost forty years, all fire dispatching had been done by uniformed firefighters in the CFD, and many people felt that "only a firefighter" could dispatch fire calls effectively.

During a twelve-month transition, all personnel in the ECC were certified in fire dispatch and underwent fire department familiarization training, which included visits to the fire departments being dispatched for a better understanding of their needs and operating conditions. Experience with the combined city-county PSAP that received 911 calls from the region eased the transition of county fire dispatch to the ECC. The city and county used the same computer-aided dispatch (CAD) product, which enabled the city and county—and UVA—to interact and communicate with minimal effort. In 2007, the transition of city fire dispatch operations into the ECC began.

The transition to ECC dispatch for Charlottesville fire services worked in three phases. In the first phase, the ECC started performing *all* call-taking functions for city fire incidents. (Because the ECC served as the combined PSAP for the city and county, it was already receiving fire calls for the city, which it transferred directly to the Charlottesville Fire Dispatch located at fire headquarters.) In the second phase, it entered the calls into the CAD to create an incident report, which was then dispatched by the CFD dispatchers. In the final phase, the ECC assumed the full dispatch operations for the city, from call taking to incident dispatch.

To maintain a smooth transition, the CFD modified some of its dispatch procedures to conform to those already in use in the county. This eased the burden on ECC dispatchers and further integrated regional public safety operations, which include provision of automatic aid by the CFD to some county areas.

In addition to establishing an oversight committee, cooperating departments can use comment cards to solicit complaints, comments, and compliments directed at all agencies, including the communications system. Any responder who fills out a comment card sends it to his or her supervisor, and it works its way up the chain of command. This process allows agency heads to manage problems jointly and relay compliments.

Another option that may prove helpful is to have liaison officers from operating departments permanently stationed in the joint center. Managers must be careful to ensure, however, that these officers work with the center's manager without disrupting operations or interfering in the chain of command.

To help build consensus, agencies can be allowed to provide input on training for both telecommunicators and field personnel. In this way, the field units and communications center can educate each other about the intricacies of their own jobs. The working relationship can also be reinforced with ride-along programs for the telecommunicators and with tours of duty in the communications center for field personnel. Monthly meetings of field representatives and communications system personnel will allow each group to express its concerns and hear the other group's concerns and questions.

Setting up a joint center by merging existing operations will require an intensive planning process. To avoid problems, the question of who will take the lead must be settled early on; generally the new management system should be in place in time to direct the planning process. An announcement should be made that on a certain day, a new communications manager will assume control of the police, fire, EMS, and other systems involved, and the affected department chiefs must demonstrate their clear-cut support for the joint center. Com-

The ECC is staffed by forty communication officers and supervisors. The goal is to have all personnel cross-trained in police, fire, and emergency medical service (EMS) dispatch. Separate certifications are maintained for each discipline. Currently, about 85 percent of staff is cross-trained.

According to Fire Chief Charles Werner, the CFD is very pleased with the new dispatching arrangements. He believes that the demands of communication assignments have grown in the areas of knowledge and technology, and that the basic qualifications for firefighter are no longer sufficient for public safety telecommunications. Serving as a fire dispatcher was a mandatory assignment for new firefighters, and most left this position as soon as they were able. The use of civilian specialists has greatly reduced turnover among dispatchers. After the transition, five of the firefighters who had been assigned to dispatch were eliminated through attrition, producing an annual savings of $109,000 for the city.

The ECC is accredited by the Commission on Accreditation for Law Enforcement Agencies (CALEA). The accreditation process includes development of written policies and guidelines, as well as compliance with key standards from third-party organizations.

Governance is provided by a board that comprises the executives from the county, city, and university; the chiefs of the police agencies, chiefs of the fire departments, a volunteer fire/EMS representative, and an environmental health and safety representative from UVA. The board meets quarterly and sets policy in conjunction with the participating agencies. Each agency is assessed a share of costs based on its share of calls for service. Some additional funding is provided by outside agencies that receive services from the ECC.

Complaints or concerns about specific incidents are handled by agency liaisons, who interact directly with a manager at the ECC. In addition, a user satisfaction survey is conducted annually, and results are published by the board, made available to users and the public, and compared from year to year.

Benefits of the consolidation include reduced call-processing times, reduced cost to the city of Charlottesville, and greater coordination of resources within the region. The consolidation of dispatch has strengthened interoperability and awareness of events and resource levels throughout the city, county, and university. The center has attracted significant grant funds because it serves all public safety agencies across all three jurisdictions.

The ECC shows that with solid management and an appropriate governance structure, effective consolidation of multijurisdictional public safety communications can be achieved. Strong preexisting relationships between agencies, methodical and well-conceived planning, and a transition pace that allows agencies to adjust to changes are all cited as factors behind the success of this consolidation.

Source: Interviews with Tom Hanson, director, Albemarle County ECC, and Charles Werner, chief, CFD.

munications center staff should be kept informed from the beginning of the planning process, and any changes in working conditions or benefits must be spelled out clearly before operations begin. Newsletters and one-on-one meetings can accomplish this.

The best opportunity for establishing a joint communications facility is when a new municipal, district, regional, or county facility is to be built. The new facility can provide a clean break with the past. It can include room for training, administrative offices, locker rooms, showers, sleeping space, and physical fitness facilities, and it should be self-sufficient in the event of a disaster.

Public safety communication systems hardware and technologies

Communication systems serve one of two purposes: the transmission of voice or the transmission of data. This section reviews major concepts and dynamic areas in the transmission of both voice and data for a fire and emergency services department.

Radio systems

What follows is a summary of radio system basics. Numerous publications from agencies such as the U.S. Fire Administration and other government sources can provide more detailed information.

Spectrum Electromagnetic radiation travels in waves, and the frequency of the waves is measured in cycles per second. (A kilohertz [kHz] is 1,000 cycles per second, and a megahertz

[MHz] is 1,000,000 cycles per second.) The radio spectrum is the full range of frequencies, from very low (subaudible) to very high (visible light).

Public safety radio systems are confined to fairly limited parts of the spectrum, in several different frequency bands:

- Very high frequency—low band: 33 MHz–46 MHz
- Very high frequency—high band: 150 MHz–174 MHz
- Ultra high frequency (UHF): 450 MHz–460 MHz
- 700–900 MHz.

Above the 800–900 MHz band are frequencies used for broadband and microwave transmissions.

The radio spectrum is a limited resource, and the FCC controls its use by licensing transmitters (by agency) and assigning frequencies. The process of regulating and assigning frequencies to users is known as frequency coordination. A frequency or band of frequencies assigned for use by a specific transmitter agency is called a channel.

Analog versus digital The original radio systems used analog technology. The analog radio signal is a continuous wave, much like the human voice. Transmitters change the amplitude of the wave to match the amplitude of the sound being transmitted, which occurs with amplitude-modulated (AM) radio; or they change the frequency in direct proportion to the sounds being transmitted, which occurs with frequency-modulated (FM) radio. In the public safety services, FM radio is used for voice communication because of its noise-rejection properties relative to AM systems.

FM transmitters can use subaudible tones to direct transmissions to specific receivers, making it possible for several agencies to share one frequency without each hearing all traffic on that frequency. The key to efficient use of the spectrum is to geographically separate agencies sharing a frequency and to limit the output of transmitters to avoid excessive interference.

Digital radio came into use for several reasons, including more efficient use of the spectrum, less noise, better clarity, and the availability of advanced features in radio systems. In a digital system, sound is converted to digital format, meaning noncontinuous electromagnetic waves. These waves are received and then converted back into analog to be played through a speaker that reproduces the original characteristics of the sound. Digital radio technology uses sampling and can correct for missing data during a transmission. However, it is not a perfect technology (see accompanying sidebar).

Digital versus analog radio transmission on the fire ground

In common fire-ground situations, transmissions from digital radios in or adjacent to high-noise conditions may be unintelligible. While some noise conditions make it too difficult for any radio to transmit a clear message, digital radios are more vulnerable than their analog counterparts to noise interference.

Analog radios rely on a relatively direct process: the user's voice (or any other sounds reaching the microphone) are translated directly into changes or modulations of the frequency. Analog transmissions can faithfully transmit both a user's voice and background noises. The latter are often an annoyance, but they can give important information to personnel monitoring the transmissions. For example, the sound of a door being forced indicates that crews may not have made entry to a structure or have encountered a locked door en route to the fire.

Digital radios, on the other hand, translate voice messages into digital data packets. The translation process is controlled by a codec (coder/decoder), and the codes are standardized in Project 25-compliant radios (see sidebar on page 468). Once the voice is sampled and converted into a digital signal, it is transmitted. The receiving radio reverses the process and converts the digital signal back into analog, where it is reproduced by the speaker on the radio. Under normal conditions, digital transmissions carry less static, enable numerous additional features, and allow more efficient use of radio spectrum. However, recent tests by the Department of Commerce's National Telecommunications and Information Administration (NTIA) have confirmed that digital radios generally perform more poorly than analog radios under high-noise conditions.[1] While the NTIA cautions that agencies should not act solely on the basis of the experiments, many agencies have opted to program their digital radios to operate in analog mode on tactical fire-ground channels.

1 See David J. Atkinson and Andrew A. Catellier, *Intelligibility of Selected Radio Systems in the Presence of Fireground Noise: Test Plan and Results*, NTIA Technical Report TR-08-453 (Washington, D.C.: National Telecommunications and Information Administration, U.S. Department of Commerce, June 2008), its.bldrdoc.gov/pub/ntia-rpt/08-453/08-453.pdf (accessed November 8, 2010).

Channel narrowbanding and rebanding A growing problem for some public safety agencies is a shortage of available radio channels, especially in large urban areas where numerous public safety agencies operate radio systems that have been in existence for many decades. When these systems were originally designed and licensed, mutual aid and joint operations were not considered. As a consequence, many new or growing fire and emergency service departments in suburban areas may be limited to a few channels, and larger cities may be unable to add channels because all available frequencies are in use within the geographic area.

Analog radio transmissions have traditionally operated with a bandwidth of 25 kHz. To avoid interference, adjacent channels need additional bandwidth between them. Digital radio signals use only 12.5 kHz per channel and need less "space" between channels to avoid interference. For this reason, digital radio is referred to as "narrowband." More narrowband channels can be defined in a given amount of radio spectrum. The FCC has mandated that all radio users operating in the traditional public safety bands must switch to narrowband (12.5 kHz) by January 1, 2013.[5] This provision applies to all legacy analog radio equipment. Analog radio will still be permitted, but it must be converted to narrowband. Agencies must plan to replace existing equipment to meet this narrowbanding deadline, and must also consider the possibility that bandwidth will be further reduced to 6.25 kHz to free more spectrum.

Trunked radio systems In conventional radio systems, a specific channel is designated for a particular use. When that channel is not in use, it remains reserved for possible use. As the number of available frequencies shrinks, great efficiencies in use of spectrum can be achieved through trunking. Trunked radio systems operate using a pool of frequencies (see the accompanying sidebar), which are assigned to conversations one call at a time via computerized control systems. Trunking technology is more complex and more costly than nontrunked technology, but because of its advantages, it is used by many larger public safety organizations.

Coverage/signal propagation The geographic area within which communications can be achieved is known as the range of the radio system. In analog systems, users know when they are nearing the limits of the system because noise increases, and it becomes increasingly difficult to understand messages received. In digital radio systems, because the signal is processed and errors are automatically corrected, there is no noticeable degradation in reception as the user nears the limits of the system's range—until, suddenly, transmission ceases. That is, digital radio systems are "all or nothing." As a result, digital radio systems have longer range than analog systems using the same power output.

Trunked radio

Telephone companies have used trunking for years to manage local telephone service.

Nontrunked (conventional) channels are like one-lane highways. Radio traffic is initiated by a party at one end of the single lane, who places a call to a recipient at the other end. No other traffic should use the channel until the recipient sends an answer back in the other direction. However, because there are often more than two users trying to use one "lane," other traffic often enters the channel during a conversation, causing interference. Even the two parties to the same conversation can interfere with each other's transmission if one cannot hear the other—as often happens when one of them is using a portable radio. The various users' radio traffic on these single-lane channels can become intermixed, and people may miss transmissions meant for them. People have to wait for their own transmissions to be acknowledged. In a conventional system with five single channels, for example, if this waiting is happening on all five channels, only five sets of radio transmissions may tie up all the channels.

Trunking unites separate single-lane channels into a limited-access highway. A computer chooses the channel that is to be used for individual messages. Multiple messages can be intermingled on the highway. Messages moving from sender to recipient can switch from channel to channel just as cars move from lane to lane on a highway as spaces open up. Channels do not have to stay idle while people wait for a reply. The computer decides which channels to use for replies and which to make available to the next radio with which someone is trying to transmit. Just as the addition of only one extra lane to a four-lane highway increases the throughput of the highway by more than 20 percent, trunking allows more communication than a regular system does on the same number of channels.

The overall performance of a radio system is determined by numerous factors, including topography, buildings, trees, power levels, antenna type and location, and possible interference from nearby transmitters. The frequency band in use can also influence coverage.

Determining radio system coverage is a specialized topic and requires a radio engineer. The most important thing for fire and emergency service managers to remember is that the usability of the system must be tested: the agency should not rely solely on calculated or forecast coverage based on software models of predicted system performance.

Interoperability DHS's SAFECOM office defines interoperability as "the ability to work seamlessly with other systems or products without any special effort."[6] The emphasis on radio system interoperability increased after the 9/11 attacks in New York. Since that time, considerable effort has been directed at formalizing processes, equipment, and procedures to permit agencies to operate together and maintain communications.

Efforts to improve interoperability are frustrated by

- Incompatible and aging communications equipment
- Limited and fragmented budget cycles and funding
- Limited and fragmented planning and coordination
- Limited and fragmented radio spectrum
- Limited equipment standards.

Fire and emergency service organizations can use SAFECOM's interoperability continuum as a tool to identify their current status as well as plan for future improvements (see Figure 16–6). The continuum, a widely accepted and useful tool for assessing where an organization stands in this critical regard, addresses interoperability as a function of five dimensions: governance, standard operating procedures, technology, training and exercises, and usage. Moving from the left to the right of Figure 16–6, the level of interoperability increases. Of course, any particular organization may be at different points on each of the five dimensions. Agencies may even be at different points with regard to different neighboring agencies.

Data systems

Digital communication technologies have created numerous opportunities for the enhanced use of information in the field. Key to this expansion in capability is the expanding availability of wireless data communication capacities that enable the rapid distribution of relatively large data files. While mobile data terminals have been in use for decades, the need to force data over radio channels has limited the quantity and type of information that could be sent. For the most part, messages were limited to short text files.

Wireless broadband, whether provided by commercial vendors through consumer networks or through dedicated public safety or government infrastructure, has made a host of

APCO Project 25

APCO Project 25 (P25) was initiated in 1989 by the Association of Public-Safety Communications Officials (APCO) International, the National Association of State Telecommunication Directors, the National Telecommunications and Information Administration, the National Communications System, and the U.S. Department of Defense. Its mission is to develop interface standards that will allow mobile and portable equipment from different manufacturers to communicate.

The first of six interface standards, the Common Air Interface, was specified in 1993. It enables subscriber units from different P25 systems to communicate. More advanced integration of radio systems is addressed in the other standards, which are in various stages of development. P25 also ensures backward compatibility from newer digital systems to older analog FM radio systems. P25 includes not only voice communications but also data.

P25 is a voluntary public-private partnership between end users of radio systems and manufacturers, developers, and vendors. Its capabilities are a requirement of many federal funding sources, and the standards are widely adopted for new digital radio systems. For more information, see apco911.org/frequency/project25/information.html.

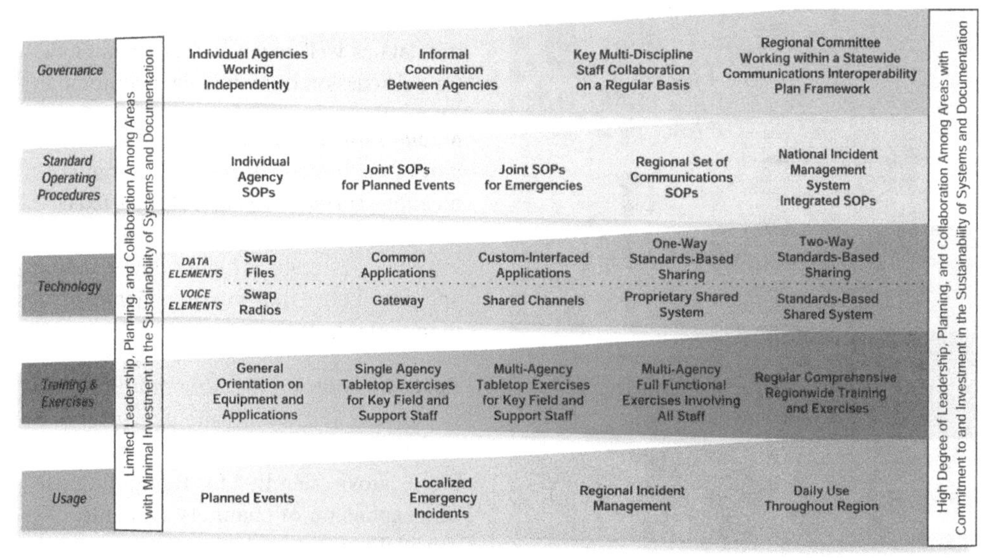

Source: Department of Homeland Security, "SAFECOM: Continuum," safecomprogram.gov/SAFECOM/tools/continuum/.

Figure 16-6 Interoperability improves the progression from left to right on the interoperability continuum developed by the U.S. Department of Homeland Security.

expanded information available to support field operations. The widespread use of mobile computer terminals in vehicles has provided a platform for the display of information as well as for the storage of data and rudimentary processing functions in the field.

Automatic vehicle location system One of the most basic data functions available to public safety agencies is automatic vehicle location (AVL) technology. While consumer-grade vehicle location units are ubiquitous and increasingly powerful, AVL penetration into public safety has been slow. The key distinguishing feature of public safety clients is the need to transmit information on vehicle position not only to the driver or operator of a particular vehicle but also back to the PSCC. Real-time vehicle location information can be used to manage system resources and can be a great aid in improving the efficiency of operations. CAD systems now routinely use GPS data to select the closest units for dispatch to an alarm. AVL also provides extensive data on vehicle travel characteristics that can be used in planning and management. Thus, fire and emergency service managers have a whole new source of information that must be managed, stored, and possibly analyzed.

Getting lost on the way to an incident should be a thing of the past. Agencies relying on AVL systems for navigation must ensure that the street database they are using is maintained and of high quality. In enterprise systems, GPS data are typically displayed against a validated governmental map or street network.

Geographic information system (GIS) A GIS is not technically a communications technology, but it is embedded in many critical aspects of communications center operations. GIS maps are used within CAD systems to define response boundaries, and incidents can be routinely geocoded or plotted to a specific location when a call is entered into the 911 system. Spatial analysis of incident response data is becoming a routine function of many PSCCs.

Video and image transmission As wireless broadband offers faster transmission of larger quantities of data, video links between field units and the communications center or command facilities are becoming more common (see Figure 16–7). With the proper infrastructure and technology, even streaming of video in real time is possible. The use of video makes real a long-awaited command and awareness aid.

User communications equipment

User, or subscriber, equipment is the hardware that ends up in the users' hands out in the field. Radio communications has become a basic part of the fire service arsenal as use of radio

Figure 16-7 Video technology is becoming commonplace in communication support vehicles.

Photo by Charles R. Jennings

and telephone equipment has proliferated. User equipment is increasingly able to transmit data as well as voice. (See Chapter 15 for a discussion of mobile data equipment.)

Mobile radios Mobile radios are a critical part of the fire and emergency communications system. Because of their fixed antenna placement, mobile radios mounted in vehicles operate at higher power output and have better transmission characteristics than portable radios.

Portable radios Portable radios are the workhorse of fire and emergency service communications. Recent designs are much more "glove friendly" for firefighting use. The expansion of channels available, especially with trunked systems, makes the use of LCD (liquid crystal display) channel displays on portable radios a desirable feature. Operation of portable radios is a subject for training so that users remain familiar with procedures for switching channels.

Cellular phones Cell phones operated on commercial networks have become an indispensible component of many agencies' communication strategies. While use of such devices can be highly cost-effective, reliability of service in times of emergency should be addressed through use of multiple providers, through agreements for priority service for preidentified public safety users, or with satellite-based equipment.

Satellite phones and radio Satellite-based telephones (Figure 16–8), Internet access, and even radio capabilities are becoming more common. While costs are prohibitive for small PSCCs, larger local centers and regional centers are beginning to integrate satellite technologies to provide redundant backup communications and connectivity. The loss of commercial cellular service or disruption of public safety communications infrastructure following a disaster creates the need for backup systems.

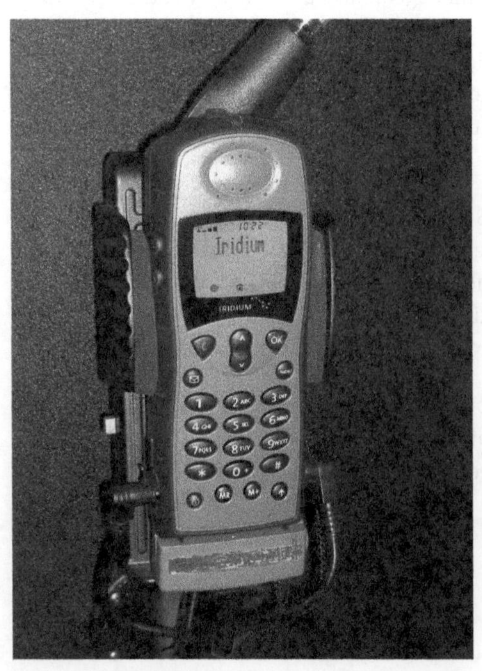

Figure 16-8 A satellite phone deployed in a communications vehicle can be removed from its mount and taken out of the vehicle.

Photo by Charles R. Jennings

Operational issues for fire and emergency service communication systems

All aspects of fire and emergency service operations—from routine activities to emergency incidents, from the firefighter in the field to the telecommunicator at the dispatch facility—involve communications. Operational concerns regarding communications cut across the organization and require coordinated attention from training, operations, and command staff in the EOC and at the emergency scene.

National Incident Management System and Incident Command System

The National Incident Management System (NIMS) and the Incident Command System (ICS) both recognize the importance of communications to the successful handling of emergency response. The key tenets of effective emergency communications, which communication systems must support, are

- Development and maintenance of a common operating picture
- Interoperability for participating resources
- Reliability, scalability, and portability, meaning that systems and solutions should be flexible and capable of adjusting as incidents grow in size
- Resiliency and redundancy, which is the ability of the communications system to withstand the loss of some components without widespread failure.

These high-level goals should drive the design of systems, including the policy and procedural components.

DHS's SAFECOM office publishes a task book for the (all-hazards) communications unit leader. DHS approval for advanced training for the communications section leader function fills a major gap in fire and emergency services training, and this training is sure to become a new standard for well-trained fire and emergency service organizations.

Initial aid agreements and mutual aid agreements

One of the key functions of a PSCC is to coordinate the responses of different agencies and jurisdictions to requests for aid. Mutual aid can be initial aid (also known as automatic aid), whereby, on the initial alarm, units from more than one entity or jurisdiction respond to the reported emergency. The communications system should facilitate such response. Maintaining awareness of unit status, which is critical to the optimal function of mutual aid systems, can be achieved through such means as linkages between CAD systems, placement of unit status monitors in respective dispatch centers, and shared alerting systems to directly notify automatic aid units.

Often, protocols such as "closest station response" can be implemented to expand automatic aid to first or even sole response to emergencies in neighboring jurisdictions. Jurisdictions have found that mutual aid agreements are well accepted by the public.

Agencies using mutual aid systems must consider radio communications interoperability, especially for incident scene operations. An often overlooked aspect of interoperability is unit designations. Ideally, unit designations are not duplicated among agencies that expect to work together. Unit designation schemes can be coordinated at the county or even regional level.

Mobile incident command posts

Mobile command units can be equipped with both cellular and satellite telephones, and both of these can be equipped to provide fax and data transmission services. Mobile units now have the capability to connect to local data networks to allow access to software and data normally available in an office environment. Other typical equipment includes radio voice logging, particularly for tactical channels (see section on next page); video recording with on-board cameras; and the capability to send video back to a dispatch or an EOC using wireless communications.

Mobile command units can vary in size from fairly modest van-based units that handle a single agency's need to elaborate units that are designed to house general staff positions and facilitate meetings among high-level staff, as well as to support multiple disciplines and agencies in coordinating communications (Figure 16–9).

Photo by Charles R. Jennings

Figure 16-9 Sioux Falls (South Dakota) Unified Incident Command Post is jointly operated by several agencies. The result is a larger, better-equipped unit than any one agency could afford on its own.

Photo by Charles R. Jennings

Figure 16-10 This radio cache trailer (with tow vehicle) in the National Capital Region (Washington, D.C.) is equipped with a generator and small workspace to manage the inventory of radios, chargers, batteries, and specialized communications equipment it carries.

Portable radio caches

A radio cache is a supply of additional radios, programmed on a jurisdiction's frequencies, which can be deployed in large-scale incidents that may draw large numbers of mutual aid responders or off-duty personnel (Figure 16–10). Caches can be useful both on short-term incidents of large magnitude and on extended operations in which numerous personnel may be cycling through the scene.

Equipment within the cache is maintained in a state of readiness with battery-charging and related support equipment. While fairly modest caches can consist of a few portable radios and extra batteries that can be delivered to a scene, many jurisdictions keep sophisticated cache systems ready; these may include specialty communications equipment as well as support personnel to assist the ICS communications leader in implementing tasks.

Cache equipment may include

- A diesel generator with a reserve fuel tank
- Portable generators for deployment at multiple sites or at locations distant from the cache location
- Portable antenna towers
- Portable radios supporting VHF, UHF, and 800 MHz bands
- Portable repeaters for all bands in use
- Interoperability devices, including gateways (network points that provide access to other networks)[7]
- Broadband trunking scanners
- Point-to-point 2.4 gigahertz (GHz) and 5.8 GHz data and voice links with a twenty-mile reach
- A portable low-speed satellite link for telephone and two-way radio
- On-board programming capabilities for all radio equipment
- A radio system analyzer, power meters, and troubleshooting tools and equipment
- A radio asset management system for distributing and tracking radios.

Primary channels and tactical channels

Primary channels are used for dispatch or initial operations. As an incident escalates, the designation of tactical channels for on-scene communications can help avoid overtaxing a single channel that is being used by incident commanders and to communicate resource requests and progress reports. The proper use of radio channel resources is a difficult topic for many organizations. Making the transition from "routine" to "working incident" communications can be a challenge, particularly for organizations with limited channels available. The separation of tactical from strategic or command functions should be considered the first step in this process.

Overloaded primary frequencies are a clear indicator of the need to begin using tactical channels. The number of tactical channels required depends on the number of personnel involved and the complexity of the incident. For highly sensitive or risky tasks (e.g., those requiring the hazardous materials team), a dedicated channel may be appropriate. Each channel in use during an incident must be monitored to maintain awareness of circumstances of the incident. Sharing frequencies with neighboring agencies is one way to use spectrum resources efficiently and ensure that enough channels are available in an emergency.

Staffing limitations at the communications center are sometimes cited as the reason that all available channels are not used during an incident. (In fact, too few supervisory staff in the field can also hamper efficient use of the radio system.) Calling in supplementary staff for the communications center is no different from calling for assistance on the fire ground.

Communications protocol

Communication managers must establish protocols that will promote effective and efficient use of communications equipment.

Jargon, codes, and plain English Each profession develops its own shorthand for use by people in the business, and the fire and emergency services are no exception. But the use of agency- or discipline-specific jargon can sometimes be an obstacle to clear communication in an emergency.

Several instructors at the Emergency Management Institute and the National Fire Academy use a simple but clear example of how jargon can affect emergency operations: The instructor asks, "What happens when you say, 'Charge the line'?" Then the class is asked if it makes a difference whether the person saying it is a police officer, a firefighter, or an electric utility line worker.

When the person issuing the order and the person receiving it are of the same discipline, each relies on the other's instinctive reaction. The police commander expects the police officers to advance rapidly, the fire service leader wants to see hose lines fill with water, and the utility crew chief expects the circuit to be energized. Each order is shorthand within the profession.

Does it matter if the receiving person and the transmitting person are of different disciplines? What might happen if the order to charge the line were passed down the chain of command from a fire service person to an electrical utility subordinate? What safety issues would be raised if this order were misinterpreted or acted on by different disciplines simultaneously? Might the advancing police walk into an area being wet down as the circuit is being energized? This issue has major implications for liaison officers and personnel operating in a unified command system, as the use of jargon can cause more than delays in operations.

A related problem arises when communication systems use numeric codes instead of a natural language. When the FCC required all radio transmissions to be entered into a written log, codes were introduced as a form of dispatcher shorthand. Some people mistakenly believed that the FCC required the use of these codes, or signals. Dispatchers then began to use the codes in actual transmissions to field units, a practice that was often formalized in written procedures.

This use of codes can lead to errors, generally in systems in which the dispatcher also gives the time over the radio as part of operational communications. Such errors occur especially from 10-00 to 10-59 in systems using "10" codes (codes that substitute numbers for commonly used phrases; e.g., "10-4" means "I understand and will comply"). Because 10-40 can be interpreted as 10:40, an operational message can be confused with the time.

Giving the time over the air began before accurate court-acceptable time-recording systems (i.e., systems whose records can be used as evidence in a lawsuit involving, for example, response times) were developed. Often the practice was codified into written policy, which has not been updated to reflect newer technology.

In the well-equipped communications center of the twenty-first century, there is no need to use codes: transmissions are recorded, and the FCC no longer requires written station logs. There is also no need to use on-air time to announce the hour over the radio system. The NIMS actually requires the use of plain language in multiagency responses. However, many organizations have resisted dropping coded language for "routine" activities.

These simple examples show that in planning sessions, the communications manager must be an advocate for both clear language and the absence of jargon. These examples also demonstrate the need for routinely updating procedures to ensure that all communications activity supports field operations and incorporates the benefits of new technology.

Fire and emergency service managers must become familiar with technology that is being sold to the general public because this technology sets public expectations. Consumer technology often "leads" public safety technology. When people can accurately find their positions in coastal waters or can call for assistance from their cars, they expect public safety services to be equally adept. In addition, effectiveness and efficiency are closely tied to technological advances. Beware the communications manager who doesn't use a smartphone!

Parroting "Parroting" refers to the practice of repeating selected critical information on the radio. Typically, dispatch retransmits or parrots key milestones, such as a size-up by a first-arriving unit or additional information received after the initial dispatch. (For example, an incident dispatched as an "activated automatic alarm" system may be updated with a call from within the building reporting a smoke condition.) The use of this technique has some merit but must be controlled. Excessive parroting, such as repeating the arrival of each unit on a multiple unit request, ties up the channel and displaces valuable communications from the scene to dispatch or vice versa.

Mayday The use of designated words for indicating a member in distress should be incorporated into standard operating procedures for radio communications. Transmission of a "mayday" message by a member in the field should trigger a predetermined response from the PSCC.

- Personnel on the frequency should cease all transmissions until the mayday is resolved. Units should break radio silence only at the direction of the incident commander.
- If unit identifiers are included on the radios, provisions should be made for relaying this information to the incident commander or other designated position in the incident command structure to assist in identifying and locating the member.
- Communications personnel should monitor all radio channels in use at an incident for transmissions that might not be heard by personnel on scene.
- Finally, information should be relayed on a channel not in use by the member or unit calling a mayday.

Analysis of such situations has shown that careful coordination with the PSCC can increase the chances for the timely rescue of missing or endangered members.

Postincident review and debriefing The postincident review or debriefing should include the PSCC. The center not only should provide audio files of on-scene radio traffic but also can include summaries of key milestones. If possible, a representative of the center should participate in the review or debriefing, and the scope of the review should include the initial report, call processing, and dispatch. Participation in these events can enhance understanding between the PSCC and field operations personnel, and can also identify areas for improvement, such as the need for clear progress reports from personnel on scene and the need to relay additional information from phone calls or other sources after personnel arrive on scene.

System acquisition and technology management

A critical component of any communications system is planning for its upgrade and eventual replacement. The quickening pace of technological advances has thrust concerns for system acquisition and technology management from a "once in a career" frequency to "once every ten years." How the planning process is managed depends on the position of the communications function in the government. Whether communications operates as a division or subpart of a fire department or is organized as a separate local or regional agency, the organizational issues will determine who the participants in the planning process are and which issues will take precedence. The overriding goal of the manager is to ensure that the needs of the public, responder agencies, and employees will be met in such a way that service is delivered efficiently.

The life cycle of a project, including the planning process, is illustrated in Figure 16–11. Knowledgeable people representing diverse interests should be part of the project planning process. This group should include personnel from the dispatch center's technical and operating realms, as well as agency managers and personnel representing end users of the system. If a PSCC serves a few agencies, each agency should have at least one representative. For centers serving more than a half-dozen agencies, it may be desirable to form an advisory committee with representatives from each agency. This committee would sign off on key aspects of the project's goals, scope, and functionality. However, it would not take on a project management role (see the section further on in this chapter on project management).

Developing a formal scope for the new project is critical. Determining what the system will and will not do is important for measuring the success of the project as well as for keeping the project's goals from "moving" over the course of the project. Similarly, developing a list

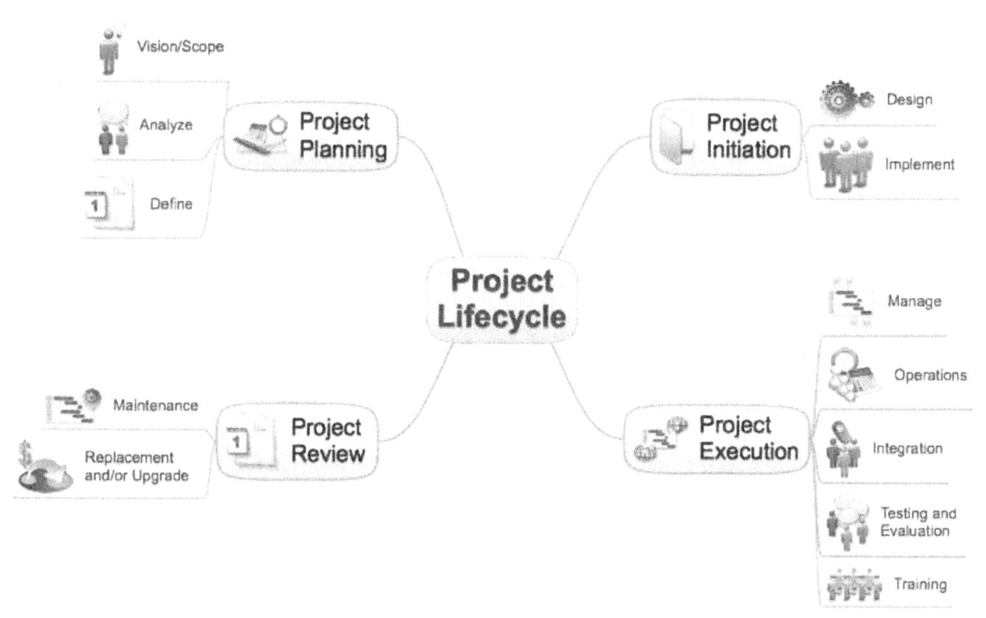

Source: Law Enforcement Information Technology Standards Council, *A Project Manager's Guide to: CAD/RMS Systems Software Acquisition* (Washington, D.C.: Bureau of Justice Assistance, n.d.), 10, theiacp.org/LinkClick.aspx?fileticket=g8QhfztgRZ0%3d&tabid=831.

Figure 16-11 The CAD/RMS Project Lifecycle comprises four activities: planning, initiation, execution, and review.

of known system deficiencies or areas of improvement can be a helpful way to refine goals. Constraints on funding and time may limit the department's ability to address all the identified deficiencies, but going through this process is helpful for prioritizing the most important concerns and for gaining buy-in from the participants.

Assessing needs and developing a requirements analysis

Although the questions of who participates and what issues take precedence may complicate planning, the planning process itself will generally be the same. It should focus on identifying detailed needs and then developing the most appropriate path forward to achieve the high-level objective. The lead person must remember that the technical knowledge of most participants in the planning process is neither as recent nor as extensive as is required. The first part of the process, therefore, may have to be training to ensure the participants' understanding.

Planning itself starts with a written needs assessment that is accepted by all parties involved: elected officials (from multiple jurisdictions, if the system is a regional one), appointed officials, responder groups, and the public. To achieve consensus, additional advisory groups may have to be convened. Defining the existing situation identifies the system's weak areas. Planners must interview all agencies that use the system. Staff must then analyze the weak areas to determine which ones can be eliminated by the use of new technology or systems. Field testing should be carried out to confirm the interview reports.

After the written needs assessment is accepted and the planning group is organized, the planners must collect the information necessary for appropriately depicting the existing situation. They can do this with field visits, technical tests, analyses of maintenance reports, surveys of end users, and interviews with field personnel. To eliminate any inaccuracies caused by missing or misinterpreted data, planners have to analyze and interpret this information in context, and their analysis must be conducted in a manner that makes it impossible for anyone to claim that the information was manipulated to control the eventual outcome. Here independent review committees or consultants can be of assistance. These precautions can assure the officials responsible for committing public funds that the need is real and that all reasonable options have been reviewed.

Once the current status of the communications system is established, planners need to review possible options for improvement. For each option, they should specify how it would address the problem areas identified earlier. If equipment is to be purchased, they should identify both the capital acquisition costs and the maintenance and operating costs over the expected life span of the equipment.

Also of concern are the costs of additional personnel and training that the operating agency will have to absorb. Many modern communication systems come with support requirements that are not at first apparent to people outside the vendor community. In deciding to commit the funding required, elected and appointed officials need to know all the costs that are involved. If they are unwilling or unable to support the investments needed to maintain or improve the level of service, alternate approaches—for example, consolidating centers or systems or contracting with another agency to provide dispatch services—must be considered. Organizational pride or a long history of independence should not be accepted excuses for inadequate support for the operational mission of the agency being served. (See Chapter 13 for more on life cycle costing.)

Planning system purchases

Planning for a new or significantly enhanced radio communications system and its supporting components is a multiyear process. Maintaining an awareness of the technology and trends among manufacturers and leading systems is crucial to knowing when the local system is becoming obsolete. Equally important is the ability to get support from the manufacturer. The best way to know where equipment stands in its product life cycle is to maintain a dialogue with the manufacturer and ensure that communications personnel participate in support groups and annual conferences such as APCO's. Costs of attendance at such events are more than offset by the benefits: increased lead time for decisions, more economical procurement, and the information needed to avoid the acquisition of unnecessary features or equipment.

The timing for replacement should be driven by manufacturer support, system performance, maintenance history, and operational needs. Any of these factors may result in an acceleration of the replacement schedule. The way an agency does *not* want to learn of the need to replace a system component is through a letter from the manufacturer announcing that it will no longer support spare parts. Worse yet is hearing from the local repair shop that it is using spare parts harvested from the neighbors' systems that are being removed from service. Similarly, an agency should not have to search for competent repair personnel and pay higher prices to repair unusual equipment. When there is only one technician left who has experience in repairing an outdated or unusual system, the agency may need to consider a replacement or upgrade.

Ideally, an agency includes communications equipment in the capital planning process. Many capital improvement plans extend from five to ten years and are updated annually. The expected lifespan of major new equipment and system components should be known at the time of acquisition. As the time frame for replacement enters the window of the capital budget, an inflation-adjusted estimate of replacement costs should be developed in consultation with the incumbent vendor or with other agencies that have recently purchased such equipment. This estimate should be the starting point for budgeting. Related costs for implementation of the system, including electrical or mechanical alterations, possible facility needs, and possible extra costs during a "switchover" period, should be estimated.

As time grows nearer for acquisition, a planning committee should be formed to gather detailed information about current and emerging technologies. The committee should include end users of each system at diverse levels to be sure that acquisition plans are based on a realistic assessment of the proposed system's strengths and weaknesses. Candid discussions with users of competing technologies should be held, and notes should be taken to be shared with other committee members.

Ensuring that funding is made available is crucial: a deferred project may result in added work as information that has been gathered must be updated. Major advances in technology or new regulations may force the planning process back to the "drawing board." Preparing a strong case with supporting materials that show managers, elected officials, and the public why a new system is needed is important for maintaining support for an acquisition project, particularly in times of fiscal scarcity.

Planners must make peace with the fact that by the time they finish the acquisition process, there may be newer products on the market. Decisions should not be based on the "buzz" at trade shows or in industry publications, but on the agency's communication needs now and through the life of the equipment.

Project management

Communications system acquisitions are high-risk undertakings because they (1) involve high costs, (2) require technical knowledge not common within the organization, (3) have a major impact on daily operations, and (4) may involve multiple vendors and manufacturers. These risk factors require that a formal management approach be used to monitor and guide the project. Large technology projects tend to go over budget and beyond schedule. A reasonable contingency factor should be built into any estimates of project costs.

Depending on the size of the project, a specialist or firm may be retained to act as project manager. At a minimum, one knowledgeable staff person with sufficient rank to interact with top management should be dedicated full time to project management for all but the most trivial undertakings. Certifications are available for project management, and the on-staff manager as well as the contracted project manager should have a combination of training and experience in managing similar projects in a public safety environment.

Consultants

One way to acquire the necessary technical knowledge that may not already be within the organization is to use consultants. Here the manager must be aware of the backgrounds of the consultant and associates. After large vendors downsized their staffs, many personnel formed consulting firms. Such firms are not independent, however, because each consultant is familiar with only one approach, and that one is the approach of only one vendor. To determine the independence of a consultant, it is important to review that consultant's previous projects to see if a preponderance of those projects ended up with one vendor.

Reference checks are a vital part of choosing a consultant. Although many states allow single-source contracting for professional services, a competitive bid process is preferable because it eliminates most complaints that the process is skewed one way or another, and it ensures that alternatives are considered.

The consultant's role in the acquisition process will depend on the technical knowledge of the communications staff. If that knowledge is general or somewhat out-of-date, the consultant can educate the staff about what is possible with current technology. If the staff's knowledge is nontechnical, the consultant can provide the engineering expertise to correctly describe the items required in the acquisition documents. Often a consultant can help assess system needs because he or she is familiar with problems that have occurred in similar systems elsewhere.

Real estate acquisition, rights-of-way to reach remote sites, and negotiation of leases for tower space can be complex issues, and a consultant with experience in these specialized areas may be helpful. Specialist consultants can be useful when communities must submit their tower and facility plans for approval at planning or zoning hearings: the consultants can provide support on such issues as tower safety, electromagnetic radiation, and television interference. Even communities that do not require planning or zoning hearings may find it beneficial to hold hearings at which the experts are available to answer questions from the public.

Consultants can also help deal with frequency coordination and the FCC licensing process. The FCC designated certain trade associations to act for it in the preliminary licensing process. The two associations that public safety officials deal with most often are APCO and the International Municipal Signal Association. The former is responsible for coordinating law enforcement frequencies and public safety frequencies as designated by the FCC. The latter, in cooperation with the International Association of Fire Chiefs, handles fire frequencies as assigned by the FCC. As the FCC manages the spectrum and adjusts to new technology and the worldwide allocation of frequencies, the process of coordinating frequencies changes. Managers who are preparing for a major project must remain familiar with the mechanism applicable to new projects.

Promoting efficiency and containing costs

The need to replace or significantly upgrade a communications system or facility presents an opportunity to consider operational and organizational alternatives that can produce major cost savings. Partnering with other agencies on interoperability, shared equipment, joint dispatch, or consolidation of services should be considered before a major investment is made.

Before choosing new technologies and equipment, the agency must weigh all initial and long-term costs and anticipate regulatory and technological developments so as to maximize the useful life of the investment. The costs should be weighed against the potential to save labor and control the need to add personnel, or to improve quality of service.

Before making any purchase, the agency must also know the manufacturer's plans for the product line, including maintenance support and parts provision. The movement toward more software-driven communication systems will challenge the ability of many smaller communication centers to keep the skills of in-house maintenance personnel up-to-date. On the other hand, contractor fees for annual maintenance of critical equipment are likely to escalate. These trends will contribute to consolidation of small communication center, as the costs of maintaining independent operations become unbearable.

Managing change and expectations in communication systems

The field of communications is very dynamic. The manager of a modern PSCC must be highly competent and energetic. Agencies that have operated for many years with no changes in technology or policy grow accustomed to one way of doing things and may find it challenging to change. Operations personnel, in particular, may not appreciate the need to adapt to new technologies or the importance of the PSCC and the challenges it faces. A reluctant boss or someone with difficulty making changes in policy and operational issues may not be appropriate for a PSCC.

Instilling a change-friendly culture is an important responsibility of each agency manager and the manager of the telecommunications staff. Telecommunicators should be made aware of the need for continuous improvement and the near-constant refinement of technology used in the center. Involving end users in the process of implementing new procedures and technologies is essential. For most telecommunicators, their console is their world. Their requests for enhanced equipment or amenities should be carefully considered. Saving a few dollars on basic equipment seldom produces overall savings.

PSCC managers must resist falling victim to a salesperson's pitch or glossy brochures or promotional videos. They should verify claims and performance expectations for new equipment and avoid making overly optimistic promises to staff or the agencies served. Heightened expectations and failure to meet them can damage the reputation of the center and undermine confidence in the new equipment.

The manager who supervises a transition from a single- to a multiagency center faces additional challenges. The advantages of improved coordination of resources and enhanced interoperability that come with being part of a multiagency center usually far outweigh any loss of local autonomy. However, the political dynamics of a PSCC will influence the degree to which individual agencies can dictate their own protocols or response policies.

If agencies served by the PSCC can agree on service-level expectations, many disputes can be avoided. Considerable flexibility can be maintained within the capabilities of most modern CAD systems, but radio designations and any codes or terminology should be consistent throughout the center to make it easy for dispatchers to transition between agencies and channels. Duplication of unit designations should not be permitted. Working through local (i.e., county or metro chiefs) associations can be very useful for resolving or avoiding regional communication issues.

Summary and future trends

The evolution of personal computers has given upper management in government a sense of how rapidly the world of technology is changing and how short computer life cycles are. Accordingly, public safety managers must continually champion the need to reserve funds for communications system upgrades. And if the communications system serves multiple agencies, fire and emergency service managers will have to ensure that improvements in their own agency's communications technology do not degrade the performance of the overall communications system. Cooperation and coordination are essential.

Perhaps most important, managers must remember that technology is only part of the solution to a fire and emergency services department's communication needs. Other components are an understanding of those needs and the careful design of a system incorporating appropriate technology. A well-managed PSCC; an adequate and trained staff with thorough knowledge of organizational procedures; and solid radio discipline, especially among end users, are all necessary for effective communication.

The increasing integration of communications equipment with software and computer equipment has made maintenance and investment in updated technology critical. As the nature of radio hardware changes, agencies will rely more on outside vendors for maintenance. Technology management and updating will become ongoing activities. Implementation of initiatives such as Next Generation 911 will require action by communication centers across the United States. Narrowbanding, the possible advent of fire-ground location technologies for tracking personnel, and other technology developments will challenge communication managers for the foreseeable future. Amid all this change, the fundamentals of planning, training, management, and quality assurance will remain critical to the communications function.

Notes

1. Presidential Commission on Law Enforcement and Administration of Justice, *The Challenge of Crime in a Free Society* (Washington, D.C.: Government Printing Office, 1967), ncjrs.gov/pdffiles1/nij/42.pdf.
2. Federal Communications Commission, "Wireless 911 Services," fcc.gov/cgb/consumerfacts/wireless911srvc.html.
3. Association of Public-Safety Communications Officials (APCO) International, *Core Competencies for Public Safety Manager/Director,* APCO ANS 1.106.1-2009 (Daytona Beach, Fla: APCO International, 2009), apcointl.org/new/commcenter911/documents/APCO-ANS1-106-1web_001.pdf.
4. APCO, "APCO Project 33: Standard for Telecommunicator Training," apcointl.com/institute/apco33.htm.
5. See Martin W. Bercovici, *FCC Narrowbanding Mandate: A Public Safety Guide for Compliance* (Washington, D.C., and Newark, N.Y.: International Association of Fire Chiefs and International Municipal Signal Association, 2006), 2, fcc.gov/pshs/docs/clearinghouse/guidelines/Narrowbanding_Booklet.pdf.
6. U.S. Department of Homeland Security, SAFECOM "Interoperability," safecomprogram.gov/SAFECOM/interoperability/default.htm (accessed November 3, 2010).
7. For a fuller explanation, see National Institute of Justice, "Interoperability Gateways/Interconnects" (November 13, 2007), ojp.usdoj.gov/nij/topics/technology/communication/gateways.htm; and Charles Jennings, "Advanced Communications," in *Fire Engineering's Handbook for Firefighter I and II,* ed. Glenn Corbett (Tulsa, Okla.: PennWell Corporation, 2009), 877.

FURTHER READINGS AND RESOURCES

This guide to further readings and resources is highly selective and represents informed judgment about basic materials of managerial interest in the dynamic field of fire and emergency services delivery. It is intended to supplement the material cited in the endnotes to individual chapters of this text with a selection of basic books and research reports on the many specific subjects within fire and emergency services management. The guide is arranged by chapter for the convenience of the reader, although some items will of course apply to several of the many functional divisions of the text. Such references will, therefore, be shown in each applicable chapter.

To help readers supplement the materials set out in the chapter listings of this guide, the following synopsis identifies some of the standard reference sources and information available in journals, yearbooks, and association publications with general application to the fire and emergency services.

A fundamental reference source for statistics of concern to fire and emergency service managers is the *Statistical Abstract of the United States,* published annually by the U.S. Census Bureau and obtainable in print from the U.S. Government Printing Office, Washington, DC 20402; on the web at census.gov/compendia/statab/; or through any U.S. Department of Commerce district office. The annual appendix titled *Guide to Sources of Statistics* is an invaluable guide to the many specialized statistical reference sources applicable to the fire and emergency services. *The Municipal Year Book,* published annually by the International City/County Management Association (ICMA) in Washington, D.C., is an authoritative reference source containing detailed guides to further sources of information—organizations as well as bibliographic materials—in local government management, including fire and emergency services. *The Fire Protection Handbook®*, published by the National Fire Protection Association (NFPA), Quincy, Mass. (and revised about every five years), contains data on loss of life and property from fire, information on the behavior of materials under fire conditions, and updates on fire protection techniques, systems, and equipment.

Several specialized fire and emergency service organizations have been described throughout this book. The major organizations presented immediately below are sources for a large variety of useful information about fire and emergency services management in general. Shown for each organization are name, website, and a short description of services; regarding the websites, readers should understand that these are subject to change and are correct at the time of publication. Next is a list of periodicals and other publications that are of value as continuing references and information sources. The balance of this guide, as described above, consists of additional references listed by chapters; this listing—mostly books—emphasizes general works that are deemed helpful for students and practitioners. These lists are not intended to be exhaustive, and readers are encouraged to continually engage with a variety of resources to stay current in the dynamic fire and emergency services field.

Associations, organizations, and websites

American Academy of Emergency Medicine (AAEM), aaem.org
The AAEM, a membership organization of Board-certified emergency physicians, is dedicated to the advancement of emergency medical care by Board-certified physicians trained in residency programs.

American College of Emergency Physicians (ACEP), acep.org
ACEP, an association of physicians, residents, and medical students, advocates for the needs of patients and emergency medical care. It also sponsors continuing medical education for its members, publishes *Annals of Emergency Medicine,* and administers grants for research through its foundation.

American Red Cross, redcross.org
The American Red Cross provides a wide range of disaster relief and preparedness services in local communities and across the globe. Local Red Cross chapters are often key partners with fire and emergency service organizations.

Association of Public Safety Communications Officers—International (APCO International), apcointl.org
The world's oldest and largest not-for-profit professional organization dedicated to the enhancement of public safety communications, APCO International publishes the magazine *Public Safety Communications* as well as numerous books and brochures.

Black Women in the Fire Service (BWFS), bwfs.org
The organization, affiliated with the International Association of Black Professional Fire Fighters, started in 1989 and is devoted to recruitment, retention, and advancement of black women in the fire and emergency services.

Center for Public Safety Excellence (CPSE), publicsafetyexcellence.org
CPSE promotes the continuous quality improvement of fire and emergency service agencies that serve communities worldwide by providing training and career resource information. As a nonprofit, 501(c)(3) corporation, CPSE supports and encourages agencies and personnel to meet international performance standards through various programs and the work of two commissions: the Commission on Fire Accreditation International (CFAI) and the Commission on Professional Credentialing (CPC).

Congressional Fire Services Institute (CFSI), cfsi.org
CFSI works with more than forty-five national fire service organizations to educate members of Congress on the important issues and challenges that face first responders, such as threats of terrorism, aging apparatus, and reduced funding.

Emergency Management Institute, training.fema.gov/EMI
One of several training facilities for the Federal Emergency Management Agency (FEMA), EMI is located in Emmitsburg, Maryland, on the grounds of the National Emergency Training Center.

Emergency Medical Services Labor Alliance (EMSLA), emsla.org
EMSLA exists to improve communication between public and private sector emergency medical service (EMS) providers. EMSLA fosters collaboration on numerous topics, including labor trends in emergency medical services, EMS systems comparison, and deployment strategies. EMSLA also acts to protect emergency medical technicians and paramedics around the world.

Everyone Goes Home, everyonegoeshome.com
Launched by the National Fallen Firefighters Foundation, Everyone Goes Home is a national initiative to prevent firefighter line-of-duty deaths and injuries. The site provides access to the Firefighter Life Safety Initiatives Research Database.

Federal Emergency Management Agency (FEMA), fema.gov
FEMA was created in 1979 to respond to the full range of disasters and emergencies through a comprehensive, risk-based emergency management program of mitigation, preparedness, response, and recovery. On March 1, 2003, FEMA became part of the U.S. Department of Homeland Security (DHS). FEMA includes the U.S. Fire Administration.

Fire Apparatus Manufacturers' Association (FAMA), fama.org
FAMA works to enhance the quality of the fire apparatus industry and emergency service community through the manufacture and sale of safe, efficient fire apparatus and equipment.

Fire Corps, firecorps.org
One of the five partner programs under Citizen Corps, Fire Corps is the FEMA initiative to involve citizens in all-hazards preparedness and resiliency. The website offers tips on initiating a program in a community as well as best practices from successful programs across the country.

Fire Department Safety Officers Association (FDSOA), fdsoa.org
Through its numerous educational seminars and publications, including a newsletter, *Health and Safety for Fire and Emergency Services Personnel,* FDSOA promotes safety standards and practices in the fire, rescue, and emergency services community.

Fire and Emergency Manufacturers and Services Association (FEMSA), femsa.org
FEMSA represents a large number of companies that supply fire and emergency service organizations with specialized equipment.

Fire 20/20, fire2020.org
Fire 20/20 is a nonprofit organization devoted to helping fire and emergency service organizations connect with their multicultural communities to improve the reach and effectiveness of diversity recruitment, retention, emergency response, and community risk reduction programs.

Governmental Accounting Standards Board (GASB), gasb.org
GASB is an organization dedicated to improving governmental accounting and financial reporting. Its values are independence, integrity, objectivity, and transparency.

Homeland Security Studies and Analysis Institute, homelandsecurity.org
A federally funded research and development center established to provide independent analysis of homeland security issues, the Homeland Security Institute is committed to supporting DHS in its efforts to prevent terrorism and enhance security, secure and manage the nation's borders, enforce and administer U.S. immigration laws, safeguard and secure cyberspace, ensure resilience to disasters, and mature and strengthen the homeland security enterprise.

Institution of Fire Engineers–United States of America Branch (IFE-USA), ife-usa.org
IFE-USA is one of thirty-nine branches of the UK-based worldwide organization devoted to the professional development of fire engineers (both fire officers and registered engineers), as well as to promoting training, encouraging good practices, and enhancing technical networks worldwide. See also the Institution of Fire Engineers (IFE) (ife.uk.org) and the Institution of Fire Engineers–Canada Branch (ife.ca).

Insurance Services Office (ISO), iso.com
ISO, an independent statistical, rating, and advisory organization, publishes the Fire Suppression Rating Schedule, which contains rating criteria for grading jurisdictions; insurance companies use the grades in setting fire insurance rates. ISO rates communities, assigns them a fire defense classification number, and then publishes a rate for structures within the rated community.

International Association of Arson Investigators (IAAI), firearson.com
Working in cooperation with other associations and law enforcement agencies to prevent and suppress the crime of arson, IAAI provides the latest information and technology in the field through annual and regional seminars, administration of the Certified Fire Investigator program, and publication of *The Fire and Arson Investigator.*

International Association of Black Professional Fire Fighters (IABPFF), iabpff.org
The IABPFF seeks to create a liaison among African-American firefighters across the nation and to promote interracial progress throughout the fire service. The Black Chief Officers Committee (bcoc.us), a committee of the IABPFF, provides a resource for coordination, networking, and building relationships.

International Association of Emergency Managers (IAEM), iaem.com
IAEM is a nonprofit educational organization dedicated to promoting the principles of emergency management; providing members with information, networking, and professional development opportunities; and advancing the emergency management profession.

International Association of Emergency Medical Services Chiefs (IAEMSC), iaemsc.org
Consisting primarily of chiefs and other leaders in EMS systems, the IAEMSC advances professionalism and networking; publishes position papers; and advocates for EMS-related legislation at the federal, state, and local levels.

International Association of Fire Chiefs (IAFC), iafc.org
The IAFC publishes a variety of informational and educational materials. Its website offers the fire service leader access to reports, research, and up-to-date accounts of activities around the world regarding a wide variety of fire/EMS service management issues. The IAFC hosts regional divisions, committees, and special-interest sections that include emergency medical services; federal and military fire services; emergency vehicle management; fire and life safety; industrial fire and life safety; metro chiefs (in conjunction with NFPA); safety health and survival; and volunteer and combination officers. Membership may be required to access some information or download reports.

International Association of Fire Fighters (IAFF), iaff.org
The IAFF was officially formed in 1918 to represent the interests of career professional firefighters across the United States and Canada. Today, through more than 3,100 local affiliates, the IAFF represents more than 298,000 full-time career firefighters and paramedics. IAFF affiliates can access numerous training, educational, and support programs for occupational health and safety, emergency medical services, hazardous materials training, etc.

International Association of Women in Fire and Emergency Services (iWomen), i-women.org
Founded in 1982 as Women in the Fire Service, iWomen serves as a network and communications vehicle for women in fire and emergency services as well as for those interested in advancing harmonious relations between men and women in the fire and emergency services. Acting as a resource for fire service leadership on issues related to women, iWomen publishes a wide array of print and video resources, as well as *FireWork* (a news bulletin) and a quarterly journal.

International City/County Management Association (ICMA), icma.org
ICMA publishes *The Municipal Year Book,* which presents data on personnel, salaries, and expenditures for fire departments compiled from annual surveys. Fire service management topics are covered frequently in ICMA reports.

International Code Council (ICC), iccsafe.org
The ICC publishes the I-Codes, a series of model building and fire prevention codes that have been adopted by fifty states and the District of Columbia as well as by multiple federal agencies.

International Fire Service Accreditation Congress (IFSAC), ifsac.org
The IFSAC is a self-governing system (i.e., members of the fire service formulate requirements) that accredits fire-related degree-granting programs at colleges and universities.

International Fire Service Training Association (IFSTA), ifsta.org
IFSTA develops and validates a complete series of training manuals published by Fire Protection Publications pertaining to all aspects of fire and emergency services.

International Municipal Signal Association (IMSA), imsasafety.org
The leading international resource for information, education, and certification for public safety, IMSA publishes study guides, manuals, and the *IMSA Journal.*

International Personnel Assessment Council (IPAC), ipacweb.org
The IPAC website offers information regarding various training opportunities for the selection practitioner as well as a variety of links to other relevant human resource websites. On-site, customized training seminars on a wide range of assessment topics delivered by human resource professionals are also available through this organization. Members have access to a newsletter, a directory of other specialists to share experiences and practices, and an annual conference.

International Society of Fire Service Instructors (ISFSI), isfsi.org
ISFSI conducts seminars on fire service education and instructor training; sponsors a reference and referral service; credentials fire and emergency service instructors; and issues numerous publications.

Lessons Learned Information Sharing, llis.gov
A program of DHS/FEMA, *LLIS.gov* serves as the national online network of lessons learned, best practices, and innovative ideas for the emergency management and homeland security communities. This information and collaboration resource helps emergency response provid-

ers and homeland security officials prevent, protect against, respond to, and recover from terrorist attacks, natural disasters, and other emergencies. *LLIS.gov* provides federal, state, and local responders and emergency managers with a wealth of information and front-line expertise on effective planning, training, and operational practices across homeland security functional areas.

Memorial Institute for the Prevention of Terrorism (MIPT), mipt.org
MIPT is a DHS training partner serving the nation's 850,000 uniformed officers and law enforcement leadership. Its mission is to enhance the public safety through training, professional development, and education.

National Association of Emergency Medical Technicians (NAEMT), naemt.org
The NAEMT promotes the interests of EMS practitioners, including respect, pay, benefits, national leadership, adequate funding for emergency medical services, and public policy.

National Association of EMS Educators (NAEMSE), naemse.org
Committed to inspiring excellence in EMS education and lifelong learning, NAEMSE hosts an annual symposium for EMS educators to attend sessions designed to help them better their teaching skills, to network with other EMS educators, and to visit the EMS exhibitors' trade show.

National Association of Hispanic Firefighters (NAHF), nahf.org
Founded in 1995, the NAHF was formed to enhance fire and life safety services through recruitment, training, mentorship, and career development of all firefighters, regardless of race, sex, color, religion, creed, and social or economic background. The NAHF encourages bilingual fire and life safety programs, and sponsors strategic partnerships with fire services in Latin America and other parts of the world.

National Association of State EMS Officials (NASEMSO), nasemso.org
An association of state EMS officials, NASEMSO strives to create a nationwide network of coordinated and accountable EMS and emergency care systems. The group assists its members in developing policy and oversight, as well as in providing vision, leadership, and resources in the development and improvement of emergency medical services and emergency care systems.

National Association of State Fire Marshals (NASFM), firemarshals.org
NASFM is committed to protecting human life, property, and the environment from fire. It is also committed to improving the efficiency and effectiveness of state fire marshals' operations. It has several ongoing projects, including juvenile fire-setter intervention, pipeline emergencies, liquefied natural gas, interoperable communications, and the residential fire safety institute.

National Board on Fire Service Professional Qualifications (NBFSPQ) (ProBoard), theproboard.org
By accrediting organizations that certify uniform members of public fire departments, both career and volunteer, the ProBoard has established an internationally recognized means of acknowledging professional achievement in the fire service and related fields.

National Emergency Management Association, nemaweb.org
NEMA is the professional association of emergency management directors from all fifty states, eight U.S. territories, and the District of Columbia. It provides national leadership and expertise in comprehensive emergency management; serves as a vital emergency management information and assistance resource; and advances continuous improvement in emergency management through strategic partnerships, innovative programs, and collaborative policy positions.

National EMS Management Association (NEMSMA), nemsma.org
NEMSMA is an organization of EMS leaders dedicated to discovery, development, and promotion of excellence in leadership and management in EMS systems, regardless of EMS system model, organizational structure, or agency affiliation.

National Fire Fighter Near-Miss Reporting System, firefighternearmiss.com
The National Fire Fighter Near-Miss Reporting System is a voluntary, confidential, nonpunitive, and secure reporting system with the goal of improving firefighter safety.

National Fire Information Council (NFIC), nfic.org
Striving to be the leading subject matter experts for the National Fire Incident Reporting System (NFIRS), the NFIC is committed to enhancing public safety through the collection and dissemination of timely, accurate, and useable fire-related emergency response information.

National Fire Protection Association (NFPA), nfpa.org
NFPA publishes numerous codes, standards, recommended practices, public education programs, and manuals in all areas of fire protection; the *Fire Protection Handbook®; NFPA Journal* (the membership magazine); and various books, as well as educational and audiovisual materials. NFPA includes the International Fire Marshals Association (IFMA), which publishes *IFMA Quarterly* to provide timely information to the fire prevention, public fire, educational, and fire investigation community.

National Institute for Occupational Safety and Health (NIOSH), cdc.gov/niosh
Part of the Centers for Disease Control and Prevention (CDC), NIOSH is responsible for conducting research on the full scope of occupational disease and injury; for investigating potentially hazardous working conditions; for recommending and disseminating information on preventing workplace disease, injury, and disability; and for providing training to occupational safety and health professionals. The NIOSH Fire Fighter Fatality Investigation and Prevention Program (cdc.gov/niosh/fire/implweb.html) is a public health practice investigation program that conducts investigations of firefighter line-of-duty deaths to formulate recommendations for preventing future deaths and injuries.

National Institute of Standards and Technology (NIST), nist.gov
The Fire.Gov (fire.gov) website provides training materials, videos, fire reconstructions, and research reports that may be of interest to the fire service. FIREDOC is the online bibliographic database of the 55,000 holdings in the Fire Research Information Services (FRIS) collection, bfrl.nist.gov/fris.

National Public Safety Telecommunications Council (NPSTC), npstc.org
NPSTC is a federation of organizations whose mission is to improve public safety communications and interoperability through collaborative leadership.

National Registry of Emergency Medical Technicians, nremt.org
The NREMT, which serves as a certification agency for emergency medical technicians and is accredited by the National Commission for Certifying Agencies, grew from a federal recommendation for national certification standards for EMS workers.

National Society of Executive Fire Officers (NSEFO), nsefo.org
The mission of the NSEFO is to support the National Fire Academy (NFA) and other federal fire programs, to support increased opportunities for executive development, and to develop and support participants in the NFA's Executive Fire Officer Program.

National Volunteer Fire Council (NVFC), nvfc.org
A nonprofit membership association representing the interests of volunteer fire, rescue, and emergency medical services, the NVFC provides information regarding legislation, standards, and regulatory issues. Through the NVFC Academy it offers a number of on-site and online training opportunities and training resources for volunteer firefighters.

National Wildfire Coordinating Group (NWCG), nwcg.gov
NWCG coordinates programs of the participating wildfire management agencies: the U.S. Department of Agriculture's Forest Service; the Department of the Interior's Bureau of Land Management, National Park Service, Bureau of Indian Affairs, and the Fish and Wildlife Service; and state forestry agencies through the National Association of State Foresters. It provides a formalized system to agree upon standards of training, equipment, qualifications, and other operational functions.

Naval Postgraduate School Center for Homeland Defense and Security, chds.us
The Naval Postgraduate School Center for Homeland Defense and Security provides homeland security graduate- and executive-level education.

North American Fire Training Directors (NAFTD), naftd.org
Made up of state, provincial, and territorial fire training directors from the United States and Canada, NAFTD trains more than a million career and volunteer fire service professionals annually. In many cases, the state or provincial fire training agency is also involved in the certification of firefighters, fire officers, fire investigators, fire inspectors, apparatus operators, and many other fire service occupations. Members serve on various professional standards

committees of NFPA. NAFTD is also involved in the International Fire Service Accreditation Congress and the National Board on Fire Service Professional Qualifications, both of which are active in fire service professionalism through certification.

Public Technology, Inc. (PTI), pti.org
PTI researches and publishes technical solutions to widespread and urgent problems facing local governments.

Responder Knowledge Base (RKB), rkb.us
The RKB mission is to provide emergency responders, purchasers, and planners with a trusted, integrated, online source of information on products, standards, certifications, grants, and other equipment-related information.

Underwriters Laboratories (UL), ul.com
UL provides independent safety services across five key business areas: product safety, environment, life and health, university, and verification services. UL conducts a wide range of basic fire and materials research in its testing facilities.

Urban and Regional Information Systems Association (URISA), urisa.org
An association of professionals using geographic information systems and other information technologies to solve challenges in state and local government, URISA sponsors conferences, produces reports, and supports volunteer activities.

U.S. Consumer Product Safety Commission, cpsc.gov
Charged with protecting the public from unreasonable risks of injury or death from thousands of types of consumer products under its jurisdiction, the CPSC is committed to protecting consumers and families from products that pose a fire, electrical, chemical, or mechanical hazard or can injure children.

U.S. Department of Homeland Security, dhs.gov
The Homeland Security Act of 2002 established DHS, combining twenty-two separate federal agencies into a single cabinet-level department with more than 230,000 employees. DHS includes FEMA and the U.S. Fire Administration.

U.S. Fire Administration (USFA), usfa.fema.gov
An arm of FEMA, the USFA publishes numerous reports and brochures on public education. Within the USFA is the National Fire Academy (usfa.dhs.gov/nfa/nfaonline) and the NFA's Executive Fire Officer Program (EFOP) (usfa.dhs.gov/nfa/efop/index.shtm). The USFA is also the home of the Fire and Emergency Services Higher Education (FESHE) program.

U.S. Occupational Safety and Health Administration (OSHA), osha.gov
To protect the health and well-being of America's workers, OSHA establishes protective standards, enforces those standards, and reaches out to employers and employees through technical assistance and consultation programs.

Periodicals and trade publications

In addition to the association journals, fire and emergency service periodicals on general topics include the following:

Fire Chief, firechief.com
Fire Engineering, fireengineering.com/index.html
Firehouse, firehouse.com/magazine
FireRescue Magazine, firefighternation.com/magazines
Journal of Emergency Medical Services, jems.com
Journal of Homeland Security and Emergency Management, bepress.com/jhsem

There are many different periodicals on special subjects—for example, arson investigation, communications, and labor relations; some of these are cited in the endnotes to the appropriate chapters. Those cited, and other special periodicals, can be obtained from the appropriate organizations.

Publications

Chapter 1 Contemporary fire and emergency services

Frederickson, George, and John Nalbandian, eds. *Future of Local Government Administration: The Hansell Symposium.* Washington, D.C.: ICMA, 2002.

International Fire Service Training Association. *Essentials of Fire Fighting.* 5th ed. Stillwater, Okla.: Fire Protection Publications, Oklahoma State University, 2008.

Jennings, Charles, ed. *Customers, Changes, and New Challenges: Reinventing the Fire Service An International Conference.* Sponsored by Institution of Fire Engineers (USA Branch) and John Jay College of Criminal Justice (CUNY). Papers presented at the Fire Department Instructor's Conference, Indianapolis, Ind., March 3–4, 2000. christianregenhardcenter.org/symposium-series/2000.htm.

Kingdon, John W. *Agendas, Alternatives, and Public Policies.* 2nd ed. New York: Longman, 2002.

National Commission on Fire Prevention and Control. *America Burning.* Washington, D.C.: U.S. Government Printing Office, 1973. usfa.dhs.gov/downloads/pdf/publications/fa-264.pdf.

Newell, Charldean, ed. *The Effective Local Government Manager.* 3rd ed. Washington, D.C.: ICMA, 2004.

Stenberg, Carl, and Susan Austin. *Managing Local Government Services.* Washington, D.C.: ICMA Press, 2007.

Weimer, David L., and Aidan R. Vining. *Policy Analysis: Concepts and Practice.* 5th ed. New York: Longman, 2010.

Wingspread V: Statements of National Significance to the Fire Service and to Those Served. A Wingspread Conference Report, International Association of Fire Chiefs Foundation, Atlanta, Ga., April 2006. Emmitsburg, Md.: U.S. Fire Administration, 2006. nationalfireheritagecenter.org/2006Wingspread.pdf.

Chapter 2 Emergency management and homeland security for fire services

Federal Emergency Management Agency (FEMA). *National Incident Management System.* Washington, D.C.: U.S. Department of Homeland Security (DHS), December 2008. fema.gov/pdf/emergency/nims/NIMS_core.pdf.

———. *National Response Framework.* Washington, D.C.: DHS, January 2008. fema.gov/pdf/emergency/nrf/nrf-core.pdf.

Haddow, George, Jane Bullock, and Damon P. Coppola. *Introduction to Emergency Management.* 4th ed. New York: Butterworth-Heinemann, 2010.

Homeland Security Council. *National Strategy for Homeland Security.* Washington, D.C, October 2007. dhs.gov/xlibrary/assets/nat_strat_homelandsecurity_2007.pdf.

International Fire Service Training Association. *Hazardous Materials for First Responders.* 4th ed. Stillwater, Okla.: Fire Protection Publications, Oklahoma State University, 2011.

Kamien, David G., ed. *The McGraw-Hill Homeland Security Handbook.* New York: The McGraw-Hill Companies, 2005.

National Commission on Terrorist Attacks upon the United States. *The 9/11 Commission Report.* New York: Norton and Co., 2004.

National Security Preparedness Group. *Tenth Anniversary Report Card: The Status of the 9/11 Commission Recommendations.* Washington, D.C.: Bipartisan Policy Center, September 2011. bipartisanpolicy.org/sites/default/files/CommissionRecommendations.pdf.

U.S. Department of Homeland Security (DHS). *National Infrastructure Protection Plan: Partnering to Enhance Protection and Resiliency.* Washington, D.C.: DHS, 2009. dhs.gov/xlibrary/assets/NIPP_Plan.pdf.

———. *Progress Made and Work Remaining in Implementing Homeland Security Missions 10 Years after 9/11.* GAO-11-881. Washington, D.C.: U.S. Government Accountability Office, September 7, 2011. gao.gov/new.items/d11881.pdf.

———. *Quadrennial Homeland Security Review Report: A Strategic Framework for a Secure Homeland.* Washington, D.C.: DHS, February 2010. dhs.gov/xlibrary/assets/qhsr_report.pdf.

U.S. House of Representatives. *A Failure of Initiative. Final Report of the Select Bipartisan Committee to Investigate the Preparation for and Response to Hurricane Katrina.* Washington, D.C.: U.S. Government Printing Office, February 15, 2006. gpoaccess.gov/katrinareport/mainreport.pdf.

Waugh, William L., Jr., and Kathleen Tierney. *Emergency Management: Principles and Practice for Local Government.* 2nd ed. Washington, D.C.: ICMA Press, 2007.

White House. *The Federal Response to Hurricane Katrina: Lessons Learned.* Washington, D.C.: Office of the President, February 23, 2006. whitehouse.gov/reports/katrina-lessons-learned.

———. *National Security Strategy.* Washington, D.C.: Office of the President, May 2010. whitehouse.gov/sites/default/files/rss_viewer/national_security_strategy.pdf.

Chapter 3 Evaluating and managing local risks

ANSFR Project. *The ANSFR Project Final Report: Recommendations for Improving Fire Risk Assessment and Management in Europe.* N.d. fire-risk.eu/resources/documents/document_display.htm?pk=88.

Bryson, John M. *Strategic Planning for Public and Nonprofit Organizations: A Guide to Strengthening and Sustaining Organizational Achievement.* 3rd ed. San Francisco: Jossey-Bass, 2004.

Center for Public Safety Excellence (CPSE). *Standards of Cover Manual.* 5th ed. Chantilly, Va.: CPSE, 2008.

Federal Emergency Management Agency. U.S. Fire Administration. *Risk Management Practices in the Fire Service.* FA-166. Washington, D.C., December 1996. usfa.dhs.gov/downloads/pdf/publications/fa-166.pdf.

Flood, Joe. *The Fires: How a Computer Formula, Big Ideas, and the Best of Intentions Burned Down New York City—and Determined the Future of Cities.* New York: Riverhead, 2010.

Hickey, Harry E. *Fire Suppression Rating Schedule Handbook.* 2nd ed. Chicago: Chicago Spectrum Press, 2002.

Jennings, Charles. "The Promise and Pitfalls of Fire Service Deployment Analysis Methods." In *Proceedings of First International Conference on Fire Service Deployment Analysis,* edited by Charles Jennings. Papers presented at the Fire Department Instructors Conference, Indianapolis, Ind., March 19–20, 1999. Alexandria, Va.: Institution of Fire Engineers, 1999. manitouinc.com/Jennings/PDFs/99IFEJ~1.pdf.

———. "Urban Fire Risk: Using GIS to Connect Fire, Census, and Assessor's Data." *Regional Science Review* 17 (1998): 105–112.

———. "Urban Residential Fires: An Empirical Analysis Using Building Stock and Socioeconomic Characteristics for Memphis, Tennessee." PhD diss., Cornell University, 1996.

Klaene, Bernard, and Russell Sanders. "Fireground Operations." In *Structural Fire Fighting.* 2nd ed. Quincy, Mass.: National Fire Protection Association, 2007.

National Fire Data Center. *Socioeconomic Factors and the Incidence of Fire.* FA-170. Emmitsburg, Md.: U.S. Fire Administration, FEMA, June 1997. usfa.dhs.gov/downloads/pdf/statistics/socio.pdf.

Peterson, William, ed. *Proceedings of Second International Conference on Fire Service Deployment Analysis.* Sponsored by Institution of Fire Engineers (USA Branch) and John Jay College of Criminal Justice (CUNY). Papers presented at the Fire Department Instructors Conference, Indianapolis, Ind., April 12–13, 2002. christianregenhardcenter.org/symposium-series/2002/start.htm.

Chapter 4 Organizing and deploying resources

Averill, Jason D., Lori Moore-Merrell, Adam Barowy, Rob Santos, Richard Peacock, Kathy A. Notarianni, and Doug Wissoker. *Report on Residential Fireground Field Experiments,* edited by

Bill Robinson. NIST Technical Note 1661. Washington, D.C.: U.S. Department of Commerce and National Institute of Science and Technology, April 27, 2010. nist.gov/customcf/get_pdf.cfm?pub_id=904607.

Begnell, Gene F. *Deployment Software Review: Executive Development.* Applied research project for the Executive Fire Officer Program. Emmitsburg, Md.: National Fire Academy, U.S. Fire Administration, September 2001. usfa.dhs.gov/pdf/efop/efo32807.pdf.

Bénichou, Noureddine, Ahmed Kashef, and George Hadjisophocleous. *Fire Department Response Model (FDRM) and Fire Department Effectiveness Model (FDEM) Theory Report.* Internal Report No. 842. Ottawa, Ontario: National Research Council Canada, March 2002. nrc-cnrc.gc.ca/obj/irc/doc/pubs/ir/ir842/ir842.pdf.

ESRI, *GIS for Fire Station Locations and Response Protocol.* An ESRI White Paper. Redlands, Calif., January 2007. esri.com/library/whitepapers/pdfs/gis-for-fire.pdf.

Goldberg, Jeffrey B. "Operations Research Models for the Deployment of Emergency Services Vehicles." *EMS Management Journal* 1, no. 1 (January–March 2004), academic.csuohio.edu/holcombj/Deployment.pdf.

Holzer, Marc, and John C. Fry. *Shared Services and Municipal Consolidation: A Critical Analysis.* Charleston, S.C.: CreateSpace, March 2011.

Jennings, Charles. "The Promise and Pitfalls of Fire Service Deployment Analysis Methods." In *Proceedings of First International Conference on Fire Service Deployment Analysis,* edited by Charles Jennings. Papers presented at the Fire Department Instructors Conference, Indianapolis, Ind., March 19–20, 1999. Alexandria, Va.: Institution of Fire Engineers, 1999. manitouinc.com/Jennings/PDFs/99IFEJ~1.pdf.

Johnson, Jerald L. *A Procedure for Evaluation of Fire Station Locations and Deployment: Executive Development.* Applied research project for the Executive Fire Officer Program. Emmitsburg, Md.: National Fire Academy, U.S. Fire Administration, December 1999. usfa.dhs.gov/pdf/efop/efo30816.pdf.

Monarchi, David E., Thomas E. Hendrick, and Donald R. Plane. "Simulation for Fire Department Policy Analysis." *Decision Sciences* 8, no. 1 (January 1977): 211–227.

Ockerhausen, Joseph, Hollis Stambaugh, and Seth Kelly. *Special Report: Fireboats: Then and Now.* USFA TR-146. Emmitsburg, Md.: U.S. Fire Administration, May 2003. usfa.dhs.gov/downloads/pdf/publications/tr-146.pdf.

Tauber, James G. "Pre-Emergency Deployment of Fire Department Resources: A Call to Action." *Fire Engineering* (October 2000). fireengineering.com/articles/print/volume-153/issue-10/features/pre-emergency-deployment-of-fire-department-resources-a-call-to-action.html.

Walker, Warren E., Jan M. Chaiken, and Edward J. Ignall, eds. *Fire Department Deployment Analysis: A Public Policy Analysis Case Study.* New York: Elsevier Science, June 1979.

Chapter 5 Emergency medical services

American College of Emergency Physicians. John A. Brennan, and Jon R. Krohmer, eds. *Principles of EMS Systems.* 3rd ed. Burlington, Mass.: Jones and Bartlett Learning, 2006.

Bergeron, J. David., Gloria Bizjak, Chris LeBaudour, and Keith Weesley. *First Responder.* 8th ed. Stillwater, Okla.: Fire Protection Publications, Oklahoma State University, 2008.

Clawson, Jeff J., Kate Boyd Dernocoeur, and Robert L. Martin, eds. *Principles of Emergency Medical Dispatch.* 2nd ed. Salt Lake City, Utah: Medical Priority Consultants, Inc., 1997.

Evans, Bruce E., and Jeff T. Dyar. *Management of EMS.* Upper Saddle River, N.J.: Brady/Prentice Hall, 2009.

Hogan, David E., and Jonathan L. Burstein, eds. *Disaster Medicine.* 2nd ed. Philadelphia: Lippincott Williams & Wilkins, 2007.

Chapter 6 Comprehensive prevention programs

Crawford, James. *Fire Prevention Organization and Management.* Upper Saddle River, N.J.: Brady/Prentice Hall Health, 2010.

DeHaan, John D., and David J. Icove. *Kirk's Fire Investigation.* 7th ed. Upper Saddle River, N.J.: Brady/Prentice Hall Health, 2011.

Diamantes, David. *Fire Prevention: Inspection and Code Enforcement.* 3rd ed. Florence, Ky.: Delmar Cengage Learning, 2006.

International Fire Service Training Association. *Building Construction Related to the Fire Service.* 3rd ed. Stillwater, Okla.: Fire Protection Publications, Oklahoma State University, 2010.

———. *Fire Inspection and Code Enforcement.* 7th ed. Stillwater, Okla.: Fire Protection Publications, Oklahoma State University, 2009.

———. *Fire Investigator.* 2nd ed. Stillwater, Okla.: Fire Protection Publications, Oklahoma State University, 2010.

———. *Fire and Life Safety Educator.* 3rd ed. Stillwater, Okla.: Fire Protection Publications, Oklahoma State University, 2011.

Klinoff, Robert W. *Introduction to Fire Protection.* 4th ed. Florence, Ky.: Delmar Cengage Learning, 2011.

Robertson, James C. *Introduction to Fire Prevention.* 7th ed. Upper Saddle River, N.J. Brady/Prentice Hall Health, 2009.

Schaenman, Philip. *Global Concepts in Residential Fire Safety.* 3 reports. Arlington, Va.: TriData Corp., October 2007.

Schaenman, Philip, Hollis Stambaugh, Christina Rossomando, Charles Jennings, and Carolyn Perroni. *Proving Public Fire Education Works.* Arlington, Va.: TriData Corp., 1990.

Senior Citizen Fire Safety Task Force. *Seniors at Risk: Creating a Culture of Fire Safety.* Montgomery County, Md., 2008. montgomerycountymd.gov/content/frs-safe/downloads/older/scfst080905.pdf.

Chapter 7 Leading and managing

Blanchard, Ken, and Michael O'Connor. *Managing by Values.* San Francisco: Berrett-Koehler Publishers, 1997.

Brunacini, Alan V. *Fire Command.* 2nd ed. Quincy, Mass.: National Fire Protection Association, 2002.

Carter, Harry R., and Erwin Rausch. *Management in the Fire Service.* 4th ed. Quincy, Mass.: National Fire Protection Association, 2007.

Compton, Dennis. *Progressive Leadership Principles, Concepts, and Tools.* Stillwater, Okla.: Fire Protection Publications, Oklahoma State University, 2010.

———. *When in Doubt, Lead! The Leader's Guide to Enhanced Employee Relations in the Fire Service.* Stillwater, Okla.: Fire Protection Publications, Oklahoma State University, 1999 (part 1), 2000 (part 2), 2001 (part 3).

Heifetz, Ronald A., and Marty Linsky. *Leadership on the Line.* Cambridge, Mass.: Harvard Business Press, 2002.

Heifetz, Ronald A., Alexander Grashow, and Marty Linsky. *The Practice of Adaptive Leadership.* Cambridge, Mass.: Harvard Business Press, 2009.

Jaques, Elliott. *Requisite Organization: A Total System for Effective Managerial Organization and Managerial Leadership for the 21st Century.* Arlington, Va.: Cason Hall & Co., 1997.

Marinucci, Richard A. *Fire Chief's Guide to Administration and Management.* Stillwater, Okla.: Fire Protection Publications, Oklahoma State University, 2008.

Romig, Dennis. *Side by Side Leadership: Achieving Outstanding Results Together.* Atlanta, Ga.: Bard Press, 2001.

Smeby, L. Charles, Jr. *Fire and Emergency Service Administration: Management and Leadership Practices.* Sudbury, Mass.: Jones and Bartlett Publishers LLC, 2006.

Stowell, Frederick M. *Fire and Emergency Services Company Officer.* 4th ed. Stillwater, Okla.: Fire Protection Publications, Oklahoma State University, 2007.

Tichy, Noel M. *The Leadership Engine.* New York: HarperBusiness, 1997.

Chapter 8 Human resource management

Aitchison, Will. *The Rights of Firefighters.* 4th ed. Portland, Ore.: Labor Relations Information System, 2010.

Chetkovich, Carol. *Real Heat: Gender and Race in the Urban Fire Service.* New Brunswick, N.J.: Rutgers University Press, 1997.

Edwards, Steven T. *Fire Service Personnel Management.* Upper Saddle River, N.J.: Brady/ Prentice Hall Health, 2009.

Fox, Kathryn A., Chris W. Hornick, and Erin Hardin. *International Association of Fire Fighters Diversity Initiative: Achieving and Retaining a Diverse Fire Service Workforce.* Washington, D.C.: International Association of Fire Fighters and CWH Research, Inc., 2006. iaff.org/hr/ media/IAFF%20Diversity%20Report.pdf.

International Association of Fire Chiefs (IAFC). *Managing Volunteer Firefighters for FLSA Compliance: A Guide for Fire Chiefs and Community Leaders.* Fairfax, Va.: IAFC, 2006. vcos.org/wp-content/uploads/2009/10/FLSAManual_Small.pdf.

International Association of Fire Fighters (IAFF). *IAFF Human Relations Manual: Recruiting Diverse First Responders.* Washington, D.C.: IAFF, 2009. iaff.org/hr/HR_Manual.pdf.

Moulder, Evelina R. *Performance Appraisals for Local Government Employees: Programs and Practices.* Special Data Issue. Washington, D.C.: ICMA, 2001.

Society for Industrial and Organization Psychology (SIOP). *Principles for the Validation and Use of Personnel Selection Procedures.* 4th ed. Bowling Green, Ohio: SIOP, 2003. siop.org/ _Principles/principles.pdf.

U.S. Fire Administration. *Many Faces, One Purpose: A Manager's Handbook on Women in Firefighting.* FA-196. Washington, D.C.: FEMA, September 1999. i-women.org/images/ pdf-files/fa-196.pdf.

U.S. Fire Administration and National Volunteer Fire Council. *Retention and Recruitment for the Volunteer Emergency Services: Challenges and Solutions.* FA-310. Emmitsburg and Greenbelt, Md., May 2007. usfa.dhs.gov/downloads/pdf/publications/fa-310.pdf.

Chapter 9 Professional development

International Association of Fire Chiefs (IAFC). *Fire Service Instructor: Principles and Practice.* Sudbury, Mass.: Jones and Bartlett Publishers LLC and the National Fire Protection Association, 2009.

———. *IAFC Officer Development Handbook.* 2nd ed. Fairfax, Va.: IAFC, August 2011. clallamfire3.org/wp-content/uploads/2010/12/OffrsHdbkFINAL3.pdf.

———. *Live Fire Training: Principles and Practice.* Sudbury, Mass.: Jones and Bartlett Publishers LLC and the National Fire Protection Association, 2010.

Stolovitch, Harold D., and Erica J. Keeps. *Telling Ain't Training.* 2nd ed. Alexandria, Va.: American Society for Training and Development Press, 2011.

Wakefield, Sarah. *Technical Training Basics.* Alexandria, Va.: American Society for Training and Development Press, 2011.

Chapter 10 Regulations, standards, and issues of liability

Bennett, Lawrence T. *Fire Service Law.* Stillwater, Okla: Fire Protection Publications, Oklahoma State University, 2008.

Brodoff, Maureen. "Liability of Fire Service Organizations for Negligent Fire Fighting." In *Fire Protection Handbook®.* 20th ed., edited by Arthur E. Cote. 2 vols. Quincy, Mass.: National Fire Protection Association, 2008.

Cote, Arthur E., and Casey C. Grant. "Codes and Standards for the Built Environment." In *Fire Protection Handbook®*. 20th ed., edited by Arthur E. Cote. 2 vols. Quincy, Mass.: National Fire Protection Association, 2008.

Hafter, Jacob L., and Victoria L. Fedor. *EMS and the Law.* Sudbury, Mass.: Jones and Bartlett Publishers LLC, 2004.

Puchovsky, Milosh T., and Morgan J. Hurley. "Performance-Based Codes and Standards for Fire Safety." In *Fire Protection Handbook®*. 20th ed., edited by Arthur E. Cote. 2 vols. Quincy, Mass.: National Fire Protection Association, 2008.

Schwartz, Arthur E. "Legal Issues for the Designer and Enforcer." In *Fire Protection Handbook®*. 20th ed., edited by Arthur E. Cote. 2 vols. Quincy, Mass.: National Fire Protection Association, 2008.

Varone, J. Curtis. *Legal Considerations for Fire and Emergency Services.* 2nd ed. Florence, Ky.: Delmar Cengage Learning, 2011.

Chapter 11 Safety, health, and survival

Angle, James S. *Occupational Safety and Health in the Emergency Services.* 2nd ed. Florence, Ky.: Delmar Cengage Learning, 2005.

Bingham, Robert C. *Street Smart Firefighting: The Common Sense Guide to Firefighter Safety and Survival.* Vienna, Va.: Valley Press, 2005.

Brannigan, Francis L., and Glenn P. Corbett. *Brannigan's Building Construction for the Fire Service.* 4th ed. Sudbury, Mass.: Jones and Bartlett Publishers LLC and the National Fire Protection Association, 2009.

Brunacini, Alan V., and Nick Brunacini. *Command Safety.* Stillwater, Okla.: Fire Protection Publications, Oklahoma State University, 2004.

Dickinson, Edward T., and Michael A. Wieder. *Emergency Incident Rehabilitation.* 2nd ed. Upper Saddle River, N.J.: Prentice Hall Health, 2003.

Elliot, Diane L., and Kerry S. Kuehl. *The Effects of Sleep Deprivation on Fire Fighters and EMS Responders.* Final Report. Fairfax, Va.: International Association of Fire Chiefs, June 2007. iafc.org/files/progsSleep_SleepDeprivationReport.pdf.

Ford, Travis. *Fire and Emergency Service Safety and Survival.* Saddle River, N.J.: Pearson Education, 2012.

International Fire Service Training Association. *Building Construction Related to the Fire Service.* 3rd ed. Stillwater, Okla.: Fire Protection Publications, Oklahoma State University, 2010.

———. *Occupational Safety, Health and Wellness.* 3rd ed. Stillwater, Okla.: Fire Protection Publications, Oklahoma State University, 2010.

International Fire Service Training Association and National Fallen Firefighters Foundation. *Understanding and Implementing the 16 Firefighter Life Safety Initiatives.* Stillwater, Okla.: Fire Protection Publications, Oklahoma State University, 2010.

Jennings, Charles. *Improving Firefighter Safety: Human Behavior and Organizational Aspects. An International Conference.* Sponsored by Institution of Fire Engineers (USA Branch) and John Jay College of Criminal Justice (CUNY). Papers presented at the Fire Department Instructor's Conference, Indianapolis, Ind., March 2–3, 2001. christianregenhardcenter.org/symposium-series/2001.htm.

LaTourrette, Tom, D. J. Peterson, James T. Bartis, Brian A. Jackson, and Ari Houser. *Protecting Emergency Responders.* Vol. 2. *Community Views of Safety and Health Risks and Personal Protection Needs.* Santa Monica, Calif.: RAND Corporation, 2003.

Malley, Kevin S., and David K. Spierer. *Get Firefighter Fit: The Complete Workout from the Former Director of the New York City Fire Department Physical Training Program.* Berkeley, Calif.: Ulysses Press, 2008.

Ockershausen, Joseph. *Special Report: The After-Action Critique: Training through Lessons Learned.* TR-159. Emmitsburg, Md.: U.S. Fire Administration, FEMA, April 2008. usfa.fema.gov/downloads/pdf/publications/tr_159.pdf.

Rios, Andreo, ed. *Rehab, Protection and Safety Measures for Firefighters and Emergency Responders.* Hauppauge, N.Y.: Nova Science Publishers, 2010.

Schneider, Ernest L. *Firefighter Fitness: A Health and Wellness Guide.* Hauppauge, N.Y.: Nova Science Publishers, 2010.

Troup, William. *Health and Wellness Guide for the Volunteer Fire Service.* Darby, Pa.: Diane Publishing, 2004.

Chapter 12 Fiscal management

Center for Public Safety Excellence (CPSE). *Fire & Emergency Services Self-Assessment Manual.* 8th ed. Chantilly, Va.: CPSE, 2009.

Gauthier, Stephen J. *Governmental Accounting, Auditing, and Financial Reporting.* Chicago: Government Finance Officers Association, 2005.

Hall, John R., Jr. *The Total Cost of Fire in the United States.* Quincy, Mass.: National Fire Protection Association, 2011. nfpa.org/assets/files/PDF/totalcostsum.pdf.

Kingdon, John W. *Agendas, Alternatives, and Public Policies.* 2nd ed. New York: Longman, 2002.

Lerner, E. Brooke, Graham Nichol, Daniel W. Spaite, Herbert G. Garrison, and Ronald F. Malo. "A Comprehensive Framework for Determining Cost of an Emergency Medical Services System." *Annals of Emergency Medicine* 49, no. 3 (2007): 304–313.

Marlowe, Justin, William C. Rivenbark, and A. John Vogt. *Capital Budgeting and Finance: A Guide for Local Governments.* 2nd ed. Washington, D.C.: ICMA Press, 2009.

McLaughlin, Thomas A. *Streetsmart Financial Basics for Nonprofit Managers.* 3rd ed. New York: Wiley, 2009.

Reiss, Claire, and Peter Young. "Risk and Reward in Local Government Management." *Public Management* 88 (January/February 2006): 10–13.

Ruppel, Warren. *Government Accounting Made Easy.* 2nd ed. New York: Wiley, 2009.

U.S. Fire Administration. *Funding Alternatives for Fire and Emergency Services.* Emmitsburg, Md.: FEMA, 1999. usfa.fema.gov/downloads/pdf/publications/fa-141.pdf.

Chapter 13 Capital resource management

Cotts, David G., and Edmond P. Rondeau. *The Facility Manager's Guide to Finance and Budgeting.* New York: American Management Association, 2007.

Cotts, David G., Kathy O. Roper, and Richard P. Payant. *The Facility Management Handbook.* 3rd ed. New York: American Management Association, 2010.

Henry, Don. *Fire Department Pumping Apparatus Maintenance.* Stillwater, Okla.: Fire Protection Publications, Oklahoma State University, 2003.

Marlowe, Justin, William C. Rivenbark, and A. John Vogt. *Capital Budgeting and Finance: A Guide for Local Governments.* 2nd ed. Washington, D.C.: ICMA Press, 2009.

Shapiro, Larry. *Fighting Fire: Trucks, Tools, and Tactics.* Minneapolis, Minn.: MBI Publishing and Motorbooks, 2008.

Wilmoth, Janet A., comp. *Fire Station Architectural Insight to Planning, Design, and Construction.* Fairfax, Va.: International Association of Fire Chiefs Foundation, 2010.

Chapter 14 Performance management

Ammons, David N., ed. *Leading Performance Management in Local Government.* Washington, D.C.: ICMA Press, 2008.

Biere, Mike. *The New Era of Enterprise Business Intelligence: Using Analytics to Achieve Global Competitive Advantage.* New York: Pearson plc (IBM Press), 2010.

Cokins, Gary. *Performance Management: Integrating Strategy Execution, Methodologies, Risk, and Analytics.* New York: Wiley, 2009.

Eckerson, Wayne W. *Performance Dashboards: Measuring, Monitoring, and Managing Your Business.* 2nd ed. New York: Wiley, 2011.

Fountain, James, Wilson Campbell, Paul Epstein, and Brett Robinson. *Report on the GASB Citizen Discussion Groups on Performance Reporting.* Norwalk, Conn.: Governmental Accounting Standards Board, July 2002. seagov.org/sea_gasb_project/reports_citizen.pdf.

Hatry, Harry. *Performance Measurement: Getting Results.* 2nd ed. Washington, D.C.: Urban Institute, 2007.

Hatry, Harry, Donald M. Fisk, John R. Hall Jr., Philip S. Schaenman, and Louise Snyder. *How Effective Are Your Community Services?* 3rd ed. Washington, D.C.: ICMA and the Urban Institute, 2006.

Hatry, Harry P., James R. Fountain Jr., Jonathan M. Sullivan, and Lorraine Kremer, eds. *Service Efforts and Accomplishments Reporting: Its Time Has Come; An Overview.* Norwalk, Conn.: Governmental Accounting Standards Board, 1990.

National Highway Traffic Safety Administration. *Leadership Guide to Quality Improvement for Emergency Medical Services (EMS) Systems.* Washington, D.C.: Public Health Service, U.S. Department of Health and Human Services, 1997. nhtsa.gov/people/injury/ems/leaderguide/.

Rummler, Geary A., and Alan P. Brache. *Improving Performance: How to Manage the White Space on the Organization Chart.* 3rd ed. San Francisco: Jossey-Bass, 2012.

Chapter 15 Information systems

GIS Technology and Applications for the Fire Service: AN ESRI White Paper. Redlands, Calif.: ESRI, March 2006. esri.com/library/whitepapers/pdfs/fire-service-gis-applications.pdf.

Haag, Stephen, and Maeve Cummings. *Management Information Systems for the Information Age.* 8th ed. New York: McGraw-Hill/Irwin, 2009.

Laudon, Kenneth, and Jane Laudon. *Essentials of Management Information Systems.* 9th ed. Upper Saddle River, N.J.: Prentice Hall, 2010.

Schulz, Jerome A. *Information Technology in Local Government: A Practical Guide for Managers.* Special Report. Washington, D.C.: ICMA, 2001.

Simon, Phil. *Why New Systems Fail: An Insider's Guide to Successful IT Projects.* Florence, Ky.: Course Technology PTR, Cengage Learning, Inc., 2010.

Stenzel, Joseph P., Gary Cokins, Karl D. Schubert, and Michael H. Hugos. *CIO Best Practices: Enabling Strategic Value with Information Technology.* 2nd ed. New York: Wiley, 2010.

U.S. Fire Administration. *Fire Data Analysis Handbook.* 2nd ed. FA-266. Emmitsburg, Md.: FEMA, January 2004. usfa.fema.gov/downloads/pdf/publications/fa-266.pdf.

———. *The National Fire Incident Reporting System.* FA-290. Emmitsburg, Md.: FEMA, January 2007. usfa.fema.gov/downloads/pdf/publications/fa-290.pdf.

Chapter 16 Communication systems and emergency communication centers

Bercovici, Martin W. *FCC Narrowbanding Mandate: A Public Safety Guide for Compliance.* Fairfax, Va., and Newark, N.Y.: International Association of Fire Chiefs and International Municipal Signal Association, 2006. iafc.org/files/commComm_Narrowbanding.pdf.

Desourdis, Robert I., Jr., David R. Smith, William D. Speights, Richard J. Dewey, and John R. DiSalvo. *Emerging Public Safety Wireless Communication Systems.* Norwood, Mass.: Artech House, 2002.

Hawkins, Dan. "Communications in the Incident Command System." COPS Interoperable Communications Technology Program. *Issue Brief* 2 (May 2007). search.org/files/pdf/IB2-CommICS.pdf.

Imel, Kathy J., and James W. Hart. *Understanding Wireless Communications in Public Safety: A Guidebook to Technology, Issues, Planning, and Management.* 2nd ed. Denver,

Colo.: National Law Enforcement and Corrections Technology Center (Rocky Mountain Region), January 2003. transition.fcc.gov/pshs/docs-best/imel-wireless03.pdf.

International Association of Fire Chiefs (IAFC). Digital Project Working Group. *Interim Report and Recommendations: Fireground Noise and Digital Radio Transmissions.* Fairfax, Va.: IAFC, May 30, 2008. iafc.org/associations/4685/files/digProj_DPWGinterimReport.pdf.

McMillian, J. Rhett. *The Primer of Public Safety Telecommunication Systems.* 3rd ed. Daytona Beach, Fla.: Association of Public-Safety Communications Officials, Inc., 2000.

National Emergency Number Association (NENA). *Public Safety Answering Point Site Selection Criteria Operations Information Document (OID).* NENA 56-506. Arlington, Va.: NENA, July 17, 2007. nena.org/sites/default/files/PSAPSiteSelectionCriteriaFINAL071707.pdf.

U.S. Fire Administration. *Special Report: Improving Firefighter Communications.* USFA-TR-099. Emmitsburg, Md.: FEMA, January 1999. usfa.fema.gov/downloads/pdf/publications/tr-099.pdf.

———. *Voice Radio Communications Guide for the Fire Service.* Emmitsburg, Md.: FEMA, October 2008. usfa.fema.gov/downloads/pdf/publications/Voice_Radio_Communications_Guide_for_the_Fire_Service.pdf.

CONTRIBUTORS

Adam K. Thiel (Editor and Chapters 1 and 9) has spent twenty years in the fire and emergency services across four states and in numerous capacities, including fire chief for a diverse and densely populated urban community in the National Capital Region; operations deputy chief for a fast-growing Arizona city; executive director of the Virginia Department of Fire Programs; firefighter, paramedic, hazardous materials technician, and company officer with the Fairfax County (Virginia) Fire and Rescue Department; deputy fire chief for a small combination fire department in North Carolina; and volunteer firefighter/rescuer in Montgomery County, Maryland.

For the past fifteen years, Chief Thiel has provided strategy, planning, leadership, and management consulting to international organizations, nonprofits, government agencies at all levels, educational institutions, and private firms. He currently chairs the National Fire Protection Association (NFPA) Technical Committee on Emergency Services Organization Risk Management, is a member of the NFPA Fire Service Section board, serves as vice-chair for the National Fire Academy Board of Visitors, is a Fire 20/20 board member, and serves on the steering committee for the George Washington University's Homeland Security Policy Institute. He has authored numerous publications, writes a regular column in *Fire Chief* magazine, and has presented at conferences throughout the country. He teaches graduate-level public administration courses, teaches in the International Association of Fire Chiefs (IAFC) New Chiefs Leadership and Executive Edge programs, and is an IAFC/International Association of Fire Fighters (IAFF) Labor-Management Initiative facilitator.

Chief Thiel earned undergraduate degrees in history and fire science from the University of North Carolina at Chapel Hill and the University of Maryland University College, respectively; he holds a master's degree in public administration from George Mason University, is finishing his doctoral degree in public administration at Arizona State University, and has completed the Virginia Executive Institute and Harvard University's Kennedy School of Government Program for Senior Executives in State and Local Government.

Charles R. Jennings, MIFireE, CFO (Editor and Chapters 3 and 16) is associate professor at John Jay College of Criminal Justice of the City University of New York, teaching in the fire science, protection management, and public administration programs. He also serves as director of the Christian Regenhard Center for Emergency Response Studies, a first-responder policy research center located at the college. His teaching and research interests include risk analysis, management, emergency service deployment, and relating community fire loss with community characteristics. With over twenty years of active service as a firefighter and officer in New York and Maryland, Dr. Jennings has held a number of fire service positions, most recently as deputy commissioner of public safety for the city of White Plains, New York. He was also chairman of the Board of Fire Commissioners for the city of Ithaca, New York, and is currently principal of Manitou, Inc., a public safety consulting firm in North America. Dr. Jennings earned a BS in journalism from the University of Maryland; an MS in fire protection management from John Jay College of Criminal Justice; and a master's degree in regional planning and a PhD in city and regional planning from Cornell University.

Donna P. Brehm (Chapter 8) is a retired Virginia Beach, Virginia, deputy fire chief. In that capacity, she was responsible for field operations, finance and budget, resources, information technology, prevention, and emergency management, and was actively engaged in department and city human resources activities from compensation and payroll to applicant and promotional processes. She has been invited to sit on promotional boards across the country. During her thirty-four years in the fire service, Chief Brehm spent twenty-one years on the NFPA 1971 committee, chaired the NFPA 1999 committee for seven years, and continues to serve the fire service as a member of the NFPA Fire Service Section Executive Board. She is currently working for a private firm specializing in the design and delivery of emergency management exercises in Virginia. She holds a master's degree in public administration from Golden Gate University.

Jennie L. Collins (Chapter 5), a battalion chief with the Prince William County (Virginia) Department of Fire and Rescue, began her career with that department in 1985. Since then she served in numerous operational and program management assignments, including positions in operations, EMS operations, training, and health and safety; she is currently the executive officer for the fire chief. She was the team leader for a firefighter line-of-duty death internal investigation and has assisted outside fire departments with firefighter significant injury investigations. Chief Collins was a governor's appointee for six years to the Virginia State EMS Advisory Board, where she also functioned as the board's chairman. She serves on numerous local, regional, and state-level committees and boards of directors, and has numerous fire- and rescue-related certifications and instructor credentials. Chief Collins has received both the Northern Virginia regional and the Virginia Governor's awards for Outstanding EMS Administrator.

Jim Crawford (Chapter 6) is the recently retired fire marshal of Vancouver, Washington, with thirty-five years of experience in the fire service. He has been a past president of the International Fire Marshals Association, a member of the Standards Council for the National Fire Protection Association, a special consultant to the U.S. Fire Administration, and adjunct faculty member for the National Fire Academy. He currently serves as chair of NFPA 1037, the professional qualifications standard for fire marshals, and as project manager for Vision 20/20. He is the author of *Fire Prevention Organization and Management* (Brady/Prentice Hall, 2010).

I. David Daniels, MHRM, MIFireE, CFO (Chapter 7) is chief executive officer of ID2 Solutions, a management consulting firm. Prior to this, he spent thirty years in the fire service in organizations in three states, including ten years as a fire chief and emergency management director. His leadership accomplishments include having helped to develop a number of public sector leaders who either serve or have served in fire, rescue, or emergency medical services in local and state government. Chief Daniels holds a bachelor's degree in fire services administration and a master's degree in human resources management, and he completed the Senior Executives in State and Local Government program at Harvard University.

David T. Endicott (Chapter 14) retired after a twenty-nine-year career with the Prince William County (Virginia) Department of Fire and Rescue, serving for twenty years as a chief officer holding positions as planning chief, training chief, communications chief, administrative chief and field battalion chief. He also served as deputy coordinator for emergency management and as public information officer. He is the owner of Endicott Associates LLC, a public safety and disaster management consultancy specializing in management and performance measurement analysis, and is a principal with and on the board of directors of All Hands Consulting, a global emergency management firm. He volunteers as administrative committee chair of the National Incident Management System Consortium; is secretary of the National Fire Protection Association (NFPA) Committee on Incident Management Professional Qualifications, which writes NFPA Standard 1026; and is a past chair of the NFPA Committee on Fire Fighter Professional Qualifications, which writes NFPA Standards 1001, 1002, 1003, and 1006.

Bruce Evans (Chapter 5, contributor) is the deputy chief at the Upper Pine Fire Protection District in Bayfield, Colorado, having retired in 2011 as the EMS chief for the North Las Vegas Fire Department after over twenty-five years in Southern Nevada emergency services. An NFPA Fire Instructor III, Chief Evans was on the faculty of the College of Southern Nevada for more than twenty years teaching various fire and EMS topics, and he is an adjunct faculty member of the National Fire Academy in the EMS, Incident Management, and Terrorism programs. In addition to co-authoring two textbooks, *Management of EMS* (Brady/Prentice

Hall, 2009), and *Crew Resource Management: Principles and Practice* (Jones and Bartlett, 2009), Chief Evans writes the bi-monthly column "EMS Viewpoints" in *Fire Chief* magazine and is on the editorial board of the *Journal of Emergency Medical Services.* He also participated with the International Fire Service Training Association (IFSTA) in developing the *Fire and Life Safety Educator* textbook, and he co-wrote IFSTA's *High-Rise Fire Fighting* manual. A longtime member of the International Association of Fire Chiefs (IAFC), he has served on the Fire Rescue Med and is on the board of the National EMS Management Association. Chief Evans is the 2010 winner of IAFC's James O. Page Leadership Award. He holds a bachelors degree in education, an associate's degree in fire management, and a master's degree in public administration.

Bruce J. Moeller (Chapter 12), currently city manager of Sunrise, Florida, spent twenty-nine years in the fire service in a variety of roles, from firefighter/paramedic to chief officer, before being appointed fire chief in 1992 of a metropolitan-sized fire agency. Active in national fire service and city management organizations, Dr. Moeller has held leadership positions in the International Association of Fire Chiefs and has served on National Fire Protection Association technical committees. He is a frequent national speaker and has authored numerous articles on fire service leadership and public management. As an adjunct professor for several universities, Dr. Moeller has taught undergraduate and graduate courses in public administration, management, labor relations, and organizational theory. He earned a BA degree in fire administration from Western Illinois University, an MPA from Northern Illinois University, and a PhD with an emphasis in public administration from Florida Atlantic University.

Wm. D. Morrison (Chapter 15) is currently retired after serving for forty years as a senior administrator of the Dallas (Texas) Fire Rescue Department's computer-assisted dispatch (CAD) system. He spent more than thirty years as the senior systems analyst for the department, which he helped to establish as an innovative leader in the use of technology. In the late 1970s, Mr. Morrison played a vital role in overseeing the development and implementation of one of the first CAD systems using mobile data computers with global positioning satellite technology. Until 2007, Dallas Fire Rescue was the only fire-rescue service using automated dispatch based on proximity to the incident. Mr. Morrison was also instrumental in developing other critical operational systems to support the fire service, including hydrant maintenance, tactical information, fire incident reporting, emergency medical incident patient reporting, and a fire security system. More recently, he participated in the replacement of the fire CAD system for a combined police and fire CAD system serving Dallas, the ninth-largest city in the United States. For seventeen years, Mr. Morrison has been a member of the National Fire Information Council (NFIC), and for six years, he served as chairman of the NFIC Systems Committee and worked with the U.S. Fire Administration's National Fire Data Center to develop the new NFIRS Version 5 reporting standard. He is also a member of the National Fire Protection Association 901 Committee on Standard Classifications for Incident Reporting and Fire Protection Data. Mr. Morrison holds a BS in economics from the University of Plano in Plano, Texas.

Kevin M. Roche (Chapter 13) is an assistant to the fire chief of the Phoenix (Arizona) Fire Department. Previously, as resource management administrator, he managed support services such as purchasing, fleet management, equipment management, and logistics. He also developed fire safety instructional materials, spoke on fire service procurement and equipment issues, and worked with fire service statistics. He began his career with the Gainesville Fire-Rescue Department in Florida, and has been a member of the Phoenix Fire Department since 1990. He has a bachelor's degree in fire protection and safety engineering technology from Oklahoma State University, and a master's degree in political science with a certificate in public administration from the University of Florida.

J. Gordon Routley (Chapter 11) is a registered fire protection engineer and a division chief in the Montreal Fire Department, assigned as the senior advisor to the director. He previously served as fire chief in Shreveport, Louisiana; as assistant to the fire chief in Phoenix, Arizona; and as health and safety officer for the Fire/EMS Department in Prince George's County, Maryland. With the National Fallen Firefighters Foundation, the International Association of Fire Chiefs, the Institution of Fire Engineers, and the National Fire Protection Association, he has been involved in numerous projects relating to firefighter occupational safety and health, including the investigation of more than thirty line-of-duty deaths.

Steve Souder (Chapter 16) is director of the Fairfax County (Virginia) Department of Public Safety Communications (DPSC), a full-service, state-of-the-art, Next Generation 911 fire-rescue-EMS and police dispatch agency for a county of approximately 1.3 million residents. He previously served as director of the Montgomery County, Maryland, and Arlington County, Virginia, 911 centers after completing a twenty-five-year career in the District of Columbia Fire Department. While in Arlington County he and his personnel had a major role in the response to the terrorist attack on the Pentagon on September 11, 2001. A nationally recognized authority on all aspects of 911 public safety communications and a frequent speaker and writer on the subject, Mr. Souder is a fifth-generation firefighter.

Jeffrey D. Stern (Chapter 2) leads the Policy Analysis Division at the Homeland Security Studies and Analysis Institute. He has served as director of the Northern Virginia Emergency Response System, as executive director of the Homeland Security Advisory Council at the Department of Homeland Security, and as a White House Fellow at the Department of the Interior and the White House, where he helped revise the president's *National Strategy for Homeland Security* in 2007. A former battalion fire chief and emergency manager with over two decades of service, he helped lead incident management teams to Hurricanes Charley (2004) and Katrina (2005), and he supported medical operations in Haiti and the Dominican Republic after the Haitian earthquake (2010). He is a PhD candidate at Virginia Tech's Center for Public Administration and Policy, holds an MPA from American University's School of Public Affairs, and has a BA in government from the College of William and Mary.

J. Curt Varone, Esq. (Chapter 10) has over thirty-seven years of experience in the fire service, having retired in 2008 as a deputy assistant chief with the Providence (Rhode Island) Fire Department. He is a practicing attorney licensed in both Rhode Island and Maine, and serves as director of the Fire Service Division of the Legal & Liability Risk Management Institute. He also served as director of the Public Fire Protection Division at the National Fire Protection Association. Mr. Varone has written two books, *Legal Considerations for Fire and Emergency Services* and *Fire Officer's Legal Handbook,* as well as the "Fire Law" column for *Firehouse* magazine. He has bachelor's degrees in biology and in fire safety, both from Providence College, and is a cum laude graduate of Suffolk University Law School in Boston, Massachusetts.

Sally Young (Chapter 4) joined the Charlotte (North Carolina) Fire Department in 1979, and as fire department planner from 1980 until her retirement at the end of 2006, she was responsible for selecting the sites for eighteen fire stations, for conducting several deployment studies, and for writing the fire department's business plan. She oversaw the department's planning and performance measurement processes, as well as the incident reporting system and the annexation process. She has also been a consultant to other fire departments in planning fire station locations. She holds a bachelor's degree in English and a master of urban administration degree, both from the University of North Carolina at Charlotte.

INDEX

Managing Fire and Emergency Services

Design
Charles Mountain, Will Kemp
ICMA, Washington, D.C.

Composition
Circle Graphics, Columbia, Maryland

Text type
Interstate, ITC Slimbach

Printing and binding
Quad/Graphics, Dubuque, Iowa

10-163